THE ANALYSIS OF
ENGINEERING STRUCTURES

THE ANALYSIS
OF
ENGINEERING STRUCTURES

BY

A. J. S. PIPPARD, M.B.E., D.Sc., F.R.S.

MEMBER AND VICE-PRESIDENT OF THE INSTITUTION OF CIVIL ENGINEERS
PROFESSOR EMERITUS OF CIVIL ENGINEERING IN THE UNIVERSITY OF LONDON AT IMPERIAL COLLEGE

AND

J. F. BAKER, O.B.E., M.A., Sc.D., F.R.S.

MEMBER OF THE INSTITUTION OF CIVIL ENGINEERS
D.SC. (WALES), HON. D.SC. (LEEDS), HON. A.R.I.B.A.
PROFESSOR OF MECHANICAL SCIENCES IN THE UNIVERSITY OF CAMBRIDGE

LONDON
EDWARD ARNOLD (PUBLISHERS) LTD.

© Copyright A. J. S. Pippard and J. F. Baker 1957

FIRST PUBLISHED 1936
SECOND EDITION 1943
REPRINTED 1944, 1945, 1948, 1950, 1953
THIRD EDITION 1957

PRINTED IN GREAT BRITAIN BY
SPOTTISWOODE, BALLANTYNE AND CO. LTD
LONDON AND COLCHESTER

PREFACE TO THE THIRD EDITION

The authors have taken the opportunity afforded by the demand for a new edition to make considerable alterations in the contents and arrangements of this book without losing sight of the original object stated in the preface to the first edition.

Little change has been made in the earlier parts of the book which seemed to present well-established essentials in a satisfactory way, but considerable alterations will be observed in most of the later chapters, many of which have been largely re-written.

Considerable revision of subject matter has been made possible by the publication of "The Steel Skeleton" (Baker) and "Studies in Elastic Structures" (Pippard), in which certain subjects dealt with in more or less detail in the two previous editions of the present book are discussed more exhaustively, and these books can be referred to by readers who may desire more complete treatments than are appropriate in a general text-book.

In particular, the chapters relating to the behaviour of steel-framed buildings and voussoir arches have been simplified by the exclusion of material now available in greater detail in the books to which reference has been made.

The treatment of arches, rings and bow-girders has been generalised by the use of the principle of super-position, a method suggested but not developed in the earlier editions, which produces more elegant solutions than the earlier treatment. The authors hope that it will commend itself to teachers and students alike.

Thanks are particularly due to Dr. A. W. Bishop of the Civil Engineering Department in Imperial College for his very great help in re-writing the chapter on retaining walls, a task which was specially necessary due to the rapid advances in the science of soil mechanics to which he has contributed so much.

One drawback to a new edition such as the present is that the elimination of misprints and errors starts once again. It is hoped that readers will be as helpful in this respect as they have been in the past and will draw the attention of the authors to any slips they may notice.

The authors have received from time to time requests for the inclusion of more illustrative examples and exercises for the use of students. This, desirable as it may be, would have had the effect of unduly lengthening the book and an alternative has been adopted. The Publishers have arranged to produce a separate volume of examples and exercises under the title "Problems in Engineering Structures" by Messrs. R. J. Ashby, M.Sc., Imperial College, and A. H. Chilver, Ph.D., University of Cambridge Engineering Department, which it is hoped will amply meet the needs of readers of the book as well as of other students of engineering structures.

In conclusion, thanks are due once more to Miss L. Chitty, M.A., for her great assistance in proof-reading.

A. J. SUTTON PIPPARD.
J. F. BAKER.

PREFACE TO THE SECOND EDITION

The preparation of a second edition of this book under present conditions was not easy in view of other demands on the authors' time. Many of the good intentions made in peace-time had to be abandoned, but it has been possible to carry out some improvements and it is hoped that the result will justify the labour of revision.

In addition to the inclusion of new material in various sections of the book, two completely new chapters have been added. One, dealing with the voussoir arch, is largely the result of an experimental study of this type of structure made by one of the authors and his associates during the years immediately preceding the war. The other, which deals with the elasto-plastic behaviour of structures, is based to a considerable extent on researches made by the other author for The Institute of Welding.

The treatment of the theory of reinforced concrete has been simplified by the omission of a number of formulas which, though useful in the preparation of design curves, tend to confuse, rather than help, the study of fundamental principles.

The authors thank those readers who have taken the trouble to point out errors. As a result, one or two serious mistakes and a number of minor ones have been corrected. It is too much to hope that all have now been eradicated and the continued help of readers will be welcomed.

A. J. SUTTON PIPPARD.

J. F. BAKER.

LONDON, 1943.

PREFACE TO FIRST EDITION

The primary object of this book is to present to the student of engineering a general outline of the theories upon which the design of structures is based. Problems of practical design have been excluded as we believe that this side of the engineer's work cannot be effectively taught by means of text-books and must be acquired by experience in the shops and drawing office.

This point of view explains the omission of certain sections commonly found in books dealing with the theory of structures, but we hope that such omissions will be compensated by the inclusion of methods of analysis which are not usually given and which in some cases appear for the first time.

It is assumed that the student is reasonably familiar with simple analytical and graphical statics since the study of these subjects forms a normal part of an intermediate course in engineering or applied mathematics. Descriptions of stress diagrams, vector diagrams, etc., have therefore been reduced to the minimum consistent with a continuous treatment of the subject.

The work during the last six years of the Steel Structures Research Committee of the Department of Scientific and Industrial Research has completely modified the outlook on the design of steel building frames. Both authors were members of this Committee, one of them being its Technical Officer for the greater part of its existence, and the results achieved are dealt with in sufficient detail to enable the student to appreciate the modern aspects of this important branch of structural engineering.

The authors are deeply indebted to Messrs. Longmans Green & Company, Limited, for their very generous permission to reproduce certain portions of books published by them * especially in connection with portions of Chapters 7 and 8 and those sections dealing with strain energy analysis.

In the troublesome work of proof-reading we have been helped by Miss L. Chitty, M.A. ; in the working of examples by Mr. S. R. Sparkes, B.Sc., and in the preparation of drawings by Mr. T. Bryce, all of the Imperial College and to them we offer our grateful thanks.

A. J. SUTTON PIPPARD.

J. F. BAKER.

September, 1936.

* "Aeroplane Structures " (A. J. S. Pippard and J. L. Pritchard) and " Strain Energy Methods of Stress Analysis " (A. J. S. Pippard).

CONTENTS

CHAPTER 1
DEFINITIONS AND GENERAL PRINCIPLES

CHAPTER 2
PRIMARY STRESS ANALYSIS OF STATICALLY DETERMINATE FRAMES

CHAPTER 3
THE STRESSES IN STRAIGHT AND CURVED BEAMS

CHAPTER 4
THEOREMS RELATING TO ELASTIC BODIES

CHAPTER 5
DISPLACEMENTS OF ELASTIC BODIES

CHAPTER 6
STRESS ANALYSIS OF REDUNDANT FRAMES

CHAPTER 7
STRUTS AND LATERALLY LOADED COLUMNS AND TIES

CHAPTER 8
CONTINUOUS BEAMS

CHAPTER 9
FRAMES WITH STIFF JOINTS

CHAPTER 10
MOMENT DISTRIBUTION METHOD

CHAPTER 11
REINFORCED CONCRETE

1*

CONTENTS

CHAPTER 12

ELASTIC ARCHES AND RINGS

PAGE

CHAPTER 13

THE SUSPENSION BRIDGE

CHAPTER 14

INFLUENCE LINES FOR STATICALLY DETERMINATE STRUCTURES: ROLLING LOADS

CHAPTER 15

INFLUENCE LINES FOR STATICALLY INDETERMINATE STRUCTURES

CHAPTER 16

THE VOUSSOIR ARCH

CONTENTS

CHAPTER 17

THE BEAM CURVED IN PLAN

CHAPTER 18

THE DESIGN OF STEEL FRAMED BUILDINGS

CHAPTER 19

THE THEORY OF MASONRY DAMS

CHAPTER 20

EARTH PRESSURE AND THE DESIGN OF EARTH RETAINING STRUCTURES

CHAPTER 21

EXPERIMENTAL STRUCTURAL ANALYSIS

CONTENTS

CHAPTER 22

PLASTIC THEORY

APPENDIX

BERRY FUNCTIONS

THE ANALYSIS OF ENGINEERING STRUCTURES

CHAPTER 1

DEFINITIONS AND GENERAL PRINCIPLES

1.1. Introduction.—Any assemblage of materials whose function is that of supporting loads is a structure. The term may be applied equally correctly to a large bridge or an aeroplane wing rib ; to a masonry dam or the steel frame of a building. The component parts of a loaded structure are in a state of stress and the laws which govern the distribution of these stresses must be studied with a view to their calculation so that the different parts of the structure may be proportioned to take them with safety.

Generally, there are several methods by which loads can be supported, and the first stage in the design of a structure is to decide the most appropriate way of solving the particular problem which is presented. For instance, in choosing a bridge to carry a railway across a river the safety of the structure is not the only criterion ; cost and appearance must be considered so that the choice of the best type is a matter requiring judgment, experience and taste.

When the general lines of the scheme have been settled the loads which the structure has to carry must be estimated as accurately as possible. The loads usually arise from a variety of causes and in the example taken will include the weight of trains, the dynamic effects of the locomotive driving wheels, the dead weight of the bridge itself and the pressure of wind on trains and structure. When these loads have been estimated the forces in the different parts of the structure must be calculated and the dimensions fixed so that the stresses will be everywhere within safe limits. This stage of the design, for which a knowledge of the theory of structures is required, will be dealt with in this book.

1.2. Classification of structures.—Structures are often classified into two main groups of framed structures and mass structures. The former comprises arrangements of separate bars or plates pinned, rivetted or welded together as in a lattice girder or roof truss and such structures depend on the geometrical properties of the arrangement to resist external loads. The latter group relies upon the weight of material in the structure to provide this resistance as in a masonry dam. This classification is not complete or very satisfactory, but is sometimes useful as a broad division.

1.3. Factor of safety and load factor.—It is impossible to determine exactly either the external loads or the internal forces to which a structure is subjected. Moreover, the materials available are subject to certain variations

1

in quality, and workmanship at times will fall below the average. It is therefore necessary in order to guard against these contingencies to allow a margin of strength over and above that which calculation indicates as being just right. This allowance is made by the introduction either of a factor of safety or a load factor and the distinction between these is important.

If the maximum stress which the material in any component of a structure can withstand is denoted by f and that component is designed so that at full load the working stress reaches f/n, n is known as the factor of safety. The maximum stress is advisably taken as the yield stress of the material and n is usually then about 2.

Another method is to multiply the external loads by a load factor N and to design the structure so that the stress under the action of this factored load system reaches the maximum value f.

In other words when a factor of safety is adopted we ensure that under full working loads the stress will nowhere exceed a safe working limit : when a load factor is used we design so that under a specified number of times the full load the structure will just reach the failing point.

In many instances these two methods yield identical results but in others there is a considerable difference.

It is impossible at this stage to indicate how these differences arise but the question will be dealt with more fully later and illustrated with reference to particular problems.

1.4. Frameworks.—An arrangement of bars, connected by joints incapable of transmitting bending moments, which can resist geometrical distortion under the action of any system of applied loads is known as a framework, pin-jointed frame, skeleton frame or truss.

When such a frame is loaded at the joints the internal forces in the bars composing it are simple tensions or compressions : loads acting on a member between its terminal joints will induce bending moments and shearing forces confined to that member. The effect of the axial forces will be to elongate or shorten the bars to the extent of their elastic strains but this elastic deformation, which is necessarily very small, is the only alteration in the configuration of the frame.

It must be emphasised that to comply with the definition, the arrangement of bars must be able to resist deformation under the action of *any* load system. An arrangement which will resist a particular load distribution but which will deform geometrically or collapse under another is not a braced frame.

A frame of which all the bars lie in one plane is known as a plane frame and will resist distortion only under systems of loads in that plane. If the bars lie in more than one plane we have a space frame which will resist distortion under loads in any direction.

1.5. Criterion for frameworks.—The simplest plane frame consists of a triangle of pin-jointed bars. If extra points are to be braced to this elementary frame each one requires the addition of two extra bars. Thus, the first 3 joints of any plane frame having j joints or nodes require 3 bars to connect them, while the remaining $j-3$ joints require $2j-6$ extra bars. If then n is the total number of bars required to brace j joints together,

$$n = 2j - 3 \qquad \qquad (1.1)$$

The simplest space frame consists of 4 joints connected by 6 members to form a skeleton tetrahedron. Additional nodes will each require 3 bars for connection to this tetrahedron, so that

$$n = 3j - 6 \quad . \quad . \quad . \quad . \quad . \quad . \quad . \quad . \quad (1.2)$$

These equations give the minimum number of bars necessary for the construction of frames with a specified number of joints and these are termed essential bars. An arrangement of bars containing less than the essential number *cannot* form a frame and will, except perhaps in special cases, collapse under load. If it contains more than the essential number the frame is said to be overbraced or redundant. If it contains the correct number of bars given by the appropriate criterion it is a simply stiff or just-stiff frame.

This statement requires certain reservations : it is assumed that the disposition of the bars is satisfactory and that their character and strength are adequate for the loads which they may have to carry.

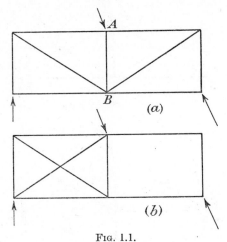

FIG. 1.1.

For example, in Fig. 1.1 six nodes are to be connected by bars to form a plane frame. Equation (1.1) shows that nine members are essential and if less are provided it is impossible to brace the points. The essential number of bars however can be disposed either as shown at (*a*) or at (*b*). The first disposition is satisfactory but in the second, one panel is overbraced while the other is unbraced. Further, although (*a*) has a satisfactory disposition of bars it is necessary to ensure that these bars can fulfil the duties imposed upon them. Under the loading shown AB will be in compression ; under another system it may be in tension. All bars must therefore be capable of taking such tensile or compressive forces as may be imposed by any possible external load system.

If a number of nodes have to be connected by bracing bars to certain fixed points it is clear that these fixed points are equivalent to an already existing frame, and the number of bars necessary to effect the bracing are 2n and 3n for plane and space frames respectively, where n is the number of free nodes.

1.6. Reactive forces.—The usual function of a frame, as already stated, is to transmit an external load system to a number of specified points, *e.g.*

the load on a bridge must be transmitted to the abutments. Since the external loading may vary, the supporting points must be capable of exerting reactive forces which will statically balance any such loading.

If a plane frame is supported at two points the reactive forces at these points together with the external loads form a system in static equilibrium and three conditions must be satisfied as follows :—

1. The algebraic sum of the components of loads and reactions parallel to any axis in the plane must be zero.
2. The algebraic sum of the components of loads and reactions parallel to another axis inclined to the original axis and in the plane must be zero.
3. The algebraic sum of the moments about any point in the plane must be zero.

It is usual but not essential to take the two axes at right angles to each other.

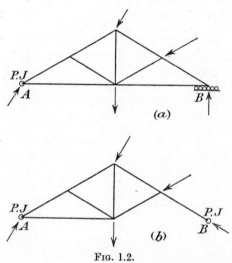

(a)

(b)

Fig. 1.2.

These conditions require three forces for their satisfaction and the nature of the supports must be such as to provide them. If one support is capable of exerting a force along one of the axes of resolution only, while the other can exert forces along both axes of resolution, the necessary conditions are satisfied. Such supports may be provided by a frictionless roller and a pin joint respectively and these supply the statically essential reactive forces.

This arrangement is illustrated in Fig. 1.2 (a) where the roof truss is supported at A on a pin joint which can exert a reaction in any direction and at B on a frictionless roller which can only exert a reaction normal to the bearing.

If both supports are pin joints both the reactive forces have components about the two chosen axes, thus introducing four unknown components. Since only three equations have to be satisfied the magnitude of these forces cannot be determined from purely statical considerations. This is an instance of a number of nodes connected to two fixed points and the number of essential bars is $2n$. In the example illustrated $n=4$ and 8 bars only are needed : a possible frame is shown at (b).

In a space frame the conditions of static equilibrium which have to be satisfied are six in number ; the components of the external loads and of the reactive forces along three separate axes must be zero and the moments of the loads and forces about those axes must also be zero. These axes are usually taken mutually perpendicular. The essential reactions for a space frame must therefore provide six component forces suitably disposed. If one support consists of a universal joint, this will account for three of the six components. Another support should then be such that movements of the supported point are restricted to a line ; this introduces two restraints. The third support should be such that movements are restricted to a plane, which only requires one restraint. The simplest illustration of the arrangement is that of the ball, groove and point used for mounting certain instruments. If more than the essential six reactive forces are provided the frame will be statically indeterminate unless the number of bars in it is correspondingly decreased.

1.7. Primary and secondary stresses.—The axial forces in the bars of a frame under loads applied to the nodes are known as the primary stresses. In actual structures the joints are seldom of the pinned type but are designed to transmit bending moments. The stresses in the bars are then no longer simple tensions and compressions but are complicated by the effects of bending. The extra stresses induced by the stiffness of the joints are known as secondary stresses ; not because they are of secondary importance but because no estimate can be made of their magnitude until the primary stresses based on the assumption of pin joints have been calculated.

1.8. Self-straining.—If a just-stiff frame has one of its members removed the remaining bars form a mechanism. It is evident therefore that the member which has been removed could within certain limits be replaced by another of a different length without causing any stresses in the remaining bars. The only effect would be an alteration in the configuration of the frame.

If, however, a *redundant* bar is to be inserted into a just-stiff frame without causing stresses in the existing bars it must be made of exactly the right length since the two joints to be connected are already fixed in position relative to each other. If by error or design the member is not of the exact length, force must be exerted to get it into position—the two points to be joined will have to be brought closer together or forced apart. Thus before any external load is applied to the frame its members are in a state of stress. This action is known as self-straining and any initial stresses must be added to those due to the external load system.

CHAPTER 2

PRIMARY STRESS ANALYSIS OF STATICALLY DETERMINATE
FRAMES

2.1. The general problem.—The first step in the analysis of any braced structure is the determination of the stresses or forces in the bars of the frame on the assumptions that they are all pinned at the ends and that all loads are applied to the joints. The internal forces are then purely tensile or compressive, and although this ideal state of affairs does not completely represent the conditions in an actual structure the determination of these primary stresses is an essential preliminary to a more exact analysis. In the present chapter an account will therefore be given of the various methods in use for calculating such stresses. Since certain of them are dealt with adequately in books on statics, which the student is presumed to have studied, it should not be necessary to elaborate them here : we shall be content to give examples which will serve as indications of the treatment.

A simply stiff framework, which will alone be considered in this chapter, can be completely analysed by the methods of statics since the number of unknowns is the same as the number of equations obtainable from the conditions of static equilibrium. The methods in use are therefore only variations of the application of the same fundamental principles.

2.2. The stress diagram.—One of the most generally useful methods is that of the stress diagram which is simply a continued application of the well-known theorem of the polygon of forces which states that if any number of forces acting at a point are in equilibrium the vector diagram representing them consists of a closed polygon. In its simplest form when only three forces are acting the polygon becomes the triangle of forces.

In a braced frame every joint is in equilibrium under the action of the forces in the bars meeting at the joint and the external loads applied there. Hence, a closed polygon can be drawn for every joint in the frame provided that not more than two unknown quantities appear at any joint. If the external loads are specified the unknowns may consist of the internal forces in two bars of the frame. For example, suppose Fig. 2.1 to represent a joint O in a frame carrying an external load W, and OA, OB and OC the bars connected to O. If the force in OA is known e.g. to be ·8W the forces in OB and OC can be determined. Using Bow's notation, ab is set out parallel to the line of action of W and equal to W to some selected scale. bc is then drawn parallel to OA and its length is made ·8W to the same scale. From c, cd is drawn parallel to OB and from a, ad is drawn parallel to OC. These lines meet at d ; cd and ad then represent to scale the magnitude of the forces in OB and OC respectively. The direction of arrows on the force polygon must be all in the same sense—in the present instance clockwise—and these arrows, transferred to the joint diagram give the direction of the forces acting through the members on the joint.

6

The two unknowns may however consist of a magnitude and a direction as illustrated by Fig. 2.2, which represents the joint at the point where a truss is pinned to a support. The forces in OA, OB and OC are known and the reactive force has to be found both in magnitude and direction.

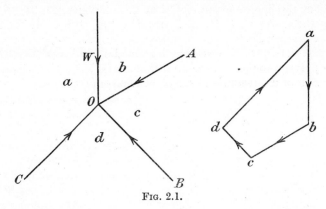

FIG. 2.1.

ab, bc and cd are drawn parallel to the lines of action of the three known forces and proportional to their magnitudes. The closing vector da then represents in magnitude and direction the reactive force at O.

This principle can be used to find graphically the reactions and primary stresses in any just-stiff braced framework, but instead of drawing separate polygons for each joint the work is simplified by combining them into one stress diagram.

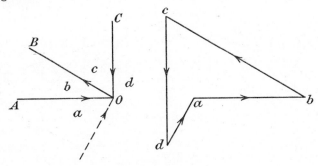

FIG. 2.2.

As an illustration the quadrangular truss shown in Fig. 2.3 will be analysed. The truss is supported on rollers at the left-hand side, the reaction there being consequently vertical, and by a pinned joint at the right-hand side where the reaction will be inclined.

The frame diagram is lettered in accordance with Bow's notation.

The first step is to determine the magnitude and line of action of the reactive forces and this may be done either by direct calculation from the static equations or graphically by the use of the funicular polygon. The process in the latter case is as follows. Set out the load line abc . . . . k to some convenient scale so that ab represents the force of 1 ton acting between A and B in magnitude and direction, bc the force between B and C and so on. Take any convenient pole O and join Oa, Ob . . . . Ok, thus completing the vector diagram. Produce the lines of action of all the forces on the frame diagram as shown.

Starting at the pinned support draw the line 01 in the space J parallel to *Oj*, cutting the line of action of HJ at 1. From 1 draw 12 in space H parallel to *Oh* to cut the line of action of GH at 2. Similarly, 23, 34, 45, etc., are drawn in the spaces G, F, E, etc., parallel to *Og*, *Of*, *Oe*, etc., until finally 89 in space A is parallel to *Oa*. Complete the funicular polygon by joining 09.

From the pole *O* of the vector diagram draw *Ol* parallel to 09 of the funicular polygon to meet the vertical from *a* at *l*. *kl* is then the magnitude and direction of the reaction at the right-hand support.

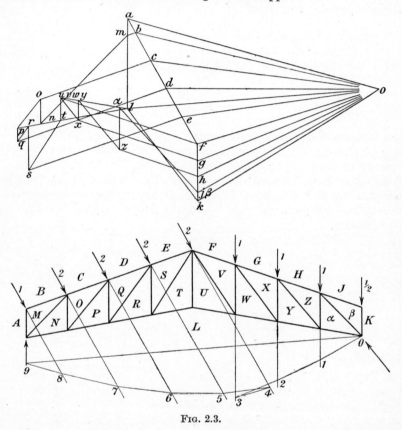

Fig. 2.3.

To draw the stress diagram we start with joint ABM. *ab* has already been drawn to represent the external force in magnitude and direction, so from *a* and *b* we draw lines *am* and *bm* parallel to forces AM and BM. *abm* is then the triangle of forces for the joint considered and the lines *am* and *bm* give the magnitudes of the forces in the bars AM and BM and the direction in which these forces act on the joint. Thus *ab* is drawn in the direction of the external force and following round the triangle we see that *bm* acts towards the joint and BM is therefore in compression. Similarly *ma* acts towards the joint and MA is also in compression.

Proceeding now to joint AMNLA we find one external reaction and three internal forces acting. Of these *la* and *am* are known so that the polygon of forces could be drawn for this joint. *la* and *am* are, however, already drawn to scale so, if *mn* and *ln* are drawn parallel to MN and LN respectively, the polygon is completed by these two additional lines. Following round the diagram in a clockwise direction to conform with the fact that *la* is an upward force we find *am* and *mn* act towards the joint, but that *nl* acts from the joint. Thus NL is in tension. Joint BCONM and remaining joints are treated in the same way in succession until the whole stress diagram is completed. The test of accuracy is obtained when the line parallel to $\alpha\beta$ in the frame diagram drawn from α in the stress diagram gives β coinciding with *j*. This gives a zero force in $j\beta$ which is obviously correct from an examination of the conditions at joint KβJ.

2.3. Ritter's method of sections.—In many cases the method of sections can be used with advantage in stress analysis, especially when a knowledge of the forces in certain members only is required.

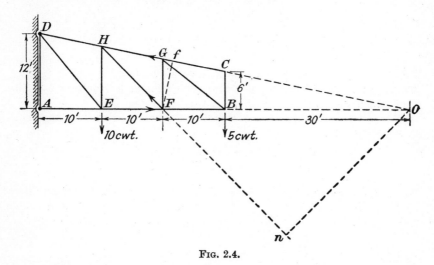

Fig. 2.4.

This method consists essentially of solving the equations of static equilibrium for a section of the framework and by judicious choice of such section the work can often be made very simple.

Fig. 2.4 shows a cantilever frame supported at A and D and carrying loads at E and B. The necessary dimensions are shown on the diagram.

The section of the frame GCBF is kept in equilibrium by the external load at B and the internal forces in GH, FH and FE which act on the joints G and F in the direction of the arrows at those joints. These four forces must therefore satisfy the conditions of static equilibrium and so the algebraic sum of their moments about any point must be zero. Now the lines of action of HG and FH meet at H and by taking moments about this point we eliminate the moments of these two forces and obtain

$$T_{EF} \times HE = 5EB$$

or
$$T_{EF} = \frac{5 \times 20}{10} = 10$$

where T_{EF} is the force in EF.

It is unnecessary to know the direction of T_{EF}. If it is assumed to be a tension and is actually a compression this will be indicated by a negative value in the result. Again by taking moments about F the moments of the forces in EF and FH are eliminated and we obtain

$$T_{HG} \times Ff = 50$$

where Ff is the perpendicular from F on the line of action of HG.

The length of Ff can often, as in the present case, be obtained geometrically, but if this is difficult it can be scaled from the frame diagram.

If DC and AB be produced to meet at O we have from the similar triangles FGf and ODA,

$$\frac{Ff}{GF} = \frac{OA}{OD}$$

or
$$Ff = \frac{8 \times 60}{\sqrt{60^2 + 12^2}} = 7 \cdot 84.$$

Hence
$$T_{HG} = \frac{50}{7 \cdot 84} = 6 \cdot 38.$$

Suppose now that the force in GF is to be calculated.

The section GCB of the frame is in equilibrium under the action of the external load at B and the internal forces GH, GF and BF.

The lines of action of GH and BF meet at O and so we take moments about this point and obtain

$$T_{GF} \times 40 = 30 \times 5$$

or
$$T_{GF} = 3 \cdot 75.$$

To calculate the force in FH we again consider the section GCBF and take moments about O where HG and EF meet.

Then
$$T_{HF} \times nO = 30 \times 5.$$

It is best here to scale nO and so solve for T_{HF}.

For the members DH, DE and AE the procedure is the same as above, but both the loads at B and E now appear in the equations.

For example T_{AE} is found by taking moments about D, the equation being

$$T_{AE} \times DA = (10 \times 10) + (30 \times 5)$$

or
$$T_{AE} = 20 \cdot 83.$$

2.4. Method of resolution at joints.—In certain simple forms of truss the forces in all the bars can be written down directly by considering the equilibrium of each joint in turn. This is a method which with a little practice is very quick and useful.

Suppose the forces in all the bars of the truss shown in Fig. 2.5 are required.

The reactions at A and B are first calculated. Consider first the equilibrium of joint A.

The vertical component of force in AE must balance the vertical reaction and so

$$T_{AE} = 12 \operatorname{cosec} 60° = 13 \cdot 85.$$

The horizontal component of T_{AE} is balanced by the force in AC or

$$T_{AC} = T_{AE} \cos 60° = 6 \cdot 925.$$

The problem may also be treated by taking AEe as the triangle of forces for the joint A, where Ee is perpendicular to AC.

Then $\qquad\qquad \dfrac{T_{AE}}{12} = \dfrac{AE}{Ee}$

or $\qquad\qquad T_{AE} = \dfrac{12 \times 8}{4\sqrt{3}} = 13 \cdot 85$

and $\qquad\qquad \dfrac{T_{AC}}{T_{AE}} = \dfrac{Ae}{AE}$

$i.e.$ $\qquad\qquad T_{AC} = \tfrac{1}{2} T_{AE} = 6 \cdot 925.$

Taking joint E next, the forces acting are $13 \cdot 85$ from AE and the vertical load at E.

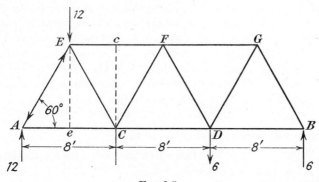

FIG. 2.5.

These can be dealt with separately. A triangle of forces for AE, EC and EF is the equilateral triangle EFC and due to the force in AE, equal forces occur in EF and EC, EF being compressive and EC tensile.

For the vertical load at E we take ECc as the triangle of forces and obtain as the total forces in the bars,

$$T_{EC} = 13 \cdot 85 - 12 \operatorname{cosec} 60° = 0$$
$$T_{EF} = -13 \cdot 85 + \tfrac{1}{2}(13 \cdot 85) = -6 \cdot 925$$

where the positive sign denotes tension and the negative sign compression.

Alternatively if a section is taken cutting EF, EC and CA the total shearing force across this section is zero, by summing forces to the left or right. Since EC is the only bar of the three which can have a vertical component of force, such component must be zero to balance the shearing force. Hence $T_{EC} = 0$.

Similarly, $T_{CF} = T_{FD} = 0$.

Therefore, by considering the equilibrium of joint F,

$$T_{EF} = T_{FG} = -6 \cdot 925.$$

Also from joint C, $T_{AC} = T_{CD} = 6 \cdot 925.$

Treating joint B in the same way as A,

$$T_{BG} = -6 \cdot 925$$

and $$T_{BD} = 3 \cdot 462.$$

Also $$T_{GD} = 6 \cdot 925$$

and the forces are all determined.

2.5. Method of tension coefficients.—The methods described in the previous paragraphs are not easily applicable to space frames and although they may

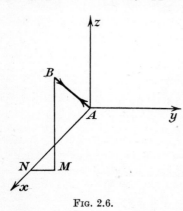

FIG. 2.6.

be adapted for the purpose analysis by their use is laborious and liable to error. The most satisfactory treatment of space frames has been very fully described by Southwell (1920). It is equally applicable to plane frames and is one of the simplest and most accurate methods of stress determination for such frames. This method was also used by Müller-Breslau. The treatment of the space frame will be considered first and its simplification when applied to a plane frame dealt with afterwards.

Let AB in Fig. 2.6 be any bar in a space frame,

T_{AB} the *tension* in this bar,

and L_{AB} the length of the bar.

The tension will be expressed in the form

$$T_{AB} = L_{AB} t_{AB}$$

where t_{AB} is known as a tension coefficient.

Through A take three mutually perpendicular axes, Ax, Ay, Az, and let the co-ordinates of A and B be (x_A, y_A, z_A) and (x_B, y_B, z_B).

Then the component of T_{AB} acting at A in the direction Ax is

$$T_{AB} \cos BAx$$

or $$T_{AB} \frac{x_B - x_A}{L_{AB}},$$

which from the expression for T_{AB} in terms of its tension coefficient can be written

$$t_{AB}(x_B - x_A).$$

Similarly, the components of T_{AB} along Ay and Az are $t_{AB}(y_B - y_A)$ and $t_{AB}(z_B - z_A)$ respectively.

At B, the other end of the bar, the components along the three axes will be

$$t_{AB}(x_A - x_B), \ t_{AB}(y_A - y_B) \text{ and } t_{AB}(z_A - z_B).$$

Suppose now that at a joint A in a space frame there are connected any number of bars AB, AC . . . . AQ, and that the components of external load acting at this joint along the directions of the x, y and z axes are X_A, Y_A and Z_A respectively. The equilibrium of the joint requires that the components of all the forces along three mutually perpendicular axes shall be zero so that the conditions for equilibrium are

$$t_{AB}(x_B-x_A)+t_{AC}(x_C-x_A)+ \ldots +t_{AQ}(x_Q-x_A)+X_A=0$$
$$t_{AB}(y_B-y_A)+t_{AC}(y_C-y_A)+ \ldots +t_{AQ}(y_Q-y_A)+Y_A=0 \qquad (2.1)$$
$$t_{AB}(z_B-z_A)+t_{AC}(z_C-z_A)+ \ldots +t_{AQ}(z_Q-z_A)+Z_A=0$$

Three equations such as these can be formed for each joint in the framework. They involve the quantities (x_B-x_A), (y_B-y_A), (z_B-z_A), etc., which are the projected lengths of the bars on the x, y and z axes respectively and therefore known from the drawings of the frame, and the unknown quantities t_{AB}, t_{AC}, etc., which are to be calculated.

For every term such as $t_{AB}(x_B-x_A)$ in one equation there will be a term $t_{AB}(x_A-x_B)$ in another equation, these being numerically equal but opposite in sign since $(x_B-x_A)=-(x_A-x_B)$. If, therefore, the x equations for all the joints are added we obtain

$$X_A+X_B+ \ldots =0$$

and similarly, by adding the y and z equations,

$$Y_A+Y_B+ \ldots =0, \qquad (2.2)$$

and

$$Z_A+Z_B+ \ldots =0.$$

These equations express three of the essential conditions for the static equilibrium of the frame as a whole, viz., that the sum of the components of the external forces along three perpendicular axes must be zero.

Again, if the first of the equations in (2.1) be multiplied by y_A and the second of these equations by $-x_A$ we obtain

$$t_{AB}(x_By_A-x_Ay_A)+t_{AC}(x_Cy_A-x_Ay_A)+ \ldots t_{AQ}(x_Qy_A-x_Ay_A)+X_Ay_A=0$$
$$t_{AB}(-y_Bx_A+y_Ax_A)+t_{AC}(-y_Cx_A+y_Ax_A)+ \ldots +t_{AQ}(-y_Qx_A+y_Ax_A)$$
$$-Y_Ax_A=0,$$

and adding these we get

$$t_{AB}(x_By_A-x_Ay_B)+t_{AC}(x_Cy_A-x_Ay_C)+ \ldots +t_{AQ}(x_Qy_A-x_Ay_Q)$$
$$+X_Ay_A-Y_Ax_A=0 \quad (2.3)$$

If this is done for the corresponding equation for each joint we shall obtain similar results to (2.3), and for every term such as $t_{AB}(x_By_A-x_Ay_B)$ there will appear another, numerically equal but opposite in sign, $t_{AB}(x_Ay_B-x_By_A)$.

Hence, by adding all these equations we obtain

$$(y_AX_A-x_AY_A)+(y_BX_B-x_BY_B)+ \ldots =0$$

and similarly from the other equations of (2.1)

$$(z_AY_A-y_AZ_A)+(z_BY_B-y_BZ_B) + \ldots =0 \qquad (2.4)$$

and

$$(x_AZ_A-z_AX_A)+(x_BZ_B-z_BX_B) + \ldots =0.$$

These equations express the remaining three essential conditions for the static equilibrium of the frame as a whole, viz., that the moments about three perpendicular axes shall be zero.

It has already been shown that the essential reactive forces for a space frame are six in number. If the frame is supported at A, B and C, for example, it is necessary for one point, say A, to be pinned, for another, B, to be restrained to move along a line in one plane, and for the third C, to be simply restrained in a plane. Thus, at A we shall have three reactive forces X_A, Y_A and Z_A, at B two reactive forces X_B, Z_B, and at C, one reactive force only, Z_C. The equations (2.2) and (2.4) enable these six unknown forces to be determined.

Having found the reactive forces the equations corresponding to (2.1) are used to find the values of the tension coefficients. It should be pointed out that these equations do not all have to be solved simultaneously and the work is neither difficult nor involved. Once the tension coefficients have been evaluated the loads in the members are found by multiplying the coefficients by the lengths of the appropriate members, *e.g.*,

$$T_{AB} = t_{AB}\sqrt{(x_B - x_A)^2 + (y_B - y_A)^2 + (z_B - z_A)^2}.$$

In forming the equations the load in a member is always assumed to be tensile and the terms in the equation are positive or negative as they tend to move the joint in the positive or negative direction of x, y or z. A negative result for the tension coefficient signifies that the force in that member is compressive.

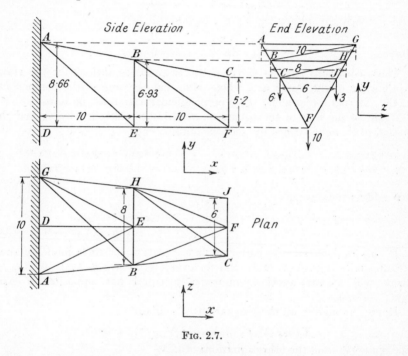

Fig. 2.7.

As an example of this method the space frame shown in Fig. 2.7 will be analysed. It consists of a cantilever structure formed of three longitudinal members ABC, GHJ and DEF braced together and arranged so that at any section they lie at the corners of an equilateral triangle.

As there are six points to be braced to the wall, eighteen members are necessary. These are provided by the six longitudinal members, six struts and six diagonal panel members.

The loading is as shown on the diagram.

Taking the co-ordinate axes positive in the directions indicated and starting with point F, the equations of equilibrium are formed as follows :—

The members meeting at this joint are FE, FC, FJ, FH, FB, and by considering first the equation for the x axis, it is clear that FC and FJ have no components.

The projection of FE on this axis is −10, that of FB is −10, and that of FH is −10, so that the equation is

$$-10t_{\text{FE}}-10t_{\text{FB}}-10t_{\text{FH}}=0.$$

Considering now the y axis, the members concerned are FC, FJ, FB and FH. The projections on the y axis of FC and FJ are both $5\cdot2$, and of FB and FH are $6\cdot93$. The load is 10 acting in a negative direction so that the equation is

$$5\cdot2t_{\text{FC}}+5\cdot2t_{\text{FJ}}+6\cdot93t_{\text{FB}}+6\cdot93t_{\text{FH}}=10.$$

Similarly, for the z axis we get

$$3t_{\text{FJ}}-3t_{\text{FC}}+4t_{\text{FH}}-4t_{\text{FB}}=0.$$

Following the same procedure at every joint the necessary equations are formed and are best set out as shown in Table 2.1.

TABLE 2.1.

Joint		Equations
F	x	$-10t_{\text{FE}}-10t_{\text{FB}}-10t_{\text{FH}}=0.$
	y	$5\cdot2t_{\text{FC}}+5\cdot2t_{\text{FJ}}+6\cdot93t_{\text{FB}}+6\cdot93t_{\text{FH}}-10=0.$
	z	$3t_{\text{FJ}}-3t_{\text{FC}}+4t_{\text{FH}}-4t_{\text{FB}}=0.$
C	x	$-10t_{\text{CB}}-10t_{\text{CH}}=0.$
	y	$-5\cdot2t_{\text{CF}}+1\cdot73t_{\text{CB}}+1\cdot73t_{\text{CH}}-6=0.$
	z	$6t_{\text{CJ}}+7t_{\text{CH}}-t_{\text{CB}}+3t_{\text{CF}}=0.$
J	x	$-10t_{\text{JH}}=0.$
	y	$1\cdot73t_{\text{JH}}-5\cdot2t_{\text{JF}}-3=0.$
	z	$-6t_{\text{JC}}+t_{\text{JH}}-3t_{\text{JF}}=0.$
E	x	$10t_{\text{EF}}-10t_{\text{ED}}-10t_{\text{EA}}-10t_{\text{EG}}=0.$
	y	$6\cdot93t_{\text{EB}}+8\cdot66t_{\text{EA}}+6\cdot93t_{\text{EH}}+8\cdot66t_{\text{EG}}=0.$
	z	$4t_{\text{EH}}-4t_{\text{EB}}+5t_{\text{EG}}-5t_{\text{EA}}=0.$
B	x	$10t_{\text{BC}}-10t_{\text{BA}}-10t_{\text{BG}}+10t_{\text{BF}}=0.$
	y	$-6\cdot93t_{\text{BE}}+1\cdot73t_{\text{BA}}+1\cdot73t_{\text{BG}}-1\cdot73t_{\text{BC}}-6\cdot93t_{\text{BF}}=0.$
	z	$8t_{\text{BH}}+9t_{\text{BG}}+t_{\text{BC}}-t_{\text{BA}}+4t_{\text{BE}}+4t_{\text{BF}}=0.$
H	x	$10t_{\text{HJ}}-10t_{\text{HG}}+10t_{\text{HC}}+10t_{\text{HF}}=0.$
	y	$1\cdot73t_{\text{HG}}-1\cdot73t_{\text{HJ}}-1\cdot73t_{\text{HC}}-6\cdot93t_{\text{HE}}-6\cdot93t_{\text{HF}}=0.$
	z	$-8t_{\text{HB}}-7t_{\text{HC}}-t_{\text{HJ}}+t_{\text{HG}}-4t_{\text{HF}}-4t_{\text{HE}}=0.$

These equations must now be solved. In the present instance joint J is taken first and the equation Jx for forces along the x axis gives $t_{\text{JH}}=0$. Substituting this value in Jy we find t_{JF} to be $-0\cdot576$ and $t_{\text{JC}}=0\cdot288$ follows at once from Jz.

If joint C be now considered it will be seen from Cx that $t_{\text{CB}}+t_{\text{CH}}=0$ which can be substituted in Cy to obtain $t_{\text{CF}}=-1\cdot15$. If we use this and the known value of t_{CJ} in Cz, an equation in t_{CH} and t_{CB} is obtained which with Cx enables these two coefficients to be evaluated.

This process is continued until all the coefficients have been determined and these, multiplied by the respective lengths of the members, give the loads in the members as set out in Table 2.2.

TABLE 2.2.

Member	Tension coefficient t	Length L	Load Lt
FC	−1·15	6·0	− 6·9
FJ	−0·576	6·0	− 3·46
FB	1·59	12·8	20·3
FE	−2·75	10·0	−27·5
FH	1·16	12·8	14·85
CB	−0·215	10·2	− 2·19
CJ	0·288	6·0	1·73
CH	0·215	12·3	2·64
JH	0	10·2	0
EB	−1·194	8·0	− 9·55
ED	−4·4	10·0	−44·0
EA	0·961	14·14	13·60
EG	0·684	14·14	9·7
EH	−0·86	8·0	− 7·08
BA	1·28	10·2	13·06
BG	0·133	13·56	1·80
BH	−0·166	8·0	− 1·328
HG	1·375	10·2	14·02

When the method of tension coefficients is applied to the stress analysis of plane frames the work is considerably simplified since there are no components along the z axis, and all the data are contained in a single view of the framework.

As an illustration the roof truss shown in Fig. 2.8 will be analysed.

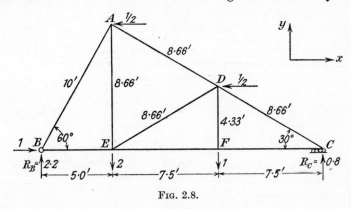

FIG. 2.8.

If R_B and R_C are the reactions at B and C respectively we obtain by taking moments about B

$$20R_C = 10 + 12 \cdot 5 - \frac{4 \cdot 33}{2} - 4 \cdot 33$$

or $$R_C = 0 \cdot 8.$$

Therefore the vertical component of $R_B = 2 \cdot 2$ and the horizontal component of $R_B = 1 \cdot 0$.

The positive directions of x and y are indicated on the diagram and the equations for the various joints in terms of tension coefficients are given in Table 2.3.

t_{CD} is obtained directly from equation Cy and is $-\cdot1846$ which is entered in the Table.

From Cx and Fx, $t_{CF}=-t_{CD}=t_{FE}$ and from Fy, $t_{FD}=\cdot231$.

The values of t_{DC} and t_{DF} thus found are substituted in Dx and Dy leaving simultaneous equations in t_{DE} and t_{DA} which give on solution $t_{DE}=-\cdot1488$ and $t_{DA}=-\cdot1025$.

t_{AB} is found directly from By and substitution of its value in Bx gives t_{BE}.

TABLE 2.3.

Joint		Equation	Bar	t	L	T
C	x	$-7\cdot5t_{CF}-7\cdot5t_{CD}=0$	CD	$-\cdot1846$	$8\cdot66$	$-1\cdot6$
	y	$4\cdot33t_{CD}+0\cdot8=0$	CF	$+\cdot1846$	$7\cdot5$	$+1\cdot385$
F	x	$t_{FC}-t_{FE}=0$	FD	$+\cdot231$	$4\cdot33$	$+1\cdot000$
	y	$4\cdot33t_{FD}-1=0$	FE	$+\cdot1846$	$7\cdot5$	$+1\cdot385$
D	x	$7\cdot5t_{DC}-7\cdot5t_{DE}-7\cdot5t_{DA}-\frac{1}{2}=0$	BA	$-\cdot254$	$10\cdot0$	$-2\cdot54$
	y	$-4\cdot33(t_{DF}+t_{DC}+t_{DE}-t_{DA})=0$	BE	$+\cdot054$	$5\cdot0$	$+0\cdot27$
A	x	$7\cdot5t_{AD}-5t_{AB}-\frac{1}{2}=0$	DE	$-\cdot1488$	$8\cdot66$	$-1\cdot29$
	y	$-8\cdot66t_{AE}-4\cdot33t_{AD}-8\cdot66t_{AB}=0$	DA	$-\cdot1025$	$8\cdot66$	$-\cdot888$
B	x	$5t_{BE}+5t_{BA}+1=0$	AE	$+\cdot305$	$8\cdot66$	$+2\cdot64$
	y	$8\cdot66t_{BA}+2\cdot2=0$				
E	x	$7\cdot5t_{EF}+7\cdot5t_{ED}-5t_{EB}=0$				
	y	$8\cdot66t_{EA}+4\cdot33t_{ED}-2=0$				

Ay then gives t_{AE}.

The remaining three equations Ax, Ex and Ey afford a check upon the accuracy of the work, since they should be satisfied when the values of the tension coefficients already found are substituted in them. Instead of calculating the reactions directly they could have been dealt with as unknown forces, V_C, V_B and H_B.

The equations for B and C would then have been :—

Joint		Equations
B	x	$5t_{BE}+5t_{BA}+H_B=0$
	y	$8\cdot66t_{BA}+V_B=0$
C	x	$-7\cdot5t_{CF}-7\cdot5t_{CD}=0$
	y	$4\cdot33t_{CD}+V_C=0$

and there would be twelve equations to solve for the nine bar forces and the three reactive forces, H_B, V_B and V_C.

REFERENCE

Southwell, R. V.   1920.   *Engineering, Lond.*, **109**, 165–8.

EXERCISES

(1) Determine by inspection the forces in the truss shown in Diagram 2a.

$(FG=-3$; $GH=HJ=-6$; $JK=-4\cdot5$;
$AC=0$; $CD=3$; $DE=4\cdot5$; $EB=0$;
$FC=GD=5$; $DJ=2\cdot5$; $EK=7\cdot5$;
$AF=CG=-4$; $HD=0$; $JE=KB=-6$.)

(2) The frame shown at 2b is pinned at A, B and C to a rigid support. Comment on the adequacy or otherwise of the bracing and if necessary modify it.

Make a neat sketch of the frame and mark on it the internal stresses in all members.

$(AD=DG=CF=GH=-W$;
$EH=EF=W$; $BE=DE=0$;
$FH=-W\sqrt2$; $AE=W\sqrt2$.)

(3) The pin-jointed frame shown at 2c is supported at A and D. The sides AB, BC and CD are equal in length. Using the method of tension coefficients, find the forces in all members of the frame.

$(AB=-5\cdot78$; $CD=-4\cdot04$; $AD=2\cdot02$;
$AC=1\cdot00$; $BC=-2\cdot89$.)

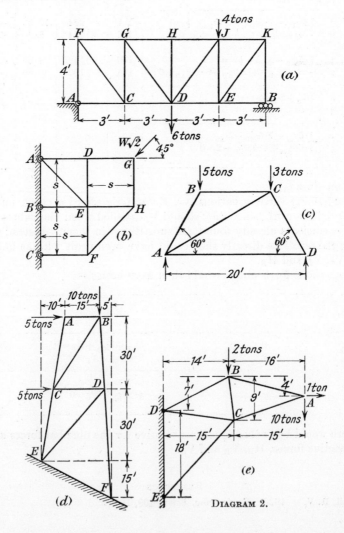

DIAGRAM 2.

(4) Determine by calculation the forces in all members of the pin-jointed frame shown in Diagram 2d.

$(AB = -5 \cdot 0$; $CD = -7 \cdot 96$; $BC = 7 \cdot 10$; $DE = 11 \cdot 07$;
$AC = 0$; $CE = 5 \cdot 99$; $BD = -15 \cdot 95$; $DF = -24 \cdot 20$.)

(5) Using the method of tension coefficients, obtain all the forces in all bars of the frame shown in Diagram 2e.

$(AB = 18 \cdot 25$; $AC = -17 \cdot 51$; $BC = -14 \cdot 58$;
$BD = 18 \cdot 00$; $CD = 3 \cdot 33$; $CE = -26 \cdot 98$.)

CHAPTER 3

THE STRESSES IN STRAIGHT AND CURVED BEAMS

3.1. Shearing force and bending moment.—The theory of flexure is fully dealt with in standard text-books on Strength of Materials. Only those portions of the subject, therefore, which are referred to in later chapters will be outlined here.

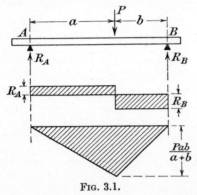

FIG. 3.1.

For our present purpose a beam can be defined as a member supporting transverse loads or subjected to other bending actions.

The *shearing force* or *shear* at any section of a beam is the algebraic sum of all the external forces, including the reactions, acting on either side of the section, resolved normal to the axis of the beam.

The *bending moment* at any section of a beam is the algebraic sum of the moments of all the applied forces, including the reactions, on either side of the section.

Shearing force and bending moment diagrams for a freely supported beam of length $a+b$ carrying a concentrated load P at a distance a from the left-hand support are shown in Fig. 3.1.

3.2. Relationship between loading, shearing force and bending moment.—In Fig. 3.2, DA and CB represent two sections of a beam under load separated by a small distance δx.

The bending moment at AD is M, and at BC is $M+\delta M$. The shearing force at AD is S, and at BC is $S+\delta S$.

The intensity of loading over the small length δx is w. Considering the

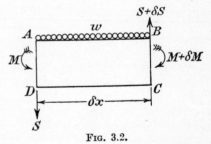

FIG. 3.2.

equilibrium of the length of the beam shown we have by equating vertical forces

$$S+w\delta x=S+\delta S,$$

whence, on making δx and δS infinitely small,

$$\frac{dS}{dx}=w,$$

and by taking moments about D

$$M+\delta M+\frac{w(\delta x)^2}{2}-(S+\delta S)\delta x-M=0$$

i.e.

$$\frac{dM}{dx}=S.$$

Putting these relationships into integral form we have

$$\int wdx = \int dS = S$$

and $$\int S dx = \int dM = M,$$

i.e. the integral of the load diagram between any limits gives the change of shearing force between those limits and the integral of the shearing force diagram similarly gives the change of bending moment.

3.3. Theory of simple bending.—The relation must now be found between the external forces acting on the beam and the internal stresses which keep it in equilibrium.

The assumptions made in the theory of simple bending and throughout this chapter are, except when otherwise stated,

(1) The beam is not stressed beyond the proportional limit of the material.
(2) Young's modulus is the same for tension and compression.
(3) A plane cross-section at right angles to the plane of bending before strain remains plane after strain.
(4) There is no resultant axial force on the beam.
(5) The cross-section of the beam is symmetrical about an axis through its centroid parallel to the plane of bending.
(6) Longitudinal fibres of the beam are free to strain independently of each other.

In Fig. 3.3, let ED, BC be two adjacent cross-sections of the beam, and after bending by pure couples applied to the ends of the beam let them be as shown at E'D', B'C'. They will clearly not be parallel since, due to bending, the fibres parallel and close to CD will have stretched, while those parallel and close to EB will have shortened. It is also clear that there is some plane between CD and EB where the material is neither stretched nor compressed. This plane is called the neutral plane or surface, and its line of intersection with the cross-section of the beam is called the neutral axis of the section.

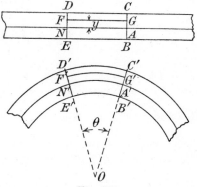

FIG. 3.3.

Let the sections E'D', B'C', inclined after bending at a small angle θ to one another, meet in a line perpendicular to the plane of the paper. Let this line intersect the plane of the paper in O. Let NA be the line in which the neutral surface cuts the plane of the paper before bending, and N'A' be that line after bending. Let y be the distance from the neutral surface of any layer of the material FG parallel to that surface.

Then if R is the radius of curvature we have

$$\frac{F'G'}{N'A'} = \frac{(R+y)\theta}{R\theta} = \frac{R+y}{R}.$$

The strain at the layer F'G' is

$$e = \frac{F'G'-FG}{FG} = \frac{F'G'-N'A'}{N'A'} = \frac{(R+y)\theta-R\theta}{R\theta} = \frac{y}{R}.$$

The longitudinal tensile stress intensity is

$$\mathrm{E}e = \mathrm{E}\frac{y}{\mathrm{R}} = p, \text{ say.}$$

This is equal to the compressive stress at the same distance below the neutral surface, so the intensity of the direct longitudinal stress at any point in the cross-section is proportional to the distance of that point from the neutral axis, reaching a maximum at the boundary farthest from the neutral surface.

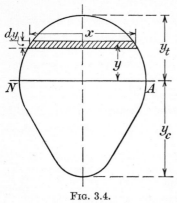

FIG. 3.4.

3.4. Moment of resistance.—The longitudinal internal forces, which are tensile on one side of the neutral surface and compressive on the other, clearly form a couple which must at any section, since the beam is in equilibrium, be equal and opposite to the bending moment at that section. This couple is called the moment of resistance.

In Fig. 3.4, let the shaded area be an elementary strip at a distance y from the neutral axis. The total force on the elementary area is $pxdy$ and the moment of this force is $pxydy$.

The total moment across the section is

$$\mathrm{M} = \int pxydy = \int \frac{\mathrm{E}y}{\mathrm{R}}xydy$$

$$= \frac{\mathrm{E}}{\mathrm{R}}\int xy^2dy$$

$$= \frac{\mathrm{EI}}{\mathrm{R}},$$

where I is the second moment of area or, as it is often but incorrectly called, the moment of inertia of the section about the neutral axis ;

therefore
$$\frac{\mathrm{M}}{\mathrm{I}} = \frac{\mathrm{E}}{\mathrm{R}} = \frac{p}{y}.$$

The maximum intensities of stress occur at the outer boundaries of the surface and if these are f_t and f_c respectively,

$$f_t = \frac{\mathrm{M}y_t}{\mathrm{I}} \text{ and } f_c = \frac{\mathrm{M}y_c}{\mathrm{I}},$$

where y_t, y_c are the distances of the tensile and compressive fibres farthest from the neutral axis.

The quantity I/y, where y is the distance of the neutral axis from the most highly stressed fibre, is called the modulus of the section and is usually denoted by Z, so that we have the relation $f = \mathrm{M}/\mathrm{Z}$. There are two moduli for every section which is not symmetrical about the neutral axis.

Since there is no axial load on the beam the sum of the forces on the elementary areas must be zero, i.e.

$$\int pxdy = 0,$$

or
$$\frac{\mathrm{E}}{\mathrm{R}}\int xydy = 0.$$

The term covered by the integral sign is the first moment of area about the neutral axis and since this is zero the neutral axis must pass through the centroid of the section.

3.5. Stresses when loads are not normal to the beam.—When a beam is subjected to an oblique load the longitudinal stress at any point in the cross-section is made up of two parts, one due to bending action and the other to the effect of the component of the oblique load along the axis of the beam. Thus in the cantilever shown in Fig. 3.5 subjected to a load P, the line of action of which makes an angle θ with the axis of the beam, the stress at a section which is x from the point of application of the load will be due to a bending

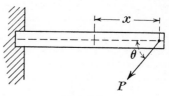

FIG. 3.5.

moment $Px \sin \theta$ and to a thrust $P \cos \theta$. The maximum compressive and tensile stresses due to bending will be $\dfrac{(Px \sin \theta)y_c}{I}$ and $\dfrac{(Px \sin \theta)y_t}{I}$ respectively, while, if A is the cross-sectional area of the beam, the stress due to the thrust will be $\dfrac{P}{A} \cos \theta$ uniformly distributed over the cross-section.

Therefore the total maximum compressive stress will be

$$\frac{(Px \sin \theta)y_c}{I} + \frac{P}{A} \cos \theta,$$

and the total maximum tensile stress will be

$$\frac{(Px \sin \theta)y_t}{I} - \frac{P}{A} \cos \theta.$$

This result assumes that the flexibility of the beam is not so great as to cause secondary effects. The general problem, when this condition is not fulfilled, will be dealt with in Chapter 7.

3.6. Unsymmetrical bending.—It was assumed in the derivation of the expression for the bending stress at any point in a beam given in paragraph 3.3 that the cross-section of the beam was symmetrical about an axis through its centroid parallel to the plane of bending. Such an axis of symmetry must be a principal axis of inertia of the cross-section and the assumption (5) of paragraph 3.3 could, in fact, have been expressed more generally as follows :

"The axis through the centroid of the cross-section of the beam parallel to the plane of bending must be a principal axis of inertia of the cross-section."

If the plane containing the applied bending moment is not parallel to a principal axis of inertia of the beam section the bending stresses cannot be found by the direct application of the formula of paragraph 3.3.

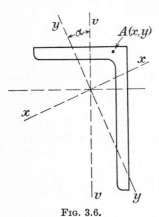

FIG. 3.6.

Fig. 3.6 shows the cross-section of a beam in the shape of an unequal angle, carrying vertical loads. The angle is supported with its short leg horizontal so that the plane of the applied bending moment is parallel to the vertical axis vv. The principal axes of inertia, about which the second moments of area of the section are a maximum and a minimum, are xx and yy respectively. Before the formula of paragraph 3.4 can be used to determine the bending stress at any point the applied bending moment must be resolved into its components about the principal axes. If, at the section under consideration, the applied bending moment acting parallel to the vertical plane vv is M, then its components in the planes parallel to xx and yy will be M sin α and M cos α respectively. At a point A (x, y) in the cross-section the bending stress due to the first of these moments will be

$$\frac{x\text{M} \sin \alpha}{\text{I}_y}$$

and due to the second,

$$\frac{y\text{M} \cos \alpha}{\text{I}_x},$$

where I_x and I_y are the second moments of area of the section about the axes xx and yy respectively.

The total bending stress at the point A due to the applied moment M is therefore

$$p = \frac{\text{M}x \sin \alpha}{\text{I}_y} + \frac{\text{M}y \cos \alpha}{\text{I}_x}.$$

Since the bending stress at the neutral axis is zero, the equation to the neutral axis is

$$\frac{x \sin \alpha}{\text{I}_y} + \frac{y \cos \alpha}{\text{I}_x} = 0.$$

In unsymmetrical bending there is a tendency for the beam to twist. This is not, in general, a serious matter in practice as a beam is usually constrained, for example, by the floor slab in the case of a floor beam and by the roof covering in the case of a purlin and the resulting torsional stresses are small. Where a beam is not so constrained particular care must be taken in its design, as even in a symmetrical section such as a solid steel I, subjected to what appears to be symmetrical bending, large torsional distortions may occur due to a small unintentional eccentricity of loading.

3.7. Distribution of shear stress.—The distribution and value of the shear stress at any section of a beam may be found as follows :—

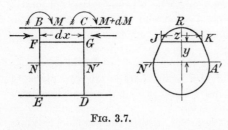

FIG. 3.7.

In Fig. 3.7, let BE, CD be two cross-sections of the beam at a small distance dx from one another, and let the bending moments at these sections be M and M+dM respectively. Let the breadth of the section at any height y be $z=$ JK.

Then the longitudinal stress intensity at height y above the neutral axis N′A′ is, as already shown,

$$p = \frac{\text{M}y}{\text{I}},$$

where I is the second moment of area of the section about N′A′.

The longitudinal thrust on any element of cross-section at BF is $pzdy$, where zdy is the area of this element, *i.e.*

$$\frac{My}{I}zdy$$

and the thrust at CG on an element at the same height is

$$\frac{(M+dM)y}{I}zdy.$$

Therefore the excess of thrust on the element of area at CG over that at BF is the difference of the above quantities,

i.e.

$$\frac{dMy}{I}zdy$$

and the total difference of thrusts on the areas CG, BF is

$$\int_{y}^{y_0}\frac{dMy}{I}zdy,$$

where y_0=BN.

But since BFGC is in equilibrium, the excess of thrust must be balanced by the longitudinal shearing force across the surface FG. Let q be the intensity of the shear stress across FG.

The shearing force across FG is

$$qzdx=\int_{y}^{y_0}\frac{dMy}{I}zdy$$

$$=\frac{dM}{I}\int_{y}^{y_0}yzdy,$$

therefore

$$q=\frac{dM}{dx}\frac{1}{Iz}\int_{y}^{y_0}yzdy=\frac{S}{Iz}\int_{y}^{y_0}yzdy$$

where S is the total shearing force on the cross-section of the beam.

Now

$$\int_{y}^{y_0}yzdy$$

is the moment of the area JRK about N′A′ and is equal to $A\bar{y}$, where A is the area of JRK and $\bar{y}$ the distance of its centroid from the neutral axis.

The shearing stress at the neutral axis is equal to $\dfrac{S\,A\bar{y}}{Ib}$ where b is the breadth of the section at the neutral axis and $A\bar{y}$ is the moment of the area of the section above the neutral axis.

The distribution of shearing stress is given for the two sections most commonly met with, *i.e.* rectangular and I sections.

Rectangular Section.—In Fig. 3.8, since $z=b=$constant

$$q=\frac{S}{I}\int_{y}^{\frac{d}{2}}ydy$$

$$=\frac{S}{2I}\left(\frac{d^2}{4}-y^2\right),$$

$$=\frac{6S}{bd^3}\left(\frac{d^2}{4}-y^2\right),$$

since

$$I=\frac{bd^3}{12}.$$

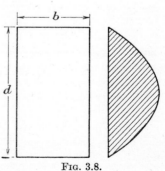

Fig. 3.8.

This is a parabola the maximum shear stress being $\dfrac{3S}{2bd}$ at the neutral axis.

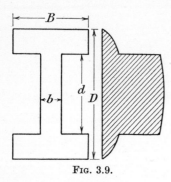

FIG. 3.9.

I *Section.*—Let dimensions be as in Fig. 3.9. Then the shear stress intensity at any height y above the neutral axis is

$\dfrac{S}{Ib} \times$ moment of area above height y about the neutral axis.

The shear stress diagram is shown in Fig. 3.9.

On the inner edge of the flange

$$q = \frac{S}{8I}(D^2 - d^2)$$

and just inside the web

$$q = \frac{S}{8I}(D^2 - d^2)\frac{B}{b}.$$

At the neutral axis the maximum shear stress is

$$\frac{S}{I}\left(\frac{D^2 - d^2}{8}\cdot\frac{B}{b} + \frac{d^2}{8}\right).$$

3.8. Deflexion of beams.—For a straight beam of uniform section we have the relation

$$\frac{1}{R} = \frac{M}{EI}.$$

In Fig. 3.10 let PQ be a small length of such a beam when deflected under

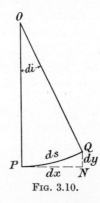

FIG. 3.10.

load. The co-ordinates of P and Q referred to rectangular axes are (x, y), $(x+\delta x)(y+\delta y)$, and the angles which the tangents at P and Q make with the axis of x are i and $i+\delta i$.

The deflexion δy is so small that δx and δs may be taken to be equal.

Then
$$\frac{1}{R} = \frac{\delta i}{\delta s} = \frac{\delta i}{\delta x},$$

but
$$i = \tan i = \frac{dy}{dx},$$

hence in the limit when δx and δy become infinitesimally small

$$\frac{1}{R} = \frac{d^2y}{dx^2},$$

therefore $\qquad \frac{dy}{dx} = \text{slope of beam} = \int \frac{1}{R} dx = \int \frac{M}{EI} dx$

between suitable limits ;

and $\qquad\qquad y = \text{deflexion} = \int\int \frac{M}{EI} dx dx$

between suitable limits.

From this and the results of paragraph 3.2 the following relations are obtained :—

$$w = \frac{dS}{dx} = \frac{d^2M}{dx^2} = EI \frac{d^4y}{dx^4}, \qquad \cdots \cdots \quad (3.1)$$

$$S = \frac{dM}{dx} = EI \frac{d^3y}{dx^3}, \qquad \cdots \cdots \quad (3.2)$$

$$M = EI \frac{d^2y}{dx^2}, \qquad \cdots \cdots \quad (3.3)$$

$$\text{slope} = i = \int \frac{Mdx}{EI}, \qquad \cdots \cdots \quad (3.4)$$

$$\text{deflexion} = y = \int\int \frac{Mdxdx}{EI} \qquad \cdots \cdots \quad (3.5)$$

These five relations are important. From them, for example, if the loading on a beam is known, the shearing force, bending moment, slope and deflexion can be obtained by successive integration, the proper constant of integration being added at each step. Alternatively, if the bending moment is given for every point along the beam, the loading, shear, deflexion and slope may be deduced.

It should be noted that $\frac{d^2y}{dx^2}$, i.e. $\frac{d}{dx}\left(\frac{dy}{dx}\right)$ is the rate of change of slope and

is positive or negative in any particular case according to the positive direction chosen for the measurement of y. Bending moments which produce a positive change of slope must therefore be taken as positive and *vice versa* in forming the equation (3.3). For example in Fig. 3.11, y is measured positive downwards from the unstrained axis of the beam and the slope, which is everywhere negative, increases with x until it reaches its maximum value of zero at the fixed end. Hence, positive bending moments are those which tend to produce concavity downwards.

The deflexion of beams loaded in different ways will now be considered in some detail.

3.9. Uniformly loaded cantilever.—Fig. 3.11 shows in its unstrained position, a cantilever of uniform cross-section and length l. The x axis is taken along the unstrained axis of the beam, which is assumed horizontal, and y is measured downwards.

Under the action of a uniformly distributed load of intensity w per unit length the " hogging " bending moment at a distance x from the free end is

$$M = \frac{wx^2}{2} = EI\frac{d^2y}{dx^2},$$

therefore

$$\frac{dy}{dx} = \frac{wx^3}{6EI} + A \quad . \quad . \quad . \quad . \quad . \quad . \quad . \quad (3.6)$$

and

$$y = \frac{wx^4}{24EI} + Ax + B \quad . \quad . \quad . \quad . \quad . \quad (3.7)$$

where A and B are constants of integration, the values of which must be found from a consideration of the end conditions of the beam.

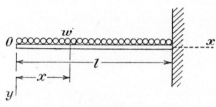

FIG. 3.11.

The cantilever will suffer no change of slope at the fixed end so when $x = l$, $\frac{dy}{dx} = 0$ and from equation (3.6),

$$A = -\frac{wl^3}{6EI}$$

and

$$\frac{dy}{dx} = \frac{wx^3}{6EI} - \frac{wl^3}{6EI}.$$

There is also no deflexion at the fixed end, i.e. $y = 0$ when $x = l$ and equation (3.7) then gives

$$B = \frac{wl^4}{8EI}$$

and

$$y = \frac{wx^4}{24EI} - \frac{wl^3x}{6EI} + \frac{wl^4}{8EI}$$

which is the equation of the deflected form of the cantilever.

3.10. Simply supported beam carrying a concentrated load.—Fig. 3.12 shows a beam of uniform cross-section and length l resting on simple supports which offer no resistance to bending. A concentrated load W is applied at a distance a from the left-hand support which is taken as the origin of co-ordinates. The supports provide vertical reactions R_A and R_B of magnitudes $\frac{W(l-a)}{l}$ and $\frac{Wa}{l}$ respectively.

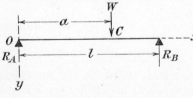

FIG. 3.12.

It is convenient in the first place to form separate expressions for the bending moments at sections to the left and right of the concentrated load respectively, thus :

$$\text{when } x < a \qquad\qquad \text{when } x > a$$

$$M = -R_A x \qquad\qquad M = -R_A x + W[x-a]$$

therefore
$$EI\frac{d^2y}{dx^2} = -R_A x \qquad\qquad EI\frac{d^2y}{dx^2} = -R_A x + W[x-a]$$

and
$$EI\frac{dy}{dx} = -R_A\frac{x^2}{2} + A \qquad\qquad EI\frac{dy}{dx} = -R_A\frac{x^2}{2} + \frac{W[x-a]^2}{2} + A'$$

where A and A′ are constants of integration.

The left-hand expression holds for all sections of the beam between the left-hand support and the point of application of the load C. The right-hand expression holds for all sections between C and the right-hand support. They will both, therefore, give the slope of the beam under the load at C, that is when $x = a$, and since we have

$$EI\left(\frac{dy}{dx}\right)_c = -R_A\frac{a^2}{2} + A \qquad\qquad EI\left(\frac{dy}{dx}\right)_c = -R_A\frac{a^2}{2} + A'$$

it follows that $A = A'$.

Using the same argument, on integrating once more it will be found that

$$EIy = -R_A\frac{x^3}{6} + Ax + B \qquad\qquad EIy = -R_A\frac{x^3}{6} + W\frac{[x-a]^3}{6} + Ax + B.$$

If it is stipulated that the terms inside the square brackets are omitted when $x < a$, the right-hand expressions are capable of expressing the bending moment, slope and deflexion at any section of the beam thus :

$$EI\frac{d^2y}{dx^2} = -R_A x + W[x-a], \quad \ldots \ldots \ldots \quad (3.8)$$

$$EI\frac{dy}{dx} = -R_A\frac{x^2}{2} + \frac{W[x-a]^2}{2} + A \quad \ldots \ldots \ldots \quad (3.9)$$

and
$$EIy = -R_A\frac{x^3}{6} + \frac{W[x-a]^3}{6} + Ax + B. \quad \ldots \ldots \quad (3.10)$$

The constants A and B are evaluated from a consideration of the end conditions. If there is no sinking of the supports under load we have $y = 0$ when $x = 0$ and from (3.10), the term in the bracket being omitted since $x < a$, we obtain $B = 0$.

When $x = l$, $y = 0$ so that

$$A = R_A\frac{l^2}{6} - \frac{W[l-a]^3}{6l} = \frac{Wa(l-a)(2l-a)}{6l}.$$

The deflexion under the load is

$$y_C = \frac{1}{EI}\left[-R_A\frac{a^3}{6} + Aa \right] = \frac{Wa^2(l-a)^2}{3EIl}.$$

The maximum deflexion will occur at the point where $\frac{dy}{dx} = 0$ which, if $a > \frac{l}{2}$, will be found in the length of beam between the left-hand support and C. In this length

$$\frac{dy}{dx} = \frac{1}{EI}\left[-R_A\frac{x^2}{2} + A \right]$$

and equating this to zero it follows that the maximum deflexion occurs at

$$x=\sqrt{\frac{a(2l-a)}{3}}.$$

Substituting this value of x in equation (3.10) we have

$$y_{\max}=\frac{W(l-a)(2al-a^2)^{3/2}}{9\sqrt{3}EIl}.$$

The method outlined above (W. H. Macaulay, 1919) can be applied to a beam carrying any number of concentrated loads W_1, W_2, W_3, etc., at distances a, b, c, etc., from the left-hand support. The expression for the bending moment at any point in the beam, from which those giving the slopes and deflexions are derived, is best found by writing down the bending moment at the section just to the left of the right-hand support, taking moments to the left of the section, thus

$$EI\frac{d^2y}{dx^2}=-R_Ax+W_1[x-a]+W_2[x-b]+W_3[x-c]+\text{ etc.}$$

Care must be taken when integrating to retain intact the expressions in the square brackets and to omit those which do not apply when considering a particular section. Errors can be avoided if it is remembered that the term inside a bracket must be omitted when, on substituting for x, it has a negative value.

3.11. Simply supported beam carrying a distributed load.—Macaulay's method will now be used to determine the deflexions of a beam carrying a load of intensity w which extends from a point at a distance a from the left-hand support to the right-hand support (Fig. 3.13).

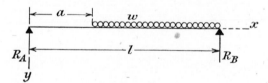

FIG. 3.13.

With the stipulation in the last paragraph the equation which holds over the whole length of the beam is

$$EI\frac{d^2y}{dx^2}=-R_Ax+\frac{w}{2}[x-a]^2. \qquad \text{. . . . . . (3.11)}$$

Upon integrating this twice we have

$$EI\frac{dy}{dx}=-R_A\frac{x^2}{2}+\frac{w}{6}[x-a]^3+A \qquad \text{. . . . . (3.12)}$$

and

$$EIy=-R_A\frac{x^3}{6}+\frac{w}{24}[x-a]^4+Ax+B. \qquad \text{. . . . (3.13)}$$

When $x=0$, $y=0$ and so $B=0$.
When $x=l$, $y=0$

so

$$0=-\frac{w(l-a)^2}{2l}\cdot\frac{l^3}{6}+\frac{w(l-a)^4}{24}+Al$$

and
$$A = \frac{w(l-a)^2(l^2+2al-a^2)}{24l}.$$

The final equation for the deflexion at any point in the beam is then

$$y = \frac{1}{EI}\left[-\frac{w(l-a)^2x^3}{12l} + \frac{w[x-a]^4}{24} + \frac{w(l-a)^2(l^2+2al-a^2)x}{24l} \right] \quad . \quad (3.14)$$

This method can only be directly used when the distributed load stretches to the right-hand support. The general case of a beam carrying a load distributed over a short length only of the span can however be covered by the use of a simple artifice.

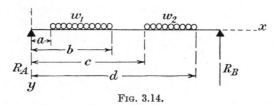

FIG. 3.14.

If beam AB carries a load of intensity w per unit length extending between points C and D which are a and b respectively from the left-hand support the behaviour of the beam is the same as if it were loaded uniformly to an intensity w over the length CB and to an intensity $-w$ over the length DB. By this arrangement the loads are made continuous to the right-hand support.

Macaulay's method can be applied and the deflexions derived as before from the equation

$$EI\frac{d^2y}{dx^2} = -R_A x + \frac{w[x-a]^2}{2} - \frac{w[x-b]^2}{2} \quad . \quad . \quad . \quad (3.15)$$

When loads of different intensities are distributed over two portions of the beam as shown in Fig. 3.14 the equation will be

$$EI\frac{d^2y}{dx^2} = -R_A x + \frac{w_1[x-a]^2}{2} - \frac{w_1[x-b]^2}{2} + \frac{w_2[x-c]^2}{2} - \frac{w_2[x-d]^2}{2} \quad . \quad (3.16)$$

3.12. Simply supported beam subjected to a couple applied at a point.— The slopes and deflexions of a beam of uniform cross-section subjected to a

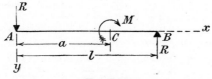

FIG. 3.15.

couple M applied to a point C at a distance a from the left-hand support (Fig. 3.15) can be found without difficulty. The reactions, R, supplied by the supports act as shown in the figure and are of magnitude $\frac{M}{l}$. If the couple is replaced by an upward vertical force $W = \frac{M}{b}$ acting through C and an equal and opposite force acting through a point at a distance b to the right of C the equations can be formed in the usual way. If, in the limit, b is made to approach zero while keeping $M=Wb$, the required solution is obtained.

A more elegant method is however to extend Macaulay's notation, and write the equation, which holds over the whole beam,

$$\mathrm{EI}\frac{d^2y}{dx^2}=\mathrm{R}x-[\mathrm{M}] \qquad . \quad . \quad . \quad . \quad . \quad (3.17)$$

the significance of the square bracket being, as before, that the term inside it shall be neglected when $x<a$.

Integrating equation (3.17) we have

$$\mathrm{EI}\frac{dy}{dx}=\frac{\mathrm{R}x^2}{2}-[\mathrm{M}(x-a)]+\mathrm{A} \quad . \quad . \quad . \quad . \quad (3.18)$$

and

$$\mathrm{EI}y=\frac{\mathrm{R}x^3}{6}-\left[\frac{\mathrm{M}(x-a)^2}{2}\right]+\mathrm{A}x+\mathrm{B}. \quad . \quad . \quad . \quad (3.19)$$

Since $y=0$ when $x=0$ and when $x=l$ we have

$$\mathrm{B}=0$$

and

$$\mathrm{A}=\frac{\mathrm{M}}{6l}(2l^2-6al+3a^2).$$

The equation for the deflexion at any point is then

$$y=\frac{1}{\mathrm{EI}}\left\{\frac{\mathrm{M}x^3}{6l}-\tfrac{1}{2}[\mathrm{M}(x-a)^2]+\frac{\mathrm{M}}{6l}(2l^2-6al+3a^2)x\right\} \quad . \quad . \quad (3.20)$$

3.13. Simply supported beam subjected to transverse loads and end couples. —General expressions which will be needed later for the slopes at the ends of a beam of uniform cross-section subjected to any system of transverse loads and to couples at its ends will now be derived.

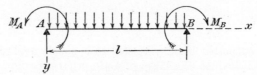

FIG. 3.16.

Fig. 3.16 shows a beam subjected to any distribution of transverse loads and to couples M_A and M_B at its ends A and B respectively.

If the hogging bending moment at a section x from the left-hand support due to the transverse loads alone is M'_x then the total bending moment at that point is

$$\mathrm{EI}\frac{d^2y}{dx^2}=\mathrm{M}'_x+\mathrm{M_A}\frac{(l-x)}{l}+\frac{x}{l}\mathrm{M_B}. \quad . \quad . \quad . \quad . \quad (3.21)$$

Multiplying equation (3.21) by x and integrating between the limits $x=0$ and $x=l$, we obtain

$$\mathrm{EI}\left[x\frac{dy}{dx}-y\right]_0^l=\int_0^l \mathrm{M}'_x x\,dx+\left[\frac{\mathrm{M_A}}{l}\left(\frac{lx^2}{2}-\frac{x^3}{3}\right)+\frac{x^3}{3l}\mathrm{M_B}\right]_0^l \quad . \quad . \quad (3.22)$$

If there is no sinking of the supports, that is to say $y=0$ when $x=0$ and also when $x=l$, equation (3.22) may be written

$$\theta_{BA}=\frac{1}{EIl}\int_0^l M_x' x\,dx+\frac{l}{6EI}(M_A+2M_B)\quad.\quad\cdots\quad(3.23)$$

where θ_{BA} is the slope of the beam at the end B where $x=l$.

Integrating (3.21) between the limits $x=0$ and $x=l$ we have

$$EI\left[\frac{dy}{dx}\right]_0^l=\int_0^l M_x'\,dx+\left[\frac{M_A}{l}\left(lx-\frac{x^2}{2}\right)+\frac{x^2}{2l}M_B\right]_0^l$$

or

$$\theta_{BA}-\theta_{AB}=\frac{1}{EI}\int_0^l M_x'\,dx+\frac{l}{2EI}(M_A+M_B)\quad.\quad\cdots\quad(3.24)$$

where θ_{AB} is the slope of the beam at the end A where $x=0$.

Substituting in this equation the value of θ_{BA} given by equation (3.23) it will be found that

$$\theta_{AB}=-\frac{1}{EI}\int_0^l M_x'\,dx+\frac{1}{EIl}\int_0^l M_x' x\,dx-\frac{l}{6EI}(2M_A+M_B)\quad.\quad.\quad(3.25)$$

Now $\int_0^l M_x'\,dx$ is the total area of the bending moment diagram due to the transverse loads alone and will be denoted by A.

$\int_0^l M_x' x\,dx$ is the moment of this area about the left-hand end of the beam where $x=0$, and will be denoted by $A\bar{x}$, $\bar{x}$ being the distance of the centroid of the area from the end where $x=0$.

Then

$$l\int_0^l M_x'\,dx-\int_0^l M_x' x\,dx=l\int_0^l M_x'\,dx-\bar{x}\int_0^l M_x'\,dx=(l-\bar{x})\int_0^l M_x'\,dx$$

which is the moment of the area of the bending moment diagram about the right-hand end of the beam where $x=l$ and will be denoted by $A\bar{x}'$, $\bar{x}'$ being the distance of the centroid of the area from the end where $x=l$.

Equations (3.23) and (3.25) may then be written

$$\theta_{BA}=\frac{l}{6EI}\left(M_A+2M_B+\frac{6A\bar{x}}{l^2}\right)\quad.\quad\cdots\quad(3.26)$$

and

$$\theta_{AB}=-\frac{l}{6EI}\left(2M_A+M_B+\frac{6A\bar{x}'}{l^2}\right)\quad.\quad\cdots\quad(3.27)$$

If the supports sink when the load is applied to the beam so that the end B has a deflexion δ relative to A, then the slope everywhere on the beam will be increased by an amount $\frac{\delta}{l}$ and the slopes at the ends will be

$$\theta_{BA}=\frac{l}{6EI}\left(M_A+2M_B+\frac{6A\bar{x}}{l^2}\right)+\frac{\delta}{l}\quad.\quad\cdots\quad(3.28)$$

$$\theta_{AB}=-\frac{l}{6EI}\left(2M_A+M_B+\frac{6A\bar{x}'}{l^2}\right)+\frac{\delta}{l}\quad.\quad\cdots\quad(3.29)$$

3.14. Encastré beam.—An encastré beam is one in which the ends are built into the supports or otherwise fixed so that the slope of the beam at those points cannot change. When load is applied the supports exert restraining moments on the ends of the beam. The magnitudes of these moments can be found directly from the expressions for the slopes at the ends of a beam derived in the preceding paragraph and the deflexion at any point can then be determined by the method set out in paragraphs 3.10–3.12.

If the axis of such a beam was originally horizontal and the end B deflects under load a distance δ relative to A, we may write from equations (3.28) and (3.29)

$$\frac{l}{6EI}\left(M_A+2M_B+\frac{6A\bar{x}}{l^2}\right)+\frac{\delta}{l}=0$$

and

$$-\frac{l}{6EI}\left(2M_A+M_B+\frac{6A\bar{x}'}{l^2}\right)+\frac{\delta}{l}=0.$$

Solving these equations we obtain

$$M_A=\frac{2A\bar{x}}{l^2}-\frac{4A\bar{x}'}{l^2}+\frac{6EI\delta}{l^2} \quad . \quad . \quad . \quad . \quad . \quad (3.30)$$

and

$$M_B=-\frac{4A\bar{x}}{l^2}+\frac{2A\bar{x}'}{l^2}-\frac{6EI\delta}{l^2}. \quad . \quad . \quad . \quad . \quad (3.31)$$

If the beam carries a uniformly distributed load of intensity w over the whole span

$$\bar{x}=\bar{x}'=\frac{l}{2}, \quad A=-\frac{2}{3}\times l\times\frac{wl^2}{8}=-\frac{wl^3}{12}$$

and the end fixing moments are

$$M_A=\frac{wl^2}{12}+\frac{6EI\delta}{l^2} \quad . \quad . \quad . \quad . \quad . \quad (3.32)$$

and

$$M_B=\frac{wl^2}{12}-\frac{6EI\delta}{l^2} \quad . \quad . \quad . \quad . \quad . \quad (3.33)$$

The effect of the downward deflexion of the end B relative to the end A is to increase the moment M_A. The importance of this increase is most easily appreciated from consideration of a special instance.

Suppose a total load of 12 tons uniformly distributed is to be carried over a span of 20 feet by means of a steel beam having a relevant second moment of area $I=220$ (ins.)[4] and a depth of 12 inches.

If the beam were simply supported at its ends the maximum bending moment, occurring at the centre of the span, would be $M_{max}=\dfrac{wl^2}{8}=360$ tons-ins. and the maximum longitudinal flexural stress would be $p_{max}=\dfrac{360\times 6}{220}=9\cdot 8$ tons/sq. in.

If the ends of the beam are encastré and no relative deflexion of the ends occurs the restraining moments exerted on the beam at the supports are

$$M_A=M_B=\frac{wl^2}{12}=240 \text{ tons-ins.}$$

This is the greatest bending moment in the beam as will be seen if the bending moment diagram for the encastré beam is drawn, and the resulting maximum longitudinal stress is $6\cdot 55$ tons per square inch.

We will now determine what relative sinking of the supports could occur before the maximum stress exceeded a permissible limit of 8 tons per square inch.

This stress would be produced by a bending moment of $\dfrac{8 \times 220}{6}$ tons-inches

so that, from equation (3.32), the limiting deflexion is

$$\frac{8 \times 220}{6} = 240 + \frac{6 \times 13,000 \times 220}{240 \times 240}\delta \qquad \text{or} \qquad \delta = 0 \cdot 18 \text{ inch.}$$

This comparatively small deflexion would produce in this particular beam, with ends encastré, an increase in the maximum stress of more than 20 per cent. No such increase in maximum stress would have been produced by the deflexion had the ends of the beam been simply supported.

3.15. Beam of varying section subjected to any load system.—The formulas derived in paragraphs 3.2 to 3.8 have been applied so far to beams of uniform cross-section throughout their length. They are applicable, however, for all practical purposes, to beams in which the cross-section is not uniform.

From equation (3.3.)

$$\frac{d^2y}{dx^2} = \frac{M}{EI}.$$

Integrating this, $\qquad \dfrac{dy}{dx} = \dfrac{1}{E}\displaystyle\int \dfrac{M}{I}dx + A$

and $\qquad y = \dfrac{1}{E}\displaystyle\int\int \dfrac{M}{I}dxdx + Ax + B.$

If $\dfrac{M}{I}$ is not an easily integrable function of x, graphical methods must be

used to determine

$$\int \frac{M}{I}dx \quad \text{and} \quad \int\int \frac{M}{I}dxdx.$$

When these integrals have been evaluated the constants of integration A and B can be found and the equations for the slopes and deflexions follow as in paragraphs 3.9–3.13.

As an example we shall consider the case of a cantilever of length L and constant depth d, which tapers linearly in plan view from a breadth b at the fixed end to nothing at the free end and carries a concentrated load W at the free end.

The relevant second moment of area at a section distance x from the free

end is $\dfrac{1}{12}\dfrac{bd^3x}{L}$ and the bending moment there is Wx so that

$$\frac{d^2y}{dx^2} = \frac{M}{EI} = \frac{12WL}{bd^3E}$$

Hence $\qquad \dfrac{dy}{dx} = \dfrac{12WLx}{bd^3E} + A$

and $\qquad y = \dfrac{6WLx^2}{bd^3E} + Ax + B.$

When $\qquad x = L, \quad \dfrac{dy}{dx} = 0 \quad$ and $\quad A = -\dfrac{12WL^2}{bd^3E}.$

When $x=L$, $y=0$ and $B=\dfrac{12WL^3}{bd^3E}-\dfrac{6WL^3}{bd^3E}=\dfrac{6WL^3}{bd^3E}$.

At the free end where the load is applied, $x=0$ and the deflexion is $\dfrac{6WL^3}{bd^3E}$.

A beam which is designed to be economical in material must vary in cross-section from point to point in a manner dependent upon the variation of the bending moment to which it is subjected.

The design of a member of this type, particularly when it forms part of a continuous structure such as one built of reinforced concrete, presents no fundamental difficulty but is laborious. A general method is, however, available (Weiskopf and Pickworth, 1937).

3.16. Moment area and shear area methods.—There is a considerable literature dealing with more specialised methods of determining the slopes and deflexions of beams.

The best known of these is the moment area method. If a beam of uniform cross-section, initially straight, is subjected to any load system so that M_x is the bending moment at any section at a distance x from the origin, which we have in earlier paragraphs taken as the left-hand end of the beam, then $\Delta\theta$, the change in angle between the tangents at two points C and D on the beam, is given by

$$\Delta\theta=\frac{1}{EI}\int_C^D M_x dx.$$

$\int_C^D M_x dx$, sometimes called the moment area, is the area of the bending moment diagram between C and D and we have the theorem : *If C and D are any two points on a beam the change in angle between the tangent at C and the tangent at D is equal to the area of the bending moment diagram between these points divided by EI, the constant flexural rigidity of the beam.*

If C is taken as the origin of co-ordinates so that x is measured from C we have, from equation (3.22),

$$x_D\theta_D-y_D+y_C=\frac{1}{EI}\int_C^D M_x x dx.$$

The left-hand side of this equation is an expression for the deflexion of C relative to the tangent at D, while the right-hand side is equivalent to the area of the bending moment diagram between C and D multiplied by the distance of the centroid of this area from C. We thus have the further theorem :—

The displacement of C relative to the tangent at D is equal to the moment of the area of the bending moment diagram between C and D about the ordinate through C divided by the flexural rigidity of the beam.

To find by this method the deflexion at the centre of a beam of span l which carries a uniformly distributed load of intensity w it must be remembered that the tangent at the centre of the length is horizontal so that the deflexion there will be equal in magnitude to the displacement of one end of the beam relative to the tangent at the centre of length.

The area of half the parabolic segment forming the bending moment diagram of the beam is $\dfrac{2}{3}\cdot\dfrac{l}{2}\cdot\dfrac{wl^2}{8}=\dfrac{wl^3}{24}$ and the distance of the centroid of this area from the end of the beam is $\dfrac{5l}{16}$ so that the required displacement is

$$\frac{wl^3}{24} \times \frac{5l}{16} \times \frac{1}{\text{EI}} = \frac{5wl^4}{384\text{EI}}.$$

The moment area method can be applied readily to beams of varying cross section.

For beams of uniform section carrying uniformly distributed loads a knowledge of the areas and the positions of the centroids of parabolic segments is required. This has led to the development of an analogous method known as the Shear Area Method (Compton & Dohrenwerd, 1936) in which use is made of the area of the shearing force diagram, which is usually a simpler figure than the bending moment diagram.

While a knowledge of these methods may be of value, the straightforward method of determining slopes and deflexions set out in paragraphs 3.9–3.15 will in all cases give results with little, if any, more labour and with much less liability to error.

Another special method is the Column Analogy (Hardy Cross, 1930) which will be dealt with later in paragraph 10.7.

3.17. Bending stresses in curved beam.—The equations for bending stress obtained in paragraph 3.3 are only valid if the beam is initially straight.

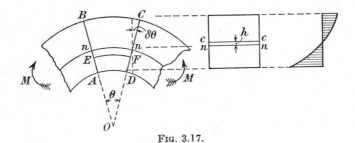

Fig. 3.17.

If it has an appreciable curvature the application of these formulas may result in serious error and a more exact treatment, which is due to Winkler, is necessary.

Fig. 3.17 shows a beam, initially curved, subjected to a bending moment M tending to straighten it. BA and CD are two adjacent cross-sections initially separated by a small angle θ. The radius of curvature of the neutral surface nn over the small length of the beam between these sections is assumed to be constant and equal to r.

The same assumptions will be made as for the case of straight beams.

Under the action of M the section CD will rotate through a small angle δθ relative to AB.

Let EF be any surface at a distance y from nn, y being assumed to be positive when measured towards O, the centre of curvature of the short length of beam under consideration. The strain of a fibre in the surface EF is

$$e = \frac{y\delta\theta}{(r-y)\theta} \qquad \qquad \qquad (3.34)$$

and, if lateral pressure between the fibres is neglected, the stress at EF is

$$f = Ee = \frac{Ey\delta\theta}{(r-y)\theta}. \qquad \cdots \qquad (3.35)$$

This is a hyperbolic curve of stress distribution as shown in Fig. 3.17 instead of the linear distribution in an initially straight beam.

Since there is no axial force acting on the beam the sum of the compressive forces in the fibres of the beam above the neutral axis must be equal to the sum of the tensile forces in the fibres below the neutral axis. If the beam is of constant width as shown in the diagram this entails that the area of the stress diagram above the neutral axis must be equal to the area of the diagram below it and so the neutral axis does not, as in the straight beam, pass through the centroid of the section but is displaced towards the centre of curvature.

For equilibrium of the cross-section we have to satisfy two conditions :

(1) That already stated above, viz. that the total force on the cross-section is zero.

(2) The sum of the moments of forces on the cross-section about nn must be equal to the applied moment M.

If dA is an element of area of the cross-section at EF these conditions may be expressed as

$$\int f dA = 0$$

$$\int f y dA = M$$

and on substituting the value of f from (3.35) we obtain

$$\frac{E\delta\theta}{\theta} \int \frac{y dA}{r-y} = 0 \qquad \cdots \qquad (3.36)$$

and

$$\frac{E\delta\theta}{\theta} \int \frac{y^2 dA}{r-y} = M. \qquad \cdots \qquad (3.37)$$

The second of these equations may be rewritten in the form

$$\frac{E\delta\theta}{\theta} \left\{ -\int y dA + \int \frac{ry dA}{r-y} \right\} = M.$$

The second integral is zero from (3.36) and the first represents the moment of area of the cross-section about nn, i.e. $-Ah$ where A is the total area of the cross-section and $-h$ is the distance of the neutral axis from the centroid.

So

$$\frac{E\delta\theta}{\theta} Ah = M$$

or

$$\frac{E\delta\theta}{\theta} = \frac{M}{Ah}. \qquad \cdots \qquad (3.38)$$

Substituting this value of $\frac{E\delta\theta}{\theta}$ in (3.35) we have

$$f = \frac{My}{Ah(r-y)}. \qquad \cdots \qquad (3.39)$$

The maximum value of f occurs in the fibre AD and the minimum value in the fibre BC, so that if the distances of these fibres from the neutral axis are y_1 and $-y_2$ respectively, we have

$$f_{max} = \frac{My_1}{Ah(r-y_1)} \left. \right\} \quad . \quad . \quad . \quad . \quad . \quad (3.40)$$

and

$$f_{min} = -\frac{My_2}{Ah(r+y_2)}$$

These equations cannot be used unless h and r are known.

Let y' be the distance of any element of cross-section from the axis through the centroid parallel to nn so that $y' = y + h$.

Substituting for y in equation (3.36) we have

$$\int \left(\frac{y'-h}{R-y'} \right) dA = 0$$

where R is the radius measured to the axis cc through the centroid.

Hence

$$\int \left(\frac{y'}{R-y'} \right) dA - \int \left(\frac{h}{R-y'} \right) dA = 0. \quad . \quad . \quad . \quad (3.41)$$

The first integral in this equation represents a modified area and will be denoted by mA,

i.e.

$$\int \left(\frac{y'}{R-y'} \right) dA = mA \quad . \quad . \quad . \quad . \quad . \quad (3.42)$$

where m is a coefficient which must be calculated. The second integral can be written in the form

$$\int \left(\frac{h}{R-y'} \right) dA = \frac{h}{R} \int \left(1 + \frac{y'}{R-y'} \right) dA = \frac{hA}{R}(1+m). \quad . \quad . \quad (3.43)$$

Substituting (3.42) and (3.43) in (3.41) we have

$$mA - \frac{hA}{R}(1+m) = 0$$

or

$$h = R\frac{m}{1+m}. \quad . \quad . \quad . \quad . \quad . \quad (3.44)$$

The value of m may be found in some instances by direct integration, in others a graphical construction is preferable.

Suppose the section of the beam consists of a rectangle of width B and depth H.

Then

$$m = \frac{1}{A} \int_{-H/2}^{H/2} \left(\frac{y'}{R-y'} \right) dA$$

where

$$dA = Bdy' \text{ and } A = BH.$$

So

$$m = \frac{1}{H} \int_{-H/2}^{H/2} \left(\frac{R}{R-y'} - 1 \right) dy'$$

or

$$m = \frac{R}{H} \log_e \frac{2R+H}{2R-H} - 1. \quad . \quad . \quad . \quad . \quad (3.45)$$

For a circular section the integration is rather lengthy but gives the result

$$m = 2\left(\frac{R^2}{a^2} - \frac{1}{2} \right) - \frac{2R}{a^2}\sqrt{R^2-a^2}$$

where a is the radius of the circle.

The value of m may also be found by taking a sufficient number of terms in the expansion of the expression $\dfrac{1}{R-y'}$, thus

$$m=\frac{1}{A}\int\frac{y'dA}{R-y'}$$

$$=\frac{1}{AR}\int y'\left(1+\frac{y'}{R}+\frac{y'^2}{R^2}+\frac{y'^3}{R^3}+\;\cdots\;\right)dA.$$

If dA can be expressed as a function of y' this series can readily be integrated. For a rectangle, for example, $dA=Bdy'$ and

$$m=\frac{B}{AR}\int_{-H/2}^{H/2}\left(y'+\frac{y'^2}{R}+\frac{y'^3}{R^2}+\frac{y'^4}{R^3}+\;\cdots\;\right)dy'$$

$$=\frac{B}{AR}\left[\frac{y'^2}{2}+\frac{y'^3}{3R}+\frac{y'^4}{4R^2}+\;\cdots\;\right]_{-H/2}^{H/2}$$

The even powers of y' vanish and we obtain

$$m=\frac{1}{HR}\left[\frac{H^3}{12R}+\frac{H^5}{80R^3}+\;\cdots\;\right]$$

or

$$m=\frac{1}{3}\left(\frac{H}{2R}\right)^2+\frac{1}{5}\left(\frac{H}{2R}\right)^4+\frac{1}{7}\left(\frac{H}{2R}\right)^6+\;\cdots$$

In the same way the value for a circle of diameter D is found to be

$$m=\frac{1}{4}\left(\frac{D}{2R}\right)^2+\frac{1}{8}\left(\frac{D}{2R}\right)^4+\frac{5}{64}\left(\frac{D}{2R}\right)^6+\;\cdots$$

If the integral cannot be evaluated readily a graphical construction may be used as follows (Fig. 3.18):

AGBG′ is the cross-section, which is shown symmetrical about the axis AB. This is not necessary, but is the usual condition. The centre of curvature is O and G′G is the axis through the centroid. The length CD of any line parallel to G′G is proportional to an element of area dA at that level. Also $FE=y'$ and $EO=R-y'$. Join OD and produce this line to cut G′G at J. From J draw JH perpendicular to EH. Then the triangles JHD, OED are similar and

$$DH:ED::JH:EO,$$

i.e.

$$DH=\frac{JH}{EO}ED=\frac{y'}{R-y'}ED$$

so DH is proportional to $\dfrac{y'}{R-y'}\,dA$ at this section.

Now consider another section KL which is above the axis G′G. As before join OL and from N the point where this line intersects G′G draw NM perpendicular to KL.

Then

$$ML=\frac{MN}{OP}PL=\frac{y'}{R-y'}dA.$$

It will be noticed that when the value of y' is negative, *i.e.* when the section considered lies above the axis through the centroid, the point on the derived figure lies inside the original diagram instead of outside it as for sections below the axis. This corresponds with the sign of the integral, which is positive when y' is positive and negative when y' is negative.

If a number of points are obtained in this way the derived figure is easily drawn and is indicated by dotted lines in Fig. 3.18.

The area included between this dotted line and the boundary of the original contour is a measure of $\frac{1}{2}\int \frac{y'}{R-y'}dA$ since one-half only of the symmetrical section shown has been treated.

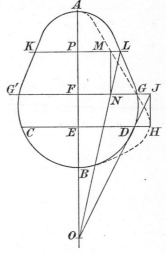

FIG. 3.18.

If the section is not symmetrical about the line AO the diagram would of course be completed by a similar process on the other side.

Once the value of m has been found, h is calculated from equation (3.44), i.e.

$h=R\left(\dfrac{m}{1+m}\right)$ and $r=R-h$. The stresses can then be found directly from equations (3.39) and (3.40).

As an example suppose a steel bar 2 inches square in cross-section bent in a circular arc having a mean radius of 8 inches is loaded by end couples of 10-inch tons and the maximum and minimum stresses are to be calculated.

In the first place m is calculated from the formula

$$m=\frac{R}{H}\log_e\frac{2R+H}{2R-H}-1$$

$$=(4\times\cdot2513145)-1=\cdot005258.$$

This may be checked by the expansion

$$m=\tfrac{1}{3}(\tfrac{1}{8})^2+\tfrac{1}{5}(\tfrac{1}{8})^4+\tfrac{1}{7}(\tfrac{1}{8})^6+\ \cdots$$
$$=\cdot005208+\cdot000048$$
$$=\cdot005256.$$

Then $\qquad\qquad h=R\left(\dfrac{m}{1+m}\right)$

$$=\frac{8\times\cdot005258}{1\cdot005258}=\cdot04184\text{ inch.}$$

Also $\qquad\qquad r=8-\cdot04184=7\cdot95816$ inches

and $\qquad\qquad f_{max}=\dfrac{My_1}{Ah(r-y_1)}$

where $\qquad\qquad y_1=1-\cdot04184=\cdot95816$

$\therefore\qquad\qquad f_{max}=\dfrac{10\times\cdot95816}{4\times\cdot04184\times7}=8\cdot18$ tons per square inch.

Also $\qquad\qquad f_{min}=\dfrac{-My_2}{Ah(r+y_2)}$

where $\qquad\qquad -y_2=-(1+\cdot04184)=-1\cdot04184.$

$\therefore\qquad\qquad f_{min}=\dfrac{-10\times1\cdot04184}{4\times\cdot04184\times9}=-6\cdot92$ tons per square inch.

If the stresses are calculated by the formulas derived for initially straight beams we obtain

$$f = \frac{10 \times 3}{4} = 7 \cdot 5 \text{ tons per square inch.}$$

The error is rather over 8 per cent. on the low side, and this error would increase rapidly with the curvature.

REFERENCES

Macaulay, W. H., 1919. *Messeng. Math.* **48**, 129.
Cross, Hardy, 1930. *Univ. of Illinois Eng. Exp. Station. Bull.* **215**.
Compton, H. B. and Dohrenwerd, C. O., 1936. *Proc. Amer. Soc. Civ. Engrs.*, **101**, 945.
Weiskopf, W. H. & Pickworth, J. W., 1937. *Proc. Amer. Soc. Civ. Engrs.*, **102**, 1.

EXERCISES

(1) A wooden cantilever 12 feet long is 10 inches deep throughout but is tapered in plan in such a way that when a load is hung on the free end the maximum fibre stress is the same at all sections.

If this fibre stress is 1,200 lb. per square inch, calculate the deflexion under the load.

$$E = 1 \cdot 5 \times 10^6 \text{ lb. per square inch.}$$

(1·66 inches)

(2) A cantilever of length L is propped at a distance L/4 from the free end to the level of the fixed end. It carries a load W at the free end. Determine the ratio of deflexions at the free end for the prop in position and the prop removed.

(0·048)

(3) A cantilever of uniform cross-section and length L carries a load W at the free end and a distributed load varying linearly from w at the free end to $3w$ at the fixed end. Calculate the deflexion at the free end.

$$\frac{L^3}{3EI}\left(W + \frac{23wL}{40}\right)$$

(4) A vertical wooden mast 50 feet high tapers linearly from 9 inches diameter at the base to 4 inches diameter at the top. At what point will the mast break under a horizontal load applied at the top ?

If the ultimate strength of the wood is 5,000 lb. per square inch, calculate the magnitude of the load which will cause failure.

(20 feet from top : 442 lb.)

(5) A cantilever of length L has a constant breadth B and a varying depth given by $K\sqrt{x}$, where K is a constant and x is the distance from the free end. The cantilever carries a load W at the free end which causes a maximum fibre stress f in the material of the beam. Find the deflexion at the free end if D is the depth of the beam at the root.

$$\left(\frac{8WL^3}{EBD^3}\right)$$

(6) A beam in cross-section is an equilateral triangle of 8-inch side, the line of the loading being perpendicular to one side.

If the total shearing force at a section is 5 tons, plot the distribution of shear stress across this section.

(Parabola with maximum value of ·27 tons per square inch at half depth)

(7) A beam freely supported over a span of 20 feet carries a load which varies uniformly from an intensity of 1 ton per foot at one end to 3 tons per foot at the other end. If the second moment of area of the beam is 300 inch units and E is 30×10^6 lb. per square inch, calculate the deflexion at the centre of the span.

(1·79 inches)

(8) A R.S.J. of $12'' \times 6'' \times \frac{1}{2}$ inch section is 12 feet long. It is fixed at one end and pinned at the other. A moment is applied to the pinned end tending to bend the beam in its strongest direction. If the maximum stress is 5 tons per square inch calculate the magnitude of the moment and the angle of slope at the pinned end of the beam.

(211·5 tons-in. ; 0·132 degrees)

(9) A beam AB of length L is freely supported at A and at a point C which is kL from the end B. If the load on AC is a uniformly distributed one of intensity w, find the value of k which will cause the upward deflexion of B to equal the downward deflexion midway between A and C.

(0·238)

(10) An encastré beam 20 feet span has a couple of 80 foot-tons applied at a point 5 feet from one support. Draw the bending moment diagram.

(11) A straight horizontal beam rests on supports 20 feet apart and overhangs each of these supports by 4 feet.

It carries loads of 10 and 8 tons at 5 and 14 feet respectively from the left-hand support.

Calculate what concentrated loads applied to the extreme ends of the beam will make it remain horizontal over both supports.

(9·55 tons at L.H. end
8·22 tons at R.H. end)

(12) The ends of a beam which carries a concentrated load at one-third of the span are so constrained that they assume slopes one-half of those which would occur if the beam were simply supported.

Sketch the bending moment and shearing force diagrams.

(End B.Ms.$=\frac{2}{27}WL$ and $\frac{1}{27}WL$
End S.Fs. $=-\frac{19}{27}W$ and $\frac{8}{27}W$)

(13) An encastré beam of span L has a second moment of area varying uniformly from I_0 at the centre to $\frac{1}{2}I_0$ at each end. It carries a load uniformly varying from an intensity w at each end to $2w$ at the centre. Calculate the bending moments at the centre and ends and the central deflexion.

$$\left(\begin{array}{l} BM \text{ at centre} \quad -\dfrac{wL^2}{12} \\[2ex] \text{,, ,, ends} \quad +\dfrac{wL^2}{12} \\[2ex] \text{Deflexion} \quad \dfrac{wL^4}{192 I_0 E} \end{array} \right.$$

(14) A circular link is made of square section steel bar of 1 inch side the junction being left unwelded.

The internal diameter is 3 inches. If the maximum stress in the steel is not to exceed 8 tons per square inch, calculate what diametrical pull the link can carry.

(·52 ton)

CHAPTER 4

THEOREMS RELATING TO ELASTIC BODIES

4.1. Elastic behaviour.—When loads are applied to a body—whether it be solid or a framework—the shape of that body is slightly changed. If on the removal of the loads the body completely regains its original shape it is said to behave elastically. The curve obtained by plotting the displacements of any point against the loads causing these displacements is in most cases a straight line, but for certain types of bodies and for certain forms of loading the load-displacement curve is not linear although the behaviour is perfectly elastic.

A thin rod of elastic material used as a tie rod, *i.e.* subjected to an axial tensile stress, may have a linear relationship between load and displacement, but if the same rod is subjected to a compressive load applied eccentrically the displacement of any point will increase at a greater rate than the load although such displacement will be elastic, *i.e.* it will disappear on the removal of the load.

Since many of the theorems relating to the behaviour of bodies under stress are only applicable if the displacements are proportional to the loads producing them, it is important to recognise the distinction between the two types of behaviour.

4.2. Principle of superposition.—*If the displacements of all points in a body are proportional to the loads causing them the effect produced upon such body by a number of forces is the sum of the effects produced by the several forces when applied separately.*

This is a most important consequence of a linear load-displacement curve and renders possible the solution of many problems which would otherwise be intractable.

Its truth is readily seen by considering the case of a rod subjected to an axial tensile load of $P+Q$.

The extension of the rod under the load, if the material obeys Hooke's law, *i.e.* if it has a linear stress strain curve, is $\dfrac{(P+Q)L}{AE}$ where L is the length of the rod, A its cross-sectional area and E is Young's modulus for the material.

But this extension is $\dfrac{PL}{AE}+\dfrac{QL}{AE}$ which is the sum of the extensions of the rod under the two separate forces P and Q.

Fig. 4.1 (*a*) illustrates the point with reference to the actual load-extension diagram for the rod. Under tensions P and Q the extensions are represented by OA and OB respectively. If $P+Q$ be applied to the rod the extension is represented by OC.

Since the triangles OBE and FGH are identical we can write

$$OC = OA + FG = OA + OB$$

or extension due to $P+Q$=extension due to P+extension due to Q.

44

Next consider a material which does not obey Hooke's law : the load extension curve for such a material is shown in Fig. 4.1 (*b*). As before, the extensions for loads P and Q are represented by OA and OB respectively. Under the action of P+Q the extension will be represented by OC and it is clear from the diagram that this is not equal to OA+OB. We are therefore unable to determine the extension of the rod under P+Q by adding those due to P and Q when applied separately.

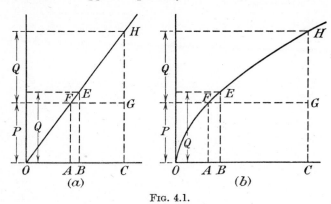

FIG. 4.1.

To illustrate the principle of superposition, let Fig. 4.2 (*a*) represent any body which obeys Hooke's law, carrying loads W_1 and W_2 as shown and supported at the points A and B.

The load system (*a*) is the sum of the two systems shown in (*b*) and (*c*), and the stress at any point, such as D, which is produced by the load system (*a*) is the algebraic sum of the stresses produced by the load systems (*b*) and (*c*), whilst the displacement at any point due to (*a*) is the algebraic sum of the displacements due to (*b*) and (*c*). For the sake of brevity this statement will be expressed in the form

$$(a)=(b)+(c).$$

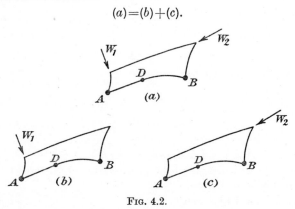

FIG. 4.2.

It is important to realise that the structures of (*a*), (*b*) and (*c*) are identical : no modification must be made. This warning is necessary since a so-called method of superposition is sometimes used in which a redundant structure is divided into two simply-stiff frames and the loading is applied half to one and half to the other. A solution obtained in this way is only approximate ;

it may in some cases be a good approximation but it cannot, in general, be exact. This method must not be confused with that now under discussion, which furnishes exact solutions.

Suppose, for example, that the encastré beam shown in Fig. 4.3 carries a uniform load of intensity $2w$ over one half of the span, and that the values of the end fixing moments M_A and M_B are required. The usual method

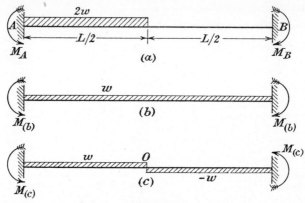

Fig. 4.3.

necessitates either the use of a planimeter or the mathematical integration of the free bending moment diagram, and is unnecessarily lengthy. The load system (a) can, however, be replaced by the two systems shown in (b) and (c) respectively in Fig. 4.3 ; (b) consists of a uniform load of intensity w acting on the whole span, while (c) consists of a downward load of intensity w over one half of the span and an upward load of intensity w over the other half.

Then $(a)=(b)+(c)$.

Now, the end fixing moment for (b) is

$$M_{(b)}=\frac{wL^2}{12}.$$

It is clear from the skew-symmetry of the arrangement that in (c) there is neither bending moment nor deflexion at O, the centre of the beam. There

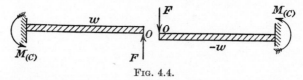

Fig. 4.4.

is, however, a shearing force F, and the two halves of the beam are in equilibrium under the actions shown in Fig. 4.4.

Considering the left half, the upward deflexion of O due to F equals the downward deflexion of O due to w.

That is, $\dfrac{FL^3}{24EI}=\dfrac{wL^4}{128EI}$;

whence $F=\dfrac{3}{16}wL,$

and $M_{(c)}=\dfrac{wL^2}{8}-\dfrac{3wL^2}{32}=\dfrac{wL^2}{32}.$

Hence $\qquad\qquad M_A = M_{(b)} + M_{(c)} = \dfrac{wL^2}{12} + \dfrac{wL^2}{32} = \dfrac{11wL^2}{96}$,

and $\qquad\qquad M_B = M_{(b)} - M_{(c)} = \dfrac{wL^2}{12} - \dfrac{wL^2}{32} = \dfrac{5wL^2}{96}$.

4.3. Strain energy.—When loads are applied to a body their points of application are displaced and the energy due to their movements is imparted to the body. If the strains are perfectly elastic this energy is stored in the body and is recoverable—when the loads are removed it is used in restoring the body to its original shape. If the strains are greater than those within which the body behaves elastically, part of the energy is used in permanently deforming the body and this portion is not recoverable. In general we are only concerned with strains of an elastic type and the energy stored under these conditions is known as strain energy. We shall also confine our attention to the case in which the load-displacement curve is linear.

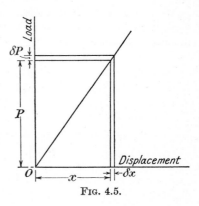

Fig. 4.5.

Fig. 4.5 represents the load displacement curve for a bar of material which obeys Hooke's law when subjected to a direct tensile or compressive force. The ordinates represent the loads applied to the bar and the abscissae the displacements. These loads are applied in such a way that no kinetic energy is created, *i.e.* the bar does not vibrate longitudinally. The work done by the load is then all stored as strain energy in the bar.

Under a load P the displacement is x and under a load $P + \delta P$ it is $x + \delta x$. The work done by the load during the increment of strain is its average value multiplied by the distance through which it moves, *i.e.* $\left(P + \dfrac{\delta P}{2}\right)\delta x$.

Since no kinetic energy is created this energy is stored in the bar and the increment of strain energy is therefore

$$\delta u = P\delta x$$

the second order term being neglected.

Since the load-displacement curve is linear

$$\delta x = \frac{L\delta P}{AE}$$

where L is the length of the bar, A is the cross-sectional area and E is Young's modulus.

Then $\qquad\qquad \delta u = \dfrac{PL}{AE}\delta P$.

Hence, the total strain energy of the bar as the load is increased from zero to P_0 is

$$u = \frac{L}{AE}\int_0^{P_0} P\,dP$$

or $\qquad\qquad u = \dfrac{P_0^2 L}{2AE}$ . . . . (4.1)

If the load is applied in such a way that kinetic energy is created the extra energy will cause the bar to vibrate. When these vibrations have ceased, however, the energy of the bar will be that found above. The strain energy in fact does not depend upon the manner in which the load is applied but only upon the final value of the load provided that the strains during vibration are not such as to cause permanent deformation, *i.e.* that the maximum stress at no time exceeds the limit of proportionality.

4.4. Force in a bar in terms of end displacements.—It is often convenient to express the force in a bar of a framework in terms of the displacements of its ends. Suppose P and Q are two nodes of a frame connected by the bar PQ.

Let the co-ordinates of P measured from any origin be (x_P, y_P, z_P) and the co-ordinates of Q be (x_Q, y_Q, z_Q).

When loads are applied to the frame P and Q will be displaced and the new co-ordinates will be

$(x_P + \alpha_P, y_P + \beta_P, z_P + \gamma_P)$ and $(x_Q + \alpha_Q, y_Q + \beta_Q, z_Q + \gamma_Q)$ respectively.

The initial length of the bar PQ is L, where

$$L^2 = (x_Q - x_P)^2 + (y_Q - y_P)^2 + (z_Q - z_P)^2$$

and the final length is $L + \delta L$, where

$$
\begin{aligned}
(L + \delta L)^2 &= (x_Q + \alpha_Q - x_P - \alpha_P)^2 + (y_Q + \beta_Q - y_P - \beta_P)^2 + (z_Q + \gamma_Q - z_P - \gamma_P)^2 \\
&= (x_Q - x_P)^2 + (\alpha_Q - \alpha_P)^2 + 2(x_Q - x_P)(\alpha_Q - \alpha_P) \\
&\quad + (y_Q - y_P)^2 + (\beta_Q - \beta_P)^2 + 2(y_Q - y_P)(\beta_Q - \beta_P) \\
&\quad + (z_Q - z_P)^2 + (\gamma_Q - \gamma_P)^2 + 2(z_Q - z_P)(\gamma_Q - \gamma_P).
\end{aligned}
$$

Substituting for the appropriate terms from the equation for L^2 and neglecting the second-order terms $(\alpha_Q - \alpha_P)^2$, $(\beta_Q - \beta_P)^2$ and $(\gamma_Q - \gamma_P)^2$ this becomes

$$(L + \delta L)^2 = L^2 + 2\{(x_Q - x_P)(\alpha_Q - \alpha_P) + (y_Q - y_P)(\beta_Q - \beta_P) + (z_Q - z_P)(\gamma_Q - \gamma_P)\}.$$

Neglecting the second-order term $(\delta L)^2$ this can be written in the form,

$$e = \frac{\delta L}{L} = \frac{(x_Q - x_P)(\alpha_Q - \alpha_P) + (y_Q - y_P)(\beta_Q - \beta_P) + (z_Q - z_P)(\gamma_Q - \gamma_P)}{L^2}$$

where e is the strain in the bar.

The stress is then Ee, and the force in the bar is AEe.

4.5. Strain energy as a function of external loads.—If PQ is any bar in a plane frame and T_{PQ} is the force in it we can write from the result of the previous paragraph

$$\frac{T_{PQ}L}{AE} = \frac{(x_Q - x_P)(\alpha_Q - \alpha_P) + (y_Q - y_P)(\beta_Q - \beta_P)}{L}$$

and multiplying both sides of this equation by $\frac{1}{2}T_{PQ}$ we obtain

$$\frac{T^2{}_{PQ}L}{2AE} = \frac{1}{2}t_{PQ}[(x_Q - x_P)(\alpha_Q - \alpha_P) + (y_Q - y_P)(\beta_Q - \beta_P)]$$

where t_{PQ} is the tension coefficient for PQ.

This can be rewritten :

$$\frac{T^2{}_{PQ}L}{2AE} = \frac{\alpha_Q t_{PQ}}{2}(x_Q - x_P) + \frac{\beta_Q t_{PQ}}{2}(y_Q - y_P) + \frac{\alpha_P t_{PQ}}{2}(x_P - x_Q) + \frac{\beta_P t_{PQ}}{2}(y_P - y_Q).$$

Similar expressions can be written for every bar of the frame : α_Q and β_Q will be common factors for all the bars connected to the joint Q so that if all the expressions are added we shall obtain

$$\sum \frac{T^2L}{2AE} = \frac{\alpha_Q}{2}\{t_{QA}(x_Q-x_A)+t_{QB}(x_Q-x_B)+ \ldots +t_{QP}(x_Q-x_P)\}$$

$$+\frac{\beta_Q}{2}\{t_{QA}(y_Q-y_A)+t_{QB}(y_Q-y_B)+ \ldots +t_{QP}(y_Q-y_P)\}$$

+similar expressions for every other joint of the frame. If X_Q and Y_Q are the components of external force along the x and y axes at joint Q the equations of equilibrium for this joint are, from equation (2.1),

$$t_{QA}(x_A-x_Q)+t_{QB}(x_B-x_Q)+ \ldots +t_{QP}(x_P-x_Q)+X_Q=0$$

and $\quad t_{QA}(y_A-y_Q)+t_{QB}(y_B-y_Q)+ \ldots +t_{QP}(y_P-y_Q)+Y_Q=0.$

Substituting the values of X_Q and Y_Q from these equations in the above we obtain

$$\sum \frac{T^2L}{2AE} = \sum \left(\frac{\alpha_Q}{2}X_Q+\frac{\beta_Q}{2}Y_Q\right)$$

the summation of the left-hand side including all the bars of the frame and that of the right-hand side all the joints.

The left-hand expression is the internal work or strain energy of the frame produced *by the action of the external loads,* so that

$$U=\tfrac{1}{2}\Sigma(\alpha_Q X_Q+\beta_Q Y_Q) \quad . \quad . \quad . \quad . \quad . \quad . \quad (4.2)$$

If W_Q is the resultant force at Q of which X_Q and Y_Q are the components, and if Δ_Q is the displacement of Q in the line of action of W_Q, we have

$$X_Q\alpha_Q+Y_Q\beta_Q=W_Q\Delta_Q$$

and (4.2) can be written

$$U=\tfrac{1}{2}\Sigma W\Delta \quad . \quad . \quad . \quad . \quad . \quad . \quad (4.3)$$

i.e. the internal work of a frame which has a linear load-displacement relationship is half the sum of the products of the external forces and their respective displacements in their own lines of action.

This result depends only on the final values of the external loads and not upon the way in which they have been applied.

For a space frame the same result is obtained in an exactly similar manner by introducing displacements and loads along the z axis of reference.

4.6. Strain energy due to bending.—Hitherto we have assumed that the bars with which we were dealing were subjected to pure tension or compression only, but as any action which stresses a body produces strain energy we shall now obtain expressions for that due to other actions.

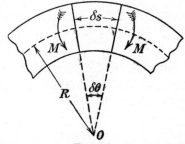

Suppose an initially straight beam to be subjected to a uniform bending moment M.

Under the action of this moment let two adjacent normal sections separated by a distance δs be inclined to each other

FIG. 4.6.

so that δs subtends an angle $\delta\theta$ at the centre of curvature as in Fig. 4.6.

Since M could be replaced by equal and opposite forces acting at the outermost tensile and compressive fibres of the beam respectively and the external work could be expressed in terms of these equivalent forces it is clear that the result obtained in the previous paragraph holds true and we can write

$$\delta U_B = \tfrac{1}{2} M \delta \theta$$

where δU_B is the strain energy of the element due to bending.

If R is the radius of curvature of the element due to the action of M,

$$R \delta \theta = \delta s$$

and

$$\delta U_B = \frac{M \delta s}{2R}.$$

But from the ordinary theory of bending,

$$\frac{1}{R} = \frac{M}{EI} \qquad \therefore \qquad \delta U_B = \frac{M^2 \delta s}{2EI}$$

and in the limit when δs is indefinitely decreased we can write

$$U_B = \int \frac{M^2 ds}{2EI} \qquad . \quad . \quad . \quad . \quad . \quad . \quad (4.4)$$

which is the expression for the strain energy due to bending.

4.7. Strain energy due to shearing force.—Let AC and BD in Fig. 4.7 be two adjacent sections of a beam, separated by a distance δs, subjected to a shearing force F which will be supposed to be uniformly distributed over the cross-section of the beam.

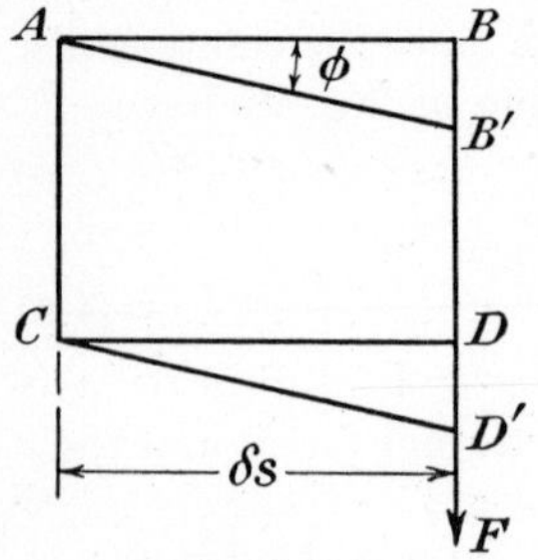

Due to F let the shear strain be ϕ so that B and D move through a distance $\phi \delta s$ to B′ and D′ respectively.

Then $\qquad \delta U_F = \tfrac{1}{2} F \phi \delta s,$

where δU_F is the strain energy of the element due to shear.

Fig. 4.7.

But $\qquad \phi = \dfrac{\text{shear stress}}{N} = \dfrac{F}{AN}$

where N is the modulus of rigidity of the material and A is the cross-sectional area of the beam.

$$\therefore \qquad \delta U_F = \frac{F^2 \delta s}{2AN}$$

and if δs is indefinitely reduced we have

$$U_F = \int \frac{F^2 ds}{2AN}. \qquad . \quad . \quad . \quad . \quad . \quad . \quad (4.5)$$

The shear stress is not in fact uniformly distributed over the cross-section : in a rectangular beam, for example, the distribution is parabolic and so the correct form of the above equation is

$$U_F = k \int \frac{F^2 ds}{2AN} \qquad . \quad . \quad . \quad . \quad . \quad . \quad (4.6)$$

where k is a coefficient which depends upon the shape of the section and the form of the loading.

4.8. Strain energy due to torsion.—Suppose that under the action of a torque T, two adjacent sections of a circular shaft δs apart are twisted

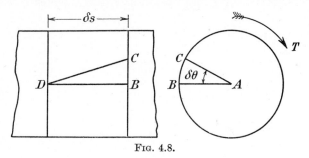

FIG. 4.8.

through an angle $\delta\theta$ relative to each other as shown in Fig. 4.8. If the outer radius of the shaft is R the shear strain ϕ is

$$\phi=\frac{BC}{BD}=\frac{R\delta\theta}{\delta s}.$$

Also,

$$\phi=q/N=\frac{TR}{NJ}$$

where q is the shear stress at the radius R, N is the modulus of rigidity of the material and J is the polar second moment of area of the shaft.

Hence

$$\frac{R\delta\theta}{\delta s}=\frac{TR}{NJ}$$

or

$$\delta\theta=\frac{T\delta s}{NJ}.$$

The internal work of the element of the shaft is $\frac{1}{2}T\delta\theta$

$\therefore$

$$\delta u=\frac{T^2\delta s}{2NJ}$$

or

$$U_T=\int\frac{T^2 ds}{2NJ}.$$

If the shaft is not circular in section, J is not the polar moment, but has a modified value which can be calculated (*e.g.* Bairstow & Pippard, 1921) although in some cases an experimental determination may be the simpler procedure. For a general discussion of this problem reference may be made to standard text books (*e.g.* Case, 1938).

4.9. The strain energy of curved beams.—When a beam has a large initial curvature the expression for the strain energy previously obtained for straight beams is not applicable.

Suppose ABCD in Fig. 4.9 is an element of a curved bar acted upon by a bending moment M, a shearing force F and an axial tension T.

From paragraph 3.17 we have

$$\frac{E\delta\theta}{\theta}=\frac{M}{Ah}$$

so that

$$\delta\theta=\frac{M\theta}{AEh}=\frac{M\delta s}{RAEh}$$

which is the decrease of angle between AB and CD due to M.

Hence, if δU_B is the strain energy of the element due to bending,

$$\delta U_B = \frac{M^2\delta s}{2RAEh}. \qquad \cdots \qquad (4.7)$$

Due to T the element elongates by an amount $\dfrac{T\delta s}{AE}$ and this *increases* the angle θ by $\dfrac{T\delta s}{RAE}$ so that the work done by T if it acted alone would be

$$\frac{T\delta s}{RAE} \times \frac{TR}{2} = \frac{T^2\delta s}{2AE}.$$

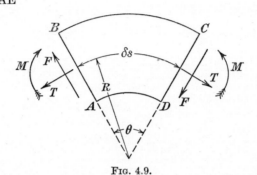

Fig. 4.9.

Part of this work, however, is done against the couple M and relieves the strain energy already stored by M. The moment used in this way is $\dfrac{MT\delta s}{RAE}$ and the net amount stored as strain energy in the element is therefore

$$\delta U_T = \frac{T^2\delta s}{2AE} - \frac{MT\delta s}{RAE}$$

$$= \frac{T\delta s}{AE}\left(\frac{T}{2} - \frac{M}{R}\right). \qquad \cdots \qquad (4.8)$$

The shearing force F will cause sliding of one section relative to the other of an amount $\dfrac{kF\delta s}{AN}$ where k is a numerical factor depending on the shape of the cross-section.

So the strain energy of the element due to shearing force is

$$\delta U_F = \frac{kF^2\delta s}{2AN} \qquad \cdots \qquad (4.9)$$

and the total strain energy of the element is

$$\delta U = \delta U_B + \delta U_T + \delta U_F$$

$$= \frac{M^2\delta s}{2RAEh} + \frac{T\delta s}{AE}\left(\frac{T}{2} - \frac{M}{R}\right) + \frac{kF^2\delta s}{2AN}$$

or

$$U = \int\left\{\frac{M^2}{2RAEh} + \frac{T}{AE}\left(\frac{T}{2} - \frac{M}{R}\right) + \frac{kF^2}{2AN}\right\}ds. \qquad \cdots \qquad (4.10)$$

The effects of T and F are very often negligible compared with that of M and with sufficient accuracy

$$U = \int\frac{M^2 ds}{2RAEh}. \qquad \cdots \qquad (4.11)$$

4.10. Clerk Maxwell's reciprocal theorem.—Suppose any elastic body, either solid or a framework, is supported in such a way that the reactive forces do no work when loads are applied to the body. This result may be obtained by fixing the points of supports in space or by allowing them to rest on frictionless bearings. In the first instance there is no movement of the supporting points and in the second, any movement is at right angles to the reactive force brought into action. The conditions for the sufficiency of the reactive forces as described in Chapter 1 must of course be observed. The body has a linear load-deflexion relation such that when loads W_1 and W_2 are applied separately in specified directions to any two points A and B in the body,

Under the action of W_1 *alone* :—
A will move $W_1\Delta_1$ in the direction of W_1.
B will move $W_1\Delta'_2$ in the direction of W_2.

Under the action of W_2 *alone* :—
A will move $W_2\Delta'_1$ in the direction of W_1.
B will move $W_2\Delta_2$ in the direction of W_2.

If these two loads are applied simultaneously at such a rate that no kinetic energy is generated W_1 grows to its maximum value while A moves through the distance $W_1\Delta_1+W_2\Delta'_1$ and W_2 grows to its maximum while B moves through $W_2\Delta_2+W_1\Delta'_2$.
Hence the total strain energy of the body is

$$U=\tfrac{1}{2}W_1(W_1\Delta_1+W_2\Delta'_1)+\tfrac{1}{2}W_2(W_2\Delta_2+W_1\Delta'_2).$$

When W_1 alone acts on the body the strain energy is $\tfrac{1}{2}W_1{}^2\Delta_1$. If W_2 is then applied to point B it will move through a distance $W_2\Delta_2$ and the strain energy due to this will be $\tfrac{1}{2}W_2{}^2\Delta_2$. At the same time it will cause the load W_1 to move through a further distance $W_2\Delta'_1$ and since the value of W_1 is constant during this movement the work done on it is $W_1W_2\Delta'_1$.
Hence the total strain energy is

$$U=\tfrac{1}{2}W_1{}^2\Delta_1+\tfrac{1}{2}W_2{}^2\Delta_2+W_1W_2\Delta'_1.$$

Since the manner in which the external loads reach their final values does not affect the value of the strain energy the two expressions are equal, *i.e.*

$$\tfrac{1}{2}W_1(W_1\Delta_1+W_2\Delta'_1)+\tfrac{1}{2}W_2(W_2\Delta_2+W_1\Delta'_2)$$
$$=\tfrac{1}{2}W_1{}^2\Delta_1+\tfrac{1}{2}W_2{}^2\Delta_2+W_1W_2\Delta'_1.$$

Whence $\qquad\qquad\tfrac{1}{2}W_1W_2\Delta'_2=\tfrac{1}{2}W_1W_2\Delta'_1$
or $\qquad\qquad\qquad\Delta'_2=\Delta'_1,$

i.e. the deflexion of B in the direction of W_2 when a unit load acts at A in the direction of W_1 is the same as the deflexion of A in the direction of W_1 when a unit load acts at B in the direction of W_2.

This is Clerk Maxwell's reciprocal theorem. In a more general form due to Betti it may be stated as follows (Southwell, 1936) :

Suppose that a number of forces P_1, P_2 ... P_n, act simultaneously upon a body which obeys Hooke's Law and that the displacements in the lines of action of these forces are respectively Δ_1, Δ_2 ... Δ_n. If these forces are replaced by a second system P'_1, P'_2 ... P'_n acting at the same points and in the same directions as those of the first system, the corresponding displacements being Δ'_1, Δ'_2 ... Δ'_n, then

$$P_1\Delta'_1+P_2\Delta'_2+\ \ldots\ +P_n\Delta'_n=P'_1\Delta_1+P'_2\Delta_2+\ \ldots\ +P'_n\Delta_n. \quad (4.12)$$

3

In addition to the forces, moments may also act on the body. If these are represented by M_q and M'_q in the first and second systems respectively, and if the corresponding displacements are θ_q and θ'_q then terms $\Sigma M_q \theta'_q$ and $\Sigma M'_q \theta_q$ will appear on the left and right-hand sides respectively of equation (4.12).

4.11. The first theorem of Castigliano.—Let any frame having a linear relationship between load and deflexion be supported in such a way that the reactive forces do no work when loads are applied to the frame. If a number of loads, $W_1, W_2 \ldots W_N$, are applied to points, 1 2, ... N of the frame let the movement of point q in the direction of W_Q due to W_P be $W_P(_p\delta_q)$ where q and p are any loaded points.

Thus the movement of point 3 in the direction of W_3 due to the load W_1 is $W_1(_1\delta_3)$, etc.

The total movement of W_1 in its own line of action is then

$$\Delta_1 = W_1(_1\delta_1) + W_2(_2\delta_1) + W_3(_3\delta_1) + \ . \ . \ . \ . \ + W_N(_N\delta_1),$$

and the movement of W_2 in its own line of action is

$$\Delta_2 = W_1(_1\delta_2) + W_2(_2\delta_2) + W_3(_3\delta_2) + \ . \ . \ . \ . \ + W_N(_N\delta_2).$$

Using the result of equation (4.3) we can write

$$\tfrac{1}{2}W_1\Delta_1 + \tfrac{1}{2}W_2\Delta_2 + \ . \ . \ . \ . \ \tfrac{1}{2}W_N\Delta_N = \sum \frac{(\alpha W_1 + \beta W_2 + \ . \ . \ . \ . \ + \nu W_N)^2 L}{2AE}$$

where $\alpha W_1 + \beta W_2 + \ . \ . \ . \ + \nu W_N$ is the force in any member due to the external load system.

If W_1 is removed the deflexions of points 1, 2, . . ., etc., are

$$\Delta_1 - W_1(_1\delta_1)$$
$$\Delta_2 - W_1(_1\delta_2)$$
$$\cdot \ \cdot \ \cdot \ \cdot \ \cdot \ \cdot$$
$$\Delta_N - W_1(_1\delta_N)$$

and as before,

$$\tfrac{1}{2}W_2\{\Delta_2 - W_1(_1\delta_2)\} + \tfrac{1}{2}W_3\{\Delta_3 - W_1(_1\delta_3)\} + \ . \ . \ . \ . \ + \tfrac{1}{2}W_N\{\Delta_N - W_1(_1\delta_N)\}$$
$$= \sum \frac{(\beta W_2 + \ . \ . \ . \ + \nu W_N)^2 L}{2AE}.$$

Subtracting this from the previous result we obtain

$$\tfrac{1}{2}W_1\Delta_1 + \tfrac{1}{2}W_2 W_1(_1\delta_2) + \tfrac{1}{2}W_3 W_1(_1\delta_3) + \ . \ . \ . \ . \ + \tfrac{1}{2}W_N W_1(_1\delta_N)$$
$$= \sum \frac{\alpha W_1(\alpha W_1 + 2\beta W_2 + \ . \ . \ . \ . \ + 2\nu W_N) L}{2AE}.$$

By Clerk Maxwell's theorem we can put $_1\delta_2 = {}_2\delta_1$, $_1\delta_3 = {}_3\delta_1$, etc., and on substituting for Δ_1 the expression becomes

$$W_1[\tfrac{1}{2}W_1(_1\delta_1) + W_2(_2\delta_1) + W_3(_3\delta_1) + \ . \ . \ . \ . \ + W_N(_N\delta_1)]$$
$$= \tfrac{1}{2}\sum \frac{\alpha W_1 L}{AE}(\alpha W_1 + 2\beta W_2 + \ . \ . \ . \ . \ + 2\nu W_N).$$

If W_1 acts alone on the frame,

$$\tfrac{1}{2}W_1^2(_1\delta_1) = \tfrac{1}{2}\sum \frac{\alpha^2 W_1^2 L}{AE}.$$

Adding this to the last result we obtain

$$W_1\Delta_1 = W_1\sum \frac{\alpha L}{AE}(\alpha W_1 + \beta W_2 + \ . \ . \ . \ . \ + \nu W_N)$$

or, $$\Delta_1 = \sum \frac{\partial u}{\partial W_1}$$

where u is the strain energy of a bar of the frame.

Hence $$\Delta_1 = \frac{\partial U}{\partial W_1} \qquad \cdot \quad \cdot \quad \cdot \quad \cdot \quad \cdot \quad \cdot \quad \cdot \quad (4.13)$$

where U is the total strain energy of the frame or, extending the result to a solid body, the total strain energy of the body.

This is the first theorem of Castigliano (1879) and states that *if the total strain energy expressed in terms of the external loads be partially differentiated with respect to any one of the external loads, the result gives the displacement of that load in its own line of action.*

Applications of this theorem will be dealt with in the next Chapter.

4.12. The second theorem of Castigliano.—Suppose a framework which obeys Hooke's law is supported in such a way that no work is done by the reactive forces, and further let this frame be subjected to a system of external loads and to self-straining forces due to the presence of imperfectly fitting redundant members.

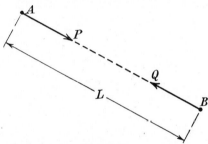

FIG. 4.10.

Let A and B in Fig. 4.10 be two adjacent nodes of the frame, the original distance between them before the application of either external or self-straining forces being L.

Suppose forces P and Q to act on the joints A and B along the line joining them as shown in the figure and let P and Q be functions of some variable R. Then if U′ is the strain energy of the frame due to the external loads and the self-straining forces we can write by the first theorem of Castigliano :—

The movement of A in the direction of $AB = \dfrac{\partial U'}{\partial P}$ and the movement of B

in the direction of $BA = \dfrac{\partial U'}{\partial Q}$.

Also $$\frac{\partial U'}{\partial R} = \frac{\partial U'}{\partial P}\frac{dP}{dR} + \frac{\partial U'}{\partial Q}\frac{dQ}{dR}.$$

If we put P=Q=R this becomes $\dfrac{\partial U'}{\partial R} = \dfrac{\partial U'}{\partial P} + \dfrac{\partial U'}{\partial Q}$ =total shortening of AB.

Suppose now that A and B are connected by a redundant bar of the frame so that R is the load in this member. Also let the original length of this bar be L−λ where λ is small compared with L.

The final length of the bar is $(L-\lambda)\left(1+\dfrac{R}{AE}\right)$, R being a tensile force.

But since the initial distance between A and B was L these points have approached each other by an amount

$$L-(L-\lambda)\left(1+\frac{R}{AE}\right)=\lambda-\frac{RL}{AE},$$

the second-order term $\frac{\lambda R}{AE}$ being neglected.

Hence
$$\lambda-\frac{RL}{AE}=\frac{\partial U'}{\partial R}.$$

Now
$$\frac{RL}{AE}=\frac{\partial}{\partial R}\left(\frac{R^2L}{2AE}\right)=\frac{\partial u}{\partial R}$$

where u is the strain energy of the bar AB.

Hence
$$\frac{\partial U'}{\partial R}+\frac{\partial u}{\partial R}=\lambda.$$

But
$$\frac{\partial U'}{\partial R}+\frac{\partial u}{\partial R}=\frac{\partial U}{\partial R}$$

where U is the total strain energy of the frame including the bar AB.

$$\therefore \qquad\qquad \frac{\partial U}{\partial R}=\lambda \quad . \quad . \quad . \quad . \quad . \quad . \quad . \quad (4.14)$$

or the partial differential coefficient of the total strain energy of a frame with respect to the load in a redundant member is equal to the initial lack of fit of that member.

Attention must be paid to the signs in using this result. In order to keep them correct the load in the member should always be made consistent with the initial lack of fit : if the member is initially too short the force R should be assumed to be tensile and if initially too long it should be assumed to be compressive.

This is the second theorem of Castigliano in its general form. If the member AB were originally of just the correct length we put $\lambda=0$ and the result is

$$\frac{\partial U}{\partial R}=0. \quad . \quad . \quad . \quad . \quad . \quad . \quad (4.15)$$

This gives the value of R which will make the strain energy of the frame a minimum and in consequence this form of the theorem is often called the principle of least work. It is, however, only a special case of the more general result.

4.13. Differential coefficients of strain energy with respect to a moment.— In the previous paragraphs the differentiation of the expression for the strain energy of an elastic body has been done with respect to an axial force. It will now be shown that the theorems of Castigliano can be extended to include the case when the action considered is a moment.

Suppose two external loads, P_1 and P_2, to act at any section of an elastic body.

Then the displacement of P_1 in its line of action $=\delta_1=\frac{\partial U}{\partial P_1}$ and the displacement of P_2 in its line of action $=\delta_2=\frac{\partial U}{\partial P_2}$.

If these loads are functions of P,

$$\frac{\partial U}{\partial P} = \frac{\partial U}{\partial P_1} \cdot \frac{dP_1}{dP} + \frac{\partial U}{\partial P_2} \cdot \frac{dP_2}{dP}$$

and if $P_1 = P_2 = P$ we have

$$\frac{\partial U}{\partial P} = \frac{\partial U}{\partial P_1} + \frac{\partial U}{\partial P_2} = \delta_1 + \delta_2.$$

If P_1 and P_2 are equal and opposite forces separated by a distance a they apply a couple $Pa = M$ to the body

and

$$\frac{1}{a} \frac{\partial U}{\partial P} = \frac{1}{a}(\delta_1 + \delta_2).$$

But

$$\frac{1}{a} \frac{\partial U}{\partial P} = \frac{\partial U}{\partial Pa} = \frac{\partial U}{\partial M}.$$

Also $\dfrac{\delta_1 + \delta_2}{a} = \theta$ is the angular rotation of the line joining the points of application of P_1 and P_2.

Hence

$$\frac{\partial U}{\partial M} = 0 \quad . \quad . \quad . \quad . \quad . \quad . \quad . \quad . \quad (4.16)$$

or the differential coefficient of the strain energy with respect to an external moment is the rotation of that moment in radians. This is a statement of the first theorem of Castigliano when the external action is a moment.

If P_1 and P_2 are internal redundant actions

$$\frac{\partial U}{\partial P_1} = \frac{\partial U}{\partial P_2} = 0$$

and then

$$\frac{\partial U}{\partial M} = 0 \quad . \quad . \quad . \quad . \quad . \quad . \quad . \quad (4.17)$$

which is the second theorem of Castigliano extended to an internal redundant moment.

4.14. Principle of Saint Venant.—This principle, known as the " elastic equivalence of statically equipollent systems of load," states that the strains which are produced in a body by the application to a small part of its surface of a system of forces statically equivalent to zero force and zero couple are of negligible magnitude at distances which are large compared with the linear dimensions of the part.

Suppose such a system of forces is divided into two parts which we will call A and B, these two parts being such that they produce equal and opposite resultant actions on the small part considered.

By Saint Venant's principle the strain at any point some distance from the part upon which A+B acts is very nearly zero. When A acts alone let the strain at this point be e. Then clearly the effect of B alone must be to cause a strain approximating to $-e$ since by the principle of superposition the effect of A+B must be the same as the sum of the separate effects. Thus the system of forces B whose resultant actions are equal in magnitude but opposite in sign to those of A produces nearly equal and opposite strains to those produced by A.

The principle of Saint Venant can therefore be restated and we may say that *forces applied at one part of an elastic structure will induce stresses which except in a region close to that part, will depend almost entirely upon their resultant action, and very little upon their distribution.*

The principle was originally stated without proof but having restated it in the form just quoted, R. V. Southwell (1923) from consideration of strain energy gave a proof which is reproduced here in its original form.

" Let us consider the case of a long girder, or braced framework, which is loaded at its two ends by forces applied in any given way ; and let us employ the symbol A to denote those regions which immediately adjoin the parts at which the forces are applied, and the symbol B for the remainder. The conditions of equilibrium require merely that the resultant action transmitted by B shall have a definite value ; but the conditions of continuity (or of compatibility of strains) will not be satisfied unless the total increase of the strain energy stored in A and B has its minimum value. Evidently, then, the equilibrium configuration may be regarded as in the nature of a compromise between the requirements of A and B. To reduce to a minimum the strain energy stored in A, the reactions between A and B would require to distribute themselves in a manner which will depend upon the distribution of the forces applied to A ; the requirements of B, on the other hand, will not vary, since there must be some definite distribution of stresses, in an otherwise unloaded body, which will entail the minimum storage of strain energy in transmitting a given resultant action.

Thus, in the process of adjustment which results in the actual distribution corresponding to equilibrium, we may picture a contest between the unloaded portions,* which strive always after ' standardisation,' and the loaded portions, which demand a particular solution for every specified distribution of the forces acting on them. As we pass from the regions of application of load through successive sections of the unloaded portion B, there will be a steady tendency for the claims of standardisation to prevail. The theorem stated in italics is an immediate deduction, and we may work back from this, by the principle of superposition, to Saint Venant's principle."

4.15. Strain energy equations in terms of tension coefficients.—In some instances it is desirable to carry through a calculation in terms of tension coefficients rather than in actual loads. The equations can readily be recast into a suitable form, as follows :—

Let P_0 be the load in any member of length L and t_p the tension coefficient for this member, so that

$$P_0 = t_p L.$$

Let R_q be the load in any redundant member, t_q its tension coefficient and l_q its length, so that

$$R_q = t_q l_q.$$

Then, $\qquad P_0 = f(W) + a t_1 l_1 + b t_2 l_2 + \ldots + q t_q l_q + \ldots + \text{etc.}$

where $f(W)$ is the contribution from the external load system.

Also $\qquad\qquad \dfrac{\partial P_0}{\partial t_q} = q l_q,$

---

* *I.e.*, portions of which the *external* surfaces are free from load.

or
$$\frac{L\partial t_p}{\partial t_q}=ql_q,$$

so that
$$\frac{\partial t_p}{\partial t_q}=\frac{ql_q}{L}.$$

Substituting these values in the expression

$$\frac{\partial u}{\partial R_q}=\frac{P_0 L}{AE}\frac{\partial P_0}{\partial R_q}$$

we have
$$\frac{\partial u}{\partial R_q}=\frac{t_p L^2}{AE}q$$

$$=\frac{t_p L^2}{AE}\frac{L\partial t_p}{l_q\partial t_q}$$

$$=\frac{t_p L^3}{AE}\left(\frac{1}{l_q}\right)\frac{\partial t_p}{\partial t_q}.$$

In general therefore the second theorem of Castigliano can be expressed in tension coefficients in the form

$$\frac{\partial U}{\partial R_q}=\sum\frac{t_p L^3}{AE}\left(\frac{1}{l_q}\right)\frac{\partial t_p}{\partial t_q}=\lambda. \quad \ldots \ldots \quad (4.18)$$

Since l_q is a divisor common to all terms we can, if λ is zero, *i.e.* if there is no self-straining, put the equation in the form

$$\sum\frac{t_p L^3}{AE}\frac{\partial t_p}{\partial t_q}=0. \quad \ldots \ldots \ldots \quad (4.19)$$

The summation extends to all members of the frame as before.

REFERENCES

Castigliano, A., 1879. *Théorème de l'équilibre des systèmes élastiques et ses applications* (English translation by E. S. Andrews " Elastic stresses in structures," 1919. Scott Greenwood).
Bairstow, L. and Pippard, A. J. S., 1921. *Proc. Instn. Civ. Engrs.*, **214**, 291.
Southwell, R. V., 1923. *Phil. Mag.*, **45**, 193.
—— 1936. " Introduction to the Theory of Elasticity." Clarendon Press.
Case, J., 1938. " Strength of Materials." Edward Arnold.

CHAPTER 5

DISPLACEMENTS OF ELASTIC BODIES

5.1. Displacement of the point of application of a single load.—If a body having a linear relationship between load and displacement is carried by supports which do no work when the body is loaded and bears a single load at any point, the displacement of that point can be calculated by a direct application of equation (4.3), which connects the strain energy with the external loads.

Thus, if W is the external load and Δ is its displacement in the line of action of W we have

$$\tfrac{1}{2}W \Delta = U$$

or

$$\Delta = \frac{2U}{W}$$

where U is the total strain energy of the body.

In a framed structure $U = \sum \dfrac{\alpha^2 W^2 L}{2AE}$ where αW is the force in any member,

so

$$\Delta = W \sum \frac{\alpha^2 L}{AE}.$$

As an example consider the steel frame shown in Fig. 5.1, which is pinned to a rigid support at A and D and carries a load of 20 tons at G. It is desired to calculate the vertical movement of the point G.

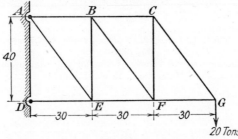

FIG. 5.1.

The work should be set out as shown in Table 5.1.

Columns 1, 2 and 3 are self-explanatory. In column 4 is entered the value of α. Since the load in any member is αW it is evident that α is the force in the member when W is made equal to unity. The required values of α may therefore be found by allowing unit load to act in the direction of W and determining the internal forces by any of the methods described in Chapter 2. In the present instance they can be written down by inspection but in a more complicated example a stress diagram or tension coefficient analysis would probably be necessary.

Column 5 is completed from the earlier columns. Since E is the same for all members it has been omitted until the final calculation. If the material

60

TABLE 5.1.

1	2	3	4	5
Member	L ins.	A sq. ins.	α	$\dfrac{\alpha^2 L}{A}$
AB	30	4	$\frac{3}{2}$	$\frac{270}{16}$
BC	30	2	$\frac{3}{4}$	$\frac{135}{16}$
DE	30	6	$-\frac{9}{4}$	$\frac{405}{16}$
EF	30	4	$-\frac{3}{2}$	$\frac{270}{16}$
FG	30	2	$-\frac{3}{4}$	$\frac{135}{16}$
AE	50	5	$\frac{5}{4}$	$\frac{250}{16}$
BF	50	5	$\frac{5}{4}$	$\frac{250}{16}$
CG	50	5	$\frac{5}{4}$	$\frac{250}{16}$
BE	40	4	-1	$\frac{160}{16}$
CF	40	4	-1	$\frac{160}{16}$

were not the same throughout the frame the appropriate value of E for each member would be entered in another column and column 5 would be $\dfrac{\alpha^2 L}{AE}$. Summing the results in column 5 we obtain $\sum \dfrac{\alpha^2 L}{A} = \dfrac{2{,}285}{16}$ and taking E as 13,000 tons per square inch,

$$\sum \frac{\alpha^2 L}{AE} = \frac{2{,}285}{16 \times 13{,}000}.$$

Hence

$$\Delta = \frac{20 \times 2{,}285}{16 \times 13{,}000} \text{ inch} = \cdot 22 \text{ inch}.$$

As an example of the application of this method to a beam we will calculate the displacement of a load placed on a simply supported beam at a point C

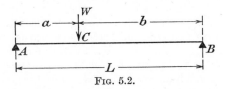

FIG. 5.2.

which is a distance a from one support and a distance b from the other as shown in Fig. 5.2.

The reaction at A is $\dfrac{b}{L}W$ and in the length AC of the beam the bending moment at a distance x from A is $\dfrac{Wbx}{L}$. From equation (4.4) we have for AC

$$U_{AC} = \frac{1}{2EI} \int_o^a M^2 dx$$

$$= \frac{W^2 b^2}{2EIL^2} \int_o^a x^2 dx$$

$$= \frac{W^2 b^2 a^3}{6EIL^2}.$$

Similarly for the length BC, taking the origin at B, we have

$$U_{BC} = \frac{W^2 a^2 b^3}{6EIL^2}.$$

The total strain energy is therefore

$$U = \frac{W^2 a^2 b^2}{6EIL^2}(a+b) = \frac{W^2 a^2 b^2}{6EIL}$$

and so

$$\Delta = \frac{2U}{W} = \frac{Wa^2 b^2}{3EIL},$$

which is a well known result obtainable by the methods of Chapter 3.

The method just described can only be used when a single load acts on the body. If more than one load is carried it is not applicable and deflexions must be calculated by one or other of the methods now to be described.

5.2. Displacements by the first theorem of Castigliano.—If the displacements of a few points only are to be determined an application of the first theorem of Castigliano is probably the most satisfactory method of obtaining

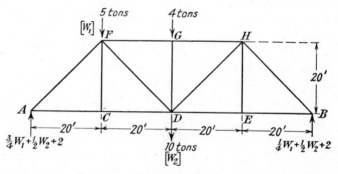

FIG. 5.3.

the result. An example will best explain the procedure and we will calculate the vertical deflexions of points F and D of the steel truss shown in Fig. 5.3.

Since the strain energy of the frame has to be differentiated with respect to the external loads at the points F and D it is necessary first of all to denote those loads by algebraic symbols and they will therefore be replaced by W_1 and W_2 respectively. The symbols will be given their numerical values only after the expressions for the deflexions have been obtained. Since the movement of the point G is not required there is no need to denote the load there by a symbol.

The required deflexions will then be

$$\Delta_F = \frac{\partial U}{\partial W_1} = \frac{1}{E} \sum \frac{P_0 L}{A} \frac{\partial P_0}{\partial W_1}$$

$$\Delta_D = \frac{\partial U}{\partial W_2} = \frac{1}{E} \sum \frac{P_0 L}{A} \frac{\partial P_0}{\partial W_2}.$$

As in all calculations of this type, the work should be systematised and Table 5.2 shows a suitable arrangement.

In the first place the force in every member must be calculated in terms of W_1, W_2 and the remaining loads, due regard being paid to signs : tensions

TABLE 5.2.

1	2	3	4			5			6		
			P_0			$\dfrac{P_0 L}{A}\dfrac{\partial P_0}{\partial W_1}$			$\dfrac{P_0 L}{A}\dfrac{\partial P_0}{\partial W_2}$		
Bar	L ins.	A ins.^{2}	W_1	W_2	Other loads	W_1	W_2	Other loads	W_1	W_2	Other loads
AC	240	2	$\frac{3}{4}$	$\frac{1}{2}$	2	67·5	45	180	45	30	120
CD	240	4	$\frac{3}{4}$	$\frac{1}{2}$	2	33·75	22·5	90	22·5	15	60
DE	240	4	$\frac{1}{4}$	$\frac{1}{2}$	2	3·75	7·5	30	7·5	15	60
EB	240	2	$\frac{1}{4}$	$\frac{1}{2}$	2	7·5	15·0	60	15	30	120
FG	240	4	$-\frac{1}{2}$	-1	-4	15	30	120	30	60	240
GH	240	4	$-\frac{1}{2}$	-1	-4	15	30	120	30	60	240
AF	$240\sqrt{2}$	3	$\dfrac{3\sqrt{2}}{4}$	$-\dfrac{\sqrt{2}}{2}$	$-2\sqrt{2}$	$90\sqrt{2}$	$60\sqrt{2}$	$240\sqrt{2}$	$60\sqrt{2}$	$40\sqrt{2}$	$160\sqrt{2}$
FC	240	2	—	—	—	—	—	—	—	—	—
FD	$240\sqrt{2}$	2	$-\dfrac{\sqrt{2}}{4}$	$\dfrac{\sqrt{2}}{2}$	$2\sqrt{2}$	$15\sqrt{2}$	$-30\sqrt{2}$	$-120\sqrt{2}$	$-30\sqrt{2}$	$60\sqrt{2}$	$240\sqrt{2}$
GD	240	2	—	—	-4	—	—	—	—	—	—
DH	$240\sqrt{2}$	2	$\dfrac{\sqrt{2}}{4}$	$\dfrac{\sqrt{2}}{2}$	$2\sqrt{2}$	$15\sqrt{2}$	$30\sqrt{2}$	$120\sqrt{2}$	$30\sqrt{2}$	$60\sqrt{2}$	$240\sqrt{2}$
HE	240	2	—	—	—	—	—	—	—	—	—
HB	$240\sqrt{2}$	3	$-\dfrac{\sqrt{2}}{4}$	$-\dfrac{\sqrt{2}}{2}$	$-2\sqrt{2}$	$10\sqrt{2}$	$20\sqrt{2}$	$80\sqrt{2}$	$20\sqrt{2}$	$40\sqrt{2}$	$160\sqrt{2}$

are positive and compressions negative. If this is done graphically it will be necessary to draw three separate diagrams—one for W_1 acting alone, one for W_2 acting alone and the third for the remaining loads. These forces are entered in column 4 ; *e.g.* the force in GH is found by using the method of sections to be $P_0=-\frac{1}{2}W_1-W_2-4$ and the sub-divisions of column 4 are completed appropriately. It may be noted here that $\dfrac{\partial P_0}{\partial W_1}$ and $\dfrac{\partial P_0}{\partial W_2}$ for this bar are respectively $-\frac{1}{2}$ and -1, *i.e.* the coefficients of W_1 and W_2 entered in the first two sub-divisions of column 4.

Columns 1, 2 and 3 give particulars of the various bars.

In columns 5 and 6 respectively are entered the values of $\dfrac{P_0 L}{A}\dfrac{\partial P_0}{\partial W_1}$ and $\dfrac{P_0 L}{A}\dfrac{\partial P_0}{\partial W_2}$, calculated from the preceding columns. As an illustration, for bar AC, $\dfrac{L}{A}=120$ and $\dfrac{\partial P_0}{\partial W_1}=\frac{3}{4}$, so that $\dfrac{L}{A}\dfrac{\partial P_0}{\partial W_1}=90$. This is multiplied by P_0 which is tabulated in column 4 and the values entered in column 5 are obtained. Similarly $\dfrac{\partial P_0}{\partial W_2}=\frac{1}{2}$ and $\dfrac{L}{A}\dfrac{\partial P_0}{\partial W_2}=60$, which again multiplied by P_0 gives the figures entered in column 6.

The table is completed and columns 5 and 6 are summed to give $\sum\dfrac{P_0 L}{A}\dfrac{\partial P_0}{\partial W_1}$ and $\sum\dfrac{P_0 L}{A}\dfrac{\partial P_0}{\partial W_2}$.

These summations give

$$326W_1 + 263W_2 + 1{,}054$$

and $\qquad\qquad 263W_1 + 493W_2 + 1{,}971$ respectively.

To obtain the deflexion at points F and D these must be divided by E which is taken to be 13,000 tons per square inch.

Hence $\qquad \Delta_F = \dfrac{1}{13{,}000}(326W_1 + 263W_2 + 1{,}054)$ inches,

and $\qquad \Delta_D = \dfrac{1}{13{,}000}(263W_1 + 493W_2 + 1{,}971)$ inches.

The numerical values of W_1 and W_2, viz. 5 tons and 10 tons respectively, are now substituted and the actual deflexions are

$$\Delta_F = \cdot410 \text{ inch}$$
and $\qquad\qquad \Delta_D = \cdot632 \text{ inch.}$

5.3. Displacement of an unloaded point.—Since the expressions for Δ_F and Δ_D in the foregoing example are valid whatever the values of W_1 and W_2 a method is at once evident for determining the displacement of an unloaded point in a structure. Suppose for example that there were no load at F and it was required to calculate the vertical deflexion at that point. A load W_F is placed at F and the previous procedure is followed, leading to the general expression for Δ_F as before. W_F is then put equal to zero and the vertical displacement of F is obtained.

5.4. Displacements in terms of stresses in the members.—Since $\dfrac{P_0}{A} = f$ is the stress in any bar the equation for the displacement of any point can be rewritten

$$\Delta = \sum \frac{fL}{E} \frac{\partial P_0}{\partial W}.$$

If then the stresses in the bars of a frame are specified it is unnecessary to set down the areas ; the displacement of any point can be found directly. If, for instance, in the previous example the frame is so designed that the stress in every loaded bar is 8 tons per square inch, the displacements of the points F and D respectively are

$$\Delta_F = \frac{1}{E}\sum fL \frac{\partial P_0}{\partial W_1}$$

and $\qquad\qquad \Delta_D = \dfrac{1}{E}\sum fL \dfrac{\partial P_0}{\partial W_2}.$

The calculations should be set out as in Table 5.3.

It must be remembered that since f is $\dfrac{P_0}{A}$ it will have the same sign as P_0.

When the specified values of W_1 and W_2 are substituted in Table 5.2, it is found that the only bars in compression are FG, GH, AF and HB. The figures for these bars in columns 5 and 6 of Table 5.3 must therefore be multiplied by -8 tons per square inch and the remainder by $+8$ tons per square inch to obtain the values of $fL\dfrac{\partial P_0}{\partial W_1}$ and $fL\dfrac{\partial P_0}{\partial W_2}$.

TABLE 5.3.

1	2	3	4	5	6
Bar	L ins.	$\dfrac{\partial P_0}{\partial W_1}$	$\dfrac{\partial P_0}{\partial W_2}$	$L\dfrac{\partial P_0}{\partial W_1}$	$L\dfrac{\partial P_0}{\partial W_2}$
AC	240	$\frac{3}{4}$	$\frac{1}{2}$	180	120
CD	240	$\frac{3}{4}$	$\frac{1}{2}$	180	120
DE	240	$\frac{1}{4}$	$\frac{1}{2}$	60	120
EB	240	$\frac{1}{4}$	$\frac{1}{2}$	60	120
FG	240	$-\frac{1}{2}$	-1	-120	-240
GH	240	$-\frac{1}{2}$	-1	-120	-240
AF	$240\sqrt{2}$	$-\dfrac{3\sqrt{2}}{4}$	$-\dfrac{\sqrt{2}}{2}$	-360	-240
FD	$240\sqrt{2}$	$-\dfrac{\sqrt{2}}{4}$	$\dfrac{\sqrt{2}}{2}$	-120	240
DH	$240\sqrt{2}$	$\dfrac{\sqrt{2}}{4}$	$\dfrac{\sqrt{2}}{2}$	120	240
HB	$240\sqrt{2}$	$-\dfrac{\sqrt{2}}{4}$	$-\dfrac{\sqrt{2}}{2}$	-120	-240

The summation of these columns then gives

$$\Delta_F = \frac{1}{E}\sum fL\frac{\partial P_0}{\partial W_1} = \frac{9,600}{13,000} = \cdot 738 \text{ inch,}$$

and
$$\Delta_D = \frac{1}{E}\sum fL\frac{\partial P_0}{\partial W_2} = \frac{15,360}{13,000} = 1\cdot 18 \text{ inches.}$$

If, as in paragraph 5.2, loads and not stresses are used, the question of sign is not so important. For example the force in FD can be expressed either as a tension of

$$-\frac{\sqrt{2}}{4}\,W_1 + \frac{\sqrt{2}}{2}\,W_2 + 2\sqrt{2} \text{ or as a compression of } \frac{\sqrt{2}}{4}\,W_1 - \frac{\sqrt{2}}{2}\,W_2 - 2\sqrt{2}.$$

The terms which affect signs are $P_0\dfrac{\partial P_0}{\partial W_1}$ and $P_0\dfrac{\partial P_0}{\partial W_2}$ and it will be seen that whichever of the two values of P_0 are used the same final result is obtained, since in the second case the signs of P_0 and both differential coefficients are changed simultaneously, leaving the products unaffected.

5.5. Displacements of beams by strain energy methods.—The first theorem of Castigliano gives an alternative method for calculating the displacements of loaded beams to that described in Chapter 3 and the strain energy analysis is often simpler.

The simple instance of a beam carrying a single load has already been dealt with by the process of equating internal and external work and as a first example this same problem, illustrated in Fig. 5.2, will be solved by applying the first theorem of Castigliano. The vertical deflexion of the point C is

$$\frac{dU}{dW} = \frac{1}{EI}\int M\frac{dM}{dW}dx.$$

At x from A, $$M_x = \frac{Wbx}{L}$$

so $$\frac{dM_x}{dW} = \frac{bx}{L},$$

and for the section AC of the beam,

$$\left[\frac{dU}{dW}\right]_{AC} = \frac{Wb^2}{EIL^2}\int_0^a x^2 dx = \frac{Wa^3b^2}{3EIL^2}.$$

Similarly for the section BC,

$$\left[\frac{dU}{dW}\right]_{BC} = \frac{Wa^2}{EIL^2}\int_0^b x^2 dx = \frac{Wa^2b^3}{3EIL^2}.$$

Hence $$\Delta_C = \frac{dU}{dW} = \frac{Wa^2b^2}{3EIL^2}(a+b) = \frac{Wa^2b^2}{3EIL}.$$

As a second example, suppose the simply supported beam shown in Fig. 5.4 has a span L and carries loads W_1 and W_2 at distances L/3 and L/4

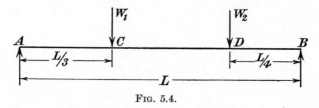

FIG. 5.4.

from the left- and right-hand supports respectively. It is desired to calculate the vertical deflexions at the loaded points. These will be

$$\Delta_C = \frac{\partial U}{\partial W_1} = \frac{1}{EI}\int M_x \frac{\partial M_x}{\partial W_1} dx$$

and $$\Delta_D = \frac{\partial U}{\partial W_2} = \frac{1}{EI}\int M_x \frac{\partial M_x}{\partial W_2} dx.$$

In the first place the reactions at A and B are found to be

$$R_A = \frac{W_2}{4} + \frac{2W_1}{3}$$

and $$R_B = \frac{3W_2}{4} + \frac{W_1}{3}.$$

Then, taking an origin at A, we have between A and C,

$$M_x = -R_A x = -x\left(\frac{W_2}{4} + \frac{2W_1}{3}\right),$$

so that $$\frac{\partial M_x}{\partial W_1} = -\frac{2x}{3} \text{ and } \frac{\partial M_x}{\partial W_2} = -\frac{x}{4}.$$

Between C and D,

$$M_x = -R_A x + W_1(x - L/3) = -\frac{W_1}{3}(L-x) - \frac{W_2}{4}x,$$

so that $$\frac{\partial M_x}{\partial W_1} = -\frac{(L-x)}{3} \text{ and } \frac{\partial M_x}{\partial W_2} = -\frac{x}{4}.$$

For the section BD of the beam we take the origin at B and then

$$M_x=-R_Bx=-x\left(\frac{3W_2}{4}+\frac{W_1}{3}\right),$$

so that $\qquad \dfrac{\partial M_x}{\partial W_1}=-\dfrac{x}{3}$ and $\dfrac{\partial M_x}{\partial W_2}=-\dfrac{3x}{4}.$

We can now write

$$\Delta_C=\frac{\partial U}{\partial W_1}=\frac{1}{EI}\Bigg[\int_0^{L/3}\tfrac{2}{3}\left(\frac{W_2}{4}+\frac{2W_1}{3}\right)x^2dx$$
$$+\int_{L/3}^{3L/4}\left\{\frac{W_1}{9}(L-x)^2+\frac{W_2}{12}x(L-x)\right\}dx+\int_0^{L/4}\left(\frac{3W_2}{4}+\frac{W_1}{3}\right)\frac{x^2}{3}dx\Bigg]$$

and

$$\Delta_D=\frac{\partial U}{\partial W_2}=\frac{1}{EI}\Bigg[\int_0^{L/3}\tfrac{1}{4}\left(\frac{W_2}{4}+\frac{2W_1}{3}\right)x^2dx$$
$$+\int_{L/3}^{3L/4}\left\{\frac{W_1x}{12}(L-x)+\frac{W_2}{16}x^2\right\}dx+\int_0^{L/4}\tfrac{3}{4}\left(\frac{3W_2}{4}+\frac{W_1}{3}\right)x^2dx\Bigg].$$

Upon integration these give

$$\Delta_C=\frac{L^3}{31104EI}(512W_1+357W_2)$$

and $\qquad\qquad \Delta_D=\dfrac{L^3}{20736EI}(238W_1+243W_2).$

Any values may now be assigned to W_1 and W_2 and the deflexions at C and D obtained.

As a final example of this method of calculation applied to simple beams we will determine the curve of deflexion for a uniformly loaded beam of span L, as shown in Fig. 5.5.

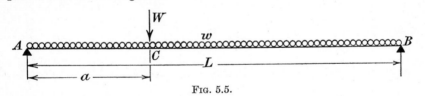

FIG. 5.5.

Assume that a concentrated load W is applied at any distance a from A. Then the deflexion at the load W is

$$\frac{dU}{dW}=\frac{1}{EI}\int M_x\frac{dM_x}{dW}dx.$$

The reaction at A is $\dfrac{wL}{2}+\left(\dfrac{L-a}{L}\right)W,$

and at B is $\qquad\qquad \dfrac{wL}{2}+\dfrac{a}{L}W.$

Consider first the section AC of the beam and take A as the origin. The bending moment at x from A is

$$M_x=-R_Ax+\frac{wx^2}{2}$$
$$=-\frac{wLx}{2}-\left(\frac{L-a}{L}\right)Wx+\frac{wx^2}{2},$$

so that
$$\frac{d\mathrm{M}}{d\mathrm{W}}=-\left(\frac{\mathrm{L}-a}{\mathrm{L}}\right)x$$

and
$$\left[\frac{d\mathrm{U}}{d\mathrm{W}}\right]_{AC}=-\frac{(\mathrm{L}-a)}{\mathrm{LEI}}\int_0^a\left\{\frac{w}{2}(x^3-\mathrm{L}x^2)-\left(\frac{\mathrm{L}-a}{\mathrm{L}}\right)\mathrm{W}x^2\right\}dx$$

$$=-\frac{(\mathrm{L}-a)a^3}{\mathrm{LEI}}\left\{\frac{w}{2}\left(\frac{a}{4}-\frac{\mathrm{L}}{3}\right)-\left(\frac{\mathrm{L}-a}{\mathrm{L}}\right)\frac{\mathrm{W}}{3}\right\}.$$

By replacing a and $\mathrm{L}-a$ by $\mathrm{L}-a$ and a respectively, we obtain
$$\left[\frac{d\mathrm{U}}{d\mathrm{W}}\right]_{BC}=-\frac{(\mathrm{L}-a)^3a}{\mathrm{LEI}}\left\{\frac{w}{2}\left(\frac{\mathrm{L}-a}{4}-\frac{\mathrm{L}}{3}\right)-\frac{a\mathrm{W}}{3\mathrm{L}}\right\}.$$

Then the deflexion at C is
$$\left[\frac{d\mathrm{U}}{d\mathrm{W}}\right]_{AC}+\left[\frac{d\mathrm{U}}{d\mathrm{W}}\right]_{BC}$$

and if W is made zero the deflexion at C due to the uniformly distributed load only is found to be
$$\Delta_C=-\frac{w(\mathrm{L}-a)a}{2\mathrm{LEI}}\left[\frac{a^3}{4}-\frac{a^2\mathrm{L}}{3}+\frac{(\mathrm{L}-a)^3}{4}-\frac{(\mathrm{L}-a)^2\mathrm{L}}{3}\right]$$

or
$$\Delta_C=\frac{wa(\mathrm{L}-a)(\mathrm{L}^2+a\mathrm{L}-a^2)}{24\mathrm{EI}}.$$

This is true for all values of a between 0 and L and is therefore the required curve of deflexion for the uniformly loaded beam.

This method can be applied to any case of bending and further examples of its use will occur in later chapters.

5.6. Calculation of reactions in continuous beams and girders.—A knowledge of the actual magnitudes of the deflexions of a beam or girder is not often required but the methods just described are useful for the calculation of reactive forces in continuous members.

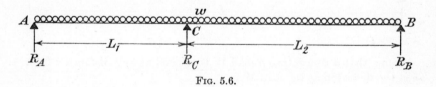

FIG. 5.6.

Suppose, for example, that the beam ACB shown in Fig. 5.6 is continuous over the support C and carries a uniformly distributed load of intensity w over the whole length $\mathrm{L}_1+\mathrm{L}_2$. The reaction at C must be found before the bending moment and shearing force diagrams can be drawn.

Let the reaction be denoted by R_C. AB may then be considered as a simply supported beam of span $\mathrm{L}_1+\mathrm{L}_2$ loaded with a uniformly distributed downward load w and an upward concentrated load R_C.

The vertical displacement at C is $\dfrac{d\mathrm{U}}{d\mathrm{R}_C}$ but if the support is rigid this displacement will be zero and the condition which determines R_C is therefore
$$\frac{d\mathrm{U}}{d\mathrm{R}_C}=0.$$

Consider first the section AC of the beam and take the origin at A. The bending moment at any point is

$$M_x = -R_A x + \frac{wx^2}{2}$$

$$= -\frac{(L_1+L_2)wx}{2} + \frac{L_2 R_C x}{L_1+L_2} + \frac{wx^2}{2}$$

and

$$\frac{dM_x}{dR_C} = \frac{L_2 x}{L_1+L_2}.$$

So,

$$\left[\frac{dU}{dR_C}\right]_{AC} = \frac{L_2}{(L_1+L_2)EI} \int_0^{L_1} \left\{ -\frac{(L_1+L_2)wx^2}{2} + \frac{L_2 R_C x^2}{L_1+L_2} + \frac{wx^3}{2} \right\} dx.$$

On integration and reduction this gives

$$\left[\frac{dU}{dR_C}\right]_{AC} = \frac{L_2}{24EI(L_1+L_2)^2}\{8R_C L_1^3 L_2 - w(L_1^5 + 5L_1^4 L_2 + 4L_1^3 L_2^2)\}.$$

Similarly we can write for the span CB

$$\left[\frac{dU}{dR_C}\right]_{BC} = \frac{L_1}{24EI(L_1+L_2)^2}\{8R_C L_2^3 L_1 - w(L_2^5 + 5L_2^4 L_1 + 4L_2^3 L_1^2)\}.$$

Adding these results we obtain

$$\frac{dU}{dR_C} = \frac{L_1 L_2}{24EI(L_1+L_2)}[8L_1 L_2 R_C - w(L_1+L_2)(L_1^2 + 3L_1 L_2 + L_2^2)]$$

and equating this result to zero we find

$$R_C = \frac{w(L_1+L_2)(L_1^2 + 3L_1 L_2 + L_2^2)}{8L_1 L_2}.$$

If $L_1 = L_2$ this gives $R_C = \frac{5}{8}W$ where W is the total load on the beam, i.e. $w(L_1+L_2)$. This is a well-known result easily obtained by the methods of Chapter 3.

If the support at C instead of being fixed in position moves a certain distance, this can readily be taken into account. Suppose for example that C sinks a distance δ when the load is applied. The movement of R_C in its own line of action is then $-\delta$ and the condition to be satisfied for the determination of R_C is

$$\frac{dU}{dR_C} = -\delta.$$

If the support is moved upwards by an amount δ the condition is

$$\frac{dU}{dR_C} = \delta.$$

This method is applicable to beams with any number of supports, e.g. suppose a continuous girder supported at its ends A and B to have a number of intermediate supports, C, D . . . . Q. The reactive forces at these supports are denoted by R_C, R_D . . . . R_Q. If the supports are fixed these forces can be evaluated by forming and solving simultaneously the equations

$$\frac{\partial U}{\partial R_C} = \frac{\partial U}{\partial R_D} = \cdots = \frac{\partial U}{\partial R_Q} = 0.$$

If any support moves under load the differential coefficient of the strain energy with respect to the force exerted there is equated to the movement of that support instead of to zero. Care must be observed in the sign ascribed to this movement as shown in the previous example.

The same principle may be applied to the calculation of reactive forces in a braced girder having more than two supports. For example, the bridge

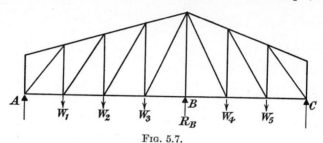

FIG. 5.7.

shown in Fig. 5.7 is supported at A, B and C and carries any system of loads. The reactive force at B, denoted by R_B, may be determined from the condition

$$\frac{dU}{dR_B} = \delta$$

where δ is, as before, the movement of the support in the direction of action of R_B. If the support is rigid, δ is zero.

The structure is subjected to the known loads W_1, W_2, etc., and the unknown load R_B. The force P_0 in any member can be expressed in terms of these external loads and so

$$\frac{dU}{dR_B} = \sum \frac{P_0 L}{AE} \frac{dP_0}{dR_B} = \delta$$

which yields an equation to determine R_B.

5.7. Calculation of the angle of rotation.—In paragraph 4.13 it was shown that the angular movement of an external couple acting on an elastic body was given by the first differential coefficient of the strain energy with respect to the moment. As an example of the application of this theorem we will calculate the slope at all points on a cantilever of length L carrying a uniform load of intensity w ; the procedure is as follows.

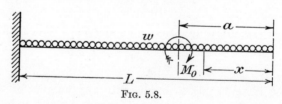

FIG. 5.8.

Apply a clockwise moment M_0 to the cantilever at a distance a from the free end as shown in Fig. 5.8.

Taking the origin at the free end of the cantilever the bending moment at any point is

$$M_x = \frac{wx^2}{2} + [M_0],$$

the second term appearing only when x is greater than a.

Then $\qquad \dfrac{d\mathrm{U}}{d\mathrm{M}_0}=\dfrac{1}{\mathrm{EI}}\int \mathrm{M}_x\dfrac{d\mathrm{M}_x}{d\mathrm{M}_0}dx=\dfrac{1}{\mathrm{EI}}\int_a^{\mathrm{L}}\left(\dfrac{wx^2}{2}+\mathrm{M}_0\right)dx$

since $\dfrac{d\mathrm{M}_x}{d\mathrm{M}_0}=0$ between $x=a$ and $x=0$.

If M_0 is made zero, $\dfrac{d\mathrm{U}}{d\mathrm{M}_0}$ is the angle of rotation of the section at a from the end due to the load w.

Therefore $\qquad \theta=\dfrac{1}{\mathrm{EI}}\int_a^{\mathrm{L}}\dfrac{wx^2}{2}dx,$

or, $\qquad \theta=\dfrac{w}{6\mathrm{EI}}(\mathrm{L}^3-a^3),$

which is the curve of slopes for all values of a from 0 to L.

This result may be checked by a direct calculation thus

$$\mathrm{EI}\dfrac{d^2y}{dx^2}=\dfrac{wx^2}{2}$$

$$\mathrm{EI}\dfrac{dy}{dx}=\dfrac{wx^3}{6}+\mathrm{A}$$

when $\qquad x=\mathrm{L},\ \dfrac{dy}{dx}=0\ ;\ \text{therefore }\mathrm{A}=-\dfrac{w\mathrm{L}^3}{6},$

and $\qquad \theta=\dfrac{dy}{dx}=\dfrac{w}{6\mathrm{EI}}(x^3-\mathrm{L}^3).$

This is the same result as by the former method, the negative sign corresponding to the direction of slope imposed by the clockwise moment M_0.

In this instance the second method is slightly more direct than the first but the application of the first theorem of Castigliano often enables results to be obtained much more simply than by any other means.

5.8. Williot-Mohr displacement diagrams.—For many purposes it is convenient to determine the displacements of all points in a braced frame and a graphical method then has advantages over those already described.

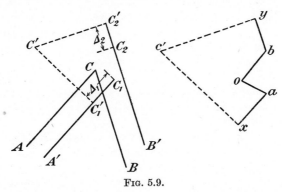

FIG. 5.9.

Let AC and BC in Fig. 5.9 represent two bars of a frame having internal forces which shorten the former by an amount Δ_1 and lengthen the latter by an amount Δ_2.

Corresponding to our convention of calling tensile stresses positive, increases in length will be treated as positive and decreases as negative.

The elastic straining of the frame will move the points A and B to new positions denoted by A′ and B′.

Suppose the bars AC and BC to be disconnected at C and let AC move to A′C_1 where A′C_1 is parallel to AC : similarly let BC move to B′C_2 where B′C_2 is parallel to BC. If we now take account of the strains of the bars, A′C_1 will shorten by Δ_1 to A′C'_1 while B′C_2 will lengthen by Δ_2 to B′C'_2.

The displaced position of C can be found by striking arcs from A′ and B′ as centres with radii A′C'_1, and B′C'_2 respectively, the point of intersection being the required position.

Since however the strains are all small compared with the lengths of the bars the arcs may be replaced by lines C'_1C' and C'_2C' drawn perpendicular to A′C'_1 and B′C'_2, giving C′ as the displaced position of C.

Suppose now that o represents the original position of point C. Draw oa, ob parallel to CC_1 and CC_2 and proportional to these distances; the points a and b then represent C_1 and C_2.

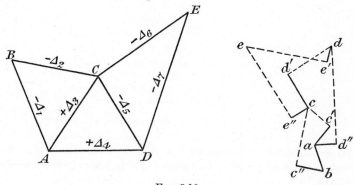

Fig. 5.10.

From a draw ax parallel to CA and proportional to Δ_1 and from b draw by parallel to BC and proportional to Δ_2. Then x and y represent the points C'_1 and C'_2. Lines from x and y perpendicular to ax and by meet at c' and oc' is the displacement of the point C of the frame to the scale chosen.

Let Fig. 5.10 be any plane frame subjected to an external load system which causes alterations in the lengths of the bars of amounts Δ_1, Δ_2, etc., as shown in the figure. It is desired to determine the displacements of all points of the frame.

These displacements must be relative to some datum so we shall assume the point A to be fixed in space and the bar AB to be fixed in direction. This choice is quite arbitrary.

Let a represent the fixed point A. Draw ab parallel to AB and equal to Δ_1. Then ab represents the displacement of B relative to A. ab is drawn from a in the direction of movement of B.

Now C moves away from A by an amount Δ_3 so we draw ac' equal to Δ_3 and parallel to AC. Similarly C moves towards B so bc'' is drawn from b equal to Δ_2 and parallel to BC. From c' and c'' draw lines $c'c$ and $c''c$ perpendicular to ac' and bc'' to meet at c. Then c is the displaced position of C relative to our datum point and direction.

To find the displacement of D the same procedure is followed. D moves towards C and away from A so cd' and ad'' are drawn in the appropriate directions parallel to CD and AD and equal to Δ_5 and Δ_4 respectively. Perpendiculars $d'd$ and $d''d$ to cd' and ad'' meet at d which is the displaced position of D.

The point e is found in the same way from the previously determined positions c and d.

Thus ab, ac, ad, ae, the displacements of B, C, D and E, are found relative to the fixed point A and the fixed direction AB. The resulting diagram is known as a Williot diagram.

The fixed point and direction were, however, chosen arbitrarily and a diagram to be of general use must give absolute displacements. If A were actually fixed in space the true displacements of the various points could be determined by superimposing upon the relative ones found by the Williot diagram a suitable rigid body rotation to correct for the inaccuracy of the assumption that the direction of AB was unchanged. This correction is effected by means of the Mohr diagram now to be described.

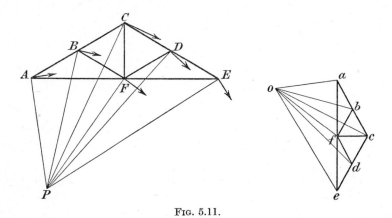

FIG. 5.11.

Let ABCDEF in Fig. 5.11 be any frame which is supposed to rotate about an instantaneous centre P through an angle θ. Any point on the frame will then move in a direction perpendicular to the line joining the point to P. The amount of the movement will be $L\theta$ where L is the distance from P to the point. Hence the movements of all points will be proportional to their distances from P. Take any pole o and draw oa, ob, etc., parallel to the displacements of A, B, etc., and proportional in length to these displacements.

Join $abcdef$ and consider the triangles PAB and oab. Since oa and ob are proportional to the displacements of A and B they are also proportional to PA and PB. Further, they are drawn parallel to the perpendiculars to PA and PB. Therefore the angle APB $=aob$ and the triangles are similar. Hence ab is perpendicular to AB and bears the same ratio to it that oa does to PA.

This is true for all other corresponding lines of the two figures and so the Mohr diagram, $abcdef$, is similar to the frame diagram and is rotated relatively to it through a right angle.

If therefore two points on the Mohr diagram can be fixed the whole diagram may be drawn and can be superimposed on the Williot diagram to give absolute displacements of all points in the frame.

The method is best illustrated by an example and we will consider the king post truss shown in Fig. 5.12. This truss is assumed to be pinned at A and mounted on rollers at B so that any movement of B relative to A takes place along the line AB. The stress diagram is drawn for the load system for which the displacements are to be calculated and the elongations and shortenings of all members of the truss are calculated from a knowledge of their internal forces and sections. These are shown marked on the frame diagram of Fig. 5.12. It will be noticed that these strains are symmetrical but we shall proceed as would be necessary in the general case leaving until later the simplification which may be introduced due to this symmetry.

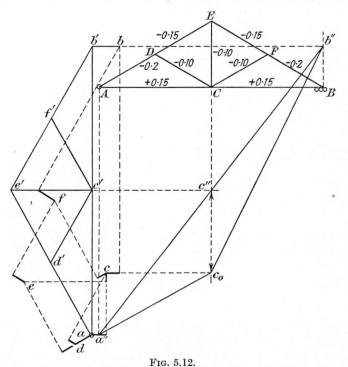

FIG. 5.12.

First, since A is fixed, we need only to assume a reference direction and for this purpose AD will be arbitrarily chosen. The Williot diagram is drawn exactly as described earlier and gives the vector ab as the displacement of B relative to A and AD. Since the displacement of B relative to A is known to be horizontal a Mohr diagram must be superimposed on the Williot diagram to make the necessary correction.

The instantaneous centre of rotation will be the fixed pin A and a rigid rotation of the frame about A will cause a displacement of B perpendicular to AB.

From a draw a line perpendicular to AB and from b draw bb' horizontally to cut this line at b'.

Then $b'a$ represents vectorially the displacement of B due to a clockwise rotation of the frame about A and the vector sum of $b'a$ and ab gives the combined effects of the rotation and of the displacement obtained from the Williot diagram.

The vector sum of $b'a$ and ab is $b'b$ and this being horizontal complies with the necessary conditions that B must move along the line AB. Hence b' is fixed as a point on the Mohr diagram which is completed by drawing on ab' a figure similar to the frame diagram.

It will be noticed that the Mohr diagram as shown in Fig. 5.11 has been rotated through two right angles so that $b'a$ and not ab' represents the displacement of B due to rotation.

The true displacement of any point, e.g. E, is then the vector sum of ae, the elastic displacement and $e'a$ the rotational displacement. This sum is $e'e$ and is measured from the point on the Mohr diagram to the corresponding one on the Williot diagram showing that E moves downwards.

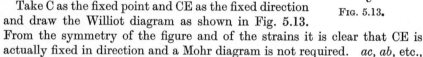

FIG. 5.13.

Due to the symmetry of strains we could obtain the results much more easily as follows.

Take C as the fixed point and CE as the fixed direction and draw the Williot diagram as shown in Fig. 5.13. From the symmetry of the figure and of the strains it is clear that CE is actually fixed in direction and a Mohr diagram is not required. ac, ab, etc., give directly the true displacements of c, b, etc., relative to A.

In Fig. 5.12 project points A, C and B vertically to cut horizontal lines from a, c' and b' at the points a'', c'' and b'' which will clearly lie on a straight line.

Also let horizontal projections of the points a, b, c cut the verticals through A, B and C at a'', b'', c_0.

Then $a''c_0b''$ is known as the displacement polygon for ACB and the vertical intercept of this polygon at any point gives the vertical displacement of that point, e.g. $c''c_0$ is the vertical displacement of point C.

This polygon is useful in dealing with certain problems in braced girders and will be referred to in later chapters.

EXERCISES

(E for steel may be taken as 13,000 tons per square inch.)

(1) A tripod is formed of steel tubes 2 inches outside diameter and ·056 inch thickness of metal. The feet of the tripod are at the apices of an equilateral triangle of 4 feet side in the horizontal plane and the tubes are each inclined at 60° to this plane.

Calculate the deflexion of the top of the tripod under a load of 1 ton hanging there.

$$(0\cdot0055\ in.)$$

(2) A vertical steel mast of height L and flexural rigidity EI is firmly built into the ground and at its centre point a steel stay of cross-sectional area A is attached. This stay is led back at 45° to the mast and firmly attached to the ground.

A load W is applied horizontally to the top of the mast in the plane of the mast and stay.

If the stay is tightened so that its point of attachment is kept in the unloaded position calculate the tension in the stay and the deflexion at the top of the mast.

$$\left(2\cdot5\sqrt{2}W,\ \frac{7WL^3}{96EI}\right)$$

(3) In the truss shown in Diagram 5a all members are of steel and are stressed to 8 tons per square inch. Calculate the vertical deflexion under the load Check your answer by means of a Williot diagram.

$$(1\cdot04\ ins.)$$

(4) The steel frame shown in Diagram 5*b* is so designed that the stress in all members is 8 tons per square inch.

Calculate the vertical deflexion of the point D under a load of 10 tons.

(0·540 in.)

(5) Calculate the deflexion of the point C in the steel frame shown at 5*c* if all members are 2 square inches in cross-sectional area. Verify the result by means of a Williot-Mohr diagram.

(0·11 in.)

(6) The frame shown at 5*d*, simply pinned at A and B, is so designed that every loaded member is stressed to 8 tons per square inch when 12 tons is carried at C.

Calculate the vertical deflexion of C under this load.

(1·108 ins.)

(7) A rolled steel joist having a second moment of area of 300 inch units and a cross-sectional area of 12 square inches is firmly attached to a rigid base and is inclined at 60° to the horizontal. The length of the joist is 20 feet and from the free end a load of 1 ton is suspended. Calculate the vertical deflexion of the load.

(0·296 in.)

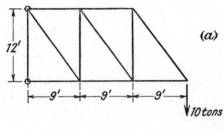

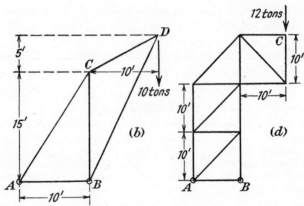

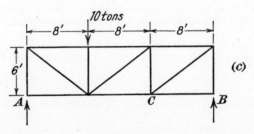

DIAGRAM 5.

(8) A steel beam of flexural rigidity EI and length L is pinned at one end to a wall. It is supported in a horizontal position by a steel wire of cross-sectional area A and modulus of elasticity E which is attached to the centre of the beam and to a point on the wall $\frac{L}{2}$ above the pinned end.

If a load is hung on the free end, calculate the deflexion at the load.

$$\left[\frac{WL}{E}\left(\frac{L^2}{12I}+\frac{4\sqrt{2}}{A}\right)\right]$$

CHAPTER 6

STRESS ANALYSIS OF REDUNDANT FRAMES

6.1. Introduction.—Suppose as in Fig. 6.1 a weight W is suspended from two wires AD and BD which are attached to a rigid support AB. The forces in these two wires are calculable simply from a knowledge of the geometry of the arrangement and provided the wires are capable of carrying these loads it is immaterial what size they are made. The movement of the point D will, however, depend upon their elastic properties as well as upon the geometry. If a third wire CD be added to the suspension the problem of load distribution is considerably modified. If we denote the force in AD by T_1 we can determine the forces in DC and DB in terms of W and T_1, and since any value can be assigned to T_1 it is evident that there are an infinite number of solutions which will satisfy the conditions of static equilibrium of the point D, *i.e.* the condition of compatibility of stresses at D is not a sufficient criterion for the determination of the force distribution.

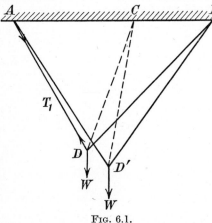

FIG. 6.1.

For any of these possible solutions the amounts by which the three wires will stretch due to the loads in them can be calculated.

If D′ is the displaced position of D, the strained lengths must be AD′, BD′ and CD′, *i.e.* arcs struck from A, C and B as centres and with radii equal to the respective strained lengths must intersect at a common point. This condition, which is known as that of compatibility of strains, enables the correct solution to be selected from the infinite number which satisfy the conditions of stress compatibility at D. The strains can only be calculated from a knowledge of the elastic properties of the wires and so the stress analysis of frameworks having redundant bracing members depends upon a knowledge of the elastic properties of all components of the structure. Several methods are available for making such an analysis, but they are essentially the same and differ only in application. The most widely used is probably the method of least work, *i.e.* an application of the second theorem of Castigliano, which was given in paragraph 4.12 and the present chapter will be devoted to illustration of this method as well as others.

Objections have been made to this treatment on the ground that it does not allow the calculator to visualise the physical significance of his procedure at every step and that it is, in fact, something of a mechanical device for obtaining results. While the authors do not agree with this view it is true that once the equations have been formed the arithmetical work is a matter

78

of routine and many designers prefer to work by graphical methods. For this reason a treatment involving the direct comparison of displacements is used in some instances and a reference to it is therefore desirable at this stage.

6.2. Stress analysis by direct comparison of displacements.—Suppose a frame such as that shown in Fig. 6.2 (*a*) which has a single redundant bar is to be analysed. In the first place any bar is chosen as the redundant member, provided that when this bar is removed from the frame the remaining or essential bars form a simply stiff structure.

In the present example it is convenient to treat CD as the redundancy and it is assumed to be removed, leaving the frame shown at (*b*).

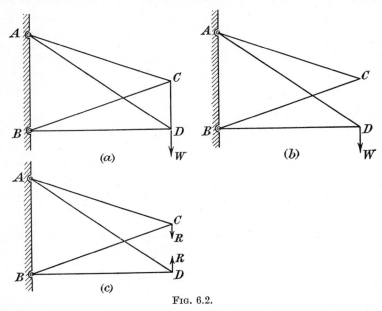

Fig. 6.2.

A Williot-Mohr diagram is now drawn for this frame and the separation of the points C and D is obtained. Let this displacement be Δ.

If the force in the redundant member CD is denoted by R the effect of this bar will be to apply loads at C and D as shown at (*c*) and a second deflexion diagram is drawn for this system and the approach of C and D is measured from it. Let this be $R\delta$.

The bar CD which applies the forces will itself stretch due to the tension in it by an amount $\dfrac{RL}{AE}$ where L is the length of CD, A is its cross-sectional area and E is the value of Young's modulus for the material.

The total separation of C and D will clearly be $\Delta - R\delta$ which must be equal to the stretch of the bar and so we obtain the relationship

$$\Delta - R\delta = \frac{RL}{AE}$$

from which

$$R = \frac{\Delta}{\left(\delta + \dfrac{L}{AE}\right)}.$$

The method, as shown in Chapter 15, can readily be extended to a structure in which there is more than one redundant member when it involves the solution of as many simultaneous equations as there are redundancies.

It should be noticed that it involves the use of displacements, which are vector quantities, and signs are therefore of fundamental importance. Strain energy, on the other hand, is a scalar quantity and complications due to the signs of the quantities involved do not occur. In a plane frame this is perhaps not a matter of serious importance, but in a space frame the consideration of signs is difficult and the method of least work has considerable advantages over that just described.

6.3. Stresses in frames with one redundancy.—The application of strain energy analysis to frames will be illustrated by a number of examples and

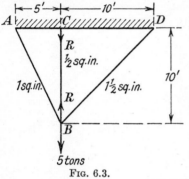

FIG. 6.3.

the simplest, involving a single redundant member will be taken first. The three steel wires AB, CB and DB in Fig. 6.3 are attached to a rigid beam at A, C and D and carry a load of 5 tons at their junction B.

The dimensions of the frame and the wires are shown on the diagram and it is desired to know how the load is distributed between the wires.

It is convenient to select CB as the redundant member. The tensile load in it is denoted by R.

In the first place it is necessary to find the forces in the two remaining wires in terms of W and R and this is best done by the use of tension coefficients. The equations for the point B are

$$\left.\begin{array}{r} -5t_{AB}+10t_{BD}=0 \\ 10(t_{AB}+t_{BD})=5-R \end{array}\right\}$$

which give
$$t_{AB}=\frac{5-R}{15} \text{ and } t_{BD}=\frac{5-R}{30}.$$

Multiplying these tension coefficients by the lengths of AB and BD respectively we have

$$T_{AB}=\frac{5-R}{15}\times\sqrt{25+100}=3\cdot725-\cdot745R$$

and
$$T_{BD}=\frac{5-R}{30}\times\sqrt{100+100}=2\cdot358-\cdot471R.$$

To determine the value of R we use the second theorem of Castigliano and put $\dfrac{dU}{dR}=0$.

Now
$$\frac{dU}{dR}=\sum\frac{P_0L}{AE}\frac{dP_0}{dR}$$

where P_0 is the load in any member, A is its area and L its length. The summation includes all members of the structure.

It is advisable in all calculations of this type, even in simple ones like the present, to arrange the work as in Table 6.1.

TABLE 6.1.

1	2	3	4	5	6
Member	L inches	A sq. inches	P_0 tons	$\dfrac{dP_0}{dR}$	$\dfrac{P_0 L}{A}\dfrac{dP_0}{dR}$
AB	134·1	1	$3\cdot725-\cdot745R$	$-\cdot745$	$-372\cdot5+74\cdot5R$
CB	120·0	0·5	R	1	240R
DB	169·6	1·5	$2\cdot358-\cdot471R$	$-\cdot471$	$-125\cdot5+25\cdot1R$

In column 1 is entered the member, in column 2 its length in inches, and in column 3, its area in square inches.   In column 4 the force in the member is entered in terms of R and the external load.   Column 5 is the value of $\dfrac{dP_0}{dR}$ which is the coefficient of R in the expression in column 4.   Column 6 is obtained by multiplication of the appropriate terms in the preceding columns.   The final result is equated to zero, E being the same for all members has been omitted.

Then, summing the three expressions in column 6 and equating to zero, we have

$$\sum\frac{P_0 L}{A}\frac{dP_0}{dR}=-498+339\cdot6R=0,$$

from which $\qquad\qquad R=1\cdot466$ tons

and finally from column 4 of the table,

$$\text{Force in AB}=2\cdot633 \text{ tons.}$$
$$\text{,,   ,, CB}=1\cdot466 \text{ ,,}$$
$$\text{,,   ,, DB}=1\cdot667 \text{ ,,}$$

As a second example of this type of problem we will consider a beam suspended by three rods as shown in Fig. 6.4 and loaded at any point.   The dimensions are shown on the diagram.   The beam is supposed to be so stiff

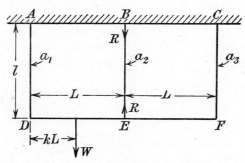

FIG. 6.4.

that it may be considered to be rigid and therefore to store no energy due to bending, while the rods are capable of taking either tensile or compressive loads.

BE will be taken as the redundant support and the tensile force in it will be denoted by R.   By taking moments about D of the forces acting on the beam we obtain

$$2LT_{CF}+RL-kWL=0$$

or
$$T_{CF}=\tfrac{1}{2}(kW-R)$$
and so
$$T_{AD}=\tfrac{1}{2}\{W(2-k)-R\}.$$

To find the value of R we put $\dfrac{dU}{dR}=0$, and tabulating as before we obtain :

TABLE 6.2.

Member	Length	A	P_0	$\dfrac{dP_0}{dR}$	$\dfrac{P_0L}{A}\dfrac{dP_0}{dR}$
AD	l	a_1	$\tfrac{1}{2}\{W(2-k)-R\}$	$-\tfrac{1}{2}$	$-\dfrac{l}{4a_1}\{W(2-k)-R\}$
BE	l	a_2	R	1	$\dfrac{l}{a_2}R$
CF	l	a_3	$\tfrac{1}{2}(kW-R)$	$-\tfrac{1}{2}$	$-\dfrac{l}{4a_3}(kW-R)$

Summing the last column we find

$$\frac{l}{4}\left\{R\left(\frac{1}{a_1}+\frac{4}{a_2}+\frac{1}{a_3}\right)-W\left(\frac{2-k}{a_1}+\frac{k}{a_3}\right)\right\}=0$$

or
$$R=\frac{W\left(\dfrac{2-k}{a_1}+\dfrac{k}{a_3}\right)}{\dfrac{1}{a_1}+\dfrac{4}{a_2}+\dfrac{1}{a_3}}$$

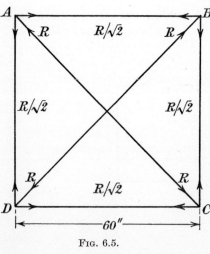

FIG. 6.5.

from which the loads in the other two rods may be found.

In both examples just considered it has been assumed that the redundant member is exactly the right length to fit into its place so that no stresses are caused in the other members when it is inserted.   The next shows how stresses due to self-straining may be calculated.

The square frame shown in Fig. 6.5 is formed of four pin-jointed steel bars, each having a cross-sectional area of 2 square inches, braced diagonally by bars of the same material each having a cross-sectional area of 1 square inch.   The diagonal AC was $\tfrac{1}{20}$ inch too long before it was forced into position and it is required to find the forces in all the bars of the frame due to this self-straining.

Since the bar AC was initially too long it will, after insertion, be in compression and so we assume that it *finally* carries a *compressive* force R. In order to determine the value of R we use the second theorem of Castigliano in its general form and evaluate

$$\frac{dU}{dR}=\frac{1}{20} \text{ inch}$$

where U is the total strain energy of the frame.

The forces in the other bars due to R acting at A and C are found by resolution at the joints and their values are shown on the diagram. The work is set out in Table 6.3.

Since the value of $\frac{dU}{dR}$ is not equated to zero the modulus E must be included in the expression. We shall take it to be 13,000 tons per square inch and summing the last column, we obtain

$$\sum\frac{P_0L}{AE}\frac{dP_0}{dR}=\frac{60R(1+2\sqrt{2})}{13,000}=\frac{1}{20}$$

or

$$R=\frac{13,000}{20\times60(1+2\sqrt{2})}=2\cdot83 \text{ tons.}$$

Thus, due simply to the lack of fit of the bar AC, the compressive force in each diagonal when it is inserted is $2\cdot83$ tons and the tensile force in each

TABLE 6.3.

Member	L	A	P_0	$\dfrac{dP_0}{dR}$	$\dfrac{P_0L}{A}\dfrac{dP_0}{dR}$
AB	60	2	$R/\sqrt{2}$	$1/\sqrt{2}$	15R
BC	,,	,,	,,	,:	,,
CD	,,	,,	,,	,,	,,
DA	,,	,,	,,	,,	,,
AC	$60\sqrt{2}$	1	$-R$	-1	$60\sqrt{2}R$
BD	,,	,,	,,	,,	,,

side of the frame is 2 tons. These forces are additional to any caused by external loads which must be calculated either separately or at the same time as those due to self-straining.

Suppose, for example, that the same frame is simply supported on a pin at A and on rollers at D and that a load W$=5$ tons is suspended from C as shown in Fig. 6.6. Assume also the same lack of fit as before in AC. We may proceed in one of two ways. If the previous calculation has already been made we can assume that we have an initially unstrained frame carrying the load W ; call R the force in the redundant member AC and find the forces in all the bars of the frame due to W and R. Then, putting $\frac{dU}{dR}=0$, we find the value of R due to the load W alone and so the forces in all the other bars. These forces must be added algebraically to those arising from the initial self-straining due to the lack of fit of AC and the sums will be the total forces. This result follows at once from the principle of super-position. Usually,

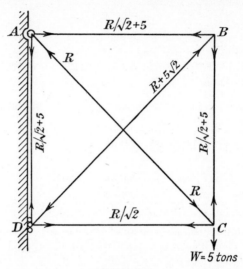

FIG. 6.6.

however, it is unnecessary to make two separate calculations and the procedure is as follows. Fig. 6.6 shows the forces in the frame under the action of the vertical load of 5 tons, R as before being the force in AC, due now, however, *to the combined effects of the external load and of self-straining.* The work is set out in Table 6.4.

TABLE 6.4.

Member	L	A	P_0	$\dfrac{dP_0}{dR}$	$\dfrac{P_0 L}{A}\dfrac{dP_0}{dR}$
AB	60	2	$\dfrac{R}{\sqrt{2}}+5$	$\dfrac{1}{\sqrt{2}}$	$30\left(\dfrac{R}{2}+\dfrac{5}{\sqrt{2}}\right)$
BC	60	2	$\dfrac{R}{\sqrt{2}}+5$	$\dfrac{1}{\sqrt{2}}$	$30\left(\dfrac{R}{2}+\dfrac{5}{\sqrt{2}}\right)$
CD	60	2	$\dfrac{R}{\sqrt{2}}$	$\dfrac{1}{\sqrt{2}}$	$15R$
DA	60	2	$\dfrac{R}{\sqrt{2}}+5$	$\dfrac{1}{\sqrt{2}}$	$15R+\dfrac{150}{\sqrt{2}}$
BD	$60\sqrt{2}$	1	$-R-5\sqrt{2}$	-1	$60\sqrt{2}(R+5\sqrt{2})$
AC	$60\sqrt{2}$	1	$-R$	-1	$60\sqrt{2}R$

From the last column, after dividing by E we have

$$\frac{dU}{dR}=\sum\frac{P_0 L}{AE}\frac{dP_0}{dR}=\frac{60R(1+2\sqrt{2})+918}{13,000}=\frac{1}{20}$$

or

$$R=\frac{\dfrac{13,000}{20}-918}{60(1+2\sqrt{2})}=-1\cdot166 \text{ tons}$$

i.e. there is a tension of $1\cdot166$ tons in AC under the combined effects of self-straining and the external load. An analysis of this result shows clearly the legitimacy of making the calculations in two parts, as outlined earlier, when it was stated that it could be done by calculating the forces due to self-straining alone and superposing the forces due to the external load alone.

In the table just obtained, if we make the external load zero and equate $\dfrac{dU}{dR}$ to the lack of fit of AC, *i.e.* to $\frac{1}{20}$ inch, we obtain $R=\dfrac{13,000}{20}/60(1+2\sqrt{2})$, *i.e.* the first term in the expression for R, agreeing with the separate calculation of the previous example.

If we now assume R is due only to the external load system we obtain the same values in the last column but must equate the sum to zero ; *i.e.* we get

$$\frac{60R(1+2\sqrt{2})+918}{13,000}=0$$

or

$$R=-\frac{918}{60(1+2\sqrt{2})}.$$

This is the second term of the combined expression and the justification for superposing results is evident.

As a further example, consider the frame shown in Fig. 6.7, which has one correctly fitted redundant bar. This is taken to be BD and the load in it is assumed to be tensile and of magnitude R.

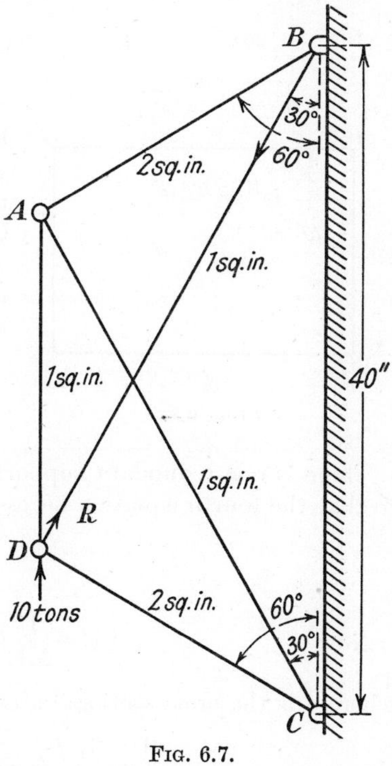

Fig. 6.7.

Proceeding as before, the loads in all bars of the frame are found in terms of R and the external force, and the strain energy equation is formed. The calculations are set out in Table 6.5.

Summing the last column but one, an equation is obtained which gives the value $R=-5\cdot45$ tons. The forces in all bars of the frame are then entered in the last column of the table.

A slightly different type of problem which may be solved by strain energy methods is exemplified by the case of a number of columns supporting a roof. For example, suppose a rectangular flat roof 20 feet × 30 feet which may be considered to be rigid, is carried on four similar stanchions placed at the corners and is loaded by a concentrated weight of 2,400 lb. acting at 10 feet from a short side and 5 feet from a long side of the roof. The

TABLE 6.5.

Member	L inches	A sq. in.	P_0	$\dfrac{dP_0}{dR}$	$\dfrac{P_0 L}{A}\dfrac{dP_0}{dR}$	P_0
AB	20	2	$-5-\dfrac{R}{\sqrt{3}}$	$-\dfrac{1}{\sqrt{3}}$	$10\left(\dfrac{5}{\sqrt{3}}+\dfrac{R}{3}\right)$	$-1 \cdot 85$
CD	20	2	$0-\dfrac{R}{\sqrt{3}}$	$-\dfrac{1}{\sqrt{3}}$	$10\left(0+\dfrac{R}{3}\right)$	$+3 \cdot 15$
AD	20	1	$-10-\dfrac{2R}{\sqrt{3}}$	$-\dfrac{2}{\sqrt{3}}$	$20\left(\dfrac{20}{\sqrt{3}}+\dfrac{4}{3}R\right)$	$-3 \cdot 70$
AC	$20\sqrt{3}$	1	$5\sqrt{3}+R$	$+1$	$20\sqrt{3}(5\sqrt{3}+R)$	$+3 \cdot 21$
BD	$20\sqrt{3}$	1	$0+R$	$+1$	$20\sqrt{3}(0+R)$	$-5 \cdot 45$

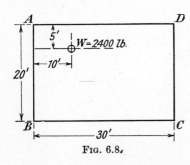

FIG. 6.8.

load in each stanchion is required. The arrangement is shown in Fig. 6.8. Denote the loads in the four stanchions by A, B, C and D. By taking moments about AB and CB in turn and equating vertical forces we obtain the following conditions for the static equilibrium of the system :

$$30(C+D)=10W$$
$$20(A+D)=15W$$
$$A+B+C+D=W.$$

There is one redundant support which is taken to be the stanchion at A so that the fourth equation necessary for the solution of the problem is

$$\frac{dU}{dA}=0.$$

Now
$$U=\frac{L}{2aE}(A^2+B^2+C^2+D^2)$$

where a is the cross-sectional area and L is the length of each stanchion.

$$\therefore \qquad \frac{dU}{dA}=\frac{L}{aE}\left(A+B\frac{dB}{dA}+C\frac{dC}{dA}+D\frac{dD}{dA}\right)=0.$$

From the first two of the above equations we obtain

$$C=\frac{W}{3}-D$$

and
$$D=\frac{3W}{4}-A.$$

Hence
$$C=A-\tfrac{5}{12}W.$$

Then from the third equation

$$B=\frac{2W}{3}-A.$$

Hence
$$\frac{dB}{dA}=-1,\ \frac{dC}{dA}=1\ \text{and}\ \frac{dD}{dA}=-1$$

and
$$\frac{aE}{L}\frac{dU}{dA}=A+\left(A-\frac{2W}{3}\right)+\left(A-\frac{5W}{12}\right)+\left(A-\frac{3W}{4}\right)=0$$

or
$$A=\tfrac{11}{24}W.$$

Substituting the value W=2,400 lb. the forces in the stanchions are

A=1,100 lb.
B= 500 lb.
C= 100 lb.
D= 700 lb.

As a final example of a structure with one redundant element the king-posted beam shown in Fig. 6.9 will be analysed.

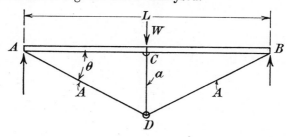

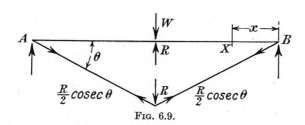

FIG. 6.9.

This structure consists of a continuous beam AB strengthened by a king post CD which is pinned to the centre of AB and braced by stays AD and BD. The beam is simply supported at A and B. Dimensions are as shown in the figure.

It is evident that if the beam consisted of two parts AC and CB pinned together at C the structure would be just-stiff and all loads in the bars would be simple tensions or compressions. The continuity at C, however, introduces a redundancy and AB is subjected to bending moments as well as axial loads. This bending must be taken into account in the analysis and differentiates the treatment of this problem from the preceding ones.

It is convenient to take the compressive force in CD as the unknown to be determined and if this is denoted by R the axial forces in the stays are $\frac{R}{2}$ cosec θ. The shears at the ends of the beam are then each $\frac{W-R}{2}$ and at any point X in BC at a distance x from B the bending moment is

$$M=\left(\frac{W-R}{2}\right)x.$$

To determine R we have the relation $\dfrac{dU}{dR}=0$ where U is the total strain energy of the frame. If we neglect the strain energy due to the axial force we have for the beam

$$\left[\frac{dU}{dR}\right]_B = \frac{2}{E_B I}\int_0^{L/2} M\frac{dM}{dR}dx,$$

since it is symmetrical and symmetrically loaded.

I is the second moment of area of the cross-section of the beam and E_B its Young's modulus.

Since
$$\frac{dM}{dR}=-\frac{x}{2}$$

$$\left[\frac{dU}{dR}\right]_B = -\frac{1}{2E_B I}\int_0^{L/2} (W-R)x^2 dx$$

$$= -\frac{L^3}{48E_B I}(W-R).$$

For the member CD

$$\left[\frac{dU}{dR}\right]_S = \frac{P_0 L'}{aE_S}\frac{dP_0}{dR}=\frac{RL\tan\theta}{2aE_S}$$

where a and L' are the cross-sectional area and length respectively of the strut CD and E_S its Young's modulus.

For the two ties

$$\left[\frac{dU}{dR}\right]_T = \frac{RL\cosec^2\theta\sec\theta}{4AE_T},$$

and
$$\frac{dU}{dR}=\frac{RL\cosec^2\theta\sec\theta}{4AE_T}+\frac{RL\tan\theta}{2aE_S}-\frac{WL^3}{48E_B I}+\frac{RL^3}{48E_B I}=0,$$

which gives

$$R=\frac{\dfrac{WL^2}{48E_B I}}{\dfrac{\cosec^2\theta\sec\theta}{4AE_T}+\dfrac{\tan\theta}{2aE_S}+\dfrac{L^2}{48E_B I}}.$$

Once this value has been determined the loads in all the bars can be found and the bending moment diagram for the beam can be plotted.

6.4. Strain energy analysis for frames with more than one redundant element.—When a frame has more than one redundant element the procedure is similar to that already explained but must be repeated for each redundancy. For example, if there are two redundant bars we denote the loads in them by R_1 and R_2 and determine the forces in the remainder of the bars in terms of R_1, R_2 and the external load system. Then U, the total strain energy, is a function of both these unknown forces and the external load, and to evaluate R_1 and R_2 we have the two simultaneous equations

$$\frac{\partial U}{\partial R_1}=\sum\frac{P_0 L}{AE}\frac{\partial P_0}{\partial R_1}=\lambda_1$$

and
$$\frac{\partial U}{\partial R_2}=\sum\frac{P_0 L}{AE}\frac{\partial P_0}{\partial R_2}=\lambda_2$$

where λ_1 and λ_2 are the initial lacks of fit in the two redundant bars.

As an illustration of the method of analysis the calculations for the airship fin rib having three redundant members shown in Fig. 6.10 are given in detail. The loading is quite arbitrary and the cross-sectional areas tabulated are those arrived at by a direct design method which will be explained later. These values have been chosen to serve as a check on the accuracy of that method. The calculation is arranged in tabular form as before. In the first four columns of Table 6.6 are entered the bar reference, its length, cross-sectional area and value of Young's modulus respectively. It will be noticed that E is not the same throughout, some of the bars being of steel and the remainder of duralumin.

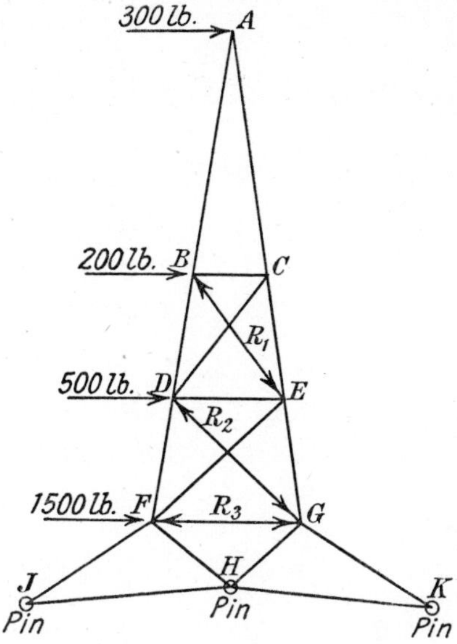

The forces in all bars are determined by resolution at the joints in terms of the external loading and the forces in the three redundant members which are taken to be R_1, R_2 and R_3 in BE, DG and FG respectively.

The force in any member can thus be expressed in the form

$$P_0 = P + \alpha R_1 + \beta R_2 + \gamma R_3$$

where P is the force due to the external load and α, β and γ are numerical coefficients. The values of P, α, β and γ are entered for each member in the sub-columns of column 5.

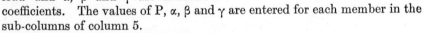

Fig. 6.10.

The equations to be formed are

$$\frac{\partial U}{\partial R_1} = \sum \frac{P_0 L}{AE} \frac{\partial P_0}{\partial R_1} = \sum \frac{P_0 L}{AE} \alpha = 0,$$

$$\frac{\partial U}{\partial R_2} = \sum \frac{P_0 L}{AE} \frac{\partial P_0}{\partial R_2} = \sum \frac{P_0 L}{AE} \beta = 0$$

and

$$\frac{\partial U}{\partial R_3} = \sum \frac{P_0 L}{AE} \frac{\partial P_0}{\partial R_3} = \sum \frac{P_0 L}{AE} \gamma = 0.$$

In column 6, therefore, we enter the values of $\dfrac{P_0 L}{AE}\alpha$ obtained by multiplying the term $\dfrac{P_0 L}{AE}$ for each member by the coefficient of R_1 in P_0, e.g. for member BD by the value $\cdot 892$.

Similarly, columns 7 and 8 are completed by multiplying the same terms $\dfrac{P_0 L}{AE}$ by the coefficients of R_2 and R_3 respectively.

Columns 6, 7 and 8 are then severally summed to obtain $\sum \dfrac{P_0 L}{AE}\alpha$, etc., and this results in the three equations :

$$
\left.
\begin{aligned}
-223{,}900 + 930R_1 + 1\cdot 75R_2 &= 0 \\
-261{,}160 + 1\cdot 75R_1 + 1060R_2 + 5\cdot 6R_3 &= 0 \\
-24{,}700 \qquad\quad + 5\cdot 61R_2 + 22\cdot 8R_3 &= 0.
\end{aligned}
\right\}
$$

TABLE 6.6.

				5				6				7				8			
				P_0				$\frac{P_0 L}{AE}\cdot\alpha\times10^6$				$\frac{P_0 L}{AE}\cdot\beta\times10^6$				$\frac{P_0 L}{AE}\cdot\gamma\times10^6$			
1	2	3	4																
Member	L In.	A Sq. in.	E $\div10^6$	Lb.	R_1	R_2	R_3	Lb.	R_1	R_2	R_3	Lb.	R_1	R_2	R_3	Lb.	R_1	R_2	R_3
AB	118	·23	10·5	2,269	—	—	—	—	—	—	—	—	—	—	—	—	—	—	—
BD	64	·25	10·5	2,269	0·892	—	—	48,260	19·36	—	—	55,350	—	—	—	—	—	—	—
DF	73	·44	10·5	4,182	—	0·838	—	—	—	—	—	22,200	—	11·08	1·97	—	—	—	—
FJ	64	·72	10·5	8,030	—	-0·327	-0·712	—	—	—	—	—	—	·904	—	48,400	—	1·97	4·29
AC	118	·23	10·5	-2,269	0·892	—	—	46,350	9·88	—	—	45,150	—	—	—	—	—	—	—
CE	64	·49	10·5	-4,182	—	0·838	—	—	—	—	—	13,940	—	5·30	—	—	—	—	—
EG	73	·92	10·5	-7,140	—	-0·327	—	—	—	—	—	—	—	·784	—	—	—	—	—
GK	64	·83	10·5	-5,815	0·559	—	-0·712	6,132	2·85	—	—	10,980	1·745	—	1·706	30,450	—	1·71	3·72
BC	26	·27	10·5	-1,200	0·362	0·645	—	6,080	·98	—	—	—	—	—	—	—	—	—	—
DE	40·1	·51	10·5	-2,278	—	—	—	—	—	1·744	—	—	—	3·11	—	—	—	—	—
FG	56·2	·50	10·5	—	—	—	-1·0	—	—	—	—	—	—	—	—	—	—	—	10·70
BE	71·7	·003	30	2,146	-1·0	—	—	-213,600	797·0	—	—	—	—	967	—	—	—	—	—
CD	71·7	·024	30	—	-1·0	-1·0	—	—	99·6	—	—	-249,000	—	70·8	—	—	—	—	—
DG	87·1	·003	30	3,526	—	-1·0	—	—	—	—	—	6,580	—	—	—	—	—	—	—
EF	87·1	·041	30	3,910	—	—	—	—	—	—	—	9,700	—	—	—	—	—	—	—
FH	39	·57	10·5	—	—	0·258	0·561	—	—	—	—	—	—	·43	·944	14,260	—	·942	2·046
HG	39	·56	10·5	-5,660	—	0·258	0·561	—	—	—	—	—	—	·44	·962	-21,020	—	·958	2·083

The solution is

$$R_1 = R_2 = 240 \text{ lb.}$$
$$R_3 = 1{,}030 \text{ lb.}$$

6.5. Stresses due to changes in temperature.—If a structure made of one material throughout, whether it be just stiff or redundant, experiences a uniform change of temperature, every bar is shortened or lengthened in the same proportion and no stresses are induced. The structure is geometrically similar to its original configuration but slightly smaller or larger.

If however a structure is made of more than one material and these have different coefficients of expansion, the effect of a temperature change depends upon whether the structure is just stiff or redundant. If the former, there will be no stresses induced since a just-stiff frame cannot be self-strained, but there will be a slight change in the geometry of the structure. This is no more important than the small changes in configuration due to the unequal stressing of the component members when the structure is loaded, but if the structure is redundant this tendency to distort may induce stresses of considerable magnitude.

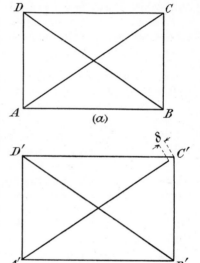

Suppose Fig. 6.11 (a) represents a rectangular frame in which all the members except AC are made of the same material having a coefficient of expansion α. AC is made of a different material, the coefficient of expansion of which is β.

If AC is removed the remaining bars form a just-stiff frame and if this frame has its temperature raised by $t°$ each member will be increased in length in the ratio $1 + \alpha t : 1$. Thus the new lengths A'B', A'D', D'C', C'B' and D'B' shown at (b) will be $1 + \alpha t$ times the lengths AB, etc., in (a) and the figure A'D'C'B' will be geometrically similar to ADCB.

FIG. 6.11.

Suppose now that the removed bar AC, of original length L, is heated to the same temperature as the remainder of the structure. Its new length will be $L(1 + \beta t)$ and not $L(1 + \alpha t)$ which would be necessary if it were to fit exactly into position in the heated frame. It is in fact short of the correct length by $\delta = L(\alpha - \beta)t$. If it is forced into position the stresses in the structure will be identical with those which would exist if the temperature of the complete redundant frame were raised through $t°$.

These stresses can be calculated exactly as for a redundant frame in which the redundant bar is initially too short. The tensile load in AC after heating is denoted by R : the forces in all bars of the frame are found in terms of R and then, if U is the strain energy, the value of R is found from the relation

$$\frac{dU}{dR} = L(\alpha - \beta)t.$$

Temperature stresses are induced not only if the structure is redundant by reason of its having more than the essential number of bars but also if the redundancy lies in the number of reactive forces.   For example, if a just-stiff roof truss is supported on a pin at one end and on rollers at the other over a span L, a rise of temperature $t°$ will cause the free end to move over the rollers a distance Lαt.   If both ends are pinned, however, this movement cannot take place and forces which stress the truss are exerted by the pins.

To calculate these forces one end of the truss may be considered free and to move a distance Lαt.   A load P is now supposed to act along the line joining the pins, of such magnitude as to restore the freed support to its original position.   P will then be the reactive force between the pin and the truss when movement due to the temperature rise is completely restricted, and if U is the strain energy of the frame in terms of P we have, by the first theorem of Castigliano,

$$\text{movement of P in its own line of action} = \frac{dU}{dP} = L\alpha t$$

from which P can be determined.

This effect is of considerable importance in connexion with metal arch ribs whose ends have to be fixed in position, and will be dealt with further when considering the stresses in such structures.

6.6. Distribution methods of stress analysis applied to pin-jointed frames. —It will be seen that the methods of determining the forces in the members of a redundant structure outlined above involve the solution of as many simultaneous equations as there are redundancies.   While this presents no difficulty mathematically the labour involved increases rapidly with the number of equations.   Experience has shown that, when hand calculating machines only are available, it is impracticable to deal successfully with a redundant structure requiring the solution of more than about fourteen equations derived by strain energy analysis.   The advent of the electronic computer makes much heavier tasks bearable (Livesley and Charlton, 1954), but as it will be a long time before designers have such aids available for their day-to-day tasks, other methods of analysis must be used.

A new process of successive approximation for determining the stresses in rigidly jointed frames which are highly redundant (Hardy Cross, 1930), focussed considerable attention on such methods.   Hardy Cross's original work will be discussed in Chapter 10, but it will be well here to outline an extension of it and also another analogous method, due to R. V. Southwell, which are applicable to pin-jointed frames.

The first step taken in applying the strain energy method was to remove all the redundant bars and to determine the forces in the members of the resulting simple frame due to the external load system.   The redundant bars were then re-inserted in the loaded frame and from energy considerations the forces induced in those bars were determined.   The extension of the Cross method, on the other hand, leaves all the bars in place but assumes that before any external load is applied all the joints are held fixed ; that is to say, in a pin-jointed structure all the pins are held by external constraints so that they cannot move.   The external loads are then applied to the joints and, since all the pins are fixed, no load can be transmitted to the members.   One joint is now released by removing the constraint which fixed its pin in position.   The external load applied to this joint then strains the members attached to it, the joint moves and easily calculable forces are induced in these members. The joint is now supposed to be fixed in its new equilibrium position and an adjacent joint is released. The out-of-balance forces acting on this second joint are the external loads applied to it and the force in the member connected to the first joint which was induced by the movement of the latter. The second joint moving into its equilibrium position induces, as a result, forces in the members connected to it. This procedure is repeated until all the joints have been released and fixed again sufficiently often to ensure that the modification in the forces brought about by further releases is small enough to be neglected. It will be seen that the method is one of successive approximation but it is not, in the ordinary sense of the term, an approximate method since by repeating the process sufficiently often any desired degree of accuracy can be obtained.

The underlying principle and the detailed procedure will be most easily appreciated from the study of a worked example but before giving this example it will be useful to develop in general terms certain expressions which are required in the analysis.

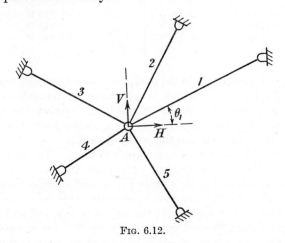

Fig. 6.12.

It will be seen from the outline already given that the method requires a knowledge of the forces in such a group of members as is shown in Fig. 6.12, due to horizontal and vertical loads H and V applied at A. If under the action of these loads the joint A suffers horizontal and vertical displacements α_A and β_A then, since the other ends of the members are prevented from moving, the tension set up in member 1 will be, with the sign convention and notation used in earlier paragraphs,

$$F_1 = -\frac{EA_1}{L_1}(\alpha_A \cos \theta_1 + \beta_A \sin \theta_1) \quad . \quad . \quad . \quad . \quad (6.1)$$

and from a consideration of the equilibrium of joint A it follows that

$$H = \sum \frac{EA_1}{L_1}(\alpha_A \cos \theta_1 + \beta_A \sin \theta_1) \cos \theta_1 \quad . \quad . \quad . \quad (6.2)$$

and

$$V = \sum \frac{EA_1}{L_1}(\alpha_A \cos \theta_1 + \beta_A \sin \theta_1) \sin \theta_1 \quad . \quad . \quad . \quad (6.3)$$

the summation in each case extending to all the members.

By solving these two simultaneous equations the unknowns α_A and β_A

4*

may be evaluated in terms of H and V and equation (6.1) then enables the force in each member connected to A to be determined.

As an illustration of the procedure the stress analysis of the frame shown in Fig. 6.7, already treated by strain energy methods, will be given. The first step is to find, from equations (6.2), (6.3) and (6.1), or by other methods, the forces developed in members AB, AC and AD when the joints B, C and D are held fixed and loads are applied to the free joint A ; also the forces developed in members DA, DB and DC when the joints A, B and C are held fixed and loads are applied to the free joint D. These forces are given in Table 6.7.

TABLE 6.7.
FORCES IN MEMBERS MEETING AT A JOINT.

	Horizontal load H at joint A	Vertical load V at joint A		Horizontal load H at joint D	Vertical load V at joint D
F_{AB}	$-0\cdot978$ H	$-0\cdot206$ V	F_{DC}	$-0\cdot978$ H	$+0\cdot206$ V
F_{AC}	$-0\cdot310$ H	$+0\cdot357$ V	F_{DB}	$-0\cdot310$ H	$-0\cdot357$ V
F_{AD}	$-0\cdot220$ H	$+0\cdot588$ V	F_{DA}	$-0\cdot220$ H	$-0\cdot588$ V

The analysis of the stresses in the complete framework may now be undertaken. It is advisable to adopt a tabular form for the calculations and a convenient arrangement is shown in Table 6.8, where the three upper columns refer to the three members meeting at the joint A and the three lower columns refer to those meeting at the joint D.

It is assumed initially that all joints are held fixed. The external vertical load+10 tons at D, is then applied. The joint D is now released, A still being fixed ; joints B and C are attached to a rigid abutment and therefore, in this particular example, are never released. Due to the external load acting at D, forces are developed in the members DA, DB and DC. Their magnitudes, read from the last column of Table 6.7, are entered in line a', Table 6.8. The joint is now in equilibrium and to indicate this a full line is drawn below the entries so far made. It must not be forgotten that the member DA is attached to joint A and therefore the force $-5\cdot88$ tons developed in it must be recorded also in the first of the upper columns, line a, where the forces in the members meeting at joint A are entered. Since joints B and C have not been released no forces have yet been developed in the members AC and AB and so in the second and third columns of line a the entries are zero. Joint D is now fixed in its new equilibrium position and joint A is released. Since there are no external loads at A the only force acting on the joint at its release is that due to the movement of D just recorded. Before A has moved into its equilibrium position, therefore, the unbalanced force acting on it is a vertical force of $+5\cdot88$ tons and so the forces developed in the members AB, AC and AD as A moves are obtained by substituting this value of V in column 3 of Table 6.7. These forces are entered in line b, Table 6.8, and at the same time the force of $+3\cdot46$ tons, developed in AD by this movement of joint A, is " carried over " to the other end of the member and entered in line b'. Joint A is now fixed in its new equilibrium position and joint D is once more released. This process of releasing and fixing joints is continued until the unbalanced force remaining at a joint is small enough to be neglected. In Table 6.8 the joints A and D have been released five and six times respectively and the unbalanced force

TABLE 6.8.

FORCES (TONS) IN MEMBERS OF FRAMEWORK.

	AD	AC	AB
a	−5·88	0·00	0·00
b	+3·46	+2·10	−1·21
	−2·04	0·00	0·00
	+1·20	+0·73	−0·42
	−0·71	0·00	0·00
	+0·42	+0·25	−0·14
	−0·24	0·00	0·00
	+0·14	+0·09	−0·05
	−0·08	0·00	0·00
	+0·05	+0·03	−0·02
	−0·03	0·00	0·00

	DA	DB	DC
a′	−5·88	−3·57	+2·06
b′	+3·46	0·00	0·00
	−2·04	−1·23	+0·71
	+1·20	0·00	0·00
	−0·71	−0·43	+0·25
	+0·42	0·00	0·00
	−0·24	−0·15	+0·09
	+0·14	0·00	0·00
	−0·08	−0·05	+0·03
	+0·05	0·00	0·00
	−0·03	−0·02	+0·01

is ·03 tons. The total forces in the members are the totals of the entries in the various columns and are

$$AD = -3\cdot71 \text{ tons.}$$
$$AB = -1\cdot84 \quad \text{,,}$$
$$AC = +3\cdot20 \quad \text{,,}$$
$$DB = -5\cdot45 \quad \text{,,}$$
$$DC = +3\cdot15 \quad \text{,,}$$

These values should be compared with those obtained by strain energy methods given in Table 6.5.

The forces in the members in this simple example were estimated to within ·01 tons of their true values after only eleven releases. The same degree of accuracy could not have been obtained so easily if the frame had been more complex as will be appreciated if the deformations suffered by the structure are considered. The percentage errors in the forces at any stage in the process are, in some degree, a measure of the difference between the shape of the frame at that stage and its final deflected form. If the frame can be so deformed before the balancing process at the joints is begun that its shape approximates to the final form, fewer cycles will be necessary to obtain any desired degree of accuracy and, if the deformation is so chosen that the loads in the members produced by it are easily calculated, a considerable saving of labour will result. Fig. 6.13 illustrates one method of producing the deformation required. A two-bay cantilever frame is shown

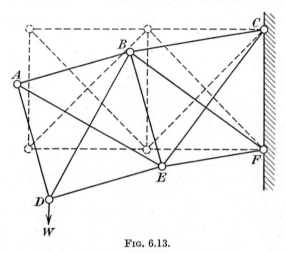

FIG. 6.13.

by broken lines in its unloaded position. When the external loads are applied, the joints of the frame are allowed to move, as shown by the full line diagram, but they are so constrained that those in the first bay, A, B, D and E, do not change their relative positions. Forces are therefore developed in the members of the second bay only and, an important point, their magnitudes are easily calculated. The joints are now held in these deformed positions and the process of releasing them one at a time, as described in the worked example, is begun. The equations for the determination of the forces developed in the members by this type of deformation are in no way complicated but for a complete discussion of the method reference should be made to a paper published by the Aeronautical Research Committee which deals with both pin-jointed and rigidly-jointed braced frames (Baker and Ockleston, 1935).

6.7. Southwell's relaxation method.—A more elegant but less practical method than that described in the previous paragraph, due to R. V. Southwell, avoids all simultaneous equations and is concerned primarily with the determination of the deformations of the structure.

It follows from paragraphs 2.5 and 4.4 that the tension coefficient of any member PQ is

$$t_{PQ} = \frac{EA}{L^3}\{(x_Q - x_P)(\alpha_Q - \alpha_P) + (y_Q - y_P)(\beta_Q - \beta_P) + (z_Q - z_P)(\gamma_Q - \gamma_P)\} \quad (6.4)$$

where x_P, y_P, z_P and x_Q, y_Q, z_Q are the co-ordinates of P and Q in their initial positions and α_P, β_P, γ_P and α_Q, β_Q, γ_Q are the components of their displacements due to strain.

As in the previous method we shall be concerned with the displacements at one end of the member while the other end is held fixed in position though free to rotate on its pin.

If the end Q is held fixed the tension coefficient of the member may be written

$$t_{PQ} = -\frac{EA}{L^3}\{(x_Q - x_P)\alpha_P + (y_Q - y_P)\beta_P + (z_Q - z_P)\gamma_P\} \quad . \quad . \quad (6.5)$$

As a result of the tension in PQ the joint P will be subjected to a force having components :

$$\left. \begin{array}{l} X_P = t_{PQ}(x_Q - x_P) \\ Y_P = t_{PQ}(y_Q - y_P) \\ Z_P = t_{PQ}(z_Q - z_P) \end{array} \right\} \quad . \quad . \quad . \quad . \quad . \quad (6.6)$$

and the fixed joint Q will be subjected to forces equal and opposite to these.

If the joint P has a number of members connected to it, their remote ends being fixed as is Q, then when P is given a displacement α_P in the x-direction and no displacements in the directions of the other axes, the components of the total force developed on the joint P are :—

in the x-direction

$$\Sigma t_{PQ}(x_Q - x_P) = -\Sigma \frac{EA}{L^3}(x_Q - x_P)^2 \alpha_P,$$

in the y-direction

$$\Sigma t_{PQ}(y_Q - y_P) = -\Sigma \frac{EA}{L^3}(x_Q - x_P)(y_Q - y_P)\alpha_P, \left.\begin{array}{l} \\ \\ \\ \\ \\ \end{array}\right\} \quad . \quad . \quad . \quad (6.7)$$

in the z-direction

$$\Sigma t_{PQ}(z_Q - z_P) = -\Sigma \frac{EA}{L^3}(x_Q - x_P)(z_Q - z_P)\alpha_P,$$

the summation including every member connected to P.

The forces developed by displacements β_P and γ_P may be found in the same way and no other preparatory calculations are needed.

The analysis of the stresses in a framework is made by giving each joint in turn that displacement in the direction of one of the co-ordinate axes which has most effect in reducing the resultant force on the joint. This process is continued until the resultant forces on the joints are small enough to be neglected. The total displacements given to the joints are then known and the forces in the members can be found from equation (6.4). The method will be illustrated by applying it to the problem dealt with in the preceding paragraph, the framework concerned being shown in Fig. 6.7.

The first step is to evaluate the constant $\dfrac{EA}{L^3}$ for each member, the units of length and force adopted being inches and tons respectively and E being taken as 13,000 tons/sq. in. These constants are $3 \cdot 250$ for members AB and CD, $1 \cdot 625$ for AD and $0 \cdot 312$ for DB and AC.

The forces on the joints due to unit displacements must next be found. When joint D is given a unit displacement in the direction of the x-axis and no displacement in the direction of the y-axis, $i.e.$ $\alpha_D = 1$ and $\beta_D = 0$, the forces exerted on the joint D by the member DC are, from equation (6.6),

$$X_D = t_{DC}(x_C - x_D) = -975$$

and $$Y_D = t_{DC}(y_C - y_D) = +564.$$

Due to the same displacement, forces are exerted by the other members meeting at the joint and it will be found from equation (6.7) that the total forces on D are, in the x-direction $-1,068$ and in the y-direction $+402$. This information is set out in line 1 (a), Table 6.9, where it is also stated that X_A and Y_A, the forces on the joint A due to this displacement, $\alpha_D = 1$, are zero.

In the same way the forces on the joints are calculated due to a unit displacement in the y-direction and no displacement in the x-direction, $i.e.$ $\beta_D = 1$ and $\alpha_D = 0$. These forces are set out in line 2 (a), Table 6.9, and it will be seen that there is a force of $+650$ in the y-direction at joint A. This follows from equation (6.6) since, due to the displacements under consideration,

$$Y_A = t_{AD}(y_D - y_A) = \frac{EA}{L^3}\{(y_D - y_A)\beta_D\}(y_D - y_A)$$

$$= 1 \cdot 625\{-20 \times -20\} = +650.$$

It will be found a convenience in the later work if the largest force at a joint due to each displacement is reduced to 1,000. This has been done in Table 6.9 ; line 1 (b), for instance, being obtained from line 1 (a) by dividing throughout by $1 \cdot 068$.

The deformation of the framework as a whole can now be considered. All the joints in the framework are initially fixed in space and the external load is applied.   Joint D will then be subjected to a force $Y_D = +10$.   The joint must next be given a displacement, all other joints being held fixed, which will reduce this force as much as possible.   A glance at Table 6.9 shows that a displacement of joint D in the y-direction is the most efficient for the purpose and that if its magnitude is one hundredth of the displacement recorded in line 2 (b), Table 6.9, the force on the joint in the y-direction will be reduced to zero.

Table 6.10 shows a convenient way of setting out these facts. The first line, p, in the table shows the conditions after the external load has been applied but before any joints have been displaced. . Line q shows the forces developed at the joints A and D, which in this particular framework are the only ones to be given displacements, by a movement of joint D in the y-direction of magnitude $0 \cdot 00797$.   The type and magnitude of this displacement are recorded in the first two columns of Table 6.10, the entry " 2 (b) " in the first column referring to line 2 (b) of Table 6.9.   The forces at the joints after the displacement has been given to D are found by adding lines p and q ; they are entered in line r.   While the force Y_D has been reduced to zero it will be seen that forces X_D and Y_A, of magnitudes $+3 \cdot 20$ and $+5 \cdot 18$ respectively, have been induced by the displacement.   Of these the latter is the greater and it will be seen from Table 6.9 that it can be made to disappear by giving joint A a displacement $0 \cdot 00518$ times that recorded in

TABLE 6.9.

FORCES (TONS) AT JOINTS DUE TO DISPLACEMENTS.

	Displacement	X_D	X_A	Y_D	Y_A
1 (a)	$\alpha_D = 1$	−1,068	0	+ 402	0
1 (b)	$\alpha_D = 0 \cdot 937$	−1,000	0	+ 377	0
2 (a)	$\beta_D = 1$	+ 402	0	−1,256	+ 650
2 (b)	$\beta_D = 0 \cdot 797$	+ 320	0	−1,000	+ 518
3 (a)	$\alpha_A = 1$	0	−1,068	0	− 402
3 (b)	$\alpha_A = 0 \cdot 937$	0	−1,000	0	− 377
4 (a)	$\beta_A = 1$	0	− 402	+ 650	−1,256
4 (b)	$\beta_A = 0 \cdot 797$	0	− 320	+ 518	−1,000

line 4 (b), Table 6.9. The forces at the joints induced by this displacement are entered in line s, Table 6.10, and those remaining after this second displacement has been completed, in line t. This process is repeated until the displacements become small enough to be neglected. In Table 6.10 a total of eighteen displacements have been made. The forces in the bars have now to be calculated. This is done by determining the total displacements given to the joints. It can be seen from columns 1 and 2, Table 6.10, that the total displacement in the x-direction suffered by joint D is

$$\alpha_D = 0 \cdot 937(0 \cdot 00320 + 0 \cdot 00124 + 0 \cdot 00075 + 0 \cdot 00020)$$
$$= 0 \cdot 937 \times 0 \cdot 00539.$$

The other displacements are

$$\beta_D = 0 \cdot 797 \times 0 \cdot 01710$$
$$\alpha_A = -0 \cdot 937 \times 0 \cdot 00311$$
$$\beta_A = 0 \cdot 797 \times 0 \cdot 01003.$$

These displacements being known the tension coefficients can be calculated from equation (6.4), thus

$$t_{DA} = \frac{EA}{L^3}(y_A - y_D)(\beta_A - \beta_D)$$
$$= 1 \cdot 625 \times 20 \times 0 \cdot 797(0 \cdot 01003 - 0 \cdot 01710) = -0 \cdot 183$$

and the force in member $DA = t_{DA} \times 20 = -3 \cdot 66$ tons.

The forces in the other members are

$$AB = -1 \cdot 92 \text{ tons.}$$
$$AC = +3 \cdot 14 \quad ,,$$
$$DB = -5 \cdot 36 \quad ,,$$
$$DC = +3 \cdot 17 \quad ,,$$

It will be seen that these values differ appreciably from those obtained for the same framework in paragraphs 6.3 and 6.6. The reason for this is that the work in Table 6.10 has not been carried far enough.

In this method, as in the one described in paragraph 6.6, it will be found economical to deform the structure by " block " displacements and rotations before the process of displacing the joints one at a time is begun (Southwell, 1935).

TABLE 6.10.

Operation	Multiplier	X_D	X_A	Y_D	Y_A	
2 (b)	+0·01000	0·00	0·00	+10·00	0·00	p
		+3·20	0·00	−10·00	+5·18	q
4 (b)	+0·00518	+3·20	0·00	0·00	+5·18	r
		0·00	−1·65	+2·68	−5·18	s
1 (b)	+0·00320	+3·20	−1·65	+2·68	0·00	t
		−3·20	0·00	+1·20	0·00	
2 (b)	+0·00388	0·00	−1·65	+3·88	0·00	
		+1·24	0·00	−3·88	+2·01	
4 (b)	+0·00201	+1·24	−1·65	0·00	+2·01	
		0·00	−0·64	+1·04	−2·01	
3 (b)	−0·00229	+1·24	−2·29	+1·04	0·00	
		0·00	+2·29	0·00	+0·86	
1 (b)	+0·00124	+1·24	0·00	+1·04	+0·86	
		−1·24	0·00	+0·47	0·00	
2 (b)	+0·00151	0·00	0·00	+1·51	+0·86	
		+0·48	0·00	−1·51	+0·78	
4 (b)	+0·00164	+0·48	0·00	0·00	+1·64	
		0·00	−0·52	+0·85	−1·64	
2 (b)	+0·00085	+0·48	−0·52	+0·85	0·00	
		+0·27	0·00	−0·85	+0·44	
1 (b)	+0·00075	+0·75	−0·52	0·00	+0·44	
		−0·75	0·00	+0·28	0·00	
3 (b)	−0·00052	0·00	−0·52	+0·28	+0·44	
		0·00	+0·52	0·00	+0·20	
4 (b)	+0·00064	0·00	0·00	+0·28	+0·64	
		0·00	−0·20	+0·33	−0·64	
2 (b)	+0·00061	0·00	−0·20	+0·61	0·00	
		+0·20	0·00	−0·61	+0·32	
4 (b)	+0·00032	+0·20	−0·20	0·00	+0·32	
		0·00	−0·10	+0·17	−0·32	
3 (b)	−0·00030	+0·20	−0·30	+0·17	0·00	
		0·00	+0·30	0·00	+0·11	
1 (b)	+0·00020	+0·20	0·00	+0·17	+0·11	
		−0·20	0·00	+0·08	0·00	
2 (b)	+0·00025	0·00	0·00	+0·25	+0·11	
		+0·08	0·00	−0·25	+0·13	
4 (b)	+0·00024	+0·08	0·00	0·00	+0·24	
		0·00	+0·08	+0·17	−0·24	
		+0·08	+0·08	+0·17	0·00	

6.8. Choice of method of stress analysis.—It is impossible to formulate general rules which will govern the method to be used in any particular case.

It is clear that less labour was involved in determining the forces in the members of the framework shown in Fig. 6.7 by strain energy methods than by either of the successive approximation methods and it is probably safe to say that when analysing the stresses in redundant structures having hinged ends the strain energy method will be found most economical if the number of redundancies does not exceed six.

There is little to choose between the two successive approximation methods except that in the second all simultaneous equations are avoided. It should be remembered, however, that it may be simpler to solve groups of two or three simultaneous equations as required by the first method than to obtain the same results by successive approximation.

6.9. Design of redundant frames.—Since the stress analysis of a redundant frame necessitates a knowledge of the cross-sectional areas of all the members it is evident that ordinary methods of design are not applicable to such a structure. The usual method is to guess sizes for all members, analyse the frame by means of strain-energy theorems, and if the stresses do not appear reasonable to make a second approximation to the sizes and go through the operation again. By this process of trial and error a suitable design can be achieved, but the procedure is laborious, especially if there are a number of redundancies, since each trial involves the solution of a number of simultaneous equations.

By a modification of the equations obtained from the second theorem of Castigliano, however, a method has been evolved which enables a much more direct approach to the problem to be made (Pippard, 1922). The results obtained by this method are not always of direct practical use and sizes obtained may have to be modified by conditions other than the stresses to be met, but it does give a structure which fulfils the conditions imposed by theoretical considerations and any necessary modifications are easily made.

Suppose that the pin-jointed frame to be designed carries a number of external loads $W_1, W_2 \ldots W_N$, and that it contains a number of redundant members the forces in which are $R_1, R_2 \ldots R_M$. By drawing stress diagrams the loads in all members of the frame can be found and we can write

$$P_0 = aW_1 + bW_2 + \ldots + nW_N + \alpha R_1 + \beta R_2 \ldots + \mu R_M,$$

where P_0 is the load in any member and $a, b \ldots n, \alpha, \beta \ldots \mu$ are numerical coefficients depending on the geometry of the frame.

The strain energy of the whole structure is

$$U = \tfrac{1}{2} \sum \frac{P_0{}^2 L}{AE}$$

and by the second theorem of Castigliano we can write

$$\frac{\partial U}{\partial R_1} = \frac{\partial U}{\partial R_2} = \ldots = \frac{\partial U}{\partial R_M} = 0.$$

Now

$$\frac{\partial U}{\partial R_1} = \sum \frac{\alpha P_0 L}{AE}$$

and P_0/A is the stress in the member $=f$.

Hence

$$\left. \begin{aligned}
\frac{\partial U}{\partial R_1} &= \sum \frac{f L \alpha}{E} = 0 \\
\frac{\partial U}{\partial R_2} &= \sum \frac{f L \beta}{E} = 0 \\
&\cdots\cdots\cdots \\
\frac{\partial U}{\partial R_M} &= \sum \frac{f L \mu}{E} = 0.
\end{aligned} \right\} \qquad \ldots \ldots \quad (6.8)$$

If, as is common, E is the same throughout, these equations become

$$\Sigma fL\alpha = \Sigma fL\beta = \ldots = \Sigma fL\mu = 0 \quad . \quad . \quad . \quad . \quad (6.9)$$

The procedure for design is as follows :—

Replace all redundant members in the structure by unknown forces R_1, R_2, etc., acting along the axes of these members. Since each member is connected to two joints of the frame, the force replacing it must be applied at both joints. The structure is now reduced to a just-stiff framework acted upon by R_1, R_2, etc., and W_1, W_2, etc. A stress diagram is drawn for the external load system, and this gives the sum of the terms

$$aW_1 + bW_2 + \ldots + nW_N$$

in the expression for P_0.

A stress diagram for the two equal forces R_1, acting on the structure, gives the values of α for all members of the frame, and similar diagrams for $R_2 \ldots R_M$ give values of $\beta \ldots \mu$. Since the values of L and E are known, the terms $L\alpha/E$, $L\beta/E \ldots L\mu/E$ are readily calculated for each member of the frame. The equations corresponding to (6.8) or (6.9) are now formed. There are the same number of equations as there are redundant members, and each equation contains terms involving the stress in one of the redundant members and the stresses in those members of the truss affected by that particular redundancy ; no other terms occur. Thus the equations connect the stresses in the various members of the structure and the next step is to select such stresses as will satisfy the equations.

It will be found convenient to begin with the equation which contains the smallest number of terms. The maximum permissible stress can be substituted for the majority of terms occurring, the remainder—which often need be no more than one in number—being adjusted to satisfy the equation. This is a very easy matter since there are any number of possible variations, all correct, and it is not a question of determining a unique solution.

Certain stresses which are fixed in the first equation will occur in other equations and these values should be substituted. The remaining equations are then dealt with in the same way and all stresses determined.

The stresses thus fixed should be tabulated and among them will be the stresses in the redundant members. The next step is to fix the *load* in each redundancy by assigning suitable areas to these members. A study of the table of internal loads helps this decision, since it shows the effect of the load in the redundant member upon the loads in the other bars. Having fixed the sizes of the redundant members and so the loads in them, the loads in all the other members of the frame can be written down and by dividing these loads by the stresses already fixed the cross-sectional areas of all members are determined.

It should be noticed that this method eliminates the solution of simultaneous equations and further, that the stresses are controlled by the designer during the process of calculation. As an example the frame shown in Fig. 6.10 will be considered (Airship Stressing Panel, 1922).

The frame is fixed at J, H and K and assuming all diagonal braces to be operative there are three redundancies. These will be taken to be FG, BE and DG.

The force in FG will be denoted by $-R_3$, that in BE by $-R_1$, and in DG by $-R_2$.

The first step is to find the internal forces in all members of the frame in terms of the external load system and R_1, R_2 and R_3. This can be done by stress diagrams or by resolution at the joints. The values obtained by the latter method are given in Table 6.11. These loads and the length of each member having been tabulated, columns 4, 5 and 6 are obtained as follows :—

Since α, β and γ are the coefficients of R_1, R_2 and R_3 respectively, their values are known from column 3 and multiplying by the term L/E we get the figures in columns 4, 5 and 6. The structure is supposed to be made of duralumin, braced diagonally by steel, having values of E of $10 \cdot 5 \times 10^6$ lb. per square inch and 30×10^6 lb. per square inch respectively.

Consider first column 4 : this enables us to form the equation $\sum \dfrac{f L \alpha}{E} = 0$ and if we denote the stress in any member AB by AB and so on, we obtain

$$5 \cdot 43 \text{ BD} + 5 \cdot 43 \text{ CE} + 1 \cdot 38 \text{ BC} + 1 \cdot 38 \text{ DE} - 2 \cdot 39 \text{ BE} - 2 \cdot 39 \text{ CD} = 0 \quad (6.10)$$

where BD, CE, etc., are the members of the truss appearing in column 4.

Similarly, from columns 5 and 6, we obtain the equations

$$5 \cdot 82 \text{ DF} - 1 \cdot 99 \text{ FJ} + 5 \cdot 82 \text{ EG} - 1 \cdot 99 \text{ GK} + 2 \cdot 46 \text{ DE}$$
$$- 2 \cdot 90 \text{ DG} - 2 \cdot 90 \text{ EF} + 0 \cdot 96 \text{ FH} + 0 \cdot 96 \text{ HG} = 0 \quad . \quad . \quad . \quad (6.11)$$
$$- 4 \cdot 34 \text{ FJ} - 4 \cdot 34 \text{ GK} - 5 \cdot 35 \text{ FG} + 2 \cdot 08 \text{ FH} + 2 \cdot 08 \text{ HG} = 0. \quad (6.12)$$

Since equation (6.12) contains the smallest number of terms, we begin with that and select any stresses to satisfy it.

Assuming that the stress in duralumin is limited to 10,000 lb. per square inch and in steel to 80,000 lb. per square inch, we put

$$\text{FH} = -\text{GK} = 8,000 \text{ lb. per square inch.}$$
$$\text{FJ} = 10,000 \quad ,, \qquad ,, \qquad ,,$$
$$\text{FG} = -2,000 \quad ,, \qquad ,, \qquad ,,$$
which gives $\qquad \text{HG} = -8,970 \quad ,, \qquad ,, \qquad ,,$

It should be noted that any other stresses which satisfy equation (6.12) would be equally correct, but we have stressed four of these members fairly equally which is reasonable.

The values above are entered in column 7, and we turn next to equation (6.10). None of the stresses appearing here have been fixed from (6.12), so we again select suitable values.

$$-\text{BE} = \text{CD} = 80,000 \text{ lb. per square inch.}$$
$$\text{BD} = 10,000 \quad ,, \qquad ,, \qquad ,,$$
$$\text{CE} = -8,000 \quad ,, \qquad ,, \qquad ,,$$
$$\text{BC} = \text{DE} = -3,928 \quad ,, \qquad ,, \qquad ,,$$

and these are also entered in column 7.

Five stresses appearing in equation (6.11) have now been fixed and substituting them, we obtain the equation

$$5 \cdot 82 \text{ DF} + 5 \cdot 82 \text{ EG} - 2 \cdot 90 \text{ DG} - 2 \cdot 90 \text{ EF} = 14,602.$$

Put $\qquad\qquad\qquad \text{DF} = 10,000 \text{ lb. per square inch.}$
$$-\text{DG} = \text{EF} = 80,000 \quad ,, \qquad ,, \qquad ,,$$
and then $\qquad\qquad \text{EG} = -7,495 \quad ,, \qquad ,, \qquad ,,$

Since members AB and AC are unaffected by the redundancies, they do not enter into the equations, so that the stresses in them can be made anything we please. They are therefore put at the maximum allowable stress,

i.e. $\qquad\qquad\qquad \text{AB} = -\text{AC} = 10,000 \text{ lb. per square inch.}$

TABLE 6.11.

Italics denote negative values.

1	2	3				4	5	6	7	8	9
	Length	Load				$\frac{L\alpha}{E}$ $\times10^6$	$\frac{L\beta}{E}$ $\times10^6$	$\frac{L\gamma}{E}$ $\times10^6$	Stress	Load	Area
Member	Ins.	Lb.	R_1	R_2	R_3				Lb./sq. in.	Lb.	Sq. in.
AB	118	2,269	—	—	—	—	—	—	10,000	2,269	0·23
BD	64	2,269	0·892	—	—	5·43	—	—	10,000	2,492	0·25
DF	73	4,182	—	0·838	—	—	5·82	—	10,000	4,392	0·44
FJ	64	8,030	—	*0·327*	*0·712*	—	*1·99*	*4·34*	10,000	7,236	0·72
AC	118	*2,269*	—	—	—	—	—	—	*10,000*	2,269	0·23
CE	64	*4,182*	0·892	—	—	5·43	—	—	*8,000*	3,959	0·49
EG	73	7,140	—	0·838	—	—	5·82	—	*7,495*	6,931	0·92
GK	64	5,815	—	*0·327*	*0·712*	—	*1·99*	*4·34*	*8,000*	6,609	0·83
BC	26	1,200	0·559	—	—	1·38	—	—	*3,928*	*1,060*	0·27
DE	40·1	2,278	0·362	0·645	—	1·38	2·46	—	*3,928*	2,020	0·51
FG	56·2	—	—	—	1·0	—	—	5·35	2,000	1,000	0·50
BE	71·7	—	*1·0*	—	—	*2·39*	—	—	80,000	250	0·003
CD	71·7	2,146	*1·0*	—	—	*2·39*	—	—	80,000	1,896	0·024
DG	87·1	—	—	*1·0*	—	—	*2·90*	—	80,000	*250*	0·003
EF	87·1	3,526	—	*1·0*	—	—	*2·90*	—	80,000	3,276	0·041
FH	39	3,910	—	0·258	0·561	—	0·96	2·08	8,000	4,536	0·57
HG	39	*5,660*	—	0·258	0·561	—	0·96	2·08	8,970	5,034	0·56

We now fix the absolute values of the loads in the redundant members, and in doing so we consider the effect these members have upon the loads in the other members.

Suppose we make $R_1=R_2=$ 250 lb.

and $R_3=1,000$ lb.

and enter these values in column 8.

We now write down the load in every member from column 3 and these loads divided by the stresses in column 7 give the required areas tabulated in column 9.

It should be emphasised that this is only one of an infinite number of solutions of this particular problem, but we have by a direct process produced a design which we know will have the stresses of column 7 when loaded as shown in Fig. 6.10 and this design has not involved the solution of any simultaneous equations.

This example was used in paragraph 6.4 as an illustration of the method of stress analysis for a structure having more than one redundant member. The areas assumed in that analysis were those found by the present method and given in Table 6.11 above. The values of R_1, R_2 and R_3 were evaluated by an application of the method of least work. This meant the solution of three simultaneous equations which gave $R_1=R_2=240$ lb. and $R_3=1,030$ lb. These figures should of course have agreed with the values assigned to R_1, R_2 and R_3 above : the small differences are due to the fact that only slide-rule accuracy was aimed at in the calculations.

6.10. Effect of curved bars in a framework.—Some members of a framework may be curved and if the structure is redundant special treatment of these members is necessary (Pippard, 1926).

Let A and B in Fig. 6.14 be two nodes of a framework connected by a circular arc of radius R and subtending an angle 2ϕ at the centre. If the frame is pin-jointed, any force transmitted between A and B must act along the line AB. Let P be such a force.

Then if Δ is the amount by which the distance AB is shortened under the action of P,

$$\Delta = \frac{dU}{dP}$$

where U is the strain-energy of the bar.

If I is the relevant second moment of area of the bar,
    A the cross-sectional area of the bar,
    E Young's modulus for the material and
    N the modulus of rigidity of the material,

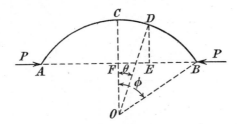

Fig. 6.14.

then at any point D on the arc where $\angle COD = \theta$ the resultant actions are :

    an axial compression $= P \cos \theta,$
    a radial shear $= P \sin \theta,$
    a bending moment $= PR (\cos \theta - \cos \phi),$

and the total strain-energy of the bar is

$$U = \frac{P^2 R}{EA} \int_0^\phi \cos^2 \theta \, d\theta + \frac{P^2 R^3}{EI} \int_0^\phi (\cos \theta - \cos \phi)^2 d\theta + \frac{P^2 R}{AN} \int_0^\phi \sin^2 \theta \, d\theta$$

where the first and second terms are the components due to axial load and bending respectively and the third term is an approximation to the unimportant component due to shear.

From this expression, when $N = \frac{2}{5}E$ we obtain

$$\Delta = \frac{PR}{AE} \left[\frac{7\phi}{2} - \frac{3 \sin 2\phi}{4} + \frac{R^2}{k^2} \left(2\phi - \frac{3 \sin 2\phi}{2} + \phi \cos 2\phi \right) \right],$$

where k is the radius of gyration of the cross-section of the bar.

If the curved bar were replaced by a straight member of the same cross-sectional dimensions but with such a value of E that Δ remained the same, the elastic properties of the frame would be unaltered.

Let E' be the modulus of elasticity of such a member. Then, under the action of P its alteration in length would be $\dfrac{2PR \sin \phi}{AE'}$ and for this to be equal to Δ we must have

$$E'=E\left[\dfrac{2\sin\phi}{\dfrac{7\phi}{2}-\dfrac{3\sin 2\phi}{4}+\dfrac{R^2}{k^2}\left(2\phi-\dfrac{3\sin 2\phi}{2}+\phi\cos 2\phi\right)}\right]\ .\ \ \ \ \text{(6.13)}$$

Any framework containing curved members can thus be simplified by replacing all such members by straight bars of the same cross-sections as the originals but with modified values of E as given by equation (6.13). Such a simplified frame will be elastically equivalent to the original and the usual methods for calculating deflexions and stresses can be employed.

The above formulas apply strictly only to circular arcs but very little error is introduced if the arc is not circular provided the maximum bow is the same.

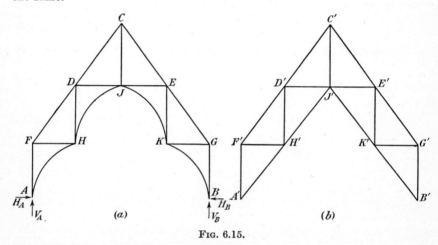

Fig. 6.15.

As an example we will consider the structure shown in Fig. 6.15 (a) which represents a roof truss of the simple hammer-beam type supported at A and B on rigid walls. There are ten joints in the truss and seventeen members are required to make it just-stiff. This number is actually provided but since both the supports are formed by pins on rigid walls a redundant reaction is introduced. This may be conveniently taken as H_A. The loading, which is not shown, will consist of dead weights and wind forces.

The value of H_A is determined from the equation $\dfrac{dU}{dH_A}=0$.

The curved members of the truss are replaced by straight bars as shown at (b) and (6.13) is used to calculate the equivalent values of E for these straight bars. The force P_0 in each member of the truss shown at (b) due to the external load system and H_A and H_B is found by any of the methods described in Chapter 2 and $\dfrac{P_0 L}{AE}\dfrac{dP_0}{dH_A}$ is calculated for each, using the equivalent value of E for the bars A'H', H'J', J'K' and K'B' and not the real value for the material. This work should be done in tabular form as shown in earlier examples and results in an expression for $\sum\dfrac{P_0 L}{AE}\dfrac{dP_0}{dH_A}$

in terms of H_A and the external loads. Equation of this expression to zero gives the value of H_A required, from which the forces in all the bars of the truss can be calculated.

Detailed examples of analyses of this type of truss will be found in a paper published by the Department of Scientific and Industrial Research (Pippard and Glanville, 1926).

6.11. Principle of superposition applied to redundant frameworks.—When a structure which has a number of redundant bars exhibits symmetry about a centre-line an application of the principle of superposition considerably reduces the work of analysis.

An example to illustrate this is shown in Fig. 6.16. It consists of a four-panel truss with counterbracing in each panel, so that there are four redundant bars. A load of 2W acts at joint D, and the bars CA, DK, FH and GB are conveniently chosen as the redundant members, the tensions in them being R_1, R_2, R_3, and R_4 respectively.

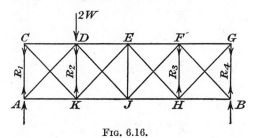

Fig. 6.16.

Using the second theorem of Castigliano, the conditions for the solution of the problem are

$$\frac{\partial U}{\partial R_1}=\frac{\partial U}{\partial R_2}=\frac{\partial U}{\partial R_3}=\frac{\partial U}{\partial R_4}=0.$$

In the ordinary way the four resulting equations must be solved simultaneously.

Suppose, however, that the load system is split into the two systems shown in Fig. 6.17. That shown in Fig. 6.17 (a) is symmetrical about EJ, the centre-line of the truss, and corresponding bars on either side of this axis must carry the same loads. It is only necessary, therefore, to assume two unknown tensions R_1', and R_2', as shown instead of four as in the case of unsymmetrical loading.

The second load system shown in (b) is skew-symmetrical, a load W acting downwards at D and an equal load acting upwards at F. The reactions are as shown, and corresponding bars on either side of the centre-line will carry equal but opposite loads. Thus, if CA has a tension R_1'', GB will have a tension of $-R_1''$; that is, a compression of $+R_1''$. Here again the number of statically indeterminate forces is two instead of four. If the load systems shown at (a) and (b) are superposed the result is 2W acting at D as in Fig. 6.16, and the original problem is thus reduced to the solution of two pairs of two simultaneous equations instead of the solution of four simultaneous equations.

The saving in work is considerable even in the present simple case, but in a problem with a larger number of redundant bars the method enables solutions to be obtained which would otherwise be impracticable. For example, twelve simultaneous equations would generally involve a prohibitive amount of work, and it is only in very exceptional circumstances that a solution would be attempted ; if, however, by the use of the principle of superposition they can be reduced to two independent sets of six each the problem, although still lengthy, is quite practicable.

The example shown in Fig. 6.16 has been solved both by the straightforward method and by using superposed load systems, and the working is given for comparison.

Numerical values have been reduced to the simplest terms to keep the arithmetical work as easy as possible.

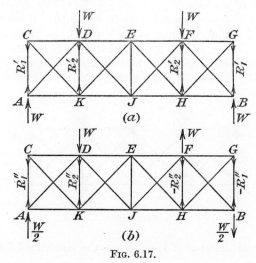

FIG. 6.17.

In each instance equations are formed of the type

$$\frac{\partial U}{\partial R} = \frac{P_0 L}{AE} \frac{\partial P_0}{\partial R} = 0,$$

where the symbols have the same significance as previously in this chapter. The material is supposed to be the same throughout.

(1) Dealing with the problem straightforwardly, the necessary four simultaneous equations are formed, the work being set out in Table 6.12. These equations are

$$\left.\begin{array}{l}
9W+40R_1-20R_2- 2R_3+ 2R_4=0 \\
9W-40R_1+44R_2+ 4R_3- 4R_4=0 \\
-9W- 4R_1+ 4R_2+44R_3-40R_4=0 \\
9W+ 2R_1- 2R_2-20R_3+40R_4=0.
\end{array}\right\}$$

The solution is
$$R_1=-0\cdot59799W$$
$$R_2=-0\cdot77006W$$
$$R_3=+0\cdot01434W$$
$$R_4=-0\cdot22643W.$$

The negative signs denote that the forces are compressive.

(2) Using the method of superposition, and dealing first with the loading shown in Fig. 6.17 (a), the equations obtained are

$$\left.\begin{array}{l}
-9W-42R_1'+22R_2'=0 \\
22R_1'-24R_2'=0
\end{array}\right\}$$

Table 6.12.

Bar	A	L	P_0 W	P_0 R_1	P_0 R_2	P_0 R_3	P_0 R_4	$\frac{P_0L}{A}\frac{\partial P_0}{\partial R_1}$ W	R_1	R_2	R_3	R_4	$\frac{P_0L}{A}\frac{\partial P_0}{\partial R_2}$ W	R_1	R_2	R_3	R_4	$\frac{P_0L}{A}\frac{\partial P_0}{\partial R_3}$ W	R_1	R_2	R_3	R_4	$\frac{P_0L}{A}\frac{\partial P_0}{\partial R_4}$ W	R_1	R_2	R_3	R_4
AC	2	1		1					$\frac{1}{2}$					$\frac{1}{2}$													
KD	2	1		-1	1		-1		$\frac{1}{2}$	$\frac{1}{2}$	$\frac{1}{2}$	$\frac{1}{2}$		$\frac{1}{2}$		$\frac{1}{2}$				$\frac{1}{2}$	$\frac{1}{2}$		$\frac{1}{2}$	$\frac{1}{2}$		
JE	2	1		-1		1																					
HF	2	1		1	1	1	-1																				
BG	2	1		-1		1																					
CD	4	1	-1	1		1		$\frac{1}{4}$	$\frac{1}{4}$	$\frac{1}{4}$			$\frac{1}{4}$	$\frac{1}{4}$	$\frac{1}{4}$			$\frac{1}{4}$		$\frac{1}{4}$	$\frac{1}{4}$		$\frac{1}{4}$	$\frac{1}{4}$	$\frac{1}{4}$	$\frac{1}{4}$
DE	4	1	-1	-1	1			$\frac{3}{8}$	$\frac{1}{4}$	$\frac{1}{4}$			$\frac{3}{8}$	$\frac{1}{4}$	$\frac{1}{4}$			$\frac{1}{8}$		$\frac{1}{4}$	$\frac{1}{4}$		$\frac{1}{8}$	$\frac{1}{4}$	$\frac{1}{4}$	$\frac{1}{4}$
EF	4	1					-1	$\frac{3}{8}$	$\frac{1}{4}$																	
FG	4	1					-1		$\frac{1}{4}$																	
AK	4	1	$\frac{3}{2}$	1					2	2				2	2				2	2				2	2	
KJ	4	1	$\frac{3}{2}$	-1					2	2				2	2				2	2				2	2	
JH	4	1	$\frac{1}{2}$				-1	3	2																	
HB	4	1	$\frac{1}{2}$				-1	1	2																	
CK	$\sqrt2$	$\sqrt2$	$-\frac{3}{\sqrt2}$	$-\sqrt2$																						
AD	$\sqrt2$	$\sqrt2$	$-\frac{1}{\sqrt2}$	$-\sqrt2$																						
DJ	$\sqrt2$	$\sqrt2$		$\sqrt2$	$-\sqrt2$		$-\sqrt2$																			
EK	$\sqrt2$	$\sqrt2$		$\sqrt2$	$-\sqrt2$	$-\sqrt2$	$-\sqrt2$																			
EH	$\sqrt2$	$\sqrt2$				$-\sqrt2$																					
FJ	$\sqrt2$	$\sqrt2$	$-\frac{1}{\sqrt2}$	$-\frac{1}{\sqrt2}$			$-\sqrt2$																			
FB	$\sqrt2$	$\sqrt2$	$-\frac{1}{\sqrt2}$	$-\frac{1}{\sqrt2}$			$-\sqrt2$																			
GH	$\sqrt2$	$\sqrt2$					$-\sqrt2$																				

which give

$$R_1' = -0 \cdot 41221W$$
$$R_2' = -0 \cdot 37786W.$$

The detailed work is set out in Table 6.13.

TABLE 6.13.

Bar	A	L	P_0			$\dfrac{P_0 L}{A} \dfrac{\partial P_0}{\partial R_1'}$			$\dfrac{P_0 L}{A} \dfrac{\partial P_0}{\partial R_2'}$		
			W	R_1'	R_2'	W	R_1'	R_2'	W	R_1'	R'
CA	2	1		1			$\frac{1}{2}$				
DK	2	1			1						$\frac{1}{2}$
CD	4	1		1			$\frac{1}{4}$				
DE	4	1	-1	-1	1	$\frac{1}{4}$	$\frac{1}{4}$	$-\frac{1}{4}$	$-\frac{1}{4}$	$-\frac{1}{4}$	$\frac{1}{4}$
AK	4	1	1	1		$\frac{1}{4}$	$\frac{1}{4}$				
KJ	4	1	1	-1	1	$-\frac{1}{4}$	$\frac{1}{4}$	$-\frac{1}{4}$	$\frac{1}{4}$	$-\frac{1}{4}$	$\frac{1}{4}$
CK	$\sqrt{2}$	$\sqrt{2}$		$-\sqrt{2}$			2				
DA	$\sqrt{2}$	$\sqrt{2}$	$-\sqrt{2}$	$-\sqrt{2}$		2	2				
DJ	$\sqrt{2}$	$\sqrt{2}$		$\sqrt{2}$	$-\sqrt{2}$		2	-2		-2	2
KE	$\sqrt{2}$	$\sqrt{2}$		$\sqrt{2}$	$-\sqrt{2}$		2	-2		-2	2
$\frac{1}{2}$ (EJ)	$\frac{1}{2}$ (2)	1		-1	1		1	-1		-1	1

The skew-symmetrical loading shown in Fig. 6.17 (b) yields the equations

$$19R_1'' - 9R_2'' = 0$$
$$-9W + 36R_1'' - 40R_2'' = 0$$

the solution being

$$R_1'' = -0 \cdot 18578W$$
$$R_2'' = -0 \cdot 39220W.$$

The numerical work is given in Table 6.14.

TABLE 6.14.

Bar	A	L	P_0			$\dfrac{P_0 L}{A} \dfrac{\partial P_0}{\partial R_1''}$			$\dfrac{P_0 L}{A} \dfrac{\partial P_0}{\partial R_2''}$		
			W	R_1''	R_2''	W	R_1''	R_2''	W	R_1''	R_2''
CA	2	1		1			$\frac{1}{2}$				
DK	2	1			1						$\frac{1}{2}$
CD	4	1		1			$\frac{1}{4}$				
DE	4	1		-1	1		$\frac{1}{4}$	$-\frac{1}{4}$		$-\frac{1}{4}$	$\frac{1}{4}$
AK	4	1	$\frac{1}{2}$	1		$\frac{1}{8}$	$\frac{1}{4}$				
KJ	4	1	$\frac{1}{2}$	-1	1	$-\frac{1}{8}$	$\frac{1}{4}$	$-\frac{1}{4}$	$\frac{1}{8}$	$-\frac{1}{4}$	$\frac{1}{4}$
CK	$\sqrt{2}$	$\sqrt{2}$		$-\sqrt{2}$			2				
DA	$\sqrt{2}$	$\sqrt{2}$	$-\dfrac{1}{\sqrt{2}}$	$-\sqrt{2}$		1	2				
DJ	$\sqrt{2}$	$\sqrt{2}$	$-\dfrac{1}{\sqrt{2}}$	$\sqrt{2}$	$-\sqrt{2}$	-1	2	-2	1	-2	2
KE	$\sqrt{2}$	$\sqrt{2}$		$\sqrt{2}$	$-\sqrt{2}$		2	-2		-2	2

The redundant forces under the original loading are then

$$R_1 = R_1' + R_1'' = -(0 \cdot 41221 + 0 \cdot 18578)W = -0 \cdot 59799W$$
$$R_2 = R_2' + R_2'' = -(0 \cdot 37786 + 0 \cdot 39220)W = -0 \cdot 77006W$$
$$R_3 = R_2' - R_2'' = -(0 \cdot 37786 - 0 \cdot 39220)W = +0 \cdot 01434W$$
$$R_4 = R_1' - R_1'' = -(0 \cdot 41221 - 0 \cdot 18578)W = -0 \cdot 22643W.$$

These results agree exactly with those obtained from the straightforward solution, but the work involved is considerably less.

It should be noted that the calculations are only required for one-half of the truss under each of the two component systems. In the case of skew-symmetrical loading the centre-post JE is unstressed and presents no difficulty; in the symmetrical loading, however, it is necessary to take a

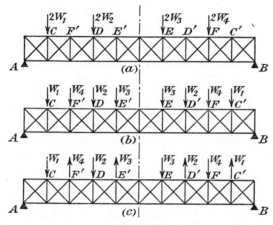

FIG. 6.18.

post of one-half the actual area carrying one-half the load when dealing with the half truss. This is indicated in Table 6.13 by the description $\frac{1}{2}$ (EJ) in the first column.

In this example the truss carried only a single concentrated load. There is, however, no difficulty in applying the same method to any load system. This is best illustrated by an example.

Suppose Fig. 6.18 (a) represents a structure carrying loads $2W_1$, $2W_2$, $2W_3$ and $2W_4$ at points C, D, E and F respectively. This system is to be replaced by symmetrical and skew-symmetrical systems which, when superposed, give the original system. Let C', D', E' and F' be the points corresponding to C, D, E and F on the other side of the centre-line of the truss.

Consider first the load $2W_1$. This is replaced by a pair of downward loads W_1 at C and C' as shown in Fig. 6.18 (b), and by downward and upward loads W_1 at C and C' respectively as shown in Fig. 6.18 (c). The other loads are dealt with similarly, and the two systems (b) and (c) result. The stress-analysis is then carried out as illustrated in the detailed example already given.

REFERENCES

Airship Stressing Panel, 1922. *Aer. Res. Cttee.*, R. & M. **800**, H.M.S.O.
Pippard, A. J. S., 1922. *Aer. Res. Cttee.* R. & M. **793**, H.M.S.O.
—— 1926. *Phil. Mag.* **1**, 254–7.
—— and Glanville, W. H., 1926. *Buil. Res. Tech. Pap.*, **2**, H.M.S.O.

Cross, H., 1930. *Proc. Amer. Soc. Civ. Engrs.*, **56**, 919–928.
Southwell, R. V., 1935. *Proc. Roy. Soc.* (A) **151**, 56–95.
Baker, J. F. and Ockleston, A. J., 1935. *Aer. Res. Cttee.*, R. & M. **1667**, H.M.S.O.
Livesley, R. K. and Charlton, T. M., 1954. *Trans. N.-E. Cst. Instn. Engrs. Shipb.* **71**, 67.

EXERCISES

(1) Three steel wires AB, CB, DB attached to points A, C and D on a rigid horizontal beam are connected at the point B which is 10 feet vertically below C.   The distances AC and CD are each 10 feet.

If AB, CB and DB are respectively 1 square inch, $\frac{1}{2}$ square inch and $1\frac{1}{2}$ square inches in cross-sectional area, calculate what load each carries when a weight of 5 tons is hung at B.

$$(AB=BD=+2\cdot22 \; tons \; ; \; BC=+1\cdot86 \; tons)$$

(2) Four equal wires OA, OB, OC and OD of length L and cross-sectional area A support a weight W midway between two walls AD and BC which are $\sqrt{2}L$ apart. The wires OD and OB are in the same straight line and at right angles to OA and OC. (See Diagram 6a.)

If the wires are initially tensioned to remain taut under load find the deflexion of O.

$$\left(\frac{WL}{2AE}\right)$$

(3) The rectangular space frame shown in Diagram 6b is pinned to a rigid wall at the corners A, B, C and D, and a couple of 1,000 inch-lb. is applied to the face EFHG, which is rigid in its own plane.

Each panel is braced and counterbraced with steel wires each of 1/100 square inch cross-sectional area.   These wires have no initial tension so that only one of each pair is operative.

All other members are of steel, having cross-sectional areas of 1/10 square inch.
Determine the loads in all the members.

$$(DE=BH=35\cdot2 \; lb.$$
$$AF=CG=43\cdot0 \; lb.$$
$$AE=CH=-28\cdot1 \; lb.$$
$$BF=GD=-38\cdot5 \; lb.)$$

(4) The pin-jointed structure shown in Diagram 6c is simply supported at L and J and carries suspended loads of 4 tons and 2 tons as shown.

The members are unstressed when the loads are removed and have the following areas :—

      EA=F'A=HA=1·06 inch²
      ED=EF=GH=1·78 inch²
      F'G=G'C=HB=FF'=2·09 inch².

Calculate the vertical deflexion under each of the applied loads.   (E=13,000 tons/square inch.)

$$(0\cdot093 \; inch \; ; \; 0\cdot071 \; inch)$$

(5) The steel beam AB shown at 6d is strengthened by a steel king post CD which is pinned to C, the centre point of the beam.   The point D is braced by steel rods to A and B which are simply supported.

Calculate the maximum central load which the beam can carry given the following data :—

    Beam :   I=250 inch units.
              Depth= 12 inches.
Strut CD : Cross-sectional area=4 square inches.
Rods AD, BD : Cross-sectional area=1 square inch.
Permissible flexural stress in beam=8 tons per square inch.

$$(36\cdot3 \; tons)$$

(6) The pin-jointed steel frame shown in Diagram 6e is attached at A, B and C to a rigid wall.

AD and CF are each $\sqrt{2}$ square inches and each diagonal is 1 square inch in area. DE and EF are rigid.   Calculate the loads in AD and CF when a load acts as shown.

$(AD = +2 \text{ tons} ;\; CF = -2 \text{ tons})$

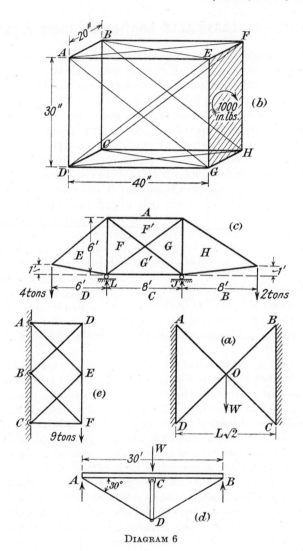

DIAGRAM 6

CHAPTER 7

STRUTS AND LATERALLY LOADED COLUMNS AND TIES

7.1. The behaviour of struts under load.—If a rod of perfectly uniform shape, perfectly straight and of homogeneous material throughout were loaded axially so that the point of application of the load coincided with the neutral axis of the rod, failure would occur by direct compression. In practice such an ideal set of conditions cannot occur. Small errors in workmanship, slight variations in the material and the practical impossibility of obtaining perfect test conditions all combine to give what is equivalent to an eccentricity of loading. This equivalent eccentricity, although small, exercises considerable influence upon the behaviour of the strut, and since it cannot in any individual case be measured, the problem of strut strength must of necessity be settled by the help of experimental data.

Before proceeding to a discussion of formulas suitable for design purposes it is necessary to consider further the behaviour of the ideal strut described above and this will depend upon the proportions of the strut, or the " slenderness ratio " ; this is the ratio of the length of the strut to the minimum radius of gyration (l/k) and appears in all rational strut formulas. The usual terms long and short struts are misleading, since absolute length has no bearing upon the behaviour of the member : a slender strut may be of any length and the important factor is the slenderness ratio. Struts will therefore be referred to as slender when the ratio l/k is large and stocky when it is small.

Suppose that a stocky strut is subjected to an axial load. The axial strain will be elastic up to a certain value of the end stress, but when this stress reaches the yield point there will be a comparatively large permanent set and the strut will have failed. If the material is ductile a further increase of stress will cause flattening of the strut, but if it is brittle there will be an actual partition of the material along planes approximately at 45° to the direction of the load, due to the shear stresses induced along such planes.

If, on the other hand, a slender strut is subjected to an axial load the behaviour is different. Under small loads the strut is in stable equilibrium and if it is displaced by a small amount it will straighten when the disturbing force is removed. For a certain value of the axial force the strut is in a state of neutral equilibrium and will remain deflected after the removal of a disturbing force. A further increase in the axial load produces a state of unstable equilibrium and any disturbing force will start a deflexion in the strut which will increase in amount until the material is overstressed due to the increasing curvature of the member. If the axial force is removed before the fibre stress has reached the limit of proportionality, the strut will become perfectly straight again and show no signs of distress. The axial load which induces this condition of elastic instability is known as the critical load, the buckling load or the Euler load, since Euler first investigated the problem. It should be noticed that in the absence of an external disturbing force all perfect struts, whether slender or stocky, will fail by direct compression.

7.2. The critical load for slender struts.—In Fig. 7.1 let AB be a slender strut of length l, of uniform cross-section and of homogeneous material. It is pin-jointed at A and B and carries an axial load P which just produces a state of neutral stability. The strut under this load is deflected a small amount a at the centre and the deflecting force is then removed. Since the strut is neutrally stable it remains deflected.

Take an origin at the centre of the deflected strut and measure x and y as shown in the figure. Then at any point

$$\frac{d^2y}{dx^2} = \frac{P}{EI}(a-y)$$

or writing $\mu^2 = \dfrac{P}{EI}$, $\dfrac{d^2y}{dx^2} + \mu^2(y-a) = 0$.

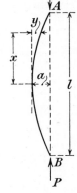

The solution of this equation is

$$y = A \sin \mu x + B \cos \mu x + a$$

where A and B are constants of integration.

When $x=0$, $y=0$ so that $B=-a$.

When $x=0$, $\dfrac{dy}{dx}=0$ and on differentiating we obtain

Fig. 7.1.

$$\frac{dy}{dx} = \mu(A \cos \mu x - B \sin \mu x),$$

from which A=0.

Then
$$y = a(1 - \cos \mu x).$$

When $x=\dfrac{l}{2}$, $y=a$ and substitution in the above equation gives

$$a \cos\frac{\mu l}{2} = 0.$$

Since by our hypothesis a cannot be zero, the solution required is

$$\cos\frac{\mu l}{2} = 0.$$

The smallest value of $\mu l/2$ which satisfies this condition is $\pi/2$ and so the critical load is defined by the condition

$$\frac{\mu l}{2} = \frac{\pi}{2}$$

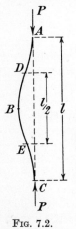

i.e.
$$\frac{Pl^2}{EI} = \pi^2$$

or
$$P = \frac{\pi^2 EI}{l^2} \qquad . \quad . \quad . \quad . \quad . \quad . \quad (7.1)$$

If instead of being pin-jointed the strut is encastré at both ends (Fig. 7.2), the slopes at the ends and at the middle are zero, and it is clear that there are inflexions at the quarter points of the strut, D and E. The portion DE can therefore be treated as a pin-jointed strut of length $l/2$, and so for this method of fixing the critical load of AC is

$$P = \frac{\pi^2 EI}{\left(\dfrac{l}{2}\right)^2} = \frac{4\pi^2 EI}{l^2}.$$

Fig. 7.2.

This result as well as those for other cases may be obtained directly by the same mathematical procedure used for the pin-jointed strut.

Critical loads for struts with different end conditions are given in Table 7.1. The encastré-free condition means that one end is not constrained in any way, *i.e.* the strut is a mast carrying an axial load. The results for the pin-encastré conditions are only approximate, but are sufficiently accurate for any practical purpose.

TABLE 7.1.

CRITICAL LOADS FOR STRUTS OF LENGTH l.

End conditions		Critical load	Equivalent length
1	2		
Pin	Pin	$\dfrac{\pi^2 EI}{l^2}$	l
Encastré	Encastré	$\dfrac{4\pi^2 EI}{l^2}$	$\dfrac{l}{2}$
Encastré	Free	$\dfrac{\pi^2 EI}{4l^2}$	$2l$
Pin	Encastré	$\dfrac{81EI}{4l^2}$	$0 \cdot 7l$

7.3. Eccentrically loaded strut.—Suppose now that a pin-jointed strut carries a load at a specified distance from the neutral axis. For any value of this load the strut assumes a definite shape and the stresses in it can be calculated. We make no assumption as to slenderness but treat the problem generally and the result is applicable to members of any slenderness ratio. It will be shown, however, that when the strut is stocky the result can be simplified.

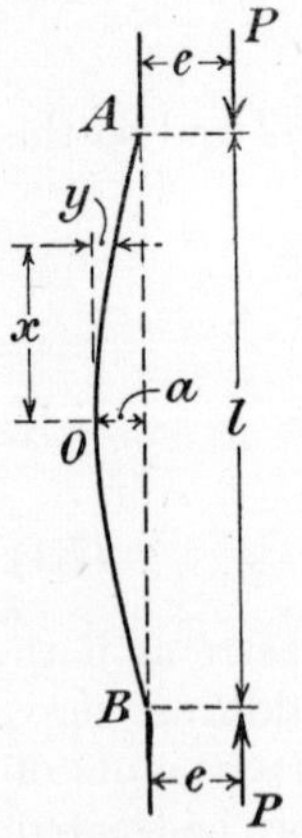

In Fig. 7.3, AB is a pin-jointed strut of length l having a load P acting at a distance e from the neutral axis.

Any value of P will produce a deflexion of the strut, owing to the bending moment which was absent under an axial load.

With the same notation as in paragraph 7.2, we have

$$\frac{d^2y}{dx^2}=\mu^2(a+e-y)$$

or

$$\frac{d^2y}{dx^2}+\mu^2(y-a-e)=0.$$

The solution of this is

$$y=(a+e)(1-\cos \mu x)$$

obtained in the same way as for the axially loaded strut.

Since $y=a$ when $x=\dfrac{l}{2}$, we have on substitution

$$a=e\left(\sec\frac{\mu l}{2}-1 \right).$$

FIG. 7.3.

The maximum bending moment in the strut, at the centre, is

$$M_0=P(a+e)=Pe \sec\frac{l}{2}\sqrt{\frac{P}{EI}}. \qquad \qquad (7.2)$$

If $I=Ak^2$ is the minimum second moment of area and h is the corresponding distance of the compressive fibre farthest from the neutral axis of the section, the maximum compressive stress in the strut is

$$p_f=\frac{P}{A}\left(1+\frac{eh}{k^2}\sec\frac{l}{2}\sqrt{\frac{P}{EI}}\right), \quad \cdots \quad (7.3)$$

where k is the minimum radius of gyration and A is the area of the cross-section.

This formula is not convenient for design purposes since P occurs in the secant term and cannot be evaluated readily. The solution necessitates either a process of trial and error or a graphical method.

7.4. Stocky struts.—In the formula of the preceding paragraph the secant term can be written as $\sec\dfrac{l}{2k}\sqrt{\dfrac{P}{AE}}$ which for small values of l/k approaches unity.

Hence for stocky columns the maximum compressive stress is

$$p_f=\frac{P}{A}\left(1+\frac{eh}{k^2}\right) \quad \cdots \quad (7.4)$$

and the maximum load which can be applied to a stocky column without permanent deformation is

$$P=\frac{p_yA}{\left(1+\dfrac{eh}{k^2}\right)}, \quad \cdots \quad (7.5)$$

where p_y is the yield stress in compression.

7.5. General strut formulas.—From the preceding work it is clear that neither the very slender nor the very stocky strut presents serious difficulty, but with few exceptions struts which are used in practice do not fall into either of these categories. They are intermediate and the real problem is to find a formula which will be sufficiently accurate to serve as a design basis for struts of any slenderness ratio.

Many such formulas for the axial load which a strut can carry have been used in the past, one of the best-known being that due to Rankine:

$$P=\frac{p_yA}{1+a(l/k)^2}. \quad \cdots \quad (7.6)$$

This is an empirical formula and the constant a should be determined experimentally. Its value for different materials is given in most books of engineering data.

If l/k is small the value of P approaches p_yA as it should and by a suitable adjustment of a, P can be made to approach the Euler value as l/k approaches infinity.

Rewriting (7.6)
$$a=\frac{p_yAk^2}{Pl^2}-\frac{k^2}{l^2},$$

and as k/l approaches zero P should approach π^2EI/l^2

i.e.
$$a=\frac{p_y}{\pi^2E}.$$

This value generally differs somewhat from the experimental one but in the absence of the more reliable figure it can be used as an approximation.

5

The Rankine formula can be written

$$p=\frac{p_y}{1+a(l/k)^2},$$

where p is the load per unit area on the end section of the strut.

It has already been shown in paragraph 7.4 that when a strut which is not slender is eccentrically loaded the ratio

$$\frac{p}{p_y}=\frac{1}{\left(1+\frac{eh}{k^2}\right)},$$

i.e. the allowable end loading is reduced by this amount due to eccentricity. If then a strut to which the Rankine formula is applied has an eccentricity of loading, an approximation to the allowable load is

$$P=\frac{p_y A}{\{1+a(l/k)^2\}\left(1+\frac{eh}{k^2}\right)}.$$

The Rankine formula is now only of historical interest and has been superseded by more rational formulas for which the essential empirical constants have been more accurately determined.

The Rankine formula makes no direct allowance for the eccentricity of loading due to slight imperfections in workmanship and material which have previously been mentioned although these would be dealt with to some extent by the empirical constant a. Later investigators however introduced such factors into their formulas and two methods have been adopted with success. In the first method the sum of all the departures from perfection is treated as an equivalent eccentricity of loading and appears in the formula as such.

The second method is to treat the sum of the imperfections as being equivalent to an initial curvature of the strut and this leads to a very useful strut formula of general applicability.

7.6. Modified Smith formula for pin-jointed struts.—If in equation (7.3) the specified eccentricity is replaced by an equivalent eccentricity to be found experimentally, a formula is obtained which is applicable to normally straight axially loaded members. This is the treatment of the problem adopted by R. H. Smith and his formula was modified by R. V. Southwell by the substitution of the yield stress, or more accurately the stress at the limit of proportionality, for the ultimate stress suggested by Smith.

The equation can be put in the form

$$p_y=p\left(1+\frac{eh}{k^2}\sec\frac{l}{2}\sqrt{\frac{p}{Ek^2}}\right),$$

from which we obtain the modified Smith formula (Jenkin, 1920)

$$P=pA=\frac{p_y A}{1+\frac{h\delta}{k^2}\sec\frac{l}{2}\sqrt{\frac{p}{Ek^2}}}, \qquad \ldots \quad \ldots \quad (7.7)$$

where P=The limiting load.

  p=The limiting average intensity of loading on the cross-section of the strut.

  A=The area of the cross-section of the strut.

  p_y=The yield point of the material.

h=The greatest distance of any point on the section from the centre line.

δ=The equivalent eccentricity of loading.

k=The minimum radius of gyration of the cross-section.

E=Young's modulus of the material.

l=Length of the strut.

This formula cannot be used directly because p appears on both sides but curves may be constructed and the results read from them.

7.7. Perry strut formula.—A formula due to Professor Perry is based on the assumption that the effect of imperfections in material and workmanship, unavoidable eccentricity of loading, etc., can be represented by a hypothetical initial curvature of the strut. The exact initial shape which is assumed for the strut does not greatly affect the final results and for ease of manipulation a cosine curve was used, as this leads to simple equations.

Let AB (Fig. 7.4) be a pin-jointed strut of length l. Take an origin at O and measure x and y as shown. The initial shape of the strut is assumed to be given by the equation

$$y_0 = c_o \cos \frac{\pi x}{l},$$

where c_o is the initial departure from straightness at the centre.

Under a load P the deflexion at x is increased by y so that

$$EI\frac{d^2y}{dx^2} = -P\left(y + c_o \cos \frac{\pi x}{l}\right),$$

i.e.

$$\frac{d^2y}{dx^2} + \mu^2\left(y + c_o \cos \frac{\pi x}{l}\right) = 0,$$

where, as before,

$$\mu^2 = \frac{P}{EI}.$$

The solution of this equation is

$$y = A \sin \mu x + B \cos \mu x + \frac{\mu^2 c_o \cos \frac{\pi x}{l}}{\frac{\pi^2}{l^2} - \mu^2},$$

where A and B are constants of integration.

When

$$x = \pm\frac{l}{2}, \quad y = 0 \quad \text{and so} \quad A = B = 0,$$

hence

$$y = \frac{Pc_o \cos \frac{\pi x}{l}}{Q - P},$$

where

$$Q = \frac{\pi^2 EI}{l^2}.$$

If A is the cross-sectional area of the strut,

put

$$\frac{P}{A} = p \quad \text{and} \quad \frac{Q}{A} = p_e.$$

Then

$$y = \frac{p}{p_e - p} c_o \cos \frac{\pi x}{l}$$

and the total deflexion at any point is

$$y+y_0=\left(\frac{p}{p_e-p}+1\right)c_0\cos\frac{\pi x}{l}$$

$$=\frac{p_e}{p_e-p}c_0\cos\frac{\pi x}{l}.$$

The maximum deflexion occurs at the centre where $x=0$ and its value is

$$y_{\max}=\frac{p_ec_0}{p_e-p},\qquad\qquad\qquad(7.8)$$

while the maximum bending moment is

$$M_{\max}=Pc_0\left(\frac{p_e}{p_e-p}\right).$$

The maximum compressive stress occurs on the concave side of the strut and is

$$p_1=\frac{Pc_0\left(\dfrac{p_e}{p_e-p}\right)a_1}{I}+\frac{P}{A},$$

where a_1 is the distance of the most stressed compressive fibre from the neutral axis.

If we put $\dfrac{c_0a_1}{k^2}=\eta$ we obtain

$$p_1=p\left(\frac{\eta p_e}{p_e-p}+1\right).\qquad\qquad(7.9)$$

Putting $p_1=p_y$, the yield stress in compression, and solving for p we find

$$p=\frac{p_y+(\eta+1)p_e}{2}-\sqrt{\left\{\frac{p_y+(\eta+1)p_e}{2}\right\}^2-p_yp_e},\qquad(7.10)$$

which is the Perry formula for the intensity of end loading which will cause the fibre stress to reach the yield point.

In a brittle material failure may occur on the tension side of the strut and following the same procedure we obtain

$$p'=\frac{(1-\eta')p_e-p_y'}{2}+\sqrt{\left\{\frac{(1-\eta')p_e-p_y'}{2}\right\}^2+p_y'p_e},\qquad(7.11)$$

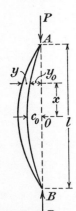

FIG. 7.4

where p' is the intensity of end loading which will cause the fibre stress to reach p_y' the ultimate stress in tension and $\eta'=\dfrac{c_0a_2}{k^2}$, where a_2 is the distance of the most stressed tension fibre from the neutral axis.

This formula, with others, was subjected to a critical examination by Andrew Robertson (1925), who made an exhaustive series of carefully controlled tests upon struts of various materials. As a result of these and tests made by other experimenters, he stated his conclusion that for all materials having a real yield the Perry formula gives good results for pin ended struts if η is taken as $\cdot001$ l/k for an average value, and $\cdot003$ l/k for a lower limit. For materials with considerable ductility but no real yield phenomena, as defined by a drop of stress, the value of p_y should be taken at the point in the stress-strain diagram where the slope is three times that in the elastic region. η is then the same as for materials with a real yield.

For materials having no yield it appears reasonable to take the ultimate stress in compression as the value of p_y and η as $\cdot015\ l/k$.   For cast iron struts this curve is slightly below the one representing tensile failure.   If the strut has end conditions other than free the values of η require modification and Robertson makes the necessary corrections by working on an equivalent length of strut given in Table 7.2.

TABLE 7.2.

End conditions	Equivalent length	η	
		Ductile	Brittle
Free	l	$\cdot003\dfrac{l}{k}$	$\cdot015\dfrac{l}{k}$
Flat	$\cdot5l$	$\cdot006\times\dfrac{\cdot5l}{k}$	$\cdot03\times\dfrac{\cdot5l}{k}$
Fixed	$\cdot5l$	$\cdot006\times\dfrac{\cdot5l}{k}$	$\cdot03\times\dfrac{\cdot5l}{k}$

It will be noticed that the numerical values of η are the same for flat and fixed ends as for free ends.   The correction on the results is introduced by the fact that the Euler crippling stress p_e is calculated for a strut of only half the length, $i.e.$ it is four times the value of the pin-ended strut.

If a strut has a real eccentricity of loading, e_o, it may be allowed for as suggested by Ayrton and Perry (1886) by replacing the term c_o, $i.e.$ the initial departure from the straight, by a term $c_1 = c_o + \tfrac{6}{5}e_o$.

Let the constant for this case be

$$\eta_1 = \frac{a_1 c_1}{k^2}.$$

Then

$$\eta_1 = \eta + \frac{6a_1 e_o}{5k^2},$$

where η is the value for the strut when there is no deliberate eccentricity of loading.

The simplest way of using the Perry formula is by a curve of p against l/k from which the maximum load for the member can be read directly.

A load factor can be incorporated by writing Np instead of p as recommended by the Steel Structures Research Committee (1931).

The formula is then

$$Np = \frac{p_y + (\eta+1)p_e}{2} - \sqrt{\left\{\frac{p_y + (\eta+1)p_e}{2}\right\}^2 - p_y p_e} \quad . \quad . \quad (7.12)$$

The Steel Structures Research Committee suggested that the following values should be used for struts of Quality A steel (British Standard Specification No. 15) :

Yield stress $=18$ tons per square inch.
Young's modulus $=13,000$ tons per square inch.
N$=2\cdot36$.
$\eta=0\cdot003\ l/k$.

Table 7.3, taken from the Report of the Committee and later included in the original British Standard Specification No. 449 (1932), gives the resulting values of p, the permissible end load in tons per square inch of cross-sectional area, for different values of l/k.

TABLE 7.3.

l/k	p	l/k	p
20	7·2	130	2·6
30	6·9	140	2·3
40	6·6	150	2·0
50	6·3	160	1·8
60	5·9	170	1·6
70	5·4	180	1·5
80	4·9	190	1·3
90	4·3	200	1·2
100	3·8	210	1·1
110	3·3	220	1·0
120	2·9	230	0·9
		240	0·9

The curve plotted from this table is shown in Fig. 7.5.

The revision of the specification B.S. 449 (1948) used the formula to calculate the permissible end load per unit area, p, for struts with a slenderness ratio in excess of 80 but with the load factor N reduced to 2·0 and the

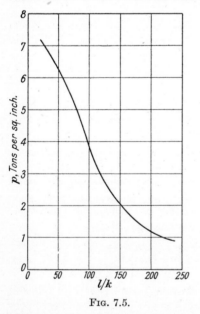

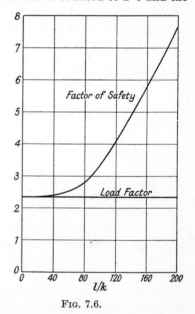

FIG. 7.5.   FIG. 7.6.

yield stress p_y, to 15·25 tons per square inch.   For values of the slenderness ratio less than 80, p was obtained by linear interpolation between its value for $l/k=80$, and 9 tons per square inch for $l/k=0$.

In Chapter 1 two methods of strength specification, by means of a load factor and a factor of safety respectively, were briefly mentioned and the

Perry formula serves as a useful illustration of the fundamental difference between them.

Since Np is the intensity of end loading which will cause the maximum fibre stress to reach the yield stress p_y, N is a load factor.

Substituting the recommended value of $\eta = \cdot 003 \, l/k$ in (7.9) we obtain

$$p_1 = p \left\{ 1 + \frac{\cdot 003 \, l/k}{1 - \frac{p}{\pi^2 E}\left(\frac{l}{k}\right)^2} \right\}.$$

Table 7.3 gives values of p for different values of l/k and on substituting these values in this formula the working fibre stress in the material is obtained.

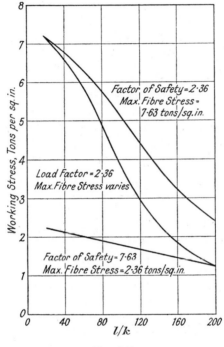

Fig. 7.7.

The factor of safety is p_y/p_1 and Fig. 7.6 shows its relation to l/k ; with a constant load factor the factor of safety varies greatly and the result emphasises in a striking manner the difference between the two methods of specifying strength in this instance.

If the design of struts were based on a constant factor of safety instead of a constant load factor very different design curves would be used. Fig. 7.7 shows the strut curve from Table 7.3 with a constant load factor of 2·36 and curves plotted from the same formula when the factor of safety is kept constant. Two such curves are given, the factors of safety being those in struts designed as at present with slenderness ratios of 20 and 200 respectively.

7.8. Members with combined loads.—Any member will deflect under lateral load by an amount depending upon the magnitude of the load and the flexural rigidity of the member. If in addition an axial thrust P is applied to the member the bending moment due to this axial load will increase the deflexion. If the flexural rigidity is large in relation to the loads, it is often sufficiently accurate to determine the deflexion Δ due to the lateral load and to add to the bending moment produced by this load a term $P\Delta$, thus neglecting the effect of the additional deflexion due to the axial load. The stress is then found from the total bending moment in the usual way.

If, however, the members are flexible, determination of the stress in this way might result in serious error and more accurate treatment is necessary as described in succeeding paragraphs.

7.9. The pin-jointed strut with a uniform lateral load.—Let AB in Fig. 7.8 be a pin-jointed member carrying an axial load P and a uniformly distributed

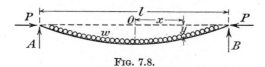

FIG. 7.8.

lateral load of intensity w. Take an origin at O, the centre of the undeflected strut and measure x and y as shown in the figure.

Then
$$M = EI\frac{d^2y}{dx^2} = -Py - \frac{w}{2}\left(\frac{l^2}{4} - x^2\right),$$

or
$$M + Py = \frac{w}{2}\left(x^2 - \frac{l^2}{4}\right).$$

Hence
$$\frac{d^2M}{dx^2} + P\frac{d^2y}{dx^2} = w,$$

or
$$\frac{d^2M}{dx^2} + \mu^2 M = w.$$

The solution is
$$M = A \sin \mu x + B \cos \mu x + \frac{w}{\mu^2}.$$

When $x = \pm\frac{l}{2}$, $M = 0$,

therefore
$$A \sin \frac{\mu l}{2} + B \cos \frac{\mu l}{2} + \frac{w}{\mu^2} = 0$$

and
$$-A \sin \frac{\mu l}{2} + B \cos \frac{\mu l}{2} + \frac{w}{\mu^2} = 0.$$

From these equations $A = 0$; $B = -\frac{w}{\mu^2} \sec \frac{\mu l}{2}$

and so
$$M = \frac{w}{\mu^2}\left(1 - \cos \mu x \sec \frac{\mu l}{2}\right).$$

The maximum value of the bending moment occurs when $x = 0$ and is

$$M_{max} = \frac{w}{\mu^2}\left(1 - \sec \frac{\mu l}{2}\right). \qquad . \quad . \quad . \quad . \quad (7.13)$$

Substituting for μ^2 and putting $\dfrac{\pi^2 EI}{l^2} = Q$, the Euler critical load, this gives

$$M_{max} = \frac{8M_0'}{\pi^2}\frac{Q}{P}\left(1 - \sec\frac{\pi}{2}\sqrt{\frac{P}{Q}}\right) \qquad \cdots \qquad (7.14)$$

where M_0' is the bending moment at the centre due to the lateral load only, i.e. $wl^2/8$.

The maximum compressive stress, at the centre of the member, is then

$$p_f = \frac{8p_b p_e}{\pi^2 p}\left(1 - \sec\frac{\pi}{2}\sqrt{\frac{p}{p_e}}\right) - p \qquad \cdots \qquad (7.15)$$

where p_b, p_e and p represent the bending stress due to lateral load alone, the Euler stress and the intensity of end loading respectively.

A problem which may arise is that of calculating the load factor of a member of this type when the normal working loads are known. For example, suppose these to be a distributed load of intensity w and an axial load P. It is required to know by what factor these loads must be increased so as to stress the material to its allowable limit.

If we call this load factor N, then p_b and p will be increased to Np_b and Np; p_f will be the yield stress p_y, and p_e which is only dependent on the size and material of the member will remain unaltered.

Equation (7.15) then becomes

$$p_y = \frac{8p_b p_e}{\pi^2 p}\left(1 - \sec\frac{\pi}{2}\sqrt{\frac{Np}{p_e}}\right) - Np \qquad \cdots \qquad (7.16)$$

which can only be solved for N by a process of trial and error and is very inconvenient. A simpler, approximate formula due to Perry, which will be derived in a later paragraph, provides a much easier solution.

If we put $\theta = \dfrac{\pi}{2}\sqrt{\dfrac{P}{Q}}$ and expand, the maximum bending moment (7.14) can be written as the series

$$M_{max} = -\frac{8M_0'}{\pi^2}\frac{Q}{P}\left(\frac{\theta^2}{\underline{2}} + \frac{5\theta^4}{\underline{4}} + \frac{61\theta^6}{\underline{6}} + \cdots\right),$$

or

$$M_{max} = -\frac{8M_0'}{\pi^2}\frac{Q}{P}\left(\frac{\pi^2 P}{8Q} + \frac{5\pi^4}{384}\frac{P^2}{Q^2} + \cdots\right),$$

i.e.

$$M_{max} = -\left(M_0' + \frac{5}{384}\frac{wl^4 P}{EI} + \cdots\right).$$

The first term in this series is the bending moment due to lateral load alone and the second is the deflexion at the centre due to the lateral load multiplied by P. It will be seen therefore that the method indicated in paragraph 7.8, which is often used for stiff members, consists of taking two terms of an infinite series. If P is small compared with Q the third term is very small and can be justifiably neglected, but this is not always so, the factored load NP often being a big fraction of Q.

7.10. Pin-jointed strut with a concentrated lateral load.—Let AB be a pin-jointed strut under an end load P and a concentrated lateral load W.

Let the dimensions be as in Fig. 7.9.

If the origin be taken at A we have for any point from $x=0$ to $x=a$

$$\mathrm{EI}\frac{d^2y}{dx^2}+\mathrm{P}y=-\left(\frac{b}{a+b}\right)x\mathrm{W}.$$

The solution is

$$y=\mathrm{A}_1 \sin \mu x+\mathrm{B}_1 \cos \mu x-\frac{\mathrm{W}}{\mathrm{P}}\left(\frac{b}{a+b}\right)x,$$

where

$$\mu^2=\frac{\mathrm{P}}{\mathrm{EI}}.$$

Since $y=0$ when $x=0$, $\mathrm{B}_1=0$.

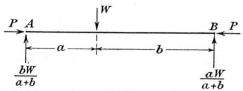

FIG. 7.9.

At $x=a$ we have

$$y_\mathrm{W}=\mathrm{A}_1 \sin \mu a-\frac{\mathrm{W}}{\mathrm{P}}\frac{ab}{a+b}.$$

By taking the origin at B we have when $x=b$, a similar expression for y_W with a and b interchanged

therefore $\mathrm{A}_1 \sin \mu a-\dfrac{\mathrm{W}}{\mathrm{P}}\dfrac{b}{a+b}a=\mathrm{A}_2 \sin \mu b-\dfrac{\mathrm{W}}{\mathrm{P}}\dfrac{a}{a+b}b.$

The two values of $\dfrac{dy}{dx}$ similarly derived are equal and opposite since W is approached from opposite sides and so

$$\mu \mathrm{A}_1 \cos \mu a-\frac{\mathrm{W}}{\mathrm{P}}\frac{b}{a+b}=-\left\{\mu \mathrm{A}_2 \cos \mu b-\frac{\mathrm{W}}{\mathrm{P}}\frac{a}{a+b}\right\}.$$

From these equations

$$\frac{\mathrm{A}_1}{\sin \mu b}=\frac{\mathrm{A}_2}{\sin \mu a}=\frac{\mathrm{W}/\mathrm{P}}{\mu \sin \mu(a+b)};$$

from $x=0$ to $x=a$

$$y=\frac{\mathrm{W}}{\mathrm{P}}\frac{\sin \mu b}{\mu \sin \mu(a+b)} \sin \mu x-\frac{\mathrm{W}}{\mathrm{P}}\left(\frac{b}{a+b}\right)x,$$

$$\frac{d^2y}{dx^2}=-\mu^2\frac{\mathrm{W}}{\mathrm{P}}\frac{\sin \mu b}{\mu \sin \mu(a+b)} \sin \mu x$$

and $\mathrm{M}=\mathrm{EI}\dfrac{d^2y}{dx^2}=-\dfrac{\mathrm{W}\sin \mu b}{\mu \sin \mu(a+b)} \sin \mu x.$

At $x=a$ $\mathrm{M}=-\dfrac{\mathrm{W}\sin \mu a \sin \mu b}{\mu \sin \mu(a+b)}.$

In particular when the load is placed at the centre of the member this becomes

$$\mathrm{M}_\mathrm{max}=-\frac{\mathrm{W}}{2\mu} \tan \frac{\mu l}{2}$$

since $a=b=\dfrac{l}{2}$.

Substituting for μ this gives

$$M_{max}=-\frac{W}{2}\sqrt{\frac{EI}{P}}\tan\frac{l}{2}\sqrt{\frac{P}{EI}}. \qquad \qquad (7.17)$$

As before, putting M_0' for the bending moment due to the lateral load alone, *i.e.* $Wl/4$, and Q for the Euler crippling load of the member, the equation can be written

$$M_{max}=-\frac{2M_0'}{\pi}\sqrt{\frac{Q}{P}}\tan\frac{\pi}{2}\sqrt{\frac{P}{Q}}, \qquad \qquad (7.18)$$

or

$$p_f=-\left(\frac{2p_b}{\pi}\sqrt{\frac{p_e}{p}}\tan\frac{\pi}{2}\sqrt{\frac{p}{p_e}}+p\right). \qquad (7.19)$$

the negative sign denoting compression.

7.11. Strut with end couples.—In Fig. 7.10 AB is a pin-jointed strut with terminal couples $-M_A$ and $-M_B$ as shown. Taking the origin at A we have

$$M=-\left\{M_A+\frac{x}{L}(M_B-M_A)+Py\right\}$$

or

$$\frac{d^2M}{dx^2}+\mu^2M=0.$$

The solution of this is

$$M=A\sin\mu x+B\cos\mu x.$$

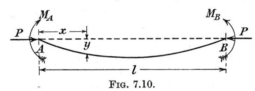

FIG. 7.10.

When $x=0$ and l, M is $-M_A$ and $-M_B$ respectively. Substituting these values we obtain

$$A=M_A\cot\mu l-M_B\operatorname{cosec}\mu l,$$
$$B=-M_A.$$

For the maximum bending moment $\dfrac{dM}{dx}=0,$

i.e.

$$\tan\mu x_0=\frac{A}{B}=\frac{M_B\operatorname{cosec}\mu l-M_A\cot\mu l}{M_A}, \qquad (7.20)$$

where x_0 is the position of the maximum bending moment.

Then
$$M_{max}=(M_A\cot\mu l-M_B\operatorname{cosec}\mu l)\sin\mu x_0-M_A\cos\mu x_0$$
i.e.
$$M_{max}=-M_A(\tan\mu x_0\sin\mu x_0+\cos\mu x_0)$$
$$=-M_A\sec\mu x_0.$$

Now
$$\sec^2\mu x_0=1+\tan^2\mu x_0=1+\left(\frac{M_B\operatorname{cosec}\mu l-M_A\cot\mu l}{M_A}\right)^2,$$

from which

$$M_{max}=-M_A\sec\mu x_0=-\sqrt{(M_A^2+M_B^2)\operatorname{cosec}^2\mu l-2M_AM_B\operatorname{cosec}\mu l\cot\mu l}.$$

When $M_A=M_B=M_0$ this becomes

$$M_{max}=-M_0\sec\frac{\mu l}{2}. \qquad \qquad (7.21)$$

7.12. Pin-jointed strut with two lateral loads.—In testing beams it is often convenient to adopt the four-point system shown in Fig. 7.11 for the application of lateral loads.

The member AB is a pin-jointed bar of length $2l$ subjected to an axial load P and having two lateral loads, each of magnitude W, symmetrically applied about the centre of AB and separated by a distance $2kl$.

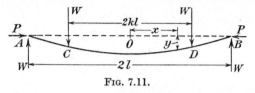

FIG. 7.11.

Taking an origin at the centre of the undeflected bar and measuring x and y as shown, we have :—

For the central part of the bar between O and D,

$$EI\frac{d^2y}{dx^2}+Py=-Wl(1-k)$$

or

$$\frac{d^2y}{dx^2}+\mu^2y=-\frac{Wl(1-k)}{EI}.$$

The solution of this is

$$y=A \sin \mu x+B \cos \mu x-\frac{Wl(1-k)}{P}$$

and so

$$\frac{dy}{dx}=\mu(A \cos \mu x-B \sin \mu x).$$

When

$$x=0, \frac{dy}{dx}=0 \text{ and so } A=0 ;$$

then

$$M=EI\frac{d^2y}{dx^2}=-EI\mu^2B \cos \mu x=-PB \cos \mu x.$$

Between D and B

$$EI\frac{d^2y}{dx^2}+Py=-W(l-x),$$

or

$$\frac{d^3y}{dx^3}+\mu^2\frac{dy}{dx}=\frac{W}{EI}.$$

The solution of this is

$$\frac{dy}{dx}=C \sin \mu x+D \cos \mu x+\frac{W}{P},$$

or

$$M=EI\frac{d^2y}{dx^2}=\mu EI(C \cos \mu x-D \sin \mu x).$$

When $x=l,$ $M=0$ and so $C=D \tan \mu l.$

Since the slope at D is continuous we have, from the slope equation above

$$-\mu B \sin \mu kl=D(\tan \mu l \sin \mu kl+\cos \mu kl)+\frac{W}{P}$$

or

$$-\mu B=D(\tan \mu l+\cot \mu kl)+\frac{W}{P} \text{cosec } \mu kl.$$

Again, the bending moments at D are the same, hence from the two bending moment equations

$$-\mu B \cos \mu kl = D(\tan \mu l \cos \mu kl - \sin \mu kl),$$

i.e.

$$-\mu B = D(\tan \mu l - \tan \mu kl)$$

and so

$$D = -\frac{W}{P} \cos \mu kl.$$

The maximum bending moment, which occurs at O, is $-\mu^2 EIB$,

i.e.

$$M_{max} = \frac{W}{\mu}\left[\tan \frac{\pi}{2}\sqrt{\frac{P}{Q}} - \tan \frac{k\pi}{2}\sqrt{\frac{P}{Q}} \right] \cos \frac{k\pi}{2}\sqrt{\frac{P}{Q}}. \quad . \quad . \quad . \quad (7.22)$$

Since the bending moment at the centre due to lateral loads alone is

$$M_0' = -Wl(1-k),$$

we have

$$M_{max} = \frac{-M_0'}{(1-k)\frac{\pi}{2}\sqrt{\frac{P}{Q}}}\left[\tan \frac{\pi}{2}\sqrt{\frac{P}{Q}} - \tan \frac{k\pi}{2}\sqrt{\frac{P}{Q}} \right] \cos \frac{k\pi}{2}\sqrt{\frac{P}{Q}}. \quad . \quad . \quad (7.23)$$

7.13. Encastré strut with a uniform lateral load.—When the ends of the member are completely restrained in direction we have, with the same notation as in paragraph 7.9 and Fig. 7.8,

$$M + Py = \frac{w}{2}\left(x^2 - \frac{l^2}{4} \right) + M_A,$$

where M_A is the fixing moment at the ends,

so

$$\frac{d^2M}{dx^2} + \mu^2 M = w,$$

the solution of which is

$$M = A \sin \mu x + B \cos \mu x + \frac{w}{\mu^2}.$$

When

$$x = \pm \frac{l}{2}, \quad M = M_A$$

and these conditions give

$$A = 0 \quad \text{and} \quad B = \left(M_A - \frac{w}{\mu^2} \right) \sec \frac{\mu l}{2};$$

therefore

$$M = \left(M_A - \frac{w}{\mu^2} \right) \sec \frac{\mu l}{2} \cos \mu x + \frac{w}{\mu^2}.$$

The shearing force at any point is

$$\frac{dM}{dx} = -\mu \left(M_A - \frac{w}{\mu^2} \right) \sec \frac{\mu l}{2} \sin \mu x,$$

which is $\frac{wl}{2}$ when $x = \frac{l}{2}$.

Hence

$$M_A = \frac{w}{\mu^2} - \frac{wl}{2\mu} \cot \frac{\mu l}{2}. \quad . \quad . \quad . \quad . \quad . \quad (7.24)$$

At the centre the maximum bending moment is

$$M_{max} = B + \frac{w}{\mu^2}$$

$$= \frac{wEI}{P} - \frac{wl}{2\mu} \operatorname{cosec} \frac{\mu l}{2}, \quad . \quad . \quad . \quad . \quad (7.25)$$

which can be written

$$M_{max}=M_0'\left\{\frac{24}{\pi^2}\frac{Q}{P}-\frac{12}{\pi}\sqrt{\frac{Q}{P}}\operatorname{cosec}\frac{\pi}{2}\sqrt{\frac{P}{Q}}\right\}. \quad . \quad . \quad . \quad (7.26)$$

7.14. Encastré strut with a central lateral load.—With the notation of paragraph 7.10 and Fig. 7.9, when $a=b=l/2$ we have, taking the origin at the centre,

$$EI\frac{d^2y}{dx^2}+Py=M_A-\frac{W}{2}\left(\frac{l}{2}-x\right)$$

or

$$\frac{d^2y}{dx^2}+\mu^2y=\frac{M_A}{EI}-\frac{W}{2EI}\left(\frac{l}{2}-x\right).$$

The solution of this is

$$y=A\sin\mu x+B\cos\mu x+\frac{1}{P}\left\{M_A-\frac{W}{2}\left(\frac{l}{2}-x\right)\right\}$$

and

$$\frac{dy}{dx}=\mu(A\cos\mu x-B\sin\mu x)+\frac{W}{2P}.$$

When $\quad x=0, \dfrac{dy}{dx}=0$ and so $A=-\dfrac{W}{2\mu P};$

when $\quad x=\dfrac{l}{2}, \dfrac{dy}{dx}=0$ and so $B=\dfrac{W}{2\mu P}\left(\operatorname{cosec}\dfrac{\mu l}{2}-\cot\dfrac{\mu l}{2}\right);$

when $\quad x=\dfrac{l}{2}, y=0,$

so

$$0=-\frac{W}{2\mu P}\left(\operatorname{cosec}\frac{\mu l}{2}-\cot\frac{\mu l}{2}\right)+\frac{M_A}{P},$$

or

$$M_A=\frac{W}{2\mu}\left(\operatorname{cosec}\frac{\mu l}{2}-\cot\frac{\mu l}{2}\right)=\frac{W}{2\mu}\tan\frac{\mu l}{4}. \quad . \quad . \quad . \quad (7.27)$$

The bending moment at the centre is

$$-Py+M_A-\frac{Wl}{4},$$

which is $\qquad\qquad -PB$ or $-\dfrac{W}{2\mu}\tan\dfrac{\mu l}{4}. \quad . \quad . \quad . \quad . \quad . \quad (7.28)$

Hence the bending moment has the same numerical value at the ends and the centre and

$$M_{max}=\pm\frac{W}{2\mu}\tan\frac{\mu l}{4}$$

$$=M_0'\left\{\frac{4}{\pi}\sqrt{\frac{Q}{P}}\tan\frac{\pi}{4}\sqrt{\frac{P}{Q}}\right\}. \quad . \quad . \quad . \quad (7.29)$$

It should be noted that M_0' is $Wl/8$ for an encastré beam with a central lateral load. Q as before $=\dfrac{\pi^2EI}{l^2}.$

7.15. Perry's approximation for a pin-jointed strut with uniform lateral load.—The secant formula given in paragraph 7.9 is an inconvenient one if it is desired to calculate the load factor from a knowledge of unit loads and the following approximation due to Perry is much easier to apply. The results given by it are very close to the exact results of the secant formula except when the end compression approaches the Euler critical load for the member.   It is assumed that the deflected form of the member is a cosine curve, so that if the central deflection is c we may write

$$y = c \cos \frac{\pi x}{l},$$

where x, y, etc., are as in Fig. 7.8.

Then
$$M_x = EI \frac{d^2 y}{dx^2} = M'_x - Py,$$

where M'_x is the bending moment at x due to the lateral load alone.

Substituting for $d^2 y/dx^2$ from the first equation we have

$$-\frac{EI\pi^2}{l^2} c \cos \frac{\pi x}{l} = M'_x - Py$$

or
$$-Qy = M'_x - Py \quad \text{where} \quad Q = \pi^2 EI/l^2 \; ;$$

so
$$y = \frac{M'_x}{P - Q}.$$

Then
$$M_x = M'_x + \left(\frac{P}{Q-P} \right) M'_x = \left(\frac{Q}{Q-P} \right) M'_x.$$

The maximum bending moment at the centre of the member is

$$M_{max} = M'_0 \left(\frac{Q}{Q-P} \right), \quad \cdot \quad \cdot \quad \cdot \quad \cdot \quad \cdot \quad (7.30)$$

where M'_0 is the central moment due to the lateral load alone $= \dfrac{wl^2}{8}$.

The maximum fibre stress is then

$$p_f = - \left[\frac{wl^2 h}{8I} \left(\frac{Q}{Q-P} \right) + \frac{P}{A} \right],$$

where A is the cross-sectional area of the strut and h is the distance from the neutral axis of the section to the outside compressive fibre.   If we write p_b for the bending stress due to the lateral load alone, p for the end load per unit area and p_e for the Euler stress as before, we can, if the material is to be stressed to the yield point p_y, express the formula as

$$p_y = p_b \left(\frac{p_e}{p_e - p} \right) + p. \quad \cdot \quad \cdot \quad \cdot \quad \cdot \quad \cdot \quad (7.31)$$

In general, if w and P represent unit loads carried by the member, the load factor N which will cause a stress p_y in the material is found from the equation

$$p_y = \frac{N w l^2}{8} \frac{h}{I} \left(\frac{Q}{Q - NP} \right) + \frac{NP}{A}. \quad \cdot \quad \cdot \quad \cdot \quad \cdot \quad (7.32)$$

This is a simple quadratic which is readily solved and the Perry equation is therefore always to be preferred to the secant formula for this class of calculation.

7.16. The analysis of strut tests.—Experimental observations in problems of elastic stability can in many instances be analysed by an elegant method due to R. V. Southwell (1932), which is particularly applicable to strut tests.

The problem of the strut with an initial curvature c has already been discussed in paragraph 7.7 where it was assumed that the initial shape of the member was a cosine curve. From this it followed that the maximum deflexion c at the centre of the strut due to an axial load P was, from equation (7.8),

$$c = \frac{c_o}{1 - P/P},$$

where P_e is the first critical or Euler load. c_o is, for actual struts, an equivalent curvature covering unavoidable departures from perfection in material and manufacture as well as in testing ; it is usually very small. The initial cosine form was assumed for the sake of simplicity but Southwell showed by a more general Fourier analysis that the expression above for c is a very good approximation to the correct solution. The curve of c plotted against P/P_e is a hyperbola passing through the point $c = c_o$, $P = 0$, and asymptotic to the line $P = P_e$.

This hyperbola can be transferred to axes with an origin at the point $(c_o, 0)$ and is then

$$c = c_o \left(\frac{P/P_e}{1 - P/P_e} \right),$$

which is again asymptotic to the line $P = P_e$ and also to the line $c = c_o$. If this expression is multiplied throughout by P_e/P we obtain

$$c - \frac{cP_e}{P} + c_o = 0, \quad . \quad . \quad . \quad . \quad . \quad . \quad (7.33)$$

which is the equation of a straight line in terms of c and c/P. If then a series of central deflexions measured in a test on a strut are plotted against those same deflexions divided by the axial loads producing them, the result will be a straight line, provided the behaviour of the strut is represented by the hyperbolic curve of the Perry result. The necessary conditions are that the initial curvature c_o shall be small compared with c, and that c shall not be so large as to impair the elasticity of the material of the strut.

Southwell showed that a number of strut tests carried out both by von Kármán and Andrew Robertson gave excellent straight lines when plotted in this way and subsequent experience has confirmed that this is usual. If values of c/P are plotted as ordinates and values of c as abscissae the slope of the resulting line to the vertical axis is clearly, from (7.33), the value of P_e and the intercept on the horizontal axis is $-c_o$. Thus, from a series of test results which do not damage the strut it is possible to deduce both the Euler critical load and the equivalent curvature of the member.

This method of analysis is not confined to strut tests but is applicable to any problem of elastic stability in which the deflexions and loading relation is hyperbolic in form.

7.17. Approximate formulas for laterally loaded struts.—It has been shown that an approximate analysis for the laterally loaded strut when the load is uniformly distributed gives the result

$$M_{max} = M'_0 \left(\frac{Q}{Q - P} \right).$$

If we modify this equation by the introduction of a constant C so that we have

$$M_{max} = M_0' \left(\frac{Q}{Q-CP} \right),$$

it is possible by a suitable choice of constants to obtain very good approximations for other cases of laterally loaded struts (Pippard, 1920). Table 7.4 gives the values of C and the errors involved by the use of these values.

TABLE 7.4.

Ends	Lateral load	C	Range of values Q/P examined	Maximum error per cent.	Remarks
Pin	Uniform	1·000	—	—	Perry formula, para. 7.15
Pin	Central	0·894	2·0–9·0	1·0	When $\frac{Q}{P} = 1 \cdot 5$, error $= 6$ per cent.
Pin	Constant B.M.	1·110	2·0–9·0	2·1	—
Encastré	Uniform	0·276	1·0–9·0	1·0	Centre of bay
		0·172	1·0–9·0	1·0	Fixing moment
Encastré	Central	0·212	1·0–9·0	0·3	Centre and fixing moments
Pin	⎧ Two equal	1·064	2·0–9·0	1·0	$k = \frac{1}{2}$ in para. 7.12
	⎨ loads spaced	1·030	2·0–9·0	1·0	$k = \frac{1}{3}$
	⎩ symmetrically	1·000	2·0–9·0	1·0	$k = \frac{1}{4}$

7.18. Members with combined bending and axial tension.—When a member is subjected to lateral bending and axial tension the maximum deflexion at the centre is less than would be produced by the lateral loads alone and the approximation referred to in paragraph 7.8 would overestimate the stress.

In the exact solution of such problems the sign of P in the differential equation is reversed and the solution is in terms of hyperbolic instead of trigonometrical functions. As an example, consider a pin-jointed bar with a uniform lateral load and an axial tension P. Then as in paragraph 7.9 we obtain

$$\frac{d^2M}{dx^2} - P\frac{d^2y}{dx^2} = w$$

the solution of which is

$$M = A \sinh \mu x + B \cosh \mu x - \frac{w}{\mu^2}.$$

When

$$x = \pm\frac{l}{2}, \quad M = 0$$

∴

$$A \sinh \frac{\mu l}{2} + B \cosh \frac{\mu l}{2} - \frac{w}{\mu^2} = 0$$

and

$$-A \sinh \frac{\mu l}{2} + B \cosh \frac{\mu l}{2} - \frac{w}{\mu^2} = 0.$$

From these equations $A = 0$ and $B = \frac{w}{\mu^2} \operatorname{sech} \frac{\mu l}{2}.$

The bending moment is

$$M = \frac{w}{\mu^2}\left(\operatorname{sech}\frac{\mu l}{2}\cosh \mu x - 1\right). \quad \cdots \quad (7.34)$$

This is a maximum when $x=0$ and its value is then

$$M_{max} = \frac{w}{\mu^2}\left(\operatorname{sech}\frac{\mu l}{2} - 1\right). \quad \cdots \quad (7.35)$$

Other problems dealing with laterally loaded ties can be solved in the same way.

7.19. Initially curved strut with end couples.—In the practical design of compression members allowance must be made for imperfections in material and workmanship which may be expected to exist in the finished structure. It was pointed out in paragraph 7.7, where the safe axial loads for pin-ended struts are tabulated, that these imperfections can be represented by an initial curvature of the axis of the member. In actual structures very few members satisfy the requirement that the ends shall be free from restraint and it is necessary, therefore, to consider the initially curved strut subjected to end couples.

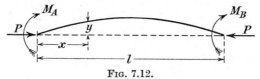

FIG. 7.12.

Suppose a strut, of uniform cross-section as shown in Fig. 7.12, to have ends which are fixed in position and to have an initial curvature defined by the equation

$$y' = \varepsilon \sin\frac{\pi x}{l}. \quad \cdots \quad (7.36)$$

It is acted on by an axial compressive load P and clockwise end couples M_A and M_B in the same plane as the curvature. The bending moment at any point at a distance x from the origin is

$$M_x = M_A - (M_A + M_B)\frac{x}{l} - Py$$

or

$$EI\frac{d^2(y-y')}{dx^2} = M_A - (M_A + M_B)\frac{x}{l} - Py, \quad \cdots \quad (7.37)$$

where I is the relevant second moment of area of the strut.

The solution of this equation is

$$y = \frac{M_A}{P}\left\{\frac{l-x}{l} - \frac{\sin\mu(l-x)}{\sin\mu l}\right\} + \frac{M_B}{P}\left\{\frac{\sin\mu x}{\sin\mu l} - \frac{x}{l}\right\} + \frac{\varepsilon\pi^2}{\pi^2 - \mu^2 l^2}\sin\frac{\pi x}{l}, \quad (7.38)$$

where

$$\mu^2 = \frac{P}{EI}.$$

Upon differentiating this expression the slope at any point is

$$\frac{dy}{dx} = \frac{M_A}{Pl}\left\{\frac{2\alpha\cos 2\alpha\left(1-\frac{x}{l}\right)}{\sin 2\alpha} - 1\right\} + \frac{M_B}{Pl}\left\{\frac{2\alpha\cos\frac{2\alpha x}{l}}{\sin 2\alpha} - 1\right\} + \frac{\varepsilon\pi^3}{l(\pi^2 - 4\alpha^2)}\cos\frac{\pi x}{l},$$

$$(7.39)$$

where

$$2\alpha = \mu l.$$

Adopting the sign convention that clockwise rotations are positive, the *changes* of slope θ_A and θ_B at the ends of the strut are given by

$$\theta_A = -\frac{M_A}{Pl}(2\alpha \cot 2\alpha - 1) - \frac{M_B}{Pl}(2\alpha \operatorname{cosec} 2\alpha - 1) - \frac{4\alpha^2 \epsilon \pi}{l(\pi^2 - 4\alpha^2)},$$

$$\theta_B = -\frac{M_A}{Pl}(2\alpha \operatorname{cosec} 2\alpha - 1) - \frac{M_B}{Pl}(2\alpha \cot 2\alpha - 1) + \frac{4\alpha^2 \epsilon \pi}{l(\pi^2 - 4\alpha^2)}.$$

Making use of the Berry functions * $f(\alpha)$ and $\phi(\alpha)$ these expressions can be written in the form

$$\theta_A = \frac{M_A l}{3EI}\phi(\alpha) - \frac{M_B l}{6EI}f(\alpha) - \frac{4\alpha^2 \epsilon \pi}{l(\pi^2 - 4\alpha^2)} \qquad . \quad . \quad . \quad (7.40)$$

and

$$\theta_B = -\frac{M_A l}{6EI}f(\alpha) + \frac{M_B l}{3EI}\phi(\alpha) + \frac{4\alpha^2 \epsilon \pi}{l(\pi^2 - 4\alpha^2)}, \qquad . \quad . \quad . \quad (7.41)$$

where $$f(\alpha) = \frac{6(2\alpha \operatorname{cosec} 2\alpha - 1)}{4\alpha^2} \quad \text{and} \quad \phi(\alpha) = \frac{3(1 - 2\alpha \cot 2\alpha)}{4\alpha^2}.$$

The solution of these equations gives

$$M_A = \frac{6EI}{l}(2Y\theta_A + X\theta_B - Z) \qquad . \quad . \quad . \quad . \quad (7.42)$$

and

$$M_B = \frac{6EI}{l}(X\theta_A + 2Y\theta_B + Z), \qquad . \quad . \quad . \quad . \quad (7.43)$$

where

$$X = \frac{f(\alpha)}{4\phi^2(\alpha) - f^2(\alpha)},$$

$$Y = \frac{\phi(\alpha)}{4\phi^2(\alpha) - f^2(\alpha)}$$

and

$$Z = \frac{4\alpha^2 \epsilon \pi}{l(\pi^2 - 4\alpha^2)}(X - 2Y).$$

These expressions, which are more general forms of the slope deflexion equations derived in paragraph 3.13, will be used later in the stress analysis of frames having members which cannot be considered perfectly straight and where the axial loads are sufficiently great to affect appreciably the flexure of the members.

This stress analysis will enable the magnitudes of the end couples and of the axial loads acting on the members of the frame to be determined.   The next step in design procedure is the determination of the maximum total stress developed in each member.   For this, the distribution of bending stress in an initially curved strut subjected to axial load and end couples must be studied.

From equations (7.37) and (7.38) the bending moment, and therefore the bending stress, at any section of such a member may be obtained and, as in paragraph 7.11, the maximum values determined.   A slight variation on this method has, however, been found useful.

It has been convenient so far in this paragraph to assume the initial shape of the axis of the member, which represents its imperfections, to be a sine curve.   There is, however, nothing axiomatic about that curve and the stresses in the member would not be seriously affected by a slight change in its initial shape so long as the versed sine remained the same.

* See Paragraph 8.4.

In calculating the safe axial loads for pin-ended struts in paragraph 7.7, the initial shape was taken to be a cosine curve. If we transfer the origin of co-ordinates from the centre of the member to one end to agree with the work of the present paragraph and substitute for the value of c_0 given in paragraph 7.7 we can write the equation of initial curvature in the form

$$y = 0 \cdot 003 \frac{lk}{a} \sin \frac{\pi x}{l}.$$

This is compared in Table 7.5, with the shape taken by an originally straight member when subjected to a uniform moment M' such that

$$M' = 0 \cdot 024 \frac{kEI}{al}.$$

TABLE 7.5.

COMPARISON OF SHAPES FOR INITIAL CURVATURE OF STRUT.

x		$\dfrac{ya}{lk}$	
		Sine curve	Beam under uniform moment
0	l	0	0
$l/8$	$7l/8$	$0 \cdot 00115$	$0 \cdot 00131$
$l/4$	$3l/4$	$0 \cdot 00212$	$0 \cdot 00225$
$3l/8$	$5l/8$	$0 \cdot 00280$	$0 \cdot 00282$
$l/2$		$0 \cdot 00300$	$0 \cdot 00300$

It is clear that no serious differences in the final results will arise if the latter shape instead of the sine curve is assumed to represent the imperfections in the member.

The shape of the initially curved strut under examination when subjected to an axial end load P and end couples M_A and M_B tending to increase the curvature of the member as in Fig. 7.13 will therefore be, for all practical

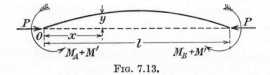

FIG. 7.13.

purposes, indistinguishable from that of an originally straight member of the same cross-section, subjected to the same axial end load P and to end couples $M_A + M'$ and $M_B + M'$ as in Fig. 7.13. The bending moment in the latter at a section a distance x from the origin is, from equations (7.37) and (7.38),

$$M'_x = (M_A + M') \frac{\sin \mu(l-x)}{\sin \mu l} + (M_B + M') \frac{\sin \mu x}{\sin \mu l}$$

and the bending moment at the corresponding section of the initially curved member is

$$M_x = (M_A + M') \frac{\sin \mu(l-x)}{\sin \mu l} + (M_B + M') \frac{\sin \mu x}{\sin \mu l} - M', \quad . \quad . \quad (7.44)$$

since it was actually unstressed before the application of the axial end load P and end couples M_A and M_B. If the maximum bending moment in the initially curved member occurs at the section x

$$(M_A + M') \cos \mu(l-x) - (M_B + M') \cos \mu x = 0$$

or

$$\tan \mu x = \operatorname{cosec} \mu l \left(\frac{M_B + M'}{M_A + M'} - \cos \mu l \right). \quad . \quad . \quad . \quad (7.45)$$

Dividing equation (7.44) throughout by the relevant modulus of section of the strut we obtain

$$\frac{f_x + f'}{f_A + f'} = \frac{\sin \mu x}{\sin \mu l} \frac{f_B + f'}{f_A + f'} + \frac{\sin \mu(l-x)}{\sin \mu l} \quad . \quad . \quad . \quad (7.46)$$

where f_x, f', f_A, etc., are the extreme fibre stresses developed in the section by the moments M_x, M', M_A, etc.

In designing a member it is essential that the maximum total stress should not rise above a certain limit p'. If the compressive axial load per unit area

is $p = \dfrac{P}{A}$ where A is the cross-sectional area of the member

$$p + f_x \not> p'.$$

When the maximum total stress reaches the limit it follows from (7.46) that

$$\frac{p' - p + f'}{f_A + f'} = \sin \mu x \operatorname{cosec} \mu l \left(\frac{f_B + f'}{f_A + f'} + \sin \mu l \cot \mu x - \cos \mu l \right). \quad . \quad (7.47)$$

For any ratio $\dfrac{f_B + f'}{f_A + f'}$ it is possible to calculate from equations (7.45) and (7.47) the value of the maximum end bending stress f_A which can be applied to a strut of any slenderness ratio carrying any axial load without raising the maximum stress at any point beyond a predetermined value p'.

These equations are much too complex for use in design, but it is a simple matter to present the results obtained from them in the form of families of curves. If M_A is always taken as the numerically greater end couple the ratio f_B/f_A must always lie within the limits ± 1. In Fig. 7.14 are plotted the values of f_A, calculated from these equations, which cause a maximum total stress of 8 tons per square inch for any ratio of f_B/f_A and for a number of values of the slenderness ratio l/k when the axial load is 6 tons per square inch and the imperfections of the members are represented by an initial curvature having a versed sine of $0 \cdot 0015 \dfrac{lk}{a}$. A more convenient way of setting out the information for design purposes is shown in Fig. 7.15. If a compression member in a structure is subjected to an axial load of 6 tons per square inch and to anti-clockwise end couples, one being $0 \cdot 6$ times the other, then the ratio $\dfrac{f_B}{f_A} = -0 \cdot 6$ and Fig. 7.15 shows that, if the slenderness ratio of the member is 90, the maximum total stress will not rise above 8 tons per square inch so long as f_A, the end bending stress due to the greater end

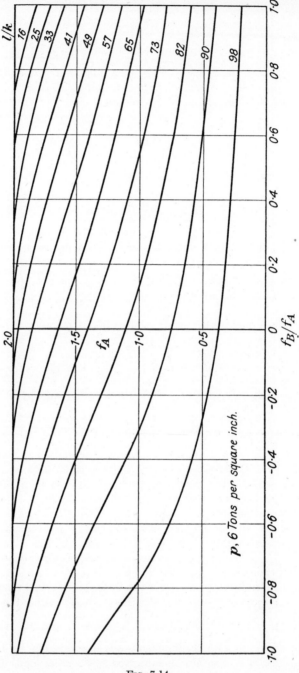

Fig. 7.14.

couple, does not rise above 1·33 tons per square inch. It must not be concluded that the result in this example would have been different if both end
couples, M_A and M_B, had acted in a clockwise direction. The designer is

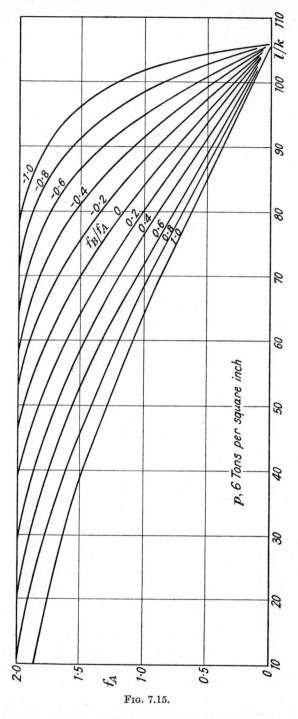

F<small>IG</small>. 7.15.

unaware of the nature of the imperfections which will be found in the member
and he must, therefore, assume that they are such as to give rise to the worst

stress conditions. This assumption is automatically made in the method outlined above.

7.20. Polar diagrams for beams with end thrusts.—Many problems of the type we have dealt with in this chapter can be solved very neatly by the aid of a polar diagram originally due to J. Ratzersdorfer (1920) but discovered independently later by H. B. Howard, (1928).

The differential equation for any laterally loaded strut is

$$EI\frac{d^2y}{dx^2}=M=-Py+M', \quad . \quad . \quad . \quad . \quad . \quad . \quad (7.48)$$

where M' is the bending moment due to the lateral loads and end moments.

Differentiating this equation twice and putting $\mu^2=\dfrac{P}{EI}$ as before, we get for a uniformly distributed lateral load of intensity w

$$\frac{d^2M}{dx^2}+\mu^2M=w.$$

The solution of this can be written either as the sum of a cosine and a sine term as hitherto in this chapter or in the form

$$M=C\cos(\mu x-\varepsilon)+\frac{w}{\mu^2}, \quad . \quad . \quad . \quad . \quad . \quad (7.49)$$

where C and ε are constants of integration replacing the A and B of the former analysis, or

$$m=M-\frac{w}{\mu^2}=C\cos(\mu x-\varepsilon). \quad . \quad . \quad . \quad . \quad (7.50)$$

The shearing force S is given by dM/dx so that we have

$$S=-\mu C\sin(\mu x-\varepsilon), \quad . \quad . \quad . \quad . \quad . \quad (7.51)$$

or in another form by differentiating (7.48)

$$S=-Pi+S', \quad . \quad . \quad . \quad . \quad . \quad . \quad (7.52)$$

where i is the slope at the point under consideration and S' is the apparent shear due to lateral loads and end moments alone.

Since x is a distance, μx is an angle measured in radians, and lengths upon the beam can therefore be represented by angles in a polar diagram. In Fig. 7.16 let OZ be any base line and O a pole on it. Draw OX$=C$ at an angle ZOX$=\varepsilon$ and on OX as diameter describe the circle OAXB. Let ON be any chord of this circle, and let angle ZON$=\mu x$.

Then ON$=$OX cos XON$=C\cos(\mu x-\varepsilon)$. Hence ON represents m to the scale to which OX represents C, and if the angles ZOA and ZOB are respectively made equal to μx_1 and μx_2, AXNBO represents the polar diagram for m between the two values of x_1 and x_2.

Again   XN$=C\sin(\mu x-\varepsilon)$

and so XN represents $-S/\mu$ from (7.51). X is termed the apex of the diagram. Positive values of μx will be measured in a clockwise direction from OZ. Positive values of m will be measured into the angle ZOB, *e.g.* OA, ON are positive. Negative values would appear from O outwards from the angle.

If we look along a radius vector in the positive direction, shearing forces will be positive if measured to the right and negative if measured to the left.

Thus the shearing force at x is $\mu(NX)$ and looking along ON it is on the left and so is negative.

A few examples will make the method of using these diagrams clear.

Example 1.   *Initially straight strut with end couples.*—In the first place consider a strut with end couples as described in paragraph 7.11 and shown in Fig. 7.10.   Here, since there are no distributed lateral loads

$$M = C \cos (\mu x - \varepsilon).$$

When $\mu x = 0$, $M = -M_A$,

and when $\mu x = \mu l$, $M = -M_B$.

In Fig. 7.17 make angle $ZOB = \mu l$ and mark off OA' and OB' equal to M_A and M_B.   Since these moments are negative they are measured outwards from the angle ZOB.

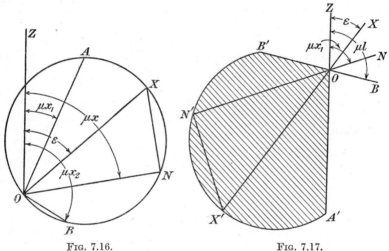

FIG. 7.16.   FIG. 7.17.

Through B', O and A' draw a circle of which OX' is a diameter.   Then $B'X'A'$ is the polar diagram for this case.

The maximum bending moment is OX' which is negative and angle $ZOX = \varepsilon$.

To find the bending moment and shearing force at a point x_1 from the origin, we make angle $ZON = \mu x_1$ and produce NO to meet the circle at N'. Then the bending moment at x_1 is given by ON' and the shearing force by $\mu(N'X')$.

The bending moment is negative, since ON' is in the negative direction : the shearing force is positive since, looking along $N'O$, *i.e.* the positive direction for moments, the line $N'X'$ is to the right.

Example 2.   *Uniformly loaded beam with positive end couples.*—This is similar to the loading shown in Fig. 7.8 but positive end moments M_A and M_B are applied at A and B respectively.   Two diagrams are shown in Fig. 7.18 to illustrate the effect of varying the size of the end moments ; the description applies to both.

Here $m = M - \dfrac{w}{\mu^2} = C \cos (\mu x - \varepsilon).$

Since the term in w is negative, we draw an arc CD in the negative sector with centre at O and of radius w/μ^2.

When $\mu x = 0$, $$m_A = M_A - \frac{w}{\mu^2}$$

and when $\mu x = \mu l$, $$m_B = M_B - \frac{w}{\mu^2}.$$

Therefore if we set off DA in the positive direction equal to M_A and CB in the positive direction equal to M_B we have

$$OA = M_A - \frac{w}{\mu^2} = m_A$$

and $$OB = M_B - \frac{w}{\mu^2} = m_B.$$

Hence, a circle drawn through B, O and A is the polar diagram for m.

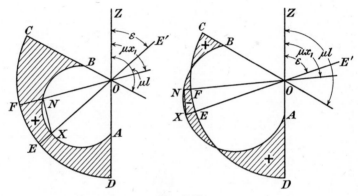

FIG. 7.18.

Draw E'OXE through the centre of this circle : OX is then C and angle ZOE' is ε. The position of the mathematical maximum or minimum value of M is defined by $\mu x = \varepsilon$ and the value of the moment here is EX, which is positive in the first diagram and negative in the second.

Draw any other radius vector ONF whose position is defined by the angle μx_1. Then the bending moment in the beam at a distance x_1 from the origin is FN and the shearing force is $+\mu(NX)$. The bending moment is positive in the first diagram and negative in the second ; the shearing force is positive in both, since if we look along the positive direction of the vector NX is drawn to the right.

Example 3. Uniformly loaded beam with a negative fixing couple at one end and a positive fixing couple at the other.—This is similar to the last, but the fixing couple at A is now in the opposite direction, *i.e.* it is $-M_A$. That at B is still M_B.

As in the previous example, the arc CD in Fig. 7.19 is drawn with centre at O and radius w/μ^2.

DA is set off in the negative direction equal to M_A and CB in the positive direction equal to M_B. A circle drawn through AOB completes the diagram as shown. X is the apex, and XE the maximum negative bending moment in the beam.

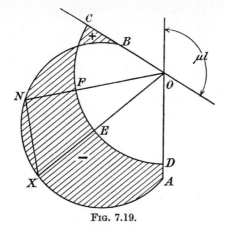

Fig. 7.19.

Example 4.   Beam with a single concentrated load, axial thrust and terminal couples.—The loading is that shown in Fig. 7.9 with the addition of positive terminal couples M_A and M_B at the two supports A and B respectively.

Here $M = C \cos(\mu x - \varepsilon)$ with different values of the constants C and ε in the two sections into which the beam is divided by the load.

To construct the diagram, mark off OA and OB equal to M_A and M_B along the radii drawn at $\mu x = 0$ and $\mu x = \mu l$ (Fig. 7.20).

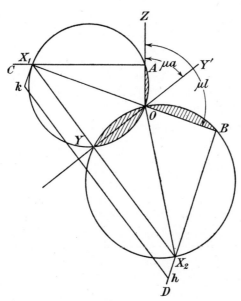

Fig. 7.20.

From A and B draw AC and BD perpendicular to the radii OA and OB. Draw the line Y'OY at the angle μa to OZ to represent the position of W on the beam.

On BD take any point h and draw hk perpendicular to OY and of length $\dfrac{W}{\mu}$.

From k draw a line kX_1 parallel to hB cutting AC in X_1 and from X_1 draw X_1X_2 parallel to hk and cutting BD in X_2.

Then X_1 and X_2 will be the apices of the polar diagrams for the two sections of the beam.

Join OX_1 and OX_2 and describe circles on these lines as diameters, completing the diagram as shown in Fig. 7.20.

The circle AOY with apex X_1 relates to the left-hand section of the beam and the circle BOY with apex X_2 relates to the right-hand section.

The conditions at the load point which must be satisfied are :

(1) The bending moment is the same on either side of the load point.
(2) The slope of the beam is the same on either side.
(3) The deflexion of the beam is the same whether considered from the left or from the right of the load point.

It will now be shown that the construction given above satisfies these conditions.

In the first place, since OYX_1 and OYX_2 are right-angled triangles, circles drawn on OX_1 and OX_2 as diameters must intersect at Y.

But OY represents the bending moment at the load point whether it be considered from the left or the right section of the beam and so the first condition is satisfied.

Again, it is evident from the construction that

$$X_1X_2 = hk = \frac{W}{\mu}.$$

The true shearing force to the left of the load

$$S_L = -(X_1Y)\mu$$

and to the right of the load

$$S_R = +(X_2Y)\mu,$$

therefore $$S_R - S_L = \mu(X_2Y + X_1Y) = W.$$

From equation (7.52) we have

$$S_L + Pi_a = S'_L,$$
$$S_R + Pi'_a = S'_R,$$

where i_a and i'_a are the slopes to left and right of the load,

therefore $$S_R - S_L + P(i'_a - i_a) = S'_R - S'_L.$$

But $S'_R - S'_L$ is the difference of the apparent shearing force in passing through the point and is W. Hence, since

$$S_R - S_L = W,$$
$$i'_a = i_a$$

and the condition of equality of slopes is satisfied.

From equation (7.48) $$M - M' = -Py$$

and, since neither M nor M' changes in passing through the load point, the deflexion of the beam is the same whether considered to the left or right of the load.

Hence, all conditions are satisfied and the diagram is proved correct.

Example 5. Initially curved strut with end couples.—The initially curved strut considered in paragraph 7.19 can be dealt with conveniently by means of a polar diagram.

If the strut is initially curved with a versed sine of $\cdot 003\dfrac{lk}{a}$ the approximate bending moment at any point due to the application of end couples M_A and M_B and of an axial compressive load P can be found as follows. In Fig. 7.21 mark off OA′ and OB′ equal to M_A+M' and M_B+M' where $M'=\cdot 024k\mathrm{EI}/al$ is the uniform moment necessary to produce the initial curvature in the strut. The circle A′X′B′O gives the moment in an originally straight member subjected to end couples M_A+M' and M_B+M'; the bending moment required in the initially curved strut is this moment less the moment M′. Thus the required moment at a point x_1 from the origin is given by the intercept N′N″ of ON between the circle A′X′B′O and the circle A″X″B″ which is drawn with centre O and radius M′.

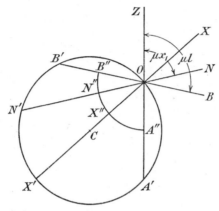

Fig. 7.21.

If OX′ is a diameter of the circle A′X′B′O the maximum bending moment in the initially curved strut will be given by the length of the intercept X′X″. It will be seen that when the centre C of this circle lies on OA′ or on OB′ or anywhere on the opposite sides of those lines from the position shown in Fig. 7.21 the maximum bending moment will be found at one or other end of the strut. When this occurs the end couples will have completely masked the strut action and there is no reason why the working stress in the strut should be cut down below the value allowed for beams subjected to flexure. The critical values of the end couples which make C lie on OA′ or on OB′ are therefore of importance.

They are given by the equation

$$\frac{M_B+M'}{M_A+M'}=\cos \mu l.$$

The maximum bending moment in a practical strut will, therefore, occur at the end where the greater couple is applied when the end couples have values defined by this equation or when the greater end couple is equal to M_A and the smaller is less than M_B or when the smaller end couple is equal to M_B and the greater exceeds M_A.

The use of polar diagrams has been extended to continuous girders and to various types of loading. For details of these extensions the reader should consult the paper (Howard, 1928) referred to at the beginning of this paragraph.

7.21. Derivation of strut formulas from polar diagrams.—The polar diagram provides a useful method for the derivation of formulas for laterally loaded struts geometrically instead of by the more usual methods of the earlier paragraphs in this chapter. This use of the diagram does not need accurate drawing as when numerical problems are solved graphically ; sketches are quite sufficient. The following examples will illustrate the method.

Example 1. *Pin-jointed strut with an eccentric thrust.*—This is dealt with analytically in paragraph 7.3 and shown in Fig. 7.3. The origin will now be taken at A and not at the centre of the strut as shown in that figure. Since there is no distributed load, M=*m*.

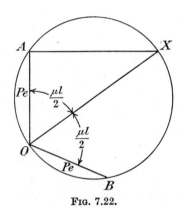

FIG. 7.22.

So, at *x*=0 and at *x*=L the value of *m* is P*e*, and the polar diagram is shown in Fig. 7.22 where OA=OB=P*e*, and angles AOX and XOB are each equal to $\dfrac{\mu l}{2}$.

Then
$$M_{max}=m_{max}=Pe \sec \frac{\mu l}{2}.$$

Also, from equation (7.48)
$$M_{max}=-Py_{max}+Pe,$$

and so at the centre of the bar $y_{max}=e\left(1-\sec \dfrac{\mu l}{2}\right)$.

Example 2. *Strut with an axial thrust and a uniformly distributed load.*— This is dealt with in paragraph 7.9 and illustrated in Fig. 7.8. Again the origin will be taken at A and not at the centre. From equation (7.50)

$$m=M-\frac{w}{\mu^2}.$$

At A and B, since there are no applied end couples, $m=-\dfrac{w}{\mu^2}$, so OA and OB in Fig. 7.23 are set off in the negative direction to represent $\dfrac{w}{\mu^2}$. The *m*-circle is then drawn through O, A and B, and m_{max} is seen to be −OX or $-\dfrac{w}{\mu^2}\sec \dfrac{\mu l}{2}$.

Hence
$$M_{max} = m_{max} + \frac{w}{\mu^2} = -\frac{w}{\mu^2} \sec \frac{\mu l}{2} + \frac{w}{\mu^2}$$

or
$$M_{max} = \left(1 - \sec \frac{\mu l}{2}\right)\frac{w}{\mu^2},$$

as in paragraph 7.9.

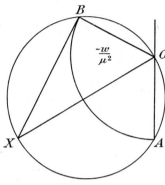

FIG. 7.23.

Example 3. Strut with an axial thrust and a concentrated load.—This is dealt with in paragraph 7.10 and illustrated in Fig. 7.9. We shall write $a+b=l$.

The polar diagram is shown in Fig. 7.24 and is generally similar to Fig. 7.20, but since there are no end couples the circles must not cut the lines ZOZ′

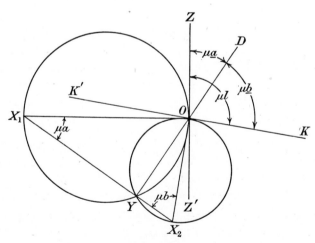

FIG. 7.24.

and KOK′, so these lines will be tangents to the appropriate circles at O. The centre of the circle for sector ZOD will therefore lie on OX_1, which is perpendicular to ZO, and the centre of the other circle will lie on OX_2, which is perpendicular to KO. The maximum value of m and therefore of M occurs at the load point and is given by OY.

Then in the diagram, since OX_1 and X_1Y are respectively perpendicular to OZ and OY, the angle $OX_1Y = \mu a$, and similarly the angle $OX_2Y = \mu b$.

Hence $\qquad$ $X_1OX_2 = \pi - \mu l.$

Now $\qquad$ $OY = OX_1 \sin \mu a.$

Also $\qquad$ $\dfrac{OX_1}{\sin \mu b} = \dfrac{X_1 X_2}{\sin \mu l},$

and so $\qquad$ $OX_1 = \dfrac{X_1 X_2 \sin \mu b}{\sin \mu l} = \dfrac{W \sin \mu b}{\mu \sin \mu l}.$

Therefore $\qquad$ $M_{max} = m_{max} = -OY = -\dfrac{W}{\mu} \dfrac{\sin \mu a \sin \mu b}{\sin \mu l}.$

If the load is central, $a = b = \dfrac{l}{2}$ and

$$M_{max} = -\left(\frac{W}{2\mu}\right) \tan \frac{\mu l}{2}.$$

These results are the same as those already found in paragraph 7.10.

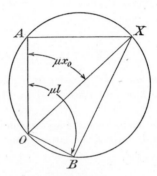

FIG. 7.25.

Example 4. *Pin-jointed strut with specified end couples.*—This is dealt with in paragraph 7.11 and shown in Fig. 7.10. The *m*-circle is shown in Fig. 7.25, but is drawn as though the end couples were positive and not negative as shown in Fig. 7.10. OX is the maximum value of *m* and therefore of M.

From the diagram,

$$OX = M_A \sec \mu x_0 = M_B \sec (\mu l - \mu x_0),$$

where $\mu x_0 = \varepsilon$ is the position of maximum bending moment in the bar.

This gives $\qquad$ $\tan \mu x_0 = \left(\dfrac{M_B}{M_A}\right) \operatorname{cosec} \mu l - \cot \mu l \ ;$

then $\qquad$ $OX^2 = M^2{}_A(1 + \tan^2 \mu x_0)$

and substituting the value of $\tan \mu x_0$, already found, we have

$$m_{max} = M_{max} = \sqrt{\{(M^2{}_A + M^2{}_B) \operatorname{cosec}^2 \mu l - 2M_A M_B \operatorname{cosec} \mu l \cot \mu l\}},$$

as in paragraph 7.11.

Example 5. *Encastré strut with axial thrust and uniformly distributed load.*—This is treated in paragraph 7.13. The end couples are unknown and must be determined in addition to the bending moment at the centre.

From equation (7.52) since the slope of the strut at the end is zero, the true shearing force is the same as the apparent shearing force, *i.e.* $\frac{1}{2}wl$. The diagram is as shown in Fig. 7.26, where AX is now known to be $\dfrac{wl}{2\mu}.$

Hence $\qquad m_{\max} = -OX = -\left(\dfrac{wl}{2\mu}\right) \operatorname{cosec} \dfrac{\mu l}{2},$

and $\qquad M_{\max} = m_{\max} + \dfrac{w}{\mu^2} = -\dfrac{wl}{2\mu} \operatorname{cosec} \dfrac{\mu l}{2} + \dfrac{w}{\mu^2}.$

The value of m at the support is

$$-OA = -AX \cot \dfrac{\mu l}{2} = -\left(\dfrac{wl}{2\mu}\right) \cot \dfrac{\mu l}{2}.$$

The end fixing moment is therefore

$$M_A = -\left(\dfrac{wl}{2\mu}\right) \cot \dfrac{\mu l}{2} + \dfrac{w}{\mu^2}.$$

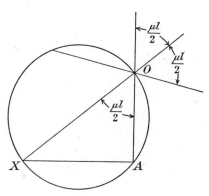

FIG. 7.26.

Example 6.   Encastré strut with axial thrust and central load.—This is dealt with in paragraph 7.16.   The m-diagram will consist of two equal circles intersecting at the point Y in Fig. 7.27.   As in the preceding example, we

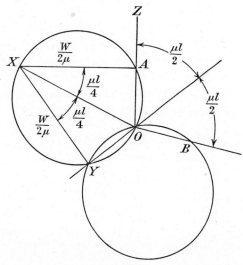

FIG. 7.27.

do not know the value of the end fixing moments, but the real and apparent shearing forces at the supports are both $\frac{1}{2}$W. So $AX = \dfrac{W}{2\mu}$. By the same reasoning, the true shearing force to the left of the load is also $\frac{1}{2}$W, and so $XY = \dfrac{W}{2\mu}$. The triangles OAX and OYX are therefore similar, and

$$AO = OY = \left(\frac{W}{2\mu}\right) \tan \frac{\mu l}{4}.$$

Since $m = M$, this is the value both of the bending moment at the centre and at the supports, the former being negative and the latter positive.

Other cases can be solved in a similar way (Pippard, 1942).

REFERENCES

Ayrton, W. E. & Perry, J., 1886. *The Engineer*, **62**, 464.
Jenkin, C. F., 1920. " Report on materials of construction used in aircraft and aircraft engines," H.M.S.O.
Pippard, A. J. S., 1920. *Aircr. Engin.*, **149**.
Ratzersdorfer, J., 1920. *Z. Flugtech.*, **7** ; **8**.
Robertson, A., 1925. *Instn. Civ. Engrs. S.E.P.*, **28**.
Howard, H. B., 1928. *Aer. Res. Cttee.* R. & M., **1233**, H.M.S.O.
Steel Structures Research Committee, 1931. First Report. H.M.S.O.
Southwell, R. V., 1932. *Proc. Roy. Soc.* (A) **135**, 601–616.
Pippard, A. J. S., 1942. *Math. Gaz.*, **26**, 119–129.

EXERCISES

(1) Compare the Perry and Rankine formulas for struts by plotting curves of axial loading against L/k for a wide range of values. Take the yield stress in the Perry formula and the constant p_y in the Rankine formula to be 18 tons per square inch ;

$$a = \frac{1}{7,500} \text{ and } \eta = \cdot 003 L/k.$$

(2) Express the secant formula for a laterally-loaded pin-jointed strut and the Perry approximation to this formula in terms of the two ratios M_0'/M_0 and P/Q where M_0' is the maximum bending moment due to the lateral load alone and M_0 the maximum bending moment due to the lateral load and end thrust P. Compare these formulas by plotting curves of M_0'/M_0 against P/Q.

(3) Use Smith's modified formula to calculate the strength of a circular steel tube 100 inches long, $2\frac{1}{8}$ inches outside diameter and $0\cdot056$ inches thick when used as a pin-jointed strut.

The equivalent eccentricity of loading may be taken to be $\dfrac{\text{length}}{600} + \dfrac{\text{internal diameter}}{40}$, the yield stress to be 28 tons per square inch and E = 13,600 tons per square inch.

(5,000 lb.)

(4) A pin-jointed rectangular wooden beam 6 inches deep by 3 inches wide and 100 inches long carries an axial thrust of 10,000 lb. and a uniform lateral load of 3 lb. per inch over its whole length.

Calculate the factor of safety under this loading and the load factor of the member if the yield stress of the material is 5,000 lb. per square inch and $E = 1\cdot6 \times 10^6$ lb. per square inch.

(6·3 : 4·8)

(5) A uniform bar of length L and flexural rigidity EI is encastré at one end and pin-jointed at the other. At the pinned end it carries a compressive load P and a moment M.

Show that the position of the maximum bending moment is given by

$$\tan \mu x = \frac{1 - \mu L \sin \mu L - \cos \mu L}{\sin \mu L - \mu L \cos \mu L},$$

where $\mu^2 = P/EI$ and x is measured from the pin-joint along the original central line of the bar.

(6) A steel tube 60 inches long, 1 inch outside diameter and ·056 inch thick is pinned at the ends and carries an axial load of 500 lb.

Calculate what lateral load, uniformly distributed, is required to produce a stress of 8 tons per square inch in the material. E = 13,600 tons per square inch.

(0·83 lb. per inch)

(7) The strut in the last question without lateral load has bending moments applied to its ends of 650 and 300 inch-lb. respectively.

Use a graphical method to determine the position and magnitude of the maximum bending moment in the strut, and the bending moment and shearing force at the centre.

(748 inch-lb. at 17·6 inches from larger end moment ; 700 inch-lb. ; −6·77 lb.)

(8) A circular steel bar 10 feet long and 2 inches diameter is pinned at the ends and carries an axial compression equal to one quarter of the Euler critical load. In addition it carries a uniformly distributed load of 10 lb. per foot and has terminal couples of 2,400 inch-lb. and −2,400 inch-lb. at the right- and left-hand supports respectively.

Determine graphically—

   (a) the position and magnitude of the maximum bending moment ;
   (b) the bending moment and shearing force at the midpoint of the span.

[(a)   −234 foot-lb. at 1·89 feet from end
(b)   −164 foot-lb. ;   46·5 lb.]

CHAPTER 8

CONTINUOUS BEAMS

8.1. The general problem of the continuous beam.—We have seen in a previous chapter that a beam requires three reactive forces to ensure equilibrium under any loading conditions which may occur ; if we assume that the beam is horizontal and that there are no horizontal forces acting upon it, two vertical reactions only are needed. If more than the essential number are provided the resultant actions at any point are statically indeterminate and their evaluation depends upon a knowledge of the elastic properties of the beam and its supports.

A common instance is that of a continuous beam supported at a number of points along its length. The beam may be of the same section throughout or may vary from span to span. The loads may be all normal to the longitudinal axis or may have components acting along this axis. The problem may be still further complicated by the nature of the supports. If these are rigid the loaded beam will not deflect at the support points ; if they are elastic such deflexions will occur. Further, the beam may be simply pinned to the supporting points or be so attached that the joints between the supports and the beam are rigid. It will be realised that any problem of this type can be analysed by making use of strain energy methods, but these are not always the most convenient and a number of other methods will be described in the present chapter.

It will be assumed unless otherwise stated that the beams are continuous and are simply pinned to their supports. Before proceeding to a discussion of the methods available for their analysis it is desirable to examine the problem generally.

Suppose a horizontal beam such as specified above and subjected to vertical loads only, rests on n supports. Two of these supports only are essential for equilibrium and the vertical reactions exerted by the remaining $n-2$ are redundant. If we denote these $n-2$ unknown forces by $R_2, R_3 \ldots R_{n-1}$ and the essential reactive forces by R_1 and R_n the values of R_1 and R_n can be expressed in terms of the external loads and of the unknowns $R_2 \ldots R_{n-1}$ by making use of the equations of static equilibrium for the beam as a whole. If the redundant supports have component movements in the lines of their action, $\delta_2, \delta_3 \ldots \delta_{n-1}$ measured from the level of the line joining support points 1 and n, an application of the first theorem of Castigliano yields the equations

$$\frac{\partial U}{\partial R_2} = \delta_2,$$

$$\frac{\partial U}{\partial R_3} = \delta_3,$$

$$\cdots \cdots \cdots$$

and $$\frac{\partial U}{\partial R_{n-1}} = \delta_{n-1}.$$

152

It should be remembered that δ_2, etc., are positive if the displacements are in the same directions as the assumed reactions. The usual behaviour is for supports to compress, *i.e.* to deflect against the directions of their action. The values of δ in the equations must then be made negative. These equations, together with the equations of static equilibrium, enable all the reactive forces to be calculated.

When they have been found the loading on the beam is completely known and the bending moment and shearing force diagrams can be plotted.

The reactive forces in general act in the opposite direction to the applied loads and the bending moments produced by them are thus of opposite sign to those due to the loads. One effect of continuity is therefore to reduce the bending moments which would occur if the member had consisted of a number of separate beams.

8.2. Wilson's method.

A continuous beam of constant section throughout its length can be analysed by a method due to Dr. George Wilson. This is in principle the same as that given in the previous paragraph in so far that the deflexions of the beam at the points of support are equated to zero in the case of rigid supports or to known values in the case of elastic supports. It differs from it however in the method of obtaining expressions for the deflexions of these points ; these are now found by making use of the equation of the elastic line of the beam. The unknown reactive forces are treated as loads and the bending moment equation is expressed in terms of the known loads and the unknown reactions. A double integration of the bending moment equation gives expressions for the deflexions at the support points and these when equated to the known movements of such points yield, with the equations of static equilibrium, the necessary equations for a complete solution of the problem.

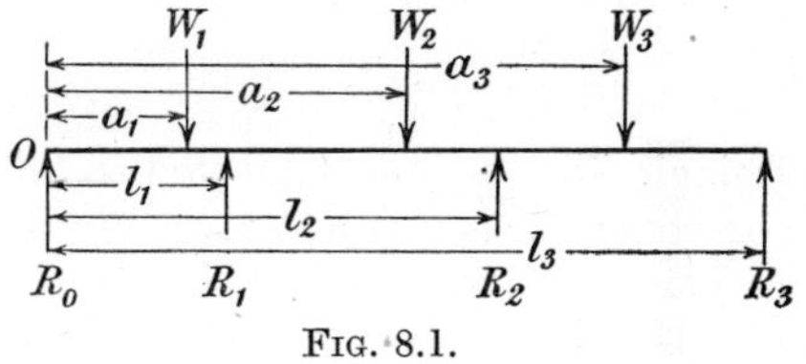

For example, suppose a beam of uniform cross-section and of length l_3 as in Fig. 8.1 is simply supported at its ends and rests on two intermediate supports at distances l_1 and

FIG. 8.1.

l_2 from the left-hand support O, while applied loads W_1, W_2 and W_3 act at distances a_1, a_2 and a_3 respectively from O.

The bending moment at a distance x from O is, using Macaulay's notation,

$$EI\frac{d^2y}{dx^2}=-R_0x+W_1[x-a_1]-R_1[x-l_1]+W_2[x-a_2]-R_2[x-l_2]+W_3[x-a_3],$$

so

$$EI\frac{dy}{dx}=-R_0\frac{x^2}{2}+\frac{W_1}{2}[x-a_1]^2-\frac{R_1}{2}[x-l_1]^2+\frac{W_2}{2}[x-a_2]^2$$
$$-\frac{R_2}{2}[x-l_2]^2+\frac{W_3}{2}[x-a_3]^2+A$$

and

$$EIy=-\frac{R_0x^3}{6}+\frac{W_1}{6}[x-a_1]^3-\frac{R_1}{6}[x-l_1]^3+\frac{W_2}{6}[x-a_2]^3$$
$$-\frac{R_2}{6}[x-l_2]^3+\frac{W_3}{6}[x-a_3]^3+Ax+B,$$

where R_0, R_1 and R_2 are the reactive forces supplied by the supports and A and B are constants of integration.

If there is no sinking of the supports when the external loads are applied, four equations result from the conditions that $y=0$ when $x=0$, l_1, l_2 and l_3 respectively. If the supports sink by specified amounts these values of y are used instead. There are six unknowns and the remaining equations necessary for their evaluation come from a consideration of the equilibrium of the beam as a whole.

Thus, summing vertical forces we have

$$R_0+R_1+R_2+R_3=W_1+W_2+W_3,$$

and taking moments about O we have

$$R_1l_1+R_2l_2+R_3l_3=W_1a_1+W_2a_2+W_3a_3.$$

The reactive forces are thus determinate and the bending moment and shearing force at any section can then be calculated.

8.3. The theorem of three moments.

—Wilson's method is useful if the beam is of constant section throughout its length but if it varies from bay to bay the equations are cumbersome. A more generally applicable method, due originally to Clapeyron, is known as the theorem of three moments. In the first place the general form of this theorem will be proved for any system of transverse loads; extensions to cover components of the axial loads will follow.

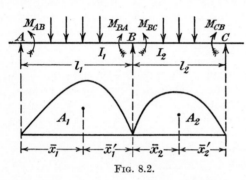

FIG. 8.2.

A continuous beam may be considered to consist of a number of single span beams subjected to known external load systems and to end moments such as M_{AB} and M_{BA} (Fig. 8.2) which are the restraints supplied by the neighbouring spans. The magnitude of these end restraining moments are such as to make the beams continuous over each support; that is to say, considering, for example, the support B, the slope at the end B of the beam AB will be the same as the slope at the end B of the beam BC.

This condition of continuity can be readily expressed in general terms from equations (3.28) and (3.29) which give the slopes at the ends of a simply supported beam subjected to transverse loads and end couples.

Suppose that the area of the bending moment diagram due to the external load system alone on the span AB, considered as a simply supported beam, is A_1 and that the distance of the centroid of this area from the end A is $\bar{x}_1$, then, from equation (3.28), the slope at the end B of AB is

$$\theta_{BA}=\frac{l_1}{6EI_1}\left[M_{AB}+2M_{BA}+\frac{6A_1\bar{x}_1}{l_1{}^2}\right]+\frac{\delta_B-\delta_A}{l_1},$$

where l_1 and I_1 are the length of AB and the relevant second moment of area of the section of the beam respectively, and δ_A and δ_B are the deflexions of the ends A and B when the external load system is applied to the continuous beam.

Similarly if A_2 is the area of the bending moment diagram due to the external load system alone on the span BC considered as simply supported, and $\bar{x}'_2$ is the distance of the centroid of this area from the end C, then the slope at the end B of BC is

$$\theta_{BC} = -\frac{l_2}{6EI_2}\left[M_{CB} + 2M_{BC} + \frac{6A_2\bar{x}'_2}{l_2{}^2}\right] + \frac{\delta_C - \delta_B}{l_2}.$$

Since the beam is continuous at B the slopes given by these expressions must be the same. Equating them we have

$$\frac{l_1}{I_1}M_{AB} + \frac{2l_1}{I_1}M_{BA} + \frac{2l_2}{I_2}M_{BC} + \frac{l_2}{I_2}M_{CB} + \frac{6A_1\bar{x}_1}{l_1 I_1} + \frac{6_2A\bar{x}'_2}{l_2 I_2}$$
$$= \frac{6E(\delta_A - \delta_B)}{l_1} + \frac{6E(\delta_C - \delta_B)}{l_2} \quad . \quad . \quad . \quad . \quad (8.1)$$

A consideration of the equilibrium of the short length of beam immediately above the support B shows that when no external couple is applied to the beam at B

$$M_{BA} = M_{BC}.$$

When, as part of the external load system, a clockwise couple M is applied to the beam at B

$$M_{BA} = M + M_{BC}. \quad . \quad . \quad . \quad . \quad (8.2)$$

For a continuous beam of n spans there will be $2n$ unknown end restraining moments. From a consideration of the slope and equilibrium of the beam at the intermediate supports, $n-1$ equations of type (8.1) and $n-1$ equations of type (8.2) may be obtained. The remaining two equations necessary for the complete determination of the end moments are obtained from a consideration of the conditions at the end supports. The moment at an end support may be known ; if, for instance, the left-hand end A of the beam is simply supported $M_{AB} = 0$. The change of slope of the beam at an end support may be known, and the required equation can be written down immediately from one of the expressions already obtained : for example, if the end C is encastré and there is no sinking of the supports, we have

$$M_{BC} + 2M_{CB} + \frac{6A_2\bar{x}_2}{l_2{}^2} = 0.$$

When the restraining moments at the supports have been evaluated the reactions at the supports may be calculated by equating the moments of internal and external forces about the various supports or by adding the shears on each side of the support algebraically.

As a particular application of the general theorem consider the beam ABCD of uniform section shown in Fig. 8.3 under a triangular distribution of load acting upwards. Let

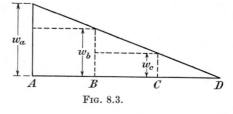

FIG. 8.3.

w_a, w_b, w_c be the intensities of loading at the supports A, B and C which remain collinear.

The B.M. due to the load on BC can be divided into two parts :

(a) Due to a uniform distributed load w_c.

(b) Due to a distributed load varying from 0 to $w_b - w_c$.

The moment of the free B.M. diagram about C is the sum of the moments of (a) and (b).

The moment from (a) is $\quad \dfrac{2l_2}{3} \cdot \dfrac{w_c l_2^2}{8} \cdot \dfrac{l_2}{2} = \dfrac{w_c l_2^4}{24}$.

To find the moment from (b) let $w_b - w_c = w_0$,

then the B.M. at a distance x from C is

$$-\frac{w_0}{6}\left(\frac{x^3}{l_2} - l_2 x\right)$$

and the moment of the B.M. diagram is $-\dfrac{w_0}{6}\displaystyle\int_0^{l_2}\left(\dfrac{x^3}{l_2} - l_2 x\right)x\,dx = \dfrac{w_0 l_2^4}{45}$.

Therefore the total moment of moment is

$$\frac{w_c l_2^4}{24} + \frac{(w_b - w_c)l_2^4}{45} = \frac{l_2^4}{360}(7w_c + 8w_b).$$

Bay AB.—To find the moment of the B.M. diagram due to (b). The area of the B.M. diagram

$$= -\frac{w_0'}{6}\int_0^{l_1}\left(\frac{x^3}{l_1} - l_1 x\right)dx$$

$$= \frac{w_0' l_1^3}{24},$$

where $w_0' = w_a - w_b$.

The moment about $B = \dfrac{w_0' l_1^4}{45}$,

therefore the distance of the C.G. from $B = \dfrac{w_0' l_1^4}{45} \cdot \dfrac{24}{w_0' l_1^3} = \dfrac{24 l_1}{45}$

and the distance of the C.G. from $A = \dfrac{21}{45}l_1 = \dfrac{7l_1}{15}$.

The moment about $A = \dfrac{7l_1}{15} \cdot \dfrac{w_0' l_1^3}{24}$

$$= \frac{7w_0' l_1^4}{360}.$$

The total moment of the area about A

$$= \frac{7w_0' l_1^4}{360} + \frac{w_b l_1^4}{24}$$

$$= \frac{l_1^4}{360}(7w_a + 8w_b).$$

Substituting in the general equation (8.1) we obtain the result

$$\frac{7}{60}w_a l_1^3 + \frac{8}{60}w_b(l_1^3 + l_2^3) + \frac{7}{60}w_c l_2^3 + M_A l_1 + 2M_B(l_1 + l_2) + M_C l_2 = 0.$$

A similar equation is found for the bays BC and CD to connect M_B, M_C and M_D. The other two necessary equations are given by the conditions of support at A and D and all fixing moments can then be evaluated.

When the spans of a continuous beam carry uniformly distributed downward loads only, no external couples being applied at the supports, the general equation (8.1) takes the simple form of the three moment equation.

$$\frac{l_1}{I_1}M_A + 2\left(\frac{l_1}{I_1}+\frac{l_2}{I_2}\right)M_B + \frac{l_2}{I_2}M_C - \frac{w_1 l_1^3}{4I_1} - \frac{w_2 l_2^3}{4I_2}$$
$$= \frac{6E(\delta_A - \delta_B)}{l_1} + \frac{6E(\delta_C - \delta_B)}{l_2}. \quad \cdots \quad (8.3)$$

It must be remembered when using the general equation that the areas A_1 and A_2 were for diagrams in which hogging bending moments were taken as positive.

As an example of the use of equation (8.3) consider the four span continuous beam ABCDE shown in Fig. 8.4. It is of uniform cross-section throughout and carries a uniformly distributed load of intensity w. The supports remain at the same level and the length of each span is l.

Since the beam is simply supported at A and E

$$M_A = M_E = 0.$$

From considerations of symmetry

$$M_B = M_D.$$

The three moment equation for ABC is

$$M_A + 4M_B + M_C - \frac{wl^2}{4} - \frac{wl^2}{4} = 0$$

and for BCD it is

$$M_B + 4M_C + M_D - \frac{wl^2}{4} - \frac{wl^2}{4} = 0.$$

Substituting for M_A and M_D these equations may be written

$$4M_B + M_C = \frac{wl^2}{2}$$

and

$$2M_B + 4M_C = \frac{wl^2}{2},$$

from which

$$M_B = M_D = \frac{3wl^2}{28}$$

and

$$M_C = \frac{wl^2}{14}.$$

The reactions at A may be found by considering the equilibrium of AB. Taking moments about B, we have

$$R_A l - \frac{wl^2}{2} + M_B = 0$$

or

$$R_A = \frac{11wl}{28}.$$

In the same way the reaction at B is found by considering the length AC. Taking moments about C we have

$$2R_A l + R_B l - 2wl^2 + M_C = 0$$

or

$$R_B = \frac{8wl}{7}.$$

For R_C, considering the whole beam and resolving vertically, we have

$$2_A R + 2 R_B + R_C = 4wl$$

or $$R_C = \frac{13wl}{14}.$$

These reactions can be found more elegantly by writing down the shears on each side of each support. Thus

the shear to the left of B is $R_{BL} = \dfrac{wl}{2} + \dfrac{M_B - M_A}{l}$

and that to the right of B is $R_{BR} = \dfrac{wl}{2} + \dfrac{M_B - M_C}{l}$,

so that the reaction at B is

$$R_B = \frac{wl}{2} + \frac{M_B - M_A}{l} + \frac{wl}{2} + \frac{M_B - M_C}{l} = \frac{8wl}{7}.$$

The shearing force diagram for the continuous beam is shown in Fig. 8.4.

The bending moment diagram can be drawn in the usual way by calculating at every section the algebraic sum of the moments of all the applied forces,

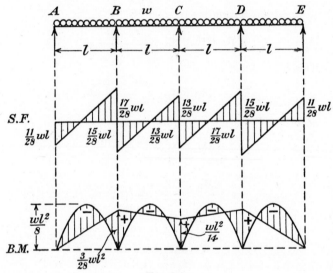

FIG. 8.4.

including the reactions, on one side of the section, but it is usually simpler to follow the method adopted in Fig. 8.4 and deal with each span separately. Span BC, for instance, may be considered to be subjected to two load systems, the first being a uniformly distributed load of intensity w and the second that due to the end couples M_B and M_C. The bending moment diagrams for these separate systems, a parabola and a trapezium respectively, are easily drawn and the net bending moment diagram for the span forming part of the continuous beam is their algebraic sum. As the uniformly distributed load causes a sagging bending moment at each section of BC and the end couples cause a hogging bending moment, the resultant diagram is formed by subtracting the trapezium from the parabola as in Fig. 8.4.

The positions of the points of contraflexure, *i.e.* where the bending moment changes sign, can be seen in the completed diagram.

The two methods given above involve the solution of simultaneous equations and though this is not usually an arduous matter in continuous beam problems it is sometimes an advantage to avoid it. This can be done by applying the moment distribution method described in Chapter 10.

8.4. The generalised theorem of three moments.—The complete solution of the problem of a continuous beam under a distributed transverse load and axial end loads was derived for the design of early biplanes (Booth and Bolas, 1915). The original solution was in too cumbersome a form for general use, but in the following year a simplified method was published (Berry, 1916) which will be followed here.

We shall consider the top spar ABC . . . of a biplane, A being the outermost support (Fig. 8.5). As in the notation used elsewhere in this chapter M_A, M_B, M_C . . . denote the fixing moments at A, B, C . . . considered positive when they tend to produce convexity upwards. The deflexion at any point

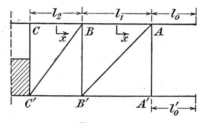

FIG. 8.5.

is denoted by y, the intensity of loading by w. Dimensions are as in Fig. 8.5. The distance of any point in a member is measured from the centre point of the span and is counted positive in the direction B to A or C to B.

As before $\mu = \sqrt{\dfrac{P}{EI}}$, where P is the total compressive end load in the span arising from the diagonal bracing and E and I have their usual significance ; also $\alpha = \dfrac{\mu l}{2}$, α being measured in radians.

Suffixes are used to denote the particular span under consideration though where there is no risk of confusion these are dropped.

The bending moment at any point is

$$M = EI \frac{d^2y}{dx^2}.$$

Taking moments about any point in AB we obtain the equation

$$EI\frac{d^2y}{dx^2} + Py = \frac{w}{2}\left(\frac{l}{2} - x\right)^2 + S_A\left(x - \frac{l}{2}\right) + M_A$$

where S_A is the shear at A.

Differentiating this equation twice we get

$$\frac{d^2M}{dx^2} + \mu^2 M = w.$$

The solution of this is

$$M = A \sin \mu x + B \cos \mu x + \frac{w}{\mu^2}, \quad \cdot \quad \cdot \quad \cdot \quad \cdot \quad (8.4)$$

where A and B are constants of integration.

When $\qquad\qquad x = \frac{l}{2}, \quad M = M_A$

and when $\qquad\qquad x = -\frac{l}{2}, \quad M = M_B.$

Therefore $\qquad\qquad M_A = A \sin \alpha + B \cos \alpha + \frac{w}{\mu^2},$

$$M_B = -A \sin \alpha + B \cos \alpha + \frac{w}{\mu^2}.$$

These give $\qquad\qquad A = \dfrac{M_A - M_B}{2 \sin \alpha}$

and $\qquad\qquad B = \dfrac{M_A + M_B}{2 \cos \alpha} - \dfrac{w}{\mu^2 \cos \alpha}.$

Substituting for A and B in (8.4) we have

$$M = \frac{M_A - M_B}{2} \frac{\sin \mu x}{\sin \alpha} + \frac{M_A + M_B}{2} \frac{\cos \mu x}{\cos \alpha} + \frac{w}{\mu^2}\left(1 - \frac{\cos \mu x}{\cos \alpha}\right) \quad \cdot \quad (8.5)$$

and integrating this equation twice we have

$$EIy = -\frac{M_A - M_B}{2} \frac{\sin \mu x}{\mu^2 \sin \alpha} - \frac{M_A + M_B}{2} \frac{\cos \mu x}{\mu^2 \cos \alpha} + \frac{w \cos \mu x}{\mu^4 \cos \alpha}$$

$$- \frac{w}{2\mu^2}\left(\frac{l^2}{4} - x^2\right) + A_1\left(x + \frac{l}{2}\right) + B_1\left(x - \frac{l}{2}\right), \quad \cdot \quad (8.6)$$

where A_1 and B_1 are constants of integration.

Now $y = 0$ when $x = \pm\frac{l}{2}$,

therefore $\qquad\qquad 0 = -\dfrac{M_A}{\mu^2} + \dfrac{w}{\mu^4} + A_1 l$

and $\qquad\qquad 0 = -\dfrac{M_B}{\mu^2} + \dfrac{w}{\mu^4} - B_1 l.$

Substituting in (8.6) we obtain

$$EIy = -\frac{M_A - M_B}{2} \frac{\sin \mu x}{\mu^2 \sin \alpha} - \frac{M_A + M_B}{2} \frac{\cos \mu x}{\mu^2 \cos \alpha} + \frac{w}{\mu^4}\left(\frac{\cos \mu x}{\cos \alpha} - 1\right)$$

$$- \frac{w}{2\mu^2}\left(\frac{l^2}{4} - x^2\right) + (M_A - M_B)\frac{x}{l\mu^2} + \frac{M_A + M_B}{2\mu^2} \quad \cdot \quad (8.7)$$

Differentiation of this gives

$$EI\frac{dy}{dx} = -\frac{M_A - M_B}{2} \frac{\cos \mu x}{\mu \sin \alpha} + \frac{M_A + M_B}{2} \frac{\sin \mu x}{\mu \cos \alpha} - \frac{w \sin \mu x}{\mu^3 \cos \alpha} + \frac{wx}{\mu^2} + \frac{M_A - M_B}{l\mu^2}. \quad (8.8)$$

The slope at B is the same whether we consider it from the point of view of the span AB or the span BC and so by using equation (8.8) for both spans in turn and equating the slopes when $x=-\dfrac{l_1}{2}$ and $x=+\dfrac{l_2}{2}$, we have

$$\frac{1}{I_1}\left(-\frac{M_A-M_B}{2}\frac{\cot \alpha_1}{\mu_1}-\frac{M_A+M_B}{2}\frac{\tan \alpha_1}{\mu_1}+\frac{w_1}{\mu_1{}^3}\tan \alpha_1-\frac{w_1 l_1}{2\mu_1{}^2}+\frac{M_A-M_B}{l_1\mu_1{}^2}\right)$$

$$=\frac{1}{I_2}\left(-\frac{M_B-M_C}{2}\frac{\cot \alpha_2}{\mu_2}+\frac{M_B+M_C}{2}\frac{\tan \alpha_2}{\mu_2}-\frac{w_2}{\mu_2{}^3}\tan \alpha_2+\frac{w_2 l_2}{2\mu_2{}^2}+\frac{M_B-M_C}{l_2\mu_2{}^2}\right).$$

This equation, on rearranging, can be written

$$\frac{l_1 M_A}{I_1}\left(\frac{3}{2}\cdot\frac{2\alpha_1\cosec 2\alpha_1-1}{\alpha_1{}^2}\right)+\frac{l_2 M_C}{I_2}\left(\frac{3}{2}\cdot\frac{2\alpha_2\cosec 2\alpha_2-1}{\alpha_2{}^2}\right)$$

$$+\frac{2l_1 M_B}{I_1}\frac{3}{4}\cdot\frac{1-2\alpha_1\cot 2\alpha_1}{\alpha_1{}^2}+\frac{2l_2 M_B}{I_2}\frac{3}{4}\cdot\frac{1-2\alpha_2\cot 2\alpha_2}{\alpha_2{}^2}$$

$$=\frac{w_1 l_1{}^3}{4I_1}\cdot 3\cdot\frac{\tan \alpha_1-\alpha_1}{\alpha_1{}^3}+\frac{w_2 l_2{}^3}{4I_2}\cdot 3\cdot\frac{\tan \alpha_2-\alpha_2}{\alpha_2{}^3},$$

or writing

$$\left.\begin{aligned}
f(\alpha)&=\frac{3}{2}\cdot\frac{2\alpha\cosec 2\alpha-1}{\alpha^2},\\[4pt]
\phi(\alpha)&=\frac{3}{4}\cdot\frac{1-2\alpha\cot 2\alpha}{\alpha^2},\\[4pt]
\psi(\alpha)&=3\cdot\frac{\tan \alpha-\alpha}{\alpha^3},
\end{aligned}\right\} \quad \cdots \cdots \quad (8.9)$$

we get

$$\frac{l_1}{I_1}M_A f(\alpha_1)+\frac{l_2}{I_2}M_C f(\alpha_2)+2M_B\left\{\frac{l_1}{I_1}\phi(\alpha_1)+\frac{l_2}{I_2}\phi(\alpha_2)\right\}=\frac{w_1 l_1{}^3}{4I_1}\psi(\alpha_1)+\frac{w_2 l_2{}^3}{4I_2}\psi(\alpha_2). \quad (8.10)$$

This is the most general form of the equation of three moments for a continuous beam.

If instead of compressions the spars carry tensions,

$$\frac{l_1}{I_1}M_A F(\alpha_1)+\frac{l_2}{I_2}M_C F(\alpha_2)+2M_B\left\{\frac{l_1}{I_1}\Phi(\alpha_1)+\frac{l_2}{I_2}\Phi(\alpha_2)\right\}$$

$$=\frac{w_1 l_1{}^3}{4I_1}\Psi(\alpha_1)+\frac{w_2 l_2{}^3}{4I_2}\Psi(\alpha_2), \quad (8.11)$$

where

$$\left.\begin{aligned}
F(\alpha)&=\frac{3}{2}\cdot\frac{1-2\alpha\cosech 2\alpha}{\alpha^2},\\[4pt]
\Phi(\alpha)&=\frac{3}{4}\cdot\frac{2\alpha\coth 2\alpha-1}{\alpha^2},\\[4pt]
\Psi(\alpha)&=3\cdot\frac{\alpha-\tanh \alpha}{\alpha^3}.
\end{aligned}\right\} \quad \cdots \cdots \quad (8.12)$$

If $\alpha=0$ the corresponding functions are unity and the ordinary equation of three moments is at once deduced from (8.10) by putting $P_1=P_2=0$. If one span is in tension and the other in compression the corresponding series of functions must be used. Suppose for example AB is in tension and BC in compression, we write

$$\frac{l_1}{I_1}M_A F(\alpha_1)+\frac{l_2}{I_2}M_C f(\alpha_2)+2M_B\left\{\frac{l_1}{I_1}\Phi(\alpha_1)+\frac{l_2}{I_2}\phi(\alpha_2)\right\}=\frac{w_1 l_1^3}{4I_1}\Psi(\alpha_1)+\frac{w_2 l_2^3}{4I_2}\psi(\alpha_2). \quad (8.13)$$

The values of the functions (8.9) and (8.12) were tabulated by Berry, to whom the results are due, and are given in the Appendix.

Maximum Bending Moment.—From equation (8.5), on putting $\mu = \dfrac{2\alpha}{l}$ and rearranging, we find that the bending moment at any point in AB is

$$M = \frac{wl^2}{4\alpha^2} - \left(\frac{wl^2}{4\alpha^2} - \frac{M_A + M_B}{2}\right)\frac{\cos \mu x}{\cos \alpha} + \frac{M_A - M_B}{2}\frac{\sin \mu x}{\sin \alpha}.$$

It is easy to show that M is a numerical maximum when

$$\tan \mu x = - \frac{\dfrac{M_A - M_B}{2}}{\dfrac{wl^2}{4\alpha^2} - \dfrac{M_A + M_B}{2}} \cot \alpha, \qquad . \quad . \quad . \quad . \quad (8.14)$$

which gives the distance from the middle of the span to the point where the bending moment is greatest.

If μx obtained from this equation is numerically greater than α there is no maximum, the bending moment increasing steadily from M_A to M_B.

But if μx is less than α,

$$M_{max} = \frac{wl^2}{4\alpha^2} - \frac{\dfrac{wl^2}{4\alpha^2} - \dfrac{M_A + M_B}{2}}{\cos \mu x \cos \alpha}. \quad . \quad . \quad . \quad . \quad . \quad (8.15)$$

The corresponding formulas for a member under tension are

$$\tanh \mu x = - \frac{\dfrac{M_A + M_B}{2}}{\dfrac{wl^2}{4\alpha^2} + \dfrac{M_A + M_B}{2}} \coth \alpha \qquad . \quad . \quad . \quad (8.16)$$

and

$$M_{max} = - \frac{wl^2}{4\alpha^2} + \frac{\dfrac{wl^2}{4\alpha^2} + \dfrac{M_A + M_B}{2}}{\cosh \mu x \cosh \alpha}. \quad . \quad . \quad . \quad (8.17)$$

For a spar subjected to neither compression nor tension we obtain

$$M = \frac{w}{2}\left(x^2 - \frac{l^2}{4}\right) + \frac{M_A + M_B}{2} + (M_A - M_B)\frac{x}{l}.$$

The maximum value occurs where $x = - \dfrac{M_A - M_B}{wl}$ $\quad . \quad . \quad . \quad . \quad (8.18)$

and is

$$M_{max} = - \frac{wl^2}{8} + \frac{M_A + M_B}{2} - \frac{(M_A - M_B)^2}{2wl^2}. \quad . \quad . \quad . \quad (8.19)$$

8.5. The continuous column.—A particular instance, to which equations similar to those derived in the last paragraph are applicable, is that of the compression member continuous through a number of storeys or panels. If such a member has imperfections represented by an initial curvature of the axis the end moments in each length may be determined from the three moment equations derived from expressions similar to (7.40) and (7.41).

Such equations would apply to a member connected to the other parts of the structure by perfectly free joints and subjected to axial loads only. These conditions are rarely found in practice. The connexion between the members will usually have some rigidity so that any change of slope of the compression member will be resisted, restraining moments being induced at the ends of each length where connexion is made to the other members in the structure. A discussion of this is outside the scope of this chapter, but a number of examples will be found in the Second Report of the Steel Structures Research Committee (Baker, 1934). In many structures such as building frames the continuous column is subjected to large moments in addition to axial loads, arising from the applications of load to the other members of the structure. This is dealt with in Chapters 10 and 18.

REFERENCES

Booth, H. and Bolas, H. 1915. Air Department, Admiralty. H.M.S.O.
Berry, A. 1916. *Trans. R. Aero. Soc. G.B.*, **1**.
Baker, J. F. 1934. Steel Structures Research Cttee. Second Report. H.M.S.O.

EXERCISES

(These exercises should be solved by all of the methods described in this Chapter.)

(1) A girder ABCD is continuous over the supports B and C and freely supported at A and D. The spans are AB = 10 feet; BC = 12 feet; CD = 15 feet. AB carries a uniformly distributed load of 1 ton per foot, BC $0 \cdot 8$ ton per foot, and CD $0 \cdot 5$ ton per foot.

Sketch neatly the bending moment and shearing force diagrams for the beam, indicating the principal values on your diagrams.

$(M_B = 10 \cdot 3$ *tons-feet*; $M_C = 11 \cdot 9$ *tons-feet*.
$R_{AR} = 3 \cdot 97$ *tons*; $R_{BR} = 4 \cdot 67$ *tons*; $R_{CR} = 4 \cdot 55$ *tons*
$R_{BL} = 6 \cdot 03$ *tons*; $R_{CL} = 4 \cdot 93$ *tons*; $R_{DL} = 2 \cdot 95$ *tons*.)

(2) A continuous girder rests on four supports A, B, C and D at the same level, and carries a uniform load of 1 ton per foot run. The spans are AB = 15 feet; BC = 20 feet and CD = 12 feet.

Determine the bending moments at the supports and the reactions on the supports.

$(M_B = 32 \cdot 7$ *tons-feet*; $M_C = 27 \cdot 8$ *tons-feet*.
$R_A = 5 \cdot 32$ *tons*; $R_B = 19 \cdot 92$ *tons*; $R_C = 18 \cdot 06$ *tons*; $R_D = 3 \cdot 70$ *tons*.)

(3) A beam AB which is 23 feet long is encastré at A and supported at points C and D, which are 8 feet and 20 feet respectively from A. The beam carries a load of 10 tons at a point 4 feet from A, 2 tons at B and a uniformly distributed load of 1 ton per foot between C and D.

Sketch the bending moment and shearing force diagrams.

CHAPTER 9

FRAMES WITH STIFF JOINTS

9.1. Stiff joints.—In earlier chapters we have dealt with the stress analysis of braced frameworks upon the assumption that the bars forming them were pinned together at the ends. Such joints as these cannot, theoretically, transmit bending moments so that when a pin-jointed frame is loaded at the nodes the forces in the component members are pure tensions or compressions. In practice it is very seldom that even an attempt is made to obtain pin joints in a frame ; connexions are usually made by rivetted or bolted joints which restrain the free movement of the ends of the members. A joint between two components of a structure which can transmit a bending moment will be referred to as a stiff joint and the degree of stiffness will depend upon the type of joint. A practical pinned joint will have some stiffness due to the friction between the pin and the members, and between

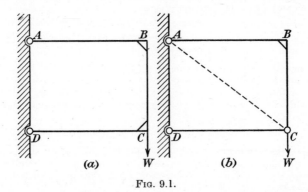

(a)   W   (b)   W

Fig. 9.1.

this degree of stiffness and that of perfect rigidity there are infinite possibilities. A convenient measure of stiffness is the change of angle between two members connected by the joint when a unit moment is applied to the members. When the joint is pinned the change of angle will be a maximum ; when it is infinitely stiff the change will be zero. This method of measuring stiffness will be defined more precisely later ; for the moment it is only necessary to appreciate the importance of stiffness as affecting stress distribution. For the present, then, joints will be considered to be rigid ; any modifications to methods of analysis when they are only partially fixed will be considered later.

To understand the function of a stiff joint in a frame, consider the simplest case of a quadrilateral frame as shown in Fig. 9.1.

If joints at B and C are to be connected to the pins A and D by a pin-jointed skeleton frame, four members AB, AC, BC and CD are essential. If, however, the joint at B is stiff, as shown at (b) in the same figure, the members AB and BC form a single cranked bar and joint C is effectively braced to A and D by this bar and DC. The diagonal member AC is

164

redundant and can be omitted. Each rigid joint is thus equivalent to a member and the frame at (a) has one redundancy.

As another example, consider the frame shown in Fig. 9.2 in which A, F and E are pinned supports to which the joints B, C and D are to be braced. For the construction of a just-stiff frame six members are required and if joints B, C and D were all pins the arrangement would be incomplete since only five bars are provided. If, however, joint B is made rigid, we have the equivalent of six members, *i.e.* five bars and one stiff joint, and the structure is just stiff. Node C is located by the cranked bar ABC and FC, while D is braced to C and E by the pin-jointed bars CD and ED. Any stiff connexions additional to that at B will introduce redundancies. Thus, the frame shown at (a) in Fig. 9.2 consists of the continuous member BCD to which the end verticals AB and ED are rigidly attached. The remaining bar FC is connected to it by a pinned joint and the equivalent number of members thus provided is made up as follows :

Five bars, AB, BC, CD, FC and ED.

One stiff joint at B and one at D.

One stiff joint at C due to the continuity of BC and CD.

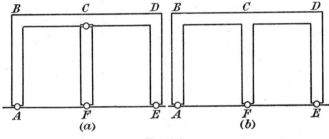

Fig. 9.2.

Eight equivalent members are thus provided and since only six are essential the frame has two redundant elements. If the vertical member FC is connected to the continuous member BCD by a rigid joint as shown at (b) in Fig. 9.2 instead of by a pin, an extra redundancy is introduced. Later examples will indicate which " members " are most conveniently taken as redundancies for the purposes of analysis.

Frames of this type are very common in engineering construction, the framed building being perhaps the best example of the use of stiff joints to replace diagonal bracing members, but rigid jointed portals occur in many other structures. Methods of analysis are therefore important and the treatment of this type of structure by the three methods of strain energy, slope deflexion and moment distribution will be described.

9.2. Strain energy analysis of stiff-jointed frames.—The general theory of this method has already been developed in earlier chapters and examples of its application to special problems will now be given. In the first place consider the portal shown in Fig. 9.3 which consists of a frame ACDB having rigid joints at C and D and pinned to fixed points at A and B. The dimensions are shown on the figure and a single load W is carried in the position indicated. All members of the frame are supposed to be of the same section. As already shown in the previous paragraph this frame has one redundancy.

If the joint B, instead of being pinned, rested on a frictionless support, ACDB would be simply a cranked beam and the bending moment diagram could be plotted without difficulty. Since B is fixed in position however, a horizontal reactive force H_B will be exerted by the pin and it is convenient to take this force as the redundant element.

Then, by the second theorem of Castigliano

$$\frac{dU}{dH_B} = 0,$$

where U is the total strain energy of the frame.

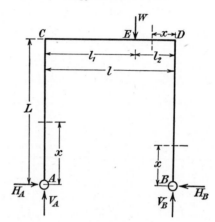

FIG. 9.3.

This strain energy is the sum of that due to bending in all members of the frame and that due to axial compression and shear. The last two components are generally negligible compared with the first, and will be ignored in the present example.

Then
$$\frac{dU}{dH_B} = \frac{1}{EI} \int M_x \frac{dM_x}{dH_B} dx = 0,$$

where M_x is the bending moment at any point and the integration extends round the whole frame.

The conditions for static equilibrium of the frame are :

$$V_A + V_B = W$$
$$H_A = H_B$$
$$V_B l = W l_1$$

which give

$$V_B = \frac{W l_1}{l} \text{ and } V_A = \frac{W l_2}{l}.$$

If
$$H_A = H_B = H,$$

then for the member BD, measuring x from B, we have

$$M_x = H x$$

and
$$\frac{dM_x}{dH} = x.$$

∴
$$\left[\frac{dU}{dH} \right]_{BD} = \frac{1}{EI} \int_0^L H x^2 dx = \frac{H L^3}{3EI}.$$

For the section DE of the top beam, measuring x from D, we have

$$M_x = HL - V_B x = HL - \frac{Wl_1 x}{l}$$

and

$$\frac{dM_x}{dH} = L.$$

$$\therefore \quad \left[\frac{dU}{dH}\right]_{DE} = \frac{L}{EI} \int_0^{l_2} \left(HL - \frac{Wl_1 x}{l}\right) dx = \frac{Ll_2}{EI}\left(HL - \frac{Wl_1 l_2}{2l}\right).$$

Similarly for AC and CE, measuring x from A and C respectively we have

$$\left[\frac{dU}{dH}\right]_{AC} = \frac{HL^3}{3EI}$$

and

$$\left[\frac{dU}{dH}\right]_{CE} = \frac{Ll_1}{EI}\left(HL - \frac{Wl_1 l_2}{2l}\right).$$

Adding the components we obtain for the whole frame, since EI is the same throughout,

$$EI\frac{dU}{dH} = \frac{2HL^3}{3} + Ll\left(HL - \frac{Wl_1 l_2}{2l}\right) = 0$$

and so

$$H = \frac{3l_1 l_2 W}{2L(2L + 3l)}.$$

If, for example, $L = 20$ feet, $l_1 = 6$ feet and $l_2 = 4$ feet, we find

$$H = \frac{18W}{700}$$

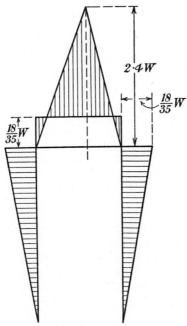

FIG. 9.4.

and the bending moment diagram for the portal is shown in Fig. 9.4 which is plotted from the equations for M_x used in the analysis.

If the structure and load system are symmetrical it is only necessary to consider one half of the structure, and as the next example we shall consider the portal shown in Fig. 9.5 which has a uniformly distributed load on the top member. The feet of the vertical members are now assumed to be rigidly fixed instead of pinned as in the first example.

If the vertical member CD were cut through at D the frame would be statically determinate, consisting simply of a double cranked cantilever built in at A and free at D. In order to restore the conditions existing before the cut was made it is necessary to impose at D a bending moment M_0, a vertical reaction V_0 and a horizontal reaction H_0. These resultant actions must be of such magnitude as to prevent the section at D from any movement either

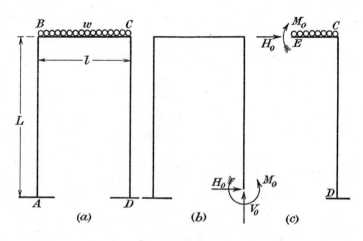

FIG. 9.5.

of translation or rotation and the conditions for this are, by the first theorem of Castigliano,

movement of D in a vertical direction $\quad = \dfrac{\partial U}{\partial V_0} = 0,$

movement of D in a horizontal direction $= \dfrac{\partial U}{\partial H_0} = 0,$

rotation of D $\quad = \dfrac{\partial U}{\partial M_0} = 0.$

The solution of these equations determines the values of the resultant actions at D in the original state of the frame.

This would be the method adopted in the general case of the problem now under consideration, e.g. if the load were not symmetrically placed on the structure or if the second moments of area of the vertical members were not equal. In the present instance, however, we are assuming symmetry both of structure and of loading and the solution may be simplified. Suppose the top member to be cut at E on the axis of symmetry of the frame as shown at (c) in the figure and the resultant actions there to be replaced by an external moment M_0 and a horizontal force H_0. From symmetry there can be no shearing force at E and the number of unknowns is reduced by one.

Then, since the section at E neither rotates nor moves laterally, M_0 and H_0 must satisfy the conditions

$$\frac{\partial U}{\partial M_0}=0 \; ; \; \frac{\partial U}{\partial H_0}=0.$$

As in the previous example we shall neglect all energy except that due to bending and then

$$\frac{\partial U}{\partial M_0}=\frac{1}{EI}\int M_x \frac{\partial M_x}{\partial M_0}dx=0$$

and

$$\frac{\partial U}{\partial H_0}=\frac{1}{EI}\int M_x \frac{\partial M_x}{\partial H_0}dx=0.$$

For the section EC, when x is measured from E we have

$$M_x=-M_0+\frac{wx^2}{2},$$

so

$$\frac{\partial M_x}{\partial M_0}=-1 \text{ and } \frac{\partial M_x}{\partial H_0}=0.$$

Hence

$$\left[\frac{\partial U}{\partial M_0}\right]_{EC}=\frac{1}{EI}\int_0^{l/2}\left(M_0-\frac{wx^2}{2}\right)dx$$

$$=\frac{1}{EI}\left[\frac{M_0 l}{2}-\frac{wl^3}{48}\right].$$

For the section CD, measuring x from C, we have

$$M_x=-M_0+\frac{wl^2}{8}-H_0 x,$$

$$\frac{\partial M_x}{\partial M_0}=-1 \text{ and } \frac{\partial M_x}{\partial H_0}=-x.$$

$$\therefore \left[\frac{\partial U}{\partial M_0}\right]_{CD}=\frac{1}{EI}\int_0^L\left(M_0-\frac{wl^2}{8}+H_0 x\right)dx=\frac{1}{EI}\left[M_0 L-\frac{wl^2 L}{8}+\frac{H_0 L^2}{2}\right]$$

and $\left[\frac{\partial U}{\partial H_0}\right]_{CD}=\frac{1}{EI}\int_0^L\left(M_0-\frac{wl^2}{8}+H_0 x\right)xdx=\frac{1}{EI}\left[\frac{M_0 L^2}{2}-\frac{wl^2 L^2}{16}+\frac{H_0 L^3}{3}\right].$

Hence, adding the appropriate terms for the half-frame, we obtain

$$\left.\begin{array}{c} M_0\left(L+\frac{l}{2}\right)-\frac{wl^2}{8}\left(L+\frac{l}{6}\right)+\frac{H_0 L^2}{2}=0 \\[2mm] \frac{M_0 L}{2}-\frac{wl^2 L}{16}+\frac{H_0 L^2}{3}=0 \end{array}\right\}.$$

The solution of these equations is

$$H_0=\frac{wl^3}{4L(L+2l)},$$

$$M_0=\frac{wl^2}{24}\left(\frac{3L+2l}{L+2l}\right)$$

and from symmetry the vertical reaction at D is $\frac{wl}{2}$.

The bending moment diagram for one half of this frame is shown in Fig. 9.6 when $L=1\cdot5l$.

A final example of structures of this type is shown in Fig. 9.7 in which the pinned supports of the vertical members are not at the same level. As in the first example the redundant element will be taken to be H_A.

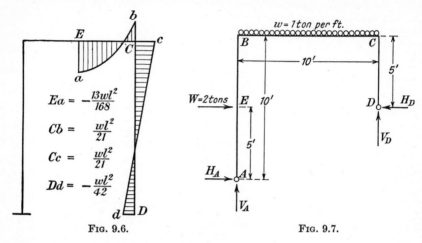

$$Ea = -\frac{13wl^2}{168}$$

$$Cb = \frac{wl^2}{21}$$

$$Cc = \frac{wl^2}{21}$$

$$Dd = -\frac{wl^2}{42}$$

FIG. 9.6.   FIG. 9.7.

The conditions for static equilibrium are
$$H_D=H_A+2$$
$$V_A+V_D=10$$
$$10V_D-5W+5H_D-50w=0, \text{ by moments about A.}$$

Substituting the specified values for W and w we obtain
$$V_A=5+0\cdot5H_A,$$
$$H_D=2+H_A,$$
$$V_D=5-0\cdot5H_A.$$

To determine H_A we have
$$\frac{dU}{dH_A}=\frac{1}{EI}\int M_x\frac{dM_x}{dH_A}dx=0.$$

For AE, measuring x from A,
$$M_x=H_Ax.$$

and
$$\left[\frac{dU}{dH_A}\right]_{AE}=\frac{1}{EI}\int_0^5 H_Ax^2dx=\frac{125H_A}{3EI}.$$

For EB, measuring x from A, we have
$$M_x=H_Ax+2(x-5),$$

and
$$\left[\frac{dU}{dH_A}\right]_{EB}=\frac{1}{EI}\int_5^{10}(H_Ax^2+2x^2-10x)dx=\frac{1}{EI}\left[\frac{875H_A}{3}+\frac{625}{3}\right].$$

For BC, measuring x from B, we have
$$M_x=10H_A+10-V_Ax+\frac{x^2}{2}$$

and substituting for V_A in terms of H_A this gives
$$M_x=H_A(10-0\cdot5x)+10-5x+\frac{x^2}{2}$$

This is an important point : V_A is a function of H_A and it is essential to substitute its value before differentiating the expression or a wrong value of $\dfrac{dM_x}{dH_A}$ will be found.

Thus
$$\frac{dM_x}{dH_A} = 10 - 0 \cdot 5x$$

and
$$\left[\frac{dU}{dH_A}\right]_{BC} = \frac{1}{EI}\int_0^{10}\left\{ H_A(10-0\cdot 5x)^2 + (100-5x) - 5x(10-0\cdot 5x) \right.$$

$$\left. + \frac{x^2}{2}(10-0\cdot 5x) \right\} dx$$

$$= \frac{1}{EI}\int_0^{10}\{H_A(10-0\cdot 5x)^2 + 100 - 55x + 7\cdot 5x^2 - 0\cdot 25x^3\}dx$$

$$= \frac{1}{EI}\left[\frac{1750}{3}H_A + 125\right].$$

For CD it is convenient to measure x from D,

then
$$M_x = H_D x = (H_A + 2)x,$$

and
$$\left[\frac{dU}{dH_A}\right]_{CD} = \frac{1}{EI}\int_0^5 (H_A+2)x^2 dx = \frac{1}{EI}\left[\frac{125}{3}H_A + \frac{250}{3}\right].$$

Adding the components we have

$$\frac{dU}{dH_A} = \frac{1}{3EI}(2875H_A + 1250) = 0$$

from which we determine

$$\left.\begin{array}{rl} H_A = & -0\cdot 4 \text{ tons} \\ V_A = & 4\cdot 8 \quad ,, \\ H_D = & 1\cdot 6 \quad ,, \\ V_D = & 5\cdot 2 \quad ,, \end{array}\right\}.$$

The bending moment diagram is shown in Fig. 9.8.

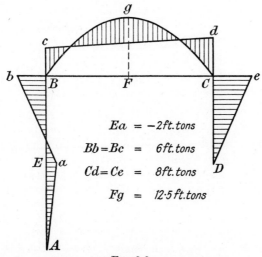

$$Ea = -2\,ft.tons$$
$$Bb = Bc = 6\,ft.tons$$
$$Cd = Ce = 8\,ft.tons$$
$$Fg = 12\cdot 5\,ft.tons$$

Fig. 9.8.

The strain energy method of analysis illustrated in the foregoing examples is very useful for simple portals but is complicated for more elaborate structures. If, for example, the structure shown at (b) in Fig. 9.2 were rigidly fixed at A, F and E it would have six redundant elements as shown by an application of the method described for determining the number of redundancies in such a frame as is also obvious if we imagine the verticals to be cut at F and E. The remaining structure is a doubly cranked cantilever ABDE held at A with a free arm CF attached. By making these cuts we have removed a moment, a vertical force and a horizontal force at both F and E and these six resultant actions may be taken as the redundant elements in an analysis. For a solution of this problem therefore we must form and solve the six simultaneous equations

$$\frac{\partial U}{\partial M_F}=\frac{\partial U}{\partial V_F}=\frac{\partial U}{\partial H_F}=\frac{\partial U}{\partial M_E}=\frac{\partial U}{\partial V_E}=\frac{\partial U}{\partial H_E}=0.$$

This is a laborious task and if the number of bays is increased beyond two the work involved may be prohibitive. Approximate methods are therefore necessary and will be discussed in Chapters 10 and 18.

9.3. Slope deflexion analysis of rigidly jointed frames.—Another method of determining the stresses in the members of a framework with stiff joints makes use of the slope deflexion expressions already set out in paragraph 3.13.

Equations are derived in much the same way as were the three moment equations for a continuous beam. In general each member of a framework is subjected, in addition to the external loads, to restraining moments at its ends transmitted through the stiff joints. These moments can be expressed in terms of the unknown slopes and deflexions at the ends of the members. By considering the equilibrium of each joint in the frame and of the frame as a whole, a sufficient number of equations can be obtained to enable all the slopes and deflexions to be evaluated. The restraining moments and the stresses at any point in the frame can then be found without difficulty.

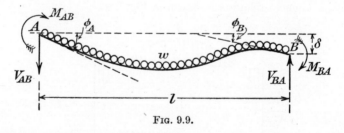

Fig. 9.9.

Though the method is capable of dealing with any type of frame, complication will be avoided here by confining attention to members of uniform cross-section carrying uniformly distributed or point loads. The usual assumption will be made that deformations due to shear and to direct stress, and also the effect of the direct thrust on the flexure of a member, are negligible.

When an initially straight horizontal member AB of uniform cross-section and length l is subjected to a uniformly distributed load of intensity w and to clockwise end couples M_{AB} and M_{BA} as shown in Fig. 9.9, where all the loads and reactions applied to the member and all changes of slope and deflexion suffered by it are shown in positive directions, ϕ_A and ϕ_B the changes of slope at A and B, are given by

$$\phi_A = \frac{l}{6EI}\left[2M_{AB}-M_{BA}+\frac{wl^2}{4}\right]+\frac{\delta}{l} \quad . \quad . \quad . \quad . \quad (9.1)$$

and

$$\phi_B = -\frac{l}{6EI}\left[M_{AB}-2M_{BA}+\frac{wl^2}{4}\right]+\frac{\delta}{l}. \quad . \quad . \quad . \quad (9.2)$$

The solution of these gives

$$M_{AB} = \frac{2EI}{l}\left[2\phi_A+\phi_B-\frac{3\delta}{l}\right]-\frac{wl^2}{12} \quad . \quad . \quad . \quad . \quad . \quad (9.3)$$

and

$$M_{BA} = \frac{2EI}{l}\left[\phi_A+2\phi_B-\frac{3\delta}{l}\right]+\frac{wl^2}{12} \quad . \quad . \quad . \quad . \quad . \quad (9.4)$$

By taking moments about A and B the reactions are found to be

$$V_{AB} = -\frac{wl}{2}+\frac{6EI}{l^2}\left[\phi_A+\phi_B-\frac{2\delta}{l}\right] \quad . \quad . \quad . \quad . \quad (9.5)$$

and

$$V_{BA} = +\frac{wl}{2}+\frac{6EI}{l^2}\left[\phi_A+\phi_B-\frac{2\delta}{l}\right] \quad . \quad . \quad . \quad . \quad (9.6)$$

The use of these equations can be illustrated by considering a symmetrical portal of the type illustrated in Fig. 9.5. When the uniformly distributed load is applied to the beam it bends, changing its slope at the ends. Since

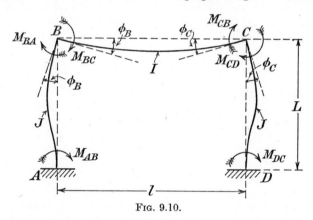

Fig. 9.10.

the joints of the portal are perfectly rigid the tops of the stanchions must suffer the same changes of slope as the ends of the beam to which they are attached, as shown in Fig. 9.10. It follows from a consideration of symmetry that $\phi_C = -\phi_B$ and that B and C have neither horizontal nor, since deformation due to direct stresses are negligible, vertical movement. It is now possible to write down relations between the changes of slope and the restraining moments applied to the ends of the members by the joints shown, Fig. 9.10, in their positive (clockwise) directions. From equation (9.3)

$$M_{BC} = \frac{2EI}{l}\phi_B-\frac{wl^2}{12} \quad . \quad . \quad . \quad . \quad . \quad (9.7)$$

also, since $\phi_A = 0$, the foot of the stanchion being rigidly fixed,

$$M_{BA} = \frac{2EJ}{L}[2\phi_B] \quad . \quad . \quad . \quad . \quad . \quad (9.8)$$

where J and L are the second moment of area and height of the stanchion respectively.

From the equilibrium of the joint B, neglecting the widths of the members, it follows that

$$M_{BA} + M_{BC} = 0 \quad . \quad . \quad . \quad . \quad . \quad . \quad . \quad (9.9)$$

so that

$$\frac{2EJ}{L}[2\phi_B] + \frac{2EI}{l}[\phi_B] - \frac{wl^2}{12} = 0$$

or

$$\phi_B = \frac{wl^2}{24\left(\dfrac{2J}{L} + \dfrac{I}{l}\right)E}.$$

Substituting in equations (9.7) and (9.8) we obtain

$$M_{BA} = -M_{BC} = \frac{\dfrac{J}{L}}{\left[\dfrac{2J}{L} + \dfrac{1}{l}\right]} \frac{wl^2}{6}$$

and from equation (9.3)

$$M_{AB} = \frac{2EJ}{L}[\phi_B] = \tfrac{1}{2}M_{BA}.$$

All the end moments are now known and the bending moment diagram for the frame may be drawn. It will be seen that for the frame of Fig. 9.5 in which the second moment of area was the same throughout,

$$M_{BC} = -\frac{l}{L+2l} \frac{wl^2}{6}$$

so that the bending moment at the centre of the beam is

$$M_0 = \frac{wl^2}{8} - \frac{l}{L+2l} \frac{wl^2}{6} = \frac{wl^2}{24}\left(\frac{3L+2l}{L+2l}\right).$$

If a comparison is made with paragraph 9.2 it will be seen that for this particular portal the slope deflexion method is more direct than the strain energy analysis since, due to symmetry and the fact that the feet of the stanchions are rigidly fixed, one change of slope is sufficient to define the shape of the loaded frame completely while two reactions have to be found by strain energy. If the portal were unsymmetrically loaded both slopes at the ends of the beam and the horizontal movement of the beam would have to be found by slope deflexion methods. This would necessitate the derivation and solution of three equations, the same number as required in the strain energy analysis so that there would be little to choose between the two methods. When the foot of a stanchion is hinged, strain energy usually has the advantage as it means one less redundancy, the fixing moment, but one more slope. For a single bay, single storey frame therefore, one or other of the methods may have the advantage but as the number of bays and storeys increases it will be found that the slope deflexion method soon becomes the more economical. This will be appreciated if the two-bay frame shown in Fig. 9.11 is examined. When the load is unsymmetrically placed, six redundant reactions would have to be found by strain energy whereas only four slopes and deflexions need to be evaluated to give the shape of the loaded frame, and therefore the reactions, completely.

Suppose both beams of the frame have the same span l and the same second moment of area I, and all the stanchions have a second moment of area J and a height h.   A load of intensity w is applied to PR.   At P, from equation (9.3),

$$M_{PR} = \frac{2EI}{l}[2\phi_P + \phi_R] - \frac{wl^2}{12} \quad \cdot \quad \cdot \quad \cdot \quad \cdot \quad (9.10)$$

also

$$M_{PQ} = \frac{2EJ}{h}\left[2\phi_P - \frac{3\delta}{h}\right], \quad \cdot \quad \cdot \quad \cdot \quad \cdot \quad (9.11)$$

where δ, the horizontal movement of P relative to Q, is the sway which will take place due to the lack of symmetry in the frame.

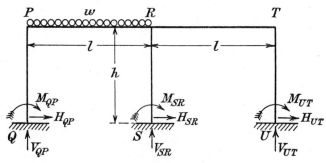

FIG. 9.11.

From a consideration of the equilibrium of joint P

$$M_{PR} + M_{PQ} = 0$$

or

$$2EK_B[2\phi_P + \phi_R] + 2EK_S\left[2\phi_P - \frac{3\delta}{h}\right] = \frac{wl^2}{12}, \quad \cdot \quad \cdot \quad (9.12)$$

where K_B and K_S are written for $\dfrac{I}{l}$ and $\dfrac{J}{h}$ respectively.

Similarly, at R, expressions for M_{RP} and M_{RT} can be obtained and

$$M_{RS} = \frac{2EJ}{h}\left[2\phi_R - \frac{3\delta}{h}\right] \quad \cdot \quad \cdot \quad \cdot \quad \cdot \quad (9.13)$$

since, owing to the assumption that deformations due to direct stress are negligible, the horizontal movement of R with respect to S must be the same as δ in equation (9.11).

From a consideration of the equilibrium of joint R which gives

$$M_{RP} + M_{RS} + M_{RT} = 0$$

it follows that

$$2EK_B[\phi_P + 2\phi_R] + \frac{wl^2}{12} + 2EK_B[2\phi_R + \phi_T] + 2EK_S\left[2\phi_R - \frac{3\delta}{h}\right] = 0 ; \quad (9.14)$$

also from the joint T

$$2EK_B[\phi_R + 2\phi_T] + 2EK_S\left[2\phi_T - \frac{3\delta}{h}\right] = 0. \quad \cdot \quad \cdot \quad (9.15)$$

An additional equation is needed before the unknowns ϕ_P, ϕ_R, ϕ_T and δ can be evaluated and this is obtained from a consideration of the equilibrium of the frame as a whole.

In Fig. 9.11 the reactions imposed on the ends of the members by the foundations are shown and the frame is in equilibrium under these reactions and the external applied load on PR.

Taking moments about U, the foot of the right-hand stanchion, we have

$$V_{QP}2l + V_{SR}l + M_{QP} + M_{SR} + M_{UT} = wl \cdot \frac{3l}{2}. \quad . \quad . \quad . \quad (9.16)$$

As the feet of the stanchions are at the same level the horizontal reactions do not appear in this equation. The reactions V_{QP} and V_{SR} are the same as those imposed on the beams at P and R and can be evaluated from equations (9.5) and (9.6). They are

$$V_{QP} = \frac{wl}{2} - \frac{6EI}{l^2}[\phi_P + \phi_R]$$

and

$$V_{SR} = \frac{wl}{2} + \frac{6EI}{l^2}[\phi_P + \phi_R] - \frac{6EI}{l^2}[\phi_R + \phi_T].$$

Substituting these expressions and those for the moments in equation (9.16) we have

$$-6EK_B[\phi_P + 2\phi_R + \phi_T] + 2EK_S\left[\phi_P + \phi_R + \phi_T - \frac{9\delta}{h}\right] = 0. \quad . \quad (9.17)$$

The unknown slopes and deflexions can be found from equations (9.12), (9.14), (9.15) and (9.17). All the end moments then follow from equations (9.3) and (9.4) and the bending moment diagram can be drawn.

Had the feet of the stanchions not been at the same level (see Fig. 9.7) the horizontal reactions H_{QP}, etc., would have appeared in equation (9.16). These reactions can be expressed in terms of the slopes and deflexions from equations (9.5) and (9.6) so that the form of equation (9.17) would not have been altered.

It is now possible to set out general equations for the rigidly jointed frame which carries the loads in a framed building. The structure considered is two dimensional and consists of a line of vertical stanchions, rigidly fixed at the base, connected by horizontal beams as shown in Fig. 9.12. The assumptions and sign conventions already given will be used. The notation is as shown in Fig. 9.12 and as follows :—

B_r is the joint where stanchion B is crossed by the rth floor.

h_r is the rth storey height, that is the height between the neutral axis of the $(r-1)$th and the rth floors.

l_{2r} = the length of the beam in the second bay of the rth floor.

d_{Br} = the distance of the faces of the stanchion from the neutral axis at B_r.

f_{Br} = the distance of the upper and lower surfaces of the beam from the neutral axis at B_r.

I_{2r} = the second moment of area of the beam in the second bay of the rth floor.

I_{Br} = the second moment of area of stanchion B in the rth storey, that is between $B_{(r-1)}$ and B_r.

θ_{Br} = the slope of the stanchion at B_r.

ϕ = the slope at the end of a beam.

δ_r = the deflexion of a stanchion in the rth storey height, that is the horizontal deflexion of the rth relative to the $(r-1)$th joint in a stanchion.

$$R_r = \frac{\delta_r}{h_r}.$$

$M^r_{BC}=$ the bending moment at the end B of the beam BC in the rth floor.

$M^B_{r(r+1)}=$ the bending moment at the end B_r of the length of stanchion $B_rB_{(r+1)}$.

V = a vertical reaction.

H = a horizontal reaction.

$$K_{1r} = \frac{I_{1r}}{l_{1r}} \; ; \; K_{Br} = \frac{I_{Br}}{h_r}.$$

$w_{2r}=$ load per unit length on the beam in the second bay of the rth floor.

It will be evident from the two-bay portal example, which has been treated in detail above, that there will be as many unknowns as there are

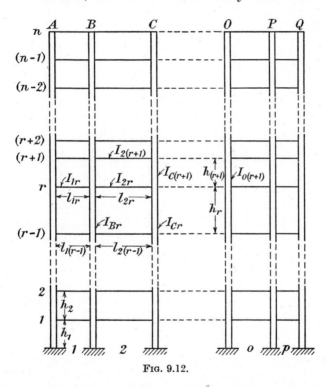

FIG. 9.12.

joints and storeys in the structure. When any load is applied, each joint will rotate and each line of beams at a floor level will suffer horizontal displacement in the plane of the frame. The equations needed for the evaluation of these slopes and displacements are derived from a consideration of the equilibrium of each joint and each storey in the frame.

Fig. 9.13 shows a typical joint with the reactions applied to it by the members. It will be assumed that the shaded portion enclosed by the beams and stanchions suffers no distortion. This is quite well justified in any practical frame. In fact the error produced by neglecting the widths of the members is usually small when the joints are rigid but it is considered worth while to include them here as they do not complicate the analysis seriously.

From the equilibrium of this joint it follows that

$$M^r_{BA} + M^B_{r(r-1)} + M^r_{BC} + M^B_{r(r+1)} + d(V^r_{BA} + V^r_{BC})$$
$$+ f(H^B_{r(r+1)} + H^B_{r(r-1)}) = 0 \quad . \quad . \quad . \quad (9.18)$$

and expressing these moments and reactions in terms of the slopes and deflexions, equations (9.3) to (9.6), we have

$$K_{1r}\left(1 + \frac{3d}{l_{1r}}\right)\theta_{Ar} + K_{Br}\left(1 + \frac{3f}{h_r}\right)\theta_{B(r-1)}$$

$$+ \left[K_{1r}\left(2 + \frac{3d}{l_{1r}}\right) + K_{2r}\left(2 + \frac{3d}{l_{2r}}\right) + K_{Br}\left(2 + \frac{3f}{h_r}\right) + K_{B(r+1)}\left(2 + \frac{3f}{h_{(r+1)}}\right)\right]\theta_{Br}$$

$$+ K_{B(r+1)}\left(1 + \frac{3f}{h_{(r+1)}}\right)\theta_{B(r+1)} + K_{2r}\left(1 + \frac{3d}{l_{2r}}\right)\theta_{Cr}$$

$$- 3K_{Br}\left(1 + \frac{2f}{h_r}\right)R_r - 3K_{B(r+1)}\left(1 + \frac{2f}{h_{(r+1)}}\right)R_{(r+1)}$$

$$+ \frac{l_{1r}}{4E}\left(d + \frac{l_{1r}}{6}\right)w_{1r} - \frac{l_{2r}}{4E}\left(d + \frac{l_{2r}}{6}\right)w_{2r} = 0. \quad . \quad . \quad . \quad . \quad . \quad . \quad (9.19)$$

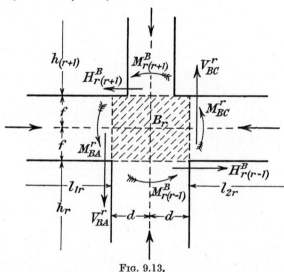

FIG. 9.13.

A similar equation can be written down for each joint in the frame. The other type of general equation can be derived by considering the equilibrium of all the stanchions in a storey but it will probably be clearer if approached in the following way.

Fig. 9.14 represents the rth storey in the frame. Imagine it cut first at XX just below the rth floor. The reactions shown at XX are those applied by the upper ends of the stanchions in the rth storey to the joints in the rth floor. That part of the frame above XX is therefore in equilibrium under these reactions and the external loads. Taking moments about the cut section in stanchion Q we obtain

$$V_A \overset{p}{\underset{1}{\Sigma}}l + V_B \overset{p}{\underset{2}{\Sigma}}l + \ldots - \overset{Q}{\underset{A}{\Sigma}}M_{r(r-1)} = \overset{n}{\underset{r}{\Sigma}}\overset{p}{\underset{1}{\Sigma}}wl.L, \quad . \quad . \quad (9.20)$$

where L is the horizontal distance from the centre of a beam to stanchion Q.

Now imagine the cuts at XX repaired and others made at YY just above the $(r-1)$th floor (Fig. 9.14). The reactions shown there are those applied to the lower ends of the stanchions by the joints in the $(r-1)$th floor. The whole of the frame above YY is therefore in equilibrium under these reactions

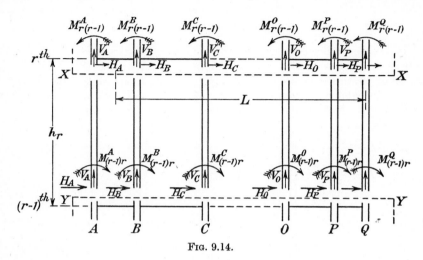

FIG. 9.14.

and the external loads. Taking moments about the cut section in stanchion Q we have

$$V_A\overset{p}{\underset{1}{\Sigma}}l+V_B\overset{p}{\underset{2}{\Sigma}}l+ \ . \ . \ . \ +\overset{Q}{\underset{A}{\Sigma}}M_{(r-1)r}=\overset{n}{\underset{r}{\Sigma}}\overset{p}{\underset{1}{\Sigma}}wl.L. \ . \ . \ . \ (9.21)$$

Subtracting equation (9.20) from (9.21) gives

$$\overset{Q}{\underset{A}{\Sigma}}(M_{r(r-1)}+M_{(r-1)r})=0, \ . \ . \ . \ . \ . \ (9.22)$$

or from equations (9.3) and (9.4)

$$\overset{Q}{\underset{A}{\Sigma}}EK_{Ar}(\theta_{Ar}+\theta_{A(r-1)}-2R_r)=0.$$

A similar equation can be obtained for each storey in the frame so that with those of type (9.19) there are sufficient for the evaluation of all the unknown slopes and deflexions from which the bending moments anywhere can be calculated.

Equations (9.19) and (9.22) have been derived for vertical floor loads only but it is not difficult to deduce from them the corresponding equations for the equally important problems involving horizontal wind loads.

If horizontal loads $W_1, W_2 \ldots W_n$ alone act from left to right at the levels of the first, second, etc., floors so that each produces a clockwise overturning moment on the structure, equation (9.19) will be unchanged except that the terms in w_{1r} and w_{2r} will disappear since these loads no longer act on the structure. Equation (9.22) is replaced by

$$\overset{Q}{\underset{A}{\Sigma}}6EK_{Ar}(\theta_{Ar}+\theta_{A(r-1)}-2R_r)+h_r\overset{n}{\underset{r}{\Sigma}}W=0. \ . \ . \ . \ (9.23)$$

If the feet of the stanchions are not at the same level and if, in addition to the horizontal loads W at the beam levels, transverse loads act on the

bottom stanchion lengths as in Fig. 9.15, consideration of the equilibrium
of the bottom storey gives in place of equation (9.23) the following :

$$\sum_A^Q \frac{1}{h_A}(M_{10}^A + M_{01}^A) + \sum_1^n W + \sum_A^Q P_A' = 0, \qquad \qquad (9.24)$$

$$\text{where } P_A' = \frac{P_A}{h_A}(h_A - a).$$

It has so far been assumed in this analysis that the effect of the direct
thrust on the flexure of a member is negligible. While, as will be shown in
Chapter 18, this is justifiable for the purposes of design of steel frames and,
in all probability, of reinforced concrete structures it is useful to derive
expressions which enable an estimate of the effect to be made.

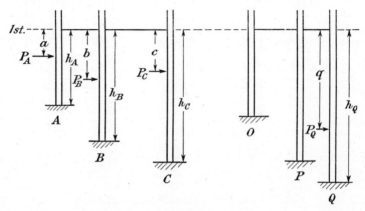

FIG. 9.15.

In a symmetrical single bay frame supporting uniformly distributed floor
loads it is not difficult to examine the effect of the flexure of the stanchions
since the reactions at the ends of the beams are independent of the end
moments.

If it is assumed that the stanchions are initially straight it will be seen
from equations (7.42) and (7.43) that the moments at the ends of a stanchion
length $A_r A_{r-1}$ may be expressed as

$$M_{r(r-1)}^A = 6EK_{Ar}(2Y_r\theta_{Ar} + X_r\theta_{A(r-1)})$$

and

$$M_{(r-1)r}^A = 6EK_{Ar}(X_r\theta_{Ar} + 2Y_r\theta_{A(r-1)})$$

where X_r and Y_r are coefficients depending on the axial load in the stanchion
length, having the values

$$X_r = \frac{f(\alpha)}{4\phi^2(\alpha) - f^2(\alpha)} \text{ and } Y_r = \frac{\phi(\alpha)}{4\phi^2(\alpha) - f^2(\alpha)}.$$

$f(\alpha)$ and $\phi(\alpha)$ are the Berry functions referred to in paragraph 8.4, and
tabulated in the Appendix, the axial compressive load in the member to be

used in evaluating them being $P = \sum_r^n \frac{w_r l}{2}$.

For a single bay frame when rigid joints are assumed and if the widths
of the members are neglected, we have from the equilibrium of joint A_r

$$M_{r(r-1)}^A + M_{r(r+1)}^A + M'_{AB} = 0,$$

or
$$3J_rX_r\theta_{A(r-1)}+(1+6J_rY_r+6L_rY_{(r+1)})\theta_{Ar}$$
$$+3L_rX_{(r+1)}\theta_{A(r+1)}=W_r, \quad . \quad . \quad . \quad . \quad . \quad (9.25)$$

where
$$J_r=\frac{K_{Ar}}{K_{1r}}, \; L_r=\frac{K_{A(r+1)}}{K_{1r}} \text{ and } W_r=\frac{w_rl^2}{24EK_{1r}}.$$

From this and the similar equations derived from a consideration of the other joints in the frame the complete solution can be obtained. By comparing the results with those found when the effect of flexure is neglected an estimate of the errors involved may be made.

9.4. Slope deflexion analysis of frames with semi-rigid joints.—In many framed structures, particularly those of steel in which bolts or rivets are used in fabrication, the joints are far from rigid. A detailed examination of the behaviour of certain riveted beam-to-stanchion connexions is made in paragraph 18.5. It is shown there that when a moment is transmitted through such connexions an appreciable relative rotation occurs between the

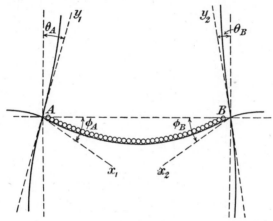

Fig. 9.16.

members joined. The relation between the moment transmitted and the relative rotation is often far from linear but as stated in Chapter 18 the only practicable method of stress analysis, for all but the simplest frames, is to assume that a linear relation does hold and to substitute for the curve connecting moment and relative rotation an arrangement of its chords. It will be well, therefore, to expand the slope deflexion equations derived in the previous paragraph to cover the condition of semi-rigidity of beam-to-stanchion connexions.

Part of a loaded frame, the beam-to-stanchion connexions of which are semi-rigid, is shown in Fig. 9.16.

Ay_1 is the tangent to the stanchion at A and θ_A is its change of slope under load.

Ax_1 is the tangent to the beam AB at A and ϕ_A is its change of slope under load.

By_2 is the tangent to the stanchion at B and θ_B is its change of slope under load.

Bx_2 is the tangent to the beam AB at B and ϕ_B is its change of slope under load.

7

Since a linear relation is assumed between the relative rotation of the members at a connexion and the moment transmitted through the connexion we may write

$$\theta_A - \phi_A = \gamma_L M_{AB} \quad \ldots \quad \ldots \quad (9.26)$$

and $$\theta_B - \phi_B = \gamma_R M_{BA}, \quad \ldots \quad \ldots \quad (9.27)$$

where γ_L and γ_R are constants depending on the connexions at A and B.

From equations (9.3) and (9.4), the moments M_{AB} and M_{BA} may be expressed in terms of ϕ_A and ϕ_B and the external load applied to AB, thus enabling equations (9.26) and (9.27) to be solved for ϕ_A and ϕ_B.

Writing α and β for $\dfrac{2EI\gamma_L}{l}$ and $\dfrac{2EI\gamma_R}{l}$ respectively we obtain

$$\phi_A = \frac{1}{(3\alpha\beta + 2\alpha + 2\beta + 1)} \left[(2\beta+1)\theta_A - \alpha\theta_B + \alpha(3\beta+1)\frac{wl^3}{24EI} \right] \quad (9.28)$$

and $$\phi_B = \frac{1}{(3\alpha\beta + 2\alpha + 2\beta + 1)} \left[-\beta\theta_A + (2\alpha+1)\theta_B - \beta(3\alpha+1)\frac{wl^3}{24EI} \right]. \quad (9.29)$$

The moments and reactions at the ends of the beam may be written in the form

$$M_{AB} = \frac{2EI}{l} \frac{1}{(3\alpha\beta + 2\alpha + 2\beta + 1)} \left[(3\beta+2)\theta_A + \theta_B - (3\beta+1)\frac{wl^3}{24EI} \right], \quad (9.30)$$

$$M_{BA} = \frac{2EI}{l} \frac{1}{(3\alpha\beta + 2\alpha + 2\beta + 1)} \left[\theta_A + (3\alpha+2)\theta_B + (3\alpha+1)\frac{wl^3}{24EI} \right], \quad (9.31)$$

$$V_A = \frac{6EI}{l^2} \frac{1}{(3\alpha\beta + 2\alpha + 2\beta + 1)} \left[(\beta+1)\theta_A \right.$$
$$\left. + (\alpha+1)\theta_B - (6\alpha\beta + 3\alpha + 5\beta + 2)\frac{wl^3}{24EI} \right], \quad (9.32)$$

$$V_B = \frac{6EI}{l^2} \frac{1}{(3\alpha\beta + 2\alpha + 2\beta + 1)} \left[(\beta+1)\theta_A \right.$$
$$\left. + (\alpha+1)\theta_B + (6\alpha\beta + 5\alpha + 3\beta + 2)\frac{wl^3}{24EI} \right]. \quad (9.33)$$

It is most usual in steel-framed buildings for the stanchion to be a continuous member the beams being connected to it as shown in Fig. 9.17. From a consideration of the equilibrium of this joint, neglecting the depth of the beam, we have

$$M^r{}_{BA} + M^B{}_{r(r-1)} + M^r{}_{BC} + M^B{}_{r(r+1)} + V^r{}_{BA}d_{Br} + V^r{}_{BC}e_{Br} = 0, \quad (9.34)$$

or substituting the values given in expressions (9.30) to (9.33) we have

$$\frac{2EK_{1r}}{(3\alpha_{1r}\beta_{1r} + 2\alpha_{1r} + 2\beta_{1r} + 1)} \left[1 + \frac{3d_{Br}}{l_{1r}}(\beta_{1r}+1) \right] \theta_{Ar} + 2EK_{Br}\theta_{B(r-1)}$$

$$+ \left[\frac{2EK_{1r}}{(3\alpha_{1r}\beta_{1r} + 2\alpha_{1r} + 2\beta_{1r} + 1)} \left\{ (3\alpha_{1r}+2) + \frac{3d_{Br}}{l_{1r}}(\alpha_{1r}+1) \right\} \right.$$

$$+ \frac{2EK_{2r}}{(3\alpha_{2r}\beta_{2r} + 2\alpha_{2r} + 2\beta_{2r} + 1)} \left\{ (3\beta_{2r}+2) + \frac{3e_{Br}}{l_{2r}}(\beta_{2r}+1) \right\}$$

$$\left. + 4EK_{Br} + 4EK_{B(r+1)} \right] \theta_{Br}$$

$$+2EK_{B(r+1)}\theta_{B(r+1)}+\frac{2EK_{2r}}{(3\alpha_{2r}\beta_{2r}+2\alpha_{2r}+2\beta_{2r}+1)}\left[1+\frac{3e_{Br}}{l_{2r}}(\alpha_{2r}+1)\right]\theta_{Cr}$$

$$-6EK_{B_r}R_r-6EK_{B(r+1)}R_{(r+1)}$$

$$+\frac{l^2_{1r}}{(3\alpha_{1r}\beta_{1r}+2\alpha_{1r}+2\beta_{1r}+1)}\left[\frac{1}{12}(3\alpha_{1r}+1)+\frac{d_{Br}}{4l_{1r}}(6\alpha_{1r}\beta_{1r}+5\alpha_{1r}+3\beta_{1r}+2)\right]w_{1r}$$

$$-\frac{l^2_{2r}}{(3\alpha_{2r}\beta_{2r}+2\alpha_{2r}+2\beta_{2r}+1)}\left[\frac{1}{12}(3\beta_{2r}+1)\right.$$

$$\left.+\frac{e_{Br}}{4l_{2r}}(6\alpha_{2r}\beta_{2r}+3\alpha_{2r}+5\beta_{2r}+2)\right]w_{2r}=0. \quad . \quad . \quad . \quad (9.35)$$

This is exactly the same form as equation (9.19), and will be found to reduce to it when the connexions are made rigid, *i.e.* when $\alpha=\beta=0$, $d_{Br}=e_{Br}$, and when the width of the beam is neglected, *i.e.* when $f=0$. An equation similar to (9.35) may be written down for each joint in the frame. The

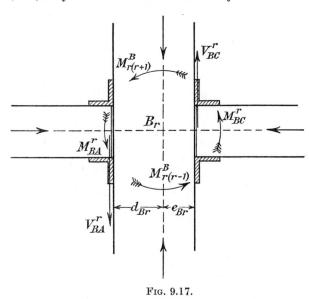

Fig. 9.17.

other set of equations needed for the evaluation of the unknown slopes comes, as before, from a consideration of the equilibrium of the stanchions in each storey. The general equations are identical with those already found for the rigid frame, that is to say for the rth storey

$$\sum_{A}^{Q}K_{Ar}(\theta_{Ar}+\theta_{A(r-1)}-2R_r)=0. \quad . \quad . \quad . \quad . \quad (9.36)$$

There are as many equations of type (9.35) as there are joints and of type (9.36) as there are storeys in the frame. A sufficient number of equations are thus provided for the evaluation of the unknown slopes θ_{A1} ... θ_{Qn} and the deflexions R_1 ... R_n. When these are known, the moments and reactions can be found from equations (9.3) to (9.6), and (9.30) to (9.33) and the stresses in the frame follow.

When horizontal wind loads alone act the same procedure is followed. This results in the equation found from a consideration of the equilibrium

of a joint being identical with equation (9.35) except that the last two terms
disappear while equation (9.23) appears in place of equation (9.36).

9.5. Rigidly jointed frame with inclined members.—The slope deflexion
method is convenient for the analysis of forms of structure other than the
rectangular frames dealt with in the preceding paragraphs. A rigidly
jointed frame with sloping posts is an interesting example.

The structure of Fig. 9.18 is of the same uniform cross-section and material
throughout and is rigidly fixed at A and D. When a uniformly distributed

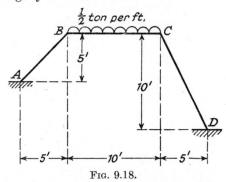

FIG. 9.18.

load of 5 tons is applied to the horizontal member BC the joints B and C
will rotate and, owing to the lack of symmetry, sway of the whole frame will
take place ; not only will B and C, the tops of the inclined posts, deflect
relative to the feet A and D, but C will deflect relative to B. The relation
between these end deflexions is the same as that which would exist if all
joints were pinned since, as set out in paragraph 9.3, it can be assumed that

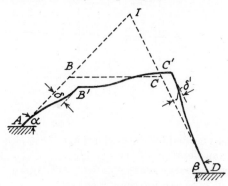

FIG. 9.19.

deformation of a member due to direct stress is negligible and all bending
displacements are small. The end B of AB can, therefore, only be displaced,
by an amount δ say, along a line BB' perpendicular to AB, Fig. 9.19 ;
similarly C can only be displaced, δ' say, along a line CC' perpendicular to
CD. The horizontal displacement of B will be $\delta \sin \alpha$ and of C, $\delta' \sin \beta$.
Since the length of BC is unaffected by bending, these horizontal displacements must be the same, *i.e.* $\delta \sin \alpha = \delta' \sin \beta$,

or
$$\delta' = \frac{\sin \alpha}{\sin \beta} \delta = \frac{\sqrt{5}}{2\sqrt{2}} \delta. \qquad . \qquad . \qquad . \qquad . \qquad (9.37)$$

The vertical displacements of B and C are $-\delta\cos\alpha$ and $-\delta'\cos\beta$ respectively so that the transverse deflexion of C relative to B is $-(\delta\cos\alpha+\delta'\cos\beta)$

or
$$-\frac{\sin(\alpha+\beta)}{\sin\beta}\delta=-\frac{3}{2\sqrt{2}}\delta. \qquad \ldots \ldots (9.38)$$

A somewhat neater approach to these expressions is to consider the members as a four-bar chain in which BC suffers a small body rotation about the instantaneous centre I which lies on the intersection of AB and DC produced (Fig. 9.19).

The moments at the ends of the members of the rigidly jointed frame can now be set out in terms of δ and the slopes ϕ_B and ϕ_C, using expressions (9.3) and (9.4). These three unknowns can then be evaluated in the usual way from a consideration of the equilibrium of the joints B and C and of the frame as a whole. It is convenient to obtain the latter in terms of end moments. Suppose H is the horizontal and V the vertical reaction at A. Taking moments about B, C and D in turn gives

$$M_{AB}+M_{BA}+5V-5H=0, \qquad \ldots \ldots (9.39)$$
$$M_{AB}+M_{CB}+15V-5H-25=0, \qquad \ldots \ldots (9.40)$$
$$M_{AB}+M_{BC}+20V+5H-50=0. \qquad \ldots \ldots (9.41)$$

On eliminating V and H from these three equations and remembering that $M_{CB}=-M_{CD}$ we obtain the equilibrium equation

$$4M_{AB}+7M_{BA}+5M_{CD}+2M_{DC}=-25 \qquad \ldots \ldots (9.42)$$

which, expressed in terms of the slopes and deflexion, is

$$\phi_B+0\cdot422\phi_C-0\cdot311\delta=-4\cdot91/EI. \qquad \ldots \ldots (9.43)$$

Consideration of the equilibrium of joints B and C yields the equations

$$\phi_B+0\cdot207\phi_C-0\cdot058\delta=4\cdot3/EI \qquad \ldots \ldots (9.44)$$
and
$$\phi_B+3\cdot790\phi_C+0\cdot129\delta=-20\cdot8/EI. \qquad \ldots \ldots (9.45)$$

The solution of these equations is

$$\phi_B=7\cdot80/EI, \quad \phi_C=-8\cdot59/EI \text{ and } \delta=29\cdot4/EI.$$

Substituting these values in expressions (9.3) and (9.4) the moments in the frame are found to be

$$M_{AB}=-1\cdot32, \ M_{BA}=0\cdot88, \ M_{CD}=-4\cdot17 \text{ and } M_{DC}=-2\cdot64 \text{ tons-ft.}$$

Multi-storey structures can be analysed in the same way, but it must be remembered that when the posts are inclined the sway of a storey not only produces a relative deflexion of the ends of the beam in that storey but in all storeys above.

9.6. Secondary stresses.—In paragraph 1.7 primary stresses were defined as the axial forces in the bars of a framework, assumed to have perfectly free pin joints, under loads applied to the nodes. The extra stresses induced by the stiffness of the joints, where they are not in fact perfect hinges, are known as secondary stresses. Other stresses, additional to the primary system, found in actual structures due to such causes as the weight of the members themselves, eccentricity in the joints and, in certain aeronautical structures, to the true distribution of external load differing from the distribution assumed in the calculation of the primary stresses, may have a claim to be included in the term secondary stresses, but it is with those arising from the stiffness of joints that we shall be concerned in this chapter.

When a pin-jointed framework is loaded at the nodes the internal forces induced in the bars are simple tensions or compressions under the action of which the bars elongate or shorten so that the geometry of the framework is altered, the angles between the bars increasing or decreasing. If, as is most usual in practice, the joints are not pinned but are made stiff, *e.g.* in a steelwork truss where the bars are riveted to a gusset plate, the angles between the bars cannot change. The result is that, as external loads are applied and the geometry of the framework is altered, restraining moments are induced at the ends of the members and give rise to secondary bending stresses.

It would be impracticable to determine all the stresses, secondary as well as primary, in such a stiff jointed truss as that shown in Fig. 10.16 (*a*) by strain energy analysis. A complete solution might be obtained using the method referred to on page 96 (Baker and Ockleston, 1935), but only after much labour.

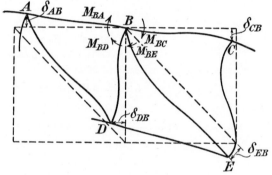

Fɪɢ. 9.20.

Fortunately, in most braced frameworks where an examination of the secondary stresses has to be made, the effect of the stiffness of the joints, while giving rise to appreciable local secondary bending stresses, is not sufficient to modify the axial forces in the members seriously. The positions of the nodes of the actual stiff-jointed framework, therefore, are very nearly the same as those which would have been observed had the joints been pinned. This being so the secondary stresses can be considered as due to the bending of the members which takes place when the nodes of the stiff-jointed framework are forced into the positions which the nodes of the pin-jointed framework would have taken up under the external load system. In moving into these positions the stiff joints would, of course, rotate and the magnitudes of these rotations must be found before the bending stresses can be evaluated.

It is not difficult, with the help of the slope deflexion expressions, to write down equations in terms of the unknown rotations. Fig. 9.20 shows a section of a rigid-jointed frame in which the secondary stresses due to a given arrangement of external loads at the nodes are to be determined. The deflexions δ_{CB}, δ_{EB}, etc., of the neighbouring joints, C, E, etc., relative to B are shown. These deflexions, according to our assumption, are the same as those which would have been observed had the given arrangement of external loads been applied to the nodes of the framework having pinned instead of rigid joints. They can be found without difficulty by means of the Williot-Mohr deflexion diagram (paragraph 5.8). Suppose the joints of the framework, Fig. 9.20, rotate through angles θ_A, θ_B, θ_C, etc., when they are forced into their deflected positions. It follows from equation (9.3) that the bending moments developed at the end B of the bar BC and at the end B of the bar BE are respectively

$$M_{BC} = \frac{2EI_{BC}}{l_{BC}}\left[2\theta_B + \theta_C - \frac{3\delta_{BC}}{l_{BC}}\right]$$

and

$$M_{BE} = \frac{2EI_{BE}}{l_{BE}}\left[2\theta_B + \theta_E - \frac{3\delta_{BE}}{l_{BE}}\right] \qquad \cdots \qquad (9.46)$$

Similar expressions may be written down for the moments at the ends of the other bars and since the joint B is in equilibrium we have, neglecting the dimensions of the gusset plate,

$$\sum \frac{2EI_{BC}}{l_{BC}}\left[2\theta_B + \theta_C - \frac{3\delta_{BC}}{l_{BC}}\right] = 0 \qquad \cdots \qquad (9.47)$$

the summation extending over all the bars meeting at B.

An equation similar to (9.47) can be obtained from a consideration of the equilibrium of each joint in the framework so that as many equations are forthcoming as there are joints in the frame and therefore, as many as there are unknowns θ_A, θ_B, θ_C, etc. The slopes can then, in theory, be evaluated and the end bending moments and the secondary bending stresses calculated. In most practical trusses the number of equations makes an exact solution impracticable and it is usual to advocate the use of an approximate method for the solution of the equations. It will be found, however, that much tedious computation is still involved and it is not proposed to explore this method further since the moment distribution method to be described in Chapter 10 is ideally suited for the determination of secondary stresses.

REFERENCE

Baker, J. F. and Ockleston, A. J. 1935. *Aer. Res. Cttee.* R. & M. **1667**, H.M.S.O.

CHAPTER 10

MOMENT DISTRIBUTION METHOD

10.1. Introduction.—The slope deflexion method, in common with strain energy analysis, suffers from the drawback that a large number of simultaneous equations have to be solved before the stresses in a highly redundant structure such as a multi-storey, multi-bay frame can be evaluated. Though the slope deflexion method is often of great value in giving general expressions for slopes and moments from which tabular data may be prepared, as shown in Chapter 18, the stresses in a particular frame can frequently be found much more easily by the moment distribution method (Cross, 1930*a*). This step-by-step method was immediately recognised as an epoch-making contribution to elastic analysis which, though applied in the first place to the determination of moments in rigidly jointed building frames, could clearly be extended to cover any form of structure (see paragraph 6.6).

Though the original paper was a model of brevity it gave rise to a long and instructive discussion in the American Society of Civil Engineers between September, 1930, and April, 1932, in the course of which Professor H. E. Wessman gave the following description.

" Other methods usually begin by making the structure simple ; in other words, by theoretically cutting restrained ends or inserting temporary hinges. End moments are then obtained by solving simultaneous equations which are functions of the angles through which the cut or pinned ends must be rotated to make the structure continuous again. The Cross method, on the other hand, starts by making the structure rigidly fixed at every joint or support and then finding fixed-end moments for any loading conditions under consideration. One joint at a time is then released and the fixed-end moments are modified to secure equilibrium at the released joint. This joint is temporarily fixed again until all other joints have been released and fixed in their new positions. Then the procedure is repeated again and again until the desired degree of accuracy is obtained."

10.2. Application to continuous beams.—The moment distribution method is most easily explained by considering its application to the determination of the moments in continuous beams.

In the three-moment method (paragraph 8.3) it was imagined that a continuous beam consisted of a number of simply supported beams to which the external load system and unknown end couples were applied ; the magnitudes of these end couples were then found from the equations for continuity of slope at the supports. In the moment distribution method the beam, before external loads are applied, is assumed to be clamped at each support so that it cannot change its slope at those points. When the loads are applied the continuous beam behaves as if it were a number of single-span encastré beams. The clamps are subjected to moments equal and opposite to the fixing moments on the beams and in general an external moment has to be applied at each support by the clamps. At one support this external moment is removed, that is to say, the beam is freed. It moves into a new position of equilibrium and in so doing modifies the end moments. The beam is clamped again in its new equilibrium position and is freed at another support. This procedure is repeated in cyclical manner until the resulting modifications in the end moments are small enough to be ignored.

Before illustrating the method by a worked example it is useful to develop in general terms certain expressions which are required in the analysis. As in paragraph 8.3 we will confine our attention to beams having a uniform cross-section between supports though the method can be applied more generally.

As the ends of each span are clamped before the load is applied, the fixed end moment which the clamp exerts on the beam is the same as the restraining moment at the end of a similarly loaded encastré beam. Expressions for this have been given in equations (3.30) and (3.31).

When the external moment at a support is removed the loaded beam behaves exactly as the same beam would do if subjected to no other action than a moment at the support equal and opposite to the external moment. This behaviour is easily followed with the help of the slope deflexion equations. As it is necessary to adopt here the sign convention in which all end moments acting on a beam are positive when clockwise it will be well to restate the slope deflexion equations.

If θ_{AB} and θ_{BA} are the changes of slope at the ends of a member of uniform cross-section due to the application of positive (clockwise) end moments M_{AB} and M_{BA} then if there is no relative deflexion of the ends we have from equations (9.1) and (9.2),

$$\theta_{BA} = \frac{l}{6EI}(-M_{AB} + 2M_{BA}) \quad . \quad . \quad . \quad . \quad (10.1)$$

and

$$\theta_{AB} = \frac{l}{6EI}(2M_{AB} - M_{BA}). \quad . \quad . \quad . \quad . \quad (10.2)$$

Solving these we obtain

$$M_{AB} = \frac{2EI}{l}(2\theta_{AB} + \theta_{BA}) \quad . \quad . \quad . \quad . \quad . \quad (10.3)$$

and

$$M_{BA} = \frac{2EI}{l}(\theta_{AB} + 2\theta_{BA}). \quad . \quad . \quad . \quad . \quad . \quad (10.4)$$

A beam subjected to a moment at the support is shown in Fig. 10.1. It is encastré at A and C and freely supported at B. A moment $\bar{M}$ is applied at B and under its action the beam moves into a new position of equilibrium rotating through an angle θ_B at B.

In moving, moments M_{BA} and M_{BC} as shown are induced at the ends of BA and BC. It is often convenient in using the moment distribution method to think of the members as

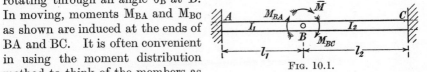

FIG. 10.1.

being joined, not directly to one another but each to a " joint " which in this instance would be the small length of beam containing the support B. Thus the moment $\bar{M}$ is applied to this " joint " and M_{BA} and M_{BC} are the moments applied by the " joint " to the ends of the members. From a consideration of the equilibrium of the " joint "

$$M_{BA} + M_{BC} = \bar{M}. \quad . \quad . \quad . \quad . \quad . \quad (10.5)$$

7*

From equation (10.4) since the end A of AB is encastré and the end B turns through an angle θ_B we have

$$M_{BA}=\frac{4EI_1}{l_1}\theta_B. \qquad \qquad \text{(10.6)}$$

Similarly

$$M_{BC}=\frac{4EI_2}{l_2}\theta_B \qquad \qquad \text{(10.7)}$$

so that

$$\overline{M}=4E\left(\frac{I_1}{l_1}+\frac{I_2}{l_2}\right)\theta_B$$

and from (10.6) and (10.7)

$$M_{BA}=\frac{\dfrac{I_1}{l_1}}{\dfrac{I_1}{l_1}+\dfrac{I_2}{l_2}}\overline{M}$$

and

$$M_{BC}=\frac{\dfrac{I_2}{l_2}}{\dfrac{I_1}{l_1}+\dfrac{I_2}{l_2}}\overline{M}. \qquad \qquad \text{(10.8)}$$

The moments induced at the ends B of AB and BC are thus proportional to the stiffness of AB and BC, the stiffness of a member being defined as its second moment of area divided by its length.

When the beam moves into its new position of equilibrium, moments are, of course, induced at the encastré ends A and C also. They can most conveniently be evaluated from equations (10.3) and (10.4). Since, in the span AB, the end A is fixed and B turns through an angle θ_B,

$$M_{AB}=\frac{2EI}{l}\theta_B \text{ and } M_{BA}=\frac{4EI}{l}\theta_B$$

so that
similarly

$$\left.\begin{array}{l}M_{AB}=\tfrac{1}{2}M_{BA}\\M_{CB}=\tfrac{1}{2}M_{BC}\end{array}\right\} \qquad \qquad \text{(10.9)}$$

Thus the restraining moment induced at the encastré end of a beam is one-half the moment applied at the other end.

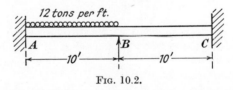

FIG. 10.2.

By means of the expressions (10.8) and (10.9) together with those for the fixed-end moments at the ends of an encastré beam, equations (3.30) and (3.31), the bending moments in continuous beams can be readily found.

Consider the beam ABC of uniform cross-section in Fig. 10.2 which is to carry a uniformly distributed load of 12 tons per foot on AB. The ends A and C are encastré and B, the mid-point of AC, is simply supported. In this and in all other examples it will be assumed, unless otherwise stated, that there is no sinking of the supports.

Before the load is applied, clamp the beam at B so that it cannot change its slope there. Apply the load. AB will then behave as an encastré beam and restraining moments will act upon it, the magnitudes of these being -100 tons-feet $\left(=\dfrac{wl^2}{12}\right)$ at A and $+100$ tons-feet at B. The latter is supplied by the clamp and no bending moment exists anywhere in BC. Now free B by removing the clamp ; the beam at B will be no longer in equilibrium since the external clockwise moment of 100 tons-feet has been removed, and will immediately accommodate itself to the new conditions, changing its slope at B until it is once more in equilibrium. This change of slope is that experienced by the beam ABC on the removal of the external moment $+100$ tons-feet, and is, therefore, the same as that produced by the application of an external moment of -100 tons-feet. The moments induced in the beam at B by this change of slope can be found by substituting $\overline{M} = -100$ tons-feet in (10.8). Since, in this particular instance, $I_1/l_1 = I_2/l_2$

$$M_{BA} = M_{BC} = -50 \text{ tons-feet.}$$

The moments, -25 tons-feet, induced at A and C are found from (10.9). The modifications in all the end moments are therefore known. Since A and C are encastré and cannot be released the beam has, by this one movement, reached its final deflected form and the exact values of the bending moments are obtained. The end moment at A was in the first, or fixed end, stage -100 tons-feet, then due to the movement of B, on the removal of the clamp, an additional moment -25 tons-feet was induced at A so that $M_{AB} = -100 - 25 = -125$ tons-feet.

At the end B of BA the fixed-end moment was $+100$ tons-feet, then on the release of the clamp the moment induced was -50 tons-feet so that

$$M_{BA} = 100 - 50 = +50 \text{ tons-feet.}$$
In the same way $\qquad M_{BC} = 0 - 50 = -50 \text{ tons-feet.}$
and $\qquad\qquad M_{CB} = 0 - 25 = -25 \text{ tons-feet.}$

The end moments being known, the bending moment diagram for ABC can be drawn.

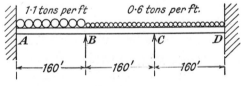

Fig. 10.3.

The process will perhaps be more easily followed from another example in which the end moments are tabulated. Fig. 10.3 shows a three-span beam ABCD of uniform cross-section throughout which is encastré at A and D and supported at B and C. A load of $1\cdot1$ tons per foot is distributed over AB and $0\cdot6$ ton per foot over BD. Each span is 160 feet long.

Clamp the beam at B and C and apply all the loads : the fixed end moments induced at the ends of the spans will be as entered in line a, Table 10.1. Release B ; the out-of-balance moment acting on the joint at B is $-(2{,}346\cdot6 - 1{,}280)$ or $-1{,}066\cdot6$ tons-feet at the instant of release. The balancing moments induced at the ends B of AB and BC as B rotates into its new equilibrium position will therefore from (10.8) be $-533\cdot3$ tons-feet. The moments carried over to the ends A and C will from (10.9) be $-266\cdot6$

TABLE 10.1.

END MOMENTS (TONS-FEET).

	A		B		C		D	
	−2,346·6	+2,346·6	−1,280·0	+1,280·0	−1,280·0	+1,280·0		a
	− 266·6	− 533·3	− 533·3	− 266·6	0·0	0·0		b
	0·0	0·0	+ 66·6	+ 133·3	+ 133·3	+ 66·6		c
	− 16·6	− 33·3	− 33·3	− 16·6	0·0	0·0		d
	0·0	0·0	+ 4·2	+ 8·3	+ 8·3	+ 4·2		e
	− 1·0	− 2·1	− 2·1	− 1·0	0·0	0·0		f
Totals .	−2,630·8	+1,777·9	−1,777·9	+1,137·4	−1,138·4	+1,350·8		

tons-feet. These end moments, induced by the movement of B, are entered in line b. The entries in columns 5 and 6 are zero because, C remaining clamped, no moments can be induced at the ends of the span CD by the movement of B. B is now clamped in its new equilibrium position and C is released. The out-of-balance moment on the joint at C is −(1,280·0 −1,280·0−266·6) or +266·6 tons-feet. The balancing moments at C will then be +133·3 tons-feet and the carry-over moments at B and D +66·6 tons-feet. These are entered in line c, Table 10.1. C is now clamped in its new equilibrium position and B is once more released. The balance of B has been upset by the moment carried over as a result of C's movement, so that at the instant of release the out-of-balance moment on joint B is −66·6 tons-feet. As B moves once more into a new equilibrium position the balancing moments induced are −33·3 tons-feet and the carry-over moments −16·6 tons-feet ; these are entered in line d. B is clamped again and so the process is continued until the modifications in the end moments brought about by further releases are small enough to be neglected. Two further releases have been made in Table 10.1. The total values of the end moments are obtained by adding the entries in each column and we find

$$M_{AB}=-2,630\cdot8, \quad M_{BA}=+1,777\cdot9, \quad M_{BC}=-1,777\cdot9.$$
$$M_{CB}=+1,137\cdot4, \quad M_{CD}=-1,138\cdot4, \quad M_{DC}=+1,350\cdot8.$$

In both these examples the ends of the continuous beam were built in or encastré. Considerably more work is entailed if the ends are simply supported.

Suppose the beam of Fig. 10.2 is simply supported at A and C. The procedure is exactly as before. All joints are clamped and the load is applied, the fixed-end moments being as shown in line a, Table 10.2. The joints have now to be released. The lay-out of Table 10.2 is slightly different from that of Table 10.1. Instead of releasing each joint separately and inserting in one line of the table the balancing and carry-over moments induced by that release, all joints are released at the same instant and the balancing moments at all the joints are entered in one line of the table while in the line below are put the carry-over moments induced by all these releases. Thus in Table 10.2, line b, the entries are the balancing moments +100, −50, −50 and 0. A line is drawn below these entries to show that

TABLE 10.2.

END MOMENTS (TONS-FEET).

A	B		C	
−100	+100	0	0	a
+100	− 50	−50	0	b
− 25	+ 50	0	−25	c
+ 25	− 25	−25	+25	d
− 12·5	+ 12·5	+12·5	−12·5	e
+ 12·5	− 12·5	−12·5	+12·5	
− 6·25	+ 6·25	+ 6·25	− 6·25	

the joints are balanced.   In line c are the carry-over moments −25, +50, 0 and −25 tons-feet induced by the balancing moments.   These carry-over moments upset the balance at the joints so that when they are once again released the balancing moments of line d come into operation and as a result the carry-over moments of line e.   It can be seen from Table 10.2 that the total end moments will be 0, +75, −75 and 0 respectively.   The physical significance of the steps shown in Table 10.2 may not be seen immediately but if the calculations are set out in the same way as those in Table 10.1, each joint in turn being released, there will be no difficulty in realising that the steps are justified.   By releasing all joints together a more concise table can be formed.

When the continuous beam has a simply supported end A it is worth while to calculate a special set of distribution factors to be used in finding the

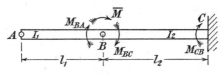

Fig. 10.4.

balancing moments when the support next to A is released.   This can be done by considering the beam ABC in Fig. 10.4 which is simply supported at A and B and is encastré at C.   If, when an external moment $\overline{M}$ is applied at B the changes of slope at A and B are θ_A and θ_B respectively then, since the end A is simply supported and C is encastré, it follows from equations (10.3) and (10.4) that

$$0 = \frac{2EI_1}{l_1}(2\theta_A + \theta_B),$$

$$M_{BA} = \frac{2EI_1}{l_1}(\theta_A + 2\theta_B)$$

and

$$M_{BC} = \frac{2EI_2}{l_2}(2\theta_B).$$

From a consideration of the equilibrium of the joint B

$$M_{BA}+M_{BC}=\overline{M}$$

so that

$$M_{BA}=\frac{\dfrac{3I_1}{l_1}}{\dfrac{3I_1}{l_1}+\dfrac{4I_2}{l_2}}\overline{M}$$

and

$$M_{BC}=\frac{\dfrac{4I_2}{l_2}}{\dfrac{3I_1}{l_1}+\dfrac{4I_2}{l_2}}\overline{M}$$

. . . . . . (10.10)

The convenience of these expressions can be judged from Table 10.3, which gives the calculation of the end moments in the continuous beam shown in Fig. 10.5 resting on the supports A, B, C and D.

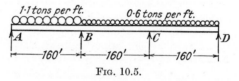

FIG. 10.5.

To avoid the calculation of special fixed-end moments for the end spans the beam is considered to be clamped initially at all the supports. When

TABLE 10.3.
END MOMENTS (TONS-FEET).

A		B		C		D	
−2,346·6	+2,346·6	−1,280·0	+1,280·0	−1,280·0	+1,280·0		a
+2,346·6	0·0	0·0	0·0	0·0	−1,280·0		b
0·0	+1,173·3	0·0	0·0	− 640·0	0·0		c
0·0	− 960·0	−1,280·0	+ 366·0	+ 274·0	0·0		d
0·0	0·0	+ 183·0	− 640·0	0·0	0·0		e
0·0	− 78·0	− 105·0	+ 366·0	+ 274·0	0·0		
0·0	0·0	+ 183·0	− 52·5	0·0	0·0		
0·0	− 78·0	− 105·0	+ 30·0	+ 22·5	0·0		
0·0	0·0	+ 15·0	− 52·5	0·0	0·0		
0·0	− 6·4	− 8·6	+ 30·0	+ 22·5	0·0		
0·0	0·0	+ 15·0	− 4·3	0·0	0·0		
0·0	− 6·4	− 8·6	+ 2·6	+ 1·7	0·0		

the load is applied the fixed-end moments produced are those shown in line a, Table 10.3. When the ends A and D are released, the resulting balancing and carry-over moments are those shown in lines b and c respectively. A and D are not clamped again but are kept free for the remainder of the process. The distribution factors by which an out-of-balance moment at B or C is to be multiplied to give the balancing moments in the beam must therefore be calculated from (10.10). Since the spans are of equal stiffnesses these factors are 3/7 and 4/7. That is to say, if the out-of-balance moment on joint B is $\overline{M}$, when the beam moves into its equilibrium position the moments induced in it will be

$$M_{BA} = \frac{3}{7}\overline{M} \text{ and } M_{BC} = \frac{4}{7}\overline{M}.$$

When B is released the out-of-balance moment is $-(2,346 \cdot 6 - 1,280 \cdot 0 + 1,173 \cdot 3)$ or $-2,239 \cdot 9$ tons-feet so that the balancing moments are -960 and $-1,280$ tons-feet approximately. These are entered in line d together with those resulting from the release of C. The carry-over moments are entered in line e. The entries in columns 1 and 2, line e, are zero since A is a free support and therefore no moment is developed there when B is released, and as no balancing moment was applied at A, line d, there is no corresponding carry-over moment to be entered at B. The process is continued as shown in the Table. The total moments after five balances are $M_{AB} = 0$; $M_{BA} = 2,391 \cdot 1 = -M_{BC}$; $M_{CB} = 1,325 \cdot 3 = -M_{CD}$ and $M_{DC} = 0$.

Though somewhat awkward for dealing with a beam on elastic supports, the moment distribution method can be used with advantage if the supports sink known distances under load. It is most convenient to assume that the deflexions of the supports take place when the load is first applied, while the beam is still clamped, that is to say so restrained as to remain horizontal at the supports. The fixed-end moments are calculated from equations (3.30) and (3.31) in which a term appears giving the modification in the moments due to the relative deflexion of the ends. The beam is then released and the balancing and carry-over moments are found as before, the initial sinking of the supports having no effect on these processes.

As an example, consider a uniform beam whose relevant second moment of area is 90 (ins.)^4, carried on supports A, B, C and D. When three concentrated loads as shown in Fig. 10.6 are applied to the beam the support B sinks a distance of $\frac{1}{10}$ inch. To find the resulting bending moments imagine the beam clamped at the supports so that when the loads are applied the

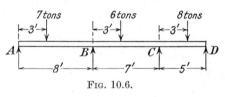

FIG. 10.6.

support B sinks $\frac{1}{10}$ inch but the beam there and at A, C and D remains horizontal. The fixed-end moments induced under these conditions are found from equations (3.30) and (3.31), taking E=13,000 tons per square inch, to be

$M_{AB} = -14 \cdot 65$ tons-feet. $M_{BA} = -1 \cdot 54$ tons-feet. $M_{BC} = 2 \cdot 40$ tons-feet. $M_{CB} = 12 \cdot 69$ tons-feet. $M_{CD} = -3 \cdot 84$ tons-feet. $M_{DC} = 5 \cdot 76$ tons-feet.

These moments are entered in the first line of Table 10.4. The beam is now released at the supports, the procedure being exactly as that described for Table 10.3 and the calculation of the end moments is completed.

10.3. Application to stiff-jointed frames.—When the moments in a frame with perfectly rigid joints are to be determined the procedure is much the same as that described in the last paragraph.

Fig. 10.7 shows a simple symmetrical portal with rigid joints and encastré feet, the bending moments in which, due to a central concentrated load of

TABLE 10.4.

END MOMENTS (TONS-FEET).

A	B		C		D
−14·65	−1·54	+2·40	+12·69	−3·84	+5·76
+14·65	0·00	0·00	0·00	0·00	−5·76
0·00	+7·33	0·00	0·00	−2·88	0·00
0·00	−3·25	−4·94	− 2·91	−3·06	0·00
0·00	0·00	−1·45	− 2·47	0·00	0·00
0·00	+0·57	+0·88	+ 1·20	+1·27	0·00
0·00	0·00	+0·60	+ 0·44	0·00	0·00
0·00	−0·24	−0·36	− 0·21	−0·23	0·00
0·00	0·00	−0·10	− 0·18	0·00	0·00
0·00	+0·04	+0·06	+ 0·09	+0·09	0·00

80 lb., are required. The members are all of the same length (100 inches) and of the same uniform cross-section and material. If all the joints are held so that they can neither rotate nor have any lateral movement then,

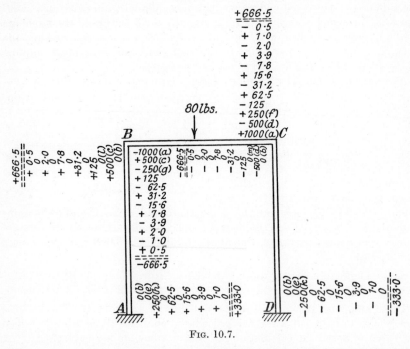

FIG. 10.7.

on the application of the load, the bending moments at the ends of the beam BC will be the same as those for a similar beam with encastré ends, and there will be no bending moments at the ends of the stanchions. These fixed-end moments are ±1,000 lb.-in. at the ends of the beams shown at a in Fig. 10.7, and zero at the ends of the stanchions, shown at b. The joint B is now released so that it is free to rotate ; before rotation the unbalanced moment on the joint was 1,000 lb.-in., on release the joint will rotate to an equilibrium position in which there will be no unbalanced moment on the joint.   The next step is, therefore, the distribution of the unbalanced moment between the members meeting at the joint in the ratio of the stiffnesses (I/l) of the members, equation (10.8).   This step is shown at c ; since the stiffnesses of the members are equal, the balancing moment applied to each member at the joint is $+500$ lb.-in.   The same process is carried out at joint C (step d).   Since the feet, A and D, of the stanchions are encastré they are not released and so no balancing moments are applied there (step e).   When a joint such as B is released and takes up its new equilibrium position, moments are induced at the other ends of the members meeting at B ; these moments must next be inserted.   For a straight member of uniform cross-section the carry-over factor is $\frac{1}{2}$, that is to say, the moment induced at one end of the member when a moment M is applied at the other is $\frac{1}{2}$M as shown in equation (10.9).   Thus the moment carried over to the end C of the member BC due to the balancing moment $+500$ lb.-in. applied at B is $+250$ lb.-in. ; this is shown as step f, Fig. 10.7.   Similarly, a moment of -250 lb.-in. is carried over from C to B (step g).   In the stanchions, moments ± 250 lb.-in. are carried over from B and C to A and D (steps h and k), but since no balancing moments were applied at the encastré feet the carry-over moments from A and D to B and C are zero (steps l and m).

The first full cycle of the process has been described.   It will be seen that at the end of it there is no longer balance at the joints ; for instance at B the out-of-balance moment is 250 lb.-in.   The same steps are therefore repeated again and again until the moments for distribution are small enough to be neglected.   In Fig. 10.7 four cycles are shown and the total values of the end moments, found by adding the figures in each column, are at B and C, $666 \cdot 5$ lb.-in. and at A and D, $333 \cdot 0$ lb.-in.   The corresponding values calculated from the slope deflexion equations are $666 \cdot 6$ and $333 \cdot 3$ lb.-in.

This example has been worked out and presented in the way suggested by Cross.   The column of figures giving the moment in a member has been written at right angles to the member concerned and therefore each time a figure relating to a stanchion is entered the diagram has to be turned through a right angle.   Though this may appear to be a small matter it leads to considerable confusion when a complicated frame is being stressed and before the method can be used for analysing complicated frames a more convenient arrangement is essential.

In Fig. 10.8 is shown a double portal with rigid joints and encastré feet carrying a concentrated load of 80 lb. at the centre of the beam PR.   As in the previous example the members are assumed to be of the same length (100 ins.) and of the same uniform cross-section and material.   The calculations of the moments in the members are given in Table 10.5 ; the upper part of the first column contains the figures relating to the end P of stanchion PQ, the lower part of this column containing the figures relating to the end Q ; columns 2 and 3 deal with the ends P and R of the beam PR and so on.

In the first step, a, the fixed-end moments $\pm 1,000$ lb.-in. are entered in the second and third columns ; at the ends of all other members the fixed-end moments are zero.   In step b the joints are released and balanced ; it has been found convenient, as shown in Table 10.5, to draw a line across the columns at each balance. There should be no difficulty in seeing that the balancing moment at the end of each member meeting at R is $-\dfrac{1,000}{3}$ lb.-in.

Extending equations (10.5)–(10.8) to the case of any number of members connected rigidly together at one joint, their far ends being encastré, we can write down the balancing moments in any one of the members having a stiffness I/l due to the application of a moment $\overline{M}$ to the joint as $\dfrac{\frac{I}{l}}{\sum \frac{I}{l}}$, the " distribution factor," multiplied by $\overline{M}$; $\sum \dfrac{I}{l}$ is, of course, the sum of the stiffnesses of all the members meeting at the joint.

Next, step c, the moment resulting from the balance is carried over to the opposite end of each member, thus, in column 3 the carry-over moment is

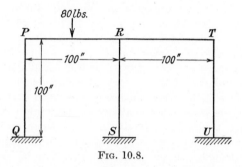

FIG. 10.8.

$+250$ lb.-in. resulting from the balancing moment of $+500$ lb.-in. applied at P (column 2, step b). With the calculations arranged in this way the out-of-balance moment at a joint can be seen at a glance and the risk of omitting any part of a step is reduced to a minimum. After the first carry-over, step c, the moment to be balanced at joint R is $+250$ lb.-in., made up of $+250$ lb.-in. in column 3 and zero moments in columns 4 and 5 ; after the second, step e, it is $+84$ lb.-in. made up of $+42$ lb.-in. in column 3, zero in column 4 and $+42$ lb.-in. in column 5 ; since the stiffnesses of the members are equal this last joint is balanced, step f, by applying the moments of -28 lb.-in. shown in columns 3, 4 and 5.

The process is continued until the necessary accuracy is obtained. In this particular example six balances were made before, at step g, the balancing moment dropped to 1 lb.-in. The total moments at the ends of the members, given in column 2 of Table 10.6, may be obtained by adding up each column of figures in Table 10.5.

It will be seen that while the balance at the joints is satisfactory the frame as a whole is not in equilibrium ; this is due to the fact that, though each joint was allowed to rotate until its equilibrium position was reached, complete freedom was not given to the structure as a whole and it was thus prevented from swaying.

Since vertical load only is applied to the frame under consideration the sum of the moments at the top and bottom of all the stanchions must, in the final state, be zero from equation (9.22). It will be seen from Table

TABLE 10.5.

Calculation of End Moments (lb.-in.)

Double Portal. Rigid Joints. Vertical Load.

1	2	3	4	5	6	7	(Step)
P	P	R	R	R	T	T	
0	−1000	+1000	0	0	0	0	a
+ 500	+ 500	− 334	− 333	− 333	0	0	b
0	− 167	+ 250	0	0	− 167	0	c
+ 83	+ 84	− 84	− 83	− 83	+ 84	+ 83	d
0	− 42	+ 42	0	+ 42	− 42	0	e
+ 21	+ 21	− 28	− 28	− 28	+ 21	+ 21	f
0	− 14	+ 11	0	+ 11	− 14	0	
+ 7	+ 7	− 7	− 7	− 7	+ 7	+ 7	
0	− 4	+ 4	0	+ 4	− 4	0	
+ 2	+ 2	− 3	− 3	− 3	+ 2	+ 2	
0	− 2	+ 1	0	+ 1	− 2	0	
+ 1	+ 1	− 1	− 1	− 1	+ 1	+ 1	g
− 68	0	0	− 69	0	0	− 68	h
+ 34	+ 34	+ 23	+ 23	+ 23	+ 34	+ 34	k
0	+ 12	+ 17	0	+ 17	+ 12	0	l
− 23	0	0	− 23	0	0	− 23	m
+ 6	+ 5	− 4	− 4	− 4	+ 5	+ 6	
0	− 2	+ 3	0	+ 3	− 2	0	
− 2	0	0	− 2	0	0	− 2	
+ 2	+ 2	− 1	− 1	− 1	+ 2	+ 2	n

Q		S		U		
0		0		0		a
0		0		0		b
+ 250		− 167		0		c
0		0		0		d
+ 42		− 42		+ 42		e
0		0		0		f
+ 11		− 14		+ 11		
0		0		0		
+ 4		− 4		+ 4		
0		0		0		
+ 1		− 2		+ 1		
0		0		0		g
− 68		− 69		− 68		h
0		0		0		k
+ 17		+ 12		+ 17		l
− 23		− 23		− 23		m
0		0		0		
+ 3		− 2		+ 3		
− 2		− 2		− 2		
0		0		0		n

10.6, column 2, that, at the stage represented by step g, Table 10.5, a residual moment of $+410$ lb.-in. exists. This means that, in preventing sway, an external horizontal force of $4 \cdot 10$ lb., acting from right to left at the level of the beam has been imposed on the frame. The next step is the removal of this force so as to allow the frame to deflect horizontally.

TABLE 10.6.
BENDING MOMENTS (LB.IN.) IN MEMBERS OF DOUBLE PORTAL FRAME.
RIGID JOINTS.
(Vertical load).

1	2	3	4	5	6
Moment	Cross method (sway neglected)	Cross method (complete solution)	Slope deflexion equations	Percentage difference between 4 and 3	Percentage difference between 4 and 2
QP	$+308$	$+235$	$+234 \cdot 4$	$0 \cdot 3$	$31 \cdot 4$
PQ	$+614$	$+563$	$+562 \cdot 5$	$0 \cdot 1$	$9 \cdot 2$
SR	-229	-313	$-312 \cdot 5$	$0 \cdot 2$	$26 \cdot 7$
RS	-455	-531	$-531 \cdot 2$	$0 \cdot 0$	$14 \cdot 3$
UT	$+ 58$	$- 15$	$- 15 \cdot 6$	$3 \cdot 9$	$471 \cdot 0$
TU	$+114$	$+ 63$	$+ 62 \cdot 5$	$0 \cdot 8$	$82 \cdot 5$
PR	-614	-563	$-562 \cdot 5$	$0 \cdot 1$	$9 \cdot 2$
RP	$+851$	$+889$	$+890 \cdot 6$	$0 \cdot 2$	$4 \cdot 4$
RT	-397	-359	$-359 \cdot 3$	$0 \cdot 1$	$10 \cdot 5$
TR	-114	$- 63$	$- 62 \cdot 5$	$0 \cdot 8$	$82 \cdot 5$

The moments induced at the ends of the members when the frame is allowed to deflect horizontally can be calculated most easily if the ends of the members are prevented from rotating while the sway takes place. It will be convenient at this stage to obtain general expressions for these moments.

Consider the behaviour of the rth storey in a frame in which all rotation of joints is prevented. Suppose a horizontal shear P acts from left to right at the level of the rth floor causing a horizontal deflexion δ of that floor relative to the $(r-1)$th. Then, from equations (9.3) and (9.4), the end moments induced in any stanchion length of height h and second moment of area J will be

$$M_{r(r-1)} = M_{(r-1)r} = -\frac{6EJ\delta}{h^2},$$

while from equation (9.23)

$$12E\delta \sum \frac{J}{h^3} = P,$$

the summation extending over all the stanchions in the storey.

It follows, therefore, that the magnitudes of the moments at the ends of a stanchion length are

$$M_{r(r-1)} = M_{(r-1)r} = -\tfrac{1}{2}P\frac{\dfrac{J}{h^2}}{\sum \dfrac{J}{h^3}} \qquad . \quad . \quad . \quad . \quad . \quad (10.11)$$

TABLE 10.7.

CALCULATION OF END MOMENTS (LB.-IN.)

DOUBLE PORTAL. RIGID JOINTS. HORIZONTAL LOAD.

1	2	3	4	5	6	7
P	P	R	R	R	T	T
−5000	0	0	−5000	0	0	−5000
+2500	+2500	+1666	+1668	+1666	+2500	+2500
0	+ 833	+1250	0	+1250	+ 833	0
−1667	0	0	−1667	0	0	−1667
+ 417	+ 417	− 278	− 278	− 278	+ 417	+ 417
0	− 139	+ 209	0	+ 209	− 139	0
− 140	0	0	− 140	0	0	− 140
+ 140	+ 140	− 93	− 93	− 93	+ 140	+ 140
0	− 46	+ 70	0	+ 70	− 46	0
− 46	0	0	− 46	0	0	− 46
+ 46	+ 46	− 31	− 31	− 31	+ 46	+ 46
0	− 16	+ 23	0	+ 23	− 16	0
− 16	0	0	− 16	0	0	− 16
+ 16	+ 16	− 10	− 10	− 10	+ 16	+ 16
0	− 5	+ 8	0	+ 8	− 5	0
− 5	0	0	− 5	0	0	− 5
+ 5	+ 5	− 4	− 4	− 4	+ 5	+ 5
0	− 2	+ 2	0	+ 2	− 2	0
− 2	0	0	− 2	0	0	− 2
+ 2	+ 2	− 1	− 1	− 1	+ 2	+ 2

Q	S	U
−5000	−5000	−5000
0	0	0
+1250	+ 834	+1250
−1667	−1667	−1667
0	0	0
+ 209	− 139	+ 209
− 140	− 140	− 140
0	0	0
+ 70	− 46	+ 70
− 46	− 46	− 46
0	0	0
+ 23	− 16	+ 23
− 16	− 16	− 16
0	0	0
+ 8	− 5	+ 8
− 5	− 5	− 5
0	0	0
+ 2	− 2	+ 2
− 2	− 2	− 2
0	0	0

In the example under consideration the moments induced when the restraining force is removed will be the same as those arising from the application to the otherwise unloaded frame of a force $+4 \cdot 10$ lb. at the level of the beams acting from left to right. Since all the stanchions are identical the moments at their ends are of the same magnitude, *viz.* $-410/6$ lb.-in. These values are inserted in their respective columns, step h, in Table 10.5 ; the entries in the beam columns 2, 3, 5 and 6 being zero as no rotations of the joints were allowed. The joints must now be released and allowed to rotate ; the balancing moments are entered at step k and the carry-over moments at step l. It will be found at this point that the sum of the moments at the ends of the stanchions again shows a residual moment, now reduced to $+137$ lb.-in. This is dealt with as before, a correcting moment of -23 lb.-in. being entered at the ends of the stanchions (step m). These last three steps, the balancing of the joints, the insertion of the carry-over moments and the correction of the residual moments, are then repeated until the necessary accuracy is obtained. The final total moments at the ends of the members found by adding up each column of figures from step a to step n, are tabulated in column 3, Table 10.6. In column 4 of this Table the moments calculated from the usual slope deflexion equations are given ; the excellent agreement between these values and those calculated by the Cross method, taking sway into account, will be seen from column 5. Column 6 shows that the neglect of the sway corrections leads to very appreciable inaccuracies.

The stressing of a frame subjected to a horizontal wind load is carried out in the way described above from step h to step n. The moments in the members of the same double portal Fig. 10.8 due to a horizontal load of 300 lb. acting from left to right at the joint P are determined in Table 10.7. Here, a horizontal shear is applied to the frame. In the first step, therefore, the joints are held so that they cannot rotate but the whole frame is allowed to sway. The moments induced at the ends of each stanchion length by this movement are found from equation (10.11) to be

$$M_{10} = M_{01} = -\tfrac{1}{2} \times 300 \times 100/3 = -5,000 \text{ lb.-in.}$$

These are entered in the first line of the table. The joints are then released and the calculation continued as before. In Table 10.7 seven balances have been carried out, giving the values of the end moments collected in Table 10.8, column 3. In practice only half this work would be necessary since, as a comparison of columns 2 and 3, Table 10.8 shows, sufficient accuracy is obtained after only four balances.

The same method can be applied when the feet of the stanchions are at different levels, Fig. 9.15. Equation (9.24) is used in making the sway correction as were equations (9.22) and (9.23) in the examples already given.

Fig. 10.9 shows a double portal frame with rigid joints and encastré feet, not at the same level, subjected to a concentrated horizontal load of 80 lb. half-way up the centre stanchion. The members of the frame are of the same uniform cross-section and material. The calculations of the moments in the members are given in Table 10.9. By step (a) all joints have been released and balanced but no sway of the frame has been allowed. At this stage it will be found by substituting the moments at the ends of the stanchions (see Table 10.10) in the left-hand side of equation (9.24), that, in preventing sway, an external horizontal force of $38 \cdot 9$ lb. acting from right

TABLE 10.8.

BENDING MOMENTS (LB.-IN.) IN MEMBERS OF DOUBLE PORTAL FRAME.

(Horizontal load).

1	2	3
Moment	Cross method (after 4 balances)	Cross method (after 7 balances)
QP	−5,324	−5,314
PQ	−3,750	−3,750
SR	−6,204	−6,250
RS	−5,588	−5,626
UT	−5,324	−5,314
TU	−3,750	−3,750
PR	+3,750	+3,750
RP	+2,793	+2,811
RT	+2,793	+2,811
TR	+3,750	+3,750

to left at the level of the beam has been imposed on the frame. The next step is the removal of this force so as to allow sway to take place but, as in the earlier examples, without allowing the joints to rotate. The moments induced at the ends of the stanchions by this movement are calculated from equation (10.11), and are entered in Table 10.9 as step (b). The joints must

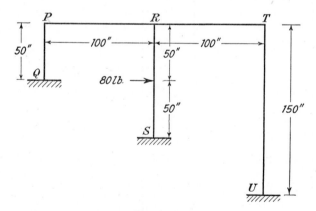

FIG. 10.9.

now be released and allowed to rotate, further sway being prevented. When the joints are once more balanced, step (c), it will be found, by substituting in equation (9.24), that the horizontal force preventing sway is 17·2 lb. This must be removed, as before, and sway allowed. The whole process between steps (b) and (c) need not be repeated since we already know the moments induced at the ends of the members by the removal of the horizontal force 38·9 lb. and the subsequent balance of the joints which introduced

ANALYSIS OF STRUCTURES

TABLE 10.9.

CALCULATION OF END MOMENTS.

DOUBLE PORTAL. FEET NOT AT SAME LEVEL. RIGID JOINTS. HORIZONTAL LOAD.

1	2	3	4	5	6	7	(Step)
P	P	R	R	R	T	T	
0	0	0	+1000	0	0	0	
0	0	− 333	− 333	− 333	0	0	
0	− 167	0	0	0	− 167	0	
+ 111	+ 56	0	0	0	+ 100	+ 67	
0	0	+ 28	0	+ 50	0	0	
0	0	− 26	− 26	− 26	0	0	
0	− 13	0	0	0	− 13	0	
+ 9	+ 4	0	0	0	+ 8	+ 5	
0	0	+ 2	0	+ 4	0	0	
0	0	− 2	− 2	− 2	0	0	a
− 837	0	0	− 209	0	0	− 93	b
+ 558	+ 279	+ 70	+ 70	+ 70	+ 56	+ 37	
0	+ 35	+ 139	0	+ 28	+ 35	0	
− 23	− 12	− 56	− 56	− 56	− 21	− 14	
0	− 28	− 6	0	− 10	− 28	0	
+ 19	+ 9	+ 5	+ 5	+ 5	+ 17	+ 11	
0	+ 2	+ 4	0	+ 8	+ 2	0	
− 1	− 1	− 4	− 4	− 4	− 1	− 1	c

Q		S		U		
0		−1000		0		
0		0		0		
0		− 167		0		
0		0		0		
+ 55		0		+ 33		
0		0		0		
0		− 13		0		
0		0		0		
+ 5		0		+ 3		
0		0		0		a
− 837		− 209		− 93		b
0		0		0		
+ 279		+ 35		+ 18		
0		0		0		
− 11		− 28		− 7		
0		0		0		
+ 10		+ 3		+ 5		
0		0		0		c

again a restraining force of $17 \cdot 2$ lb. If, therefore, these moments, Column (4), Table 10.10, are multiplied by $\dfrac{17 \cdot 2}{(38 \cdot 9 - 17 \cdot 2)}$ the additional moments to produce final balance result. These are entered in Table 10.10 as step (d).

TABLE 10.10.

BENDING MOMENTS (LB.-IN.) IN MEMBERS OF PORTAL, SHOWN IN FIG. 10.9,
AT VARIOUS STAGES IN THE CALCULATION.

1	2	3	4	5	6
Moment	At step (a)	At step (c)	Induced between steps (a) and (c) [Col. (3) − Col. (2)]	Added at step (d)	Total [Col. (3) + Col. (5)]
QP	+ 60	− 499	−559	−443	− 942
PQ	+ 120	− 164	−284	−225	− 389
PR	− 120	+ 164	+284	+225	+ 389
RP	− 331	− 179	+152	+120	− 59
RS	+ 639	+ 445	−194	−154	+ 291
SR	−1180	−1379	−199	−158	−1537
RT	− 307	− 266	+ 41	+ 33	− 233
TR	− 72	− 12	+ 60	+ 48	+ 36
TU	+ 72	+ 12	− 60	− 48	− 36
UT	+ 36	− 41	− 77	− 61	− 102

10.4. Frames with semi-rigid joints.—There is no difficulty in extending the moment distribution method to include frames with semi-rigid beam-to-stanchion connexions. Fig. 10.10 represents part of such a frame. It will

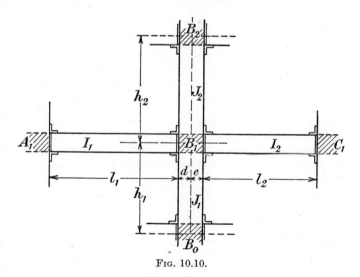

FIG. 10.10.

be found most convenient to consider the parts of the stanchions at the levels of the beams, shown cross-hatched at B_1, etc., as the joints which are in turn fixed and released. The assumption will be made in the first place that the widths of the members may be neglected without giving rise to serious errors. The fixed-end moments, distribution and carry-over factors can then be deduced directly from the general expressions given in paragraph 9.4.

When a uniformly distributed load w per unit length is applied to a beam of uniform cross-section, such as A_1B_1, Fig. 10.10, the fixed-end moments are

and

$$\left. \begin{aligned} M_{AB} &= \frac{-(3\beta+1)wl^2}{12(3\alpha\beta+2\alpha+2\beta+1)} \\[2mm] M_{BA} &= \frac{(3\alpha+1)wl^2}{12(3\alpha\beta+2\alpha+2\beta+1)} \end{aligned} \right\} \begin{aligned} &\text{Fixed-end} \\ &\text{moments.} \end{aligned}$$

where α and β are the constants for the connexions at the ends A and B, and l is the length of the beam. These expressions are derived from equations (9.30) and (9.31) by making $\theta_A = \theta_B = 0$.

The carry-over factors can be found quite simply. Suppose a moment M_{AB} is applied to the end A of a beam AB, the other end B being attached by a semi-rigid connexion to a stanchion which is clamped so that it cannot rotate.

From equation (9.4) we have

$$M_{BA} = \frac{2EI}{l}[\phi_A + 2\phi_B]. \quad . \quad . \quad . \quad . \quad (10.12)$$

Since the stanchion does not rotate we obtain, from equation (9.27)

$$\phi_B = -\frac{\beta l}{2EI}M_{BA} \quad . \quad . \quad . \quad . \quad (10.13)$$

and from (10.12) and (10.13)

$$\frac{2EI}{l}\phi_A = (1+2\beta)M_{BA}. \quad . \quad . \quad . \quad . \quad (10.14)$$

But, from equation (9.3)

$$M_{AB} = \frac{2EI}{l}[2\phi_A + \phi_B]$$

or, from (10.13) and (10.14)

$$M_{AB} = (2+3\beta)M_{BA},$$

so that if a moment M_{AB} is applied to one end A of a beam the moment induced at the other end B is $M_{AB}/(2+3\beta)$. It can be shown in the same way that if a moment M_{BA} is applied to the end B the moment induced at the other end A attached to a rigid support by a semi-rigid connexion is $M_{BA}/(2+3\alpha)$.

We may say, therefore, that from the end A to the end B

$$\left. \begin{aligned} &\text{the carry-over factor is } \frac{1}{(2+3\beta)} \\ &\text{and from the end B to the end A} \\ &\text{the carry-over factor is } \frac{1}{(2+3\alpha)} \end{aligned} \right\} \begin{aligned} &\text{Carry-over} \\ &\text{factors.} \end{aligned}$$

where α and β are the constants for the connexions at the ends A and B of the beam.

For all stanchion lengths the carry-over factor will be $\frac{1}{2}$, as before.

The distribution factors may be obtained from a consideration of Fig. 10.10. If the joint B_1 is rotated through an angle θ while the neighbouring joints

A_1, B_2, C_1 and B_0 are kept fixed the total moment acting on the joint B_1 will be, when the widths of the members are neglected,

$$M^1{}_{BA}+M^B{}_{12}+M^1{}_{BC}+M^B{}_{10}$$

$$=\left[\frac{2EI_1(3\alpha_1+2)}{l_1(3\alpha_1\beta_1+2\alpha_1+2\beta_1+1)}+\frac{4EJ_2}{h_2}+\frac{2EI_2(3\beta_2+2)}{l_2(3\alpha_2\beta_2+2\alpha_2+2\beta_2+1)}+\frac{4EJ_1}{h_1}\right]\theta$$

$$=2EY\theta \text{ (say).} \quad \text{See equation (9.35).}$$

The distribution factors by which an unbalanced moment at B_1 must be multiplied to give the balancing moments at the ends of the members meeting at the joint are therefore,

for B_1A_1 .. $\dfrac{I_1}{l_1Y}\dfrac{(3\alpha_1+2)}{(3\alpha_1\beta_1+2\alpha_1+2\beta_1+1)}$

for B_1B_2 .. $\dfrac{2J_2}{h_2Y}$

for B_1C_1 .. $\dfrac{I_2}{l_2Y}\dfrac{(3\beta_2+2)}{(3\alpha_2\beta_2+2\alpha_2+2\beta_2+1)}$ Distribution factors.

for B_1B_0 .. $\dfrac{2J_1}{h_1Y}$

The various factors for any particular frame with semi-rigid beam connexions may be evaluated from these general expressions. Once they are

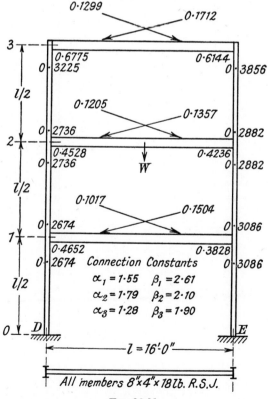

FIG. 10.11.

TABLE 10.11.

CALCULATION OF END MOMENTS.　THREE-STOREY, SINGLE-BAY FRAME.

SEMI-RIGID CONNEXIONS.　VERTICAL LOAD.

0	0	0	0
0	0	0	0
+0·00623			−0·00572
−0·00038			−0·00038
−0·00189	−0·00396	+0·00375	+0·00235
+0·00042	+0·00064	−0·00051	−0·00025
−0·00030	0	0	−0·00030
−0·00025	−0·00051	+0·00065	+0·00041
+0·00033	+0·00011	−0·00007	−0·00025
−0·00012	0	0	−0·00012
−0·00010	−0·00022	+0·00027	+0·00017
+0·00007	+0·00005	−0·00003	−0·00004
−0·00005	0	0	−0·00005
−0·00002	−0·00005	+0·00007	+0·00005

↓

0	0	−0·04549	+0·03969	0	0
+0·01245	+0·01245	+0·02059	−0·01681	−0·01144	−0·01144
0	0	−0·00228	+0·00248	0	0
−0·00038	−0·00038	0	0	−0·00038	−0·00038
+0·00083	+0·00083	+0·00138	−0·00072	−0·00050	−0·00050
−0·00095	−0·00078	−0·00010	+0·00017	+0·00118	+0·00094
−0·00030	−0·00024	0	0	−0·00030	−0·00024
+0·00065	+0·00065	+0·00107	−0·00074	−0·00050	−0·00050
−0·00013	−0·00006	−0·00010	+0·00013	+0·00021	+0·00014
−0·00012	−0·00012	0	0	−0·00012	−0·00012
+0·00014	+0·00014	+0·00024	−0·00010	−0·00007	−0·00007
−0·00005	−0·00003	−0·00001	+0·00003	+0·00009	+0·00007
−0·00005	−0·00006	0	0	−0·00005	−0·00006
+0·00005	+0·00005	+0·00010	−0·00003	−0·00002	−0·00002

0	0	0	0	0	0
0	0	0	0	0	0
0	+0·00623	0	0	0	−0·00572
0	−0·00038	0	0	0	−0·00038
−0·00156	−0·00156	−0·00272	+0·00234	+0·00188	+0·00188
0	+0·00042	+0·00035	−0·00028	0	−0·00025
−0·00012	−0·00024	0	0	−0·00012	−0·00024
−0·00011	−0·00011	−0·00019	+0·00034	+0·00027	+0·00027
0	+0·00033	+0·00005	−0·00002	0	−0·00025
−0·00006	−0·00012	0	0	−0·00006	−0·00012
−0·00005	−0·00005	−0·00009	+0·00017	+0·00014	+0·00014
0	+0·00007	+0·00003	−0·00001	0	−0·00004
−0·00003	−0·00006	0	0	−0·00003	−0·00006
0	0	0	+0·00005	+0·00004	+0·00004

0	0
0	0
0	0
0	0
0	0
−0·00078	+0·00094
−0·00012	−0·00012
0	0
−0·00006	+0·00014
−0·00006	−0·00006
0	0
−0·00003	+0·00007
−0·00003	−0·00003
0	0

[*All entries to be multiplied by Wl where W is the concentrated load and l is the length of the beam.*]

obtained, exactly the same procedure is adopted as that already described for the rigid frames.

Table 10.11 gives the detailed calculations of the bending moments in a three-storey, single-bay frame carrying a central concentrated load W on the middle beam. The dimensions of the frame and the values of the constants of the beam connexions are given in Fig. 10.11 where will also be found the distribution factors grouped around each joint and the carry-over factors placed above each beam.

The only difference between the procedure adopted in Table 10.11 and that given for the rigid frame in Table 10.5 is that in the former the sway correction is not made separately at the end of the calculation but is included in each cycle as for the wind load of Table 10.7. Thus, each time the joints are balanced and the carry-over moments inserted, the residual moment in the stanchions is determined and the necessary correction made.

The total moments from Table 10.11 and those calculated by the slope deflexion equations are given in Table 10.12.

TABLE 10.12.

BENDING MOMENTS IN MEMBERS OF THREE-STOREY FRAME.

SEMI-RIGID CONNEXIONS.   VERTICAL LOAD.

Moment	Cross	Slope deflexion	Percentage difference
D_0D_1	$-0.00094\ Wl$	$-0.00092\ Wl$	2·2
D_1D_0	$-0.00212\ Wl$	$-0.00209\ Wl$	1·4
D_1D_2	$+0.00473\ Wl$	$+0.00478\ Wl$	1·0
D_2D_1	$+0.01218\ Wl$	$+0.01222\ Wl$	0·3
D_2D_3	$+0.01190\ Wl$	$+0.01191\ Wl$	0·1
D_3D_2	$+0.00413\ Wl$	$+0.00417\ Wl$	1·0
E_0E_1	$+0.00108\ Wl$	$+0.00109\ Wl$	1·0
E_1E_0	$+0.00193\ Wl$	$+0.00192\ Wl$	0·5
E_1E_2	$-0.00453\ Wl$	$-0.00453\ Wl$	0·0
E_2E_1	$-0.01245\ Wl$	$-0.01243\ Wl$	0·2
E_2E_3	$-0.01214\ Wl$	$-0.01213\ Wl$	0·1
E_3E_2	$-0.00394\ Wl$	$-0.00393\ Wl$	0·3

In certain cases frequently found in practice to-day, where the beams are attached to the flanges of the stanchions by connexions which are far from rigid, appreciable errors arise when the members are assumed for purposes of calculation to be represented by their neutral axes. The moment distribution method can, however, be expanded to take into account the widths of the stanchions and so give accurate results without adding any serious complication to the work.

A new set of distribution factors must first be obtained. If the joint B_1, Fig. 10.10, is rotated through an angle θ while the neighbouring joints are fixed, the total moment acting on the joint B_1 will be, when the widths of the stanchions are not neglected,

$$M^1{}_{BA}+M^B{}_{12}+M^1{}_{BC}+M^B{}_{10}+dV^1{}_{BA}+eV^1{}_{BC}$$

where d and e are the distances of the left- and right-hand faces of the stanchion from the neutral axis at B_1, or

$$\left[\frac{2EI_1}{l_1}\frac{(3\alpha_1+2)}{(3\alpha_1\beta_1+2\alpha_1+2\beta_1+1)}+\frac{4EJ_2}{h_2}\right.$$

$$+\frac{2EI_2}{l_2}\frac{(3\beta_2+2)}{(3\alpha_2\beta_2+2\alpha_2+2\beta_2+1)}+\frac{4EJ_1}{h_1}$$

$$+\frac{6EI_1d}{l_1{}^2}\frac{(\alpha_1+1)}{(3\alpha_1\beta_1+2\alpha_1+2\beta_1+1)}$$

$$\left.+\frac{6EI_2e}{l_2{}^2}\frac{(\beta_2+1)}{(3\alpha_2\beta_2+2\alpha_2+2\beta_2+1)}\right]\theta.$$

$$=2EZ\theta \text{ (say). See equation (9.35).}$$

The distribution factors by which an unbalanced moment at B_1 must be multiplied to give the balancing moments and reactions at the ends of the members meeting at the joint are therefore

for moment on B_1A_1, $\dfrac{I_1}{l_1Z}\dfrac{(3\alpha_1+2)}{(3\alpha_1\beta_1+2\alpha_1+2\beta_1+1)}$

for moment on B_1B_2, $\dfrac{2J_2}{h_2Z}$

for moment on B_1C_1, $\dfrac{I_2}{l_2Z}\dfrac{(3\beta_2+2)}{(3\alpha_2\beta_2+2\alpha_2+2\beta_2+1)}$ Distribution Factors.

for moment on B_1B_0, $\dfrac{2J_1}{h_1Z}$

for reaction on B_1A_1, $\dfrac{3I_1}{l_1{}^2Z}\dfrac{(\alpha_1+1)}{(3\alpha_1\beta_1+2\alpha_1+2\beta_1+1)}$

for reaction on B_1C_1, $\dfrac{3I_2}{l_2{}^2Z}\dfrac{(\beta_2+1)}{(3\alpha_2\beta_2+2\alpha_2+2\beta_2+1)}$

It should be noted that the last two of these factors give the reactions at the ends of the beams, while the first four give moments.

For all stanchion lengths the carry-over factor will be $\frac{1}{2}$, as usual.

The fixed-end moments

$$M_{AB}=\frac{-(3\beta+1)wl^2}{12(3\alpha\beta+2\alpha+2\beta+1)}$$

and

$$M_{BA}=\frac{(3\alpha+1)wl^2}{12(3\alpha\beta+2\alpha+2\beta+1)}$$

Fixed-end Moments.

are unchanged.

In addition, fixed-end reactions must now be set down. They are

$$V_{AB}=\frac{-(6\alpha\beta+3\alpha+5\beta+2)wl}{4(3\alpha\beta+2\alpha+2\beta+1)}$$

and

$$V_{BA}=\frac{(6\alpha\beta+5\alpha+3\beta+2)wl}{4(3\alpha\beta+2\alpha+2\beta+1)}$$

Fixed-end Reactions.

derived from equations (9.32) and (9.33) by making $\theta_A=\theta_B=0$.

Since the reactions as well as the moments at the ends of the beams are to be calculated, there is now no necessity to derive general expressions for carry-over factors. If a balancing moment +M and a balancing reaction +V are applied to one end of a beam of length l, then a moment $-(M-Vl)$ and a reaction +V must be carried over to the other end.

A simple example will make the process clear. A single-storey two-bay semi-rigid frame with stanchions 10 in. wide is shown in Fig. 10.12. The distribution factors are entered around each joint. It will be seen from Table 10.13, where the detailed calculations are given, that four more columns are used than in the similar case worked out in Table 10.5. These columns, 3, 4, 8 and 9, contain the reactions at the ends of the beams.

The usual procedure is adopted. All joints are, in the first place, held fixed. The central load of 80 lb. applied to beam AC then gives rise to fixed-end moments of ∓ 450 lb.-in. and fixed-end reactions of ∓ 40 lb. at A and C, entered in columns 2, 5, 3 and 4, step (a).

The joints are next released and allowed to take up new equilibrium positions. The out-of-balance moment acting at joint A, on release, is made

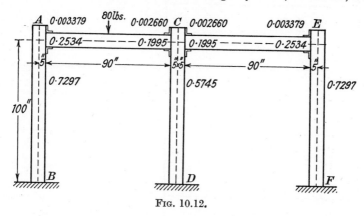

FIG. 10.12.

up of the moment -450 lb.-in., column 2, at the end of the beam and the moment -40×5 lb.-in. due to the eccentric beam reaction, column 3. The total out-of-balance moment is, therefore, 650 lb.-in. and it is distributed in step (b), on the joint taking up its new equilibrium position, into three balancing moments, $+474 \cdot 3$ lb.-in. (column 1) on AB, $+164 \cdot 7$ lb.-in. (column 2) on AC and $+11 \cdot 0$ lb.-in. arising from the balancing reaction $+2 \cdot 196$ lb. (column 3). These values inserted in step (b) are found directly by multiplying the appropriate distribution factors by 650. In the same way, balancing moments and reactions are found for joint C and entered in columns 4 to 8.

The carry-over moments and reactions are next inserted, step (c). The reaction and moment at the end A of AC arising from the balancing reaction $-1 \cdot 729$ lb. and the balancing moment $-129 \cdot 7$ lb.-in. applied at the end C are $-1 \cdot 729$ lb. and $-(-129 \cdot 7 + 90 \times 1 \cdot 729)$ lb.-in. or $-25 \cdot 9$ lb.-in. respectively ; these will be found in columns 3 and 2, step (c). Similarly, the reaction and moment carried over to the end C of AC are $+2 \cdot 196$ lb. and $-(164 \cdot 7 - 90 \times 2 \cdot 196)$ lb.-in. or $+33 \cdot 0$ lb.-in. When the sway correction, step (d), has been applied as described in earlier cases, the first cycle of operations is complete.

TABLE 10.13.

CALCULATION OF END MOMENTS AND BEAM REACTIONS. DOUBLE PORTAL. SEMI-RIGID CONNEXIONS. VERTICAL LOAD.

	1	2	3	4	5	6	7	8	9	10	11
	A	A	A	C	C	C	C	C	E	E	E
	0 +474.3	−450.0 +164.7	−40.0 +2.196	+40.0 −1.729	+450.0 −129.7	0 −373.4	0 −129.7	0 −1.729	0 0	0 0	0 0
a	−25.2 +43.6	−25.9 +15.1	−1.729 +0.202	+2.196 0 −0.050	+33.0 −3.8	0 −25.2 −10.8	0 −3.8	0 −0.050	−1.729 0 +0.202	−25.9 +15.1	0 −25.2 +43.6
b	0 −19.1 −14.7	−0.7 +5.1	−0.050 +0.068	+0.202 0 +0.029	+3.1 −2.2	−19.1 +6.3	+3.1 0 +2.2	+0.202 0 +0.029	−0.050 0 +0.068	−0.7 +5.1	0 −19.1 +14.7
c	+8.9 −6.1	+0.4 +2.1	+0.029 +0.028	+0.068 0 +0.016	+1.0 +1.2	0 +8.9 −3.6	+1.0 +1.2	+0.068 0 +0.016	+0.029 0 +0.028	+0.4 +2.1	+8.9 +6.1
d	−4.0 +2.6	+0.3 +0.9	+0.016 +0.012	+0.028 0 +0.007	+0.5 +0.5	−4.0 −1.6	+0.5 +0.5	+0.028 0 +0.007	+0.016 0 +0.012	+0.3 +0.9	+4.0 +2.6

B

	0 0
	+237.2 −25.2
	+21.8 −19.1
	+7.4 −8.9
	+3.1 −4.0

D

	0 0
	−186.7 −25.2
	−5.4 −19.1
	+3.2 −8.9
	+1.8 −4.0

F

	0 0
	0 −25.2
	+21.8 −19.1
	+7.4 −8.9
	+3.1 −4.0

The moments at the ends of the members resulting from the five cycles shown in Table 10.13 are collected in Table 10.14, together with the values calculated from the slope deflexion equations and those found when the widths of the stanchions are neglected and all members are represented by their neutral axes.

TABLE 10.14.

BENDING MOMENTS (LB.-IN.) IN STANCHIONS OF TWO-BAY SEMI-RIGID FRAME WITH STANCHIONS OF FINITE WIDTH.

Moment	Stanchions of finite width		Members represented by neutral axes
	Cross	Slope deflexion	Cross
BA	+212·3	+211·4	+170·0
AB	+484·1	+483·1	+384·0
DC	−244·3	−245·9	−193·0
CD	−429·9	−431·6	−342·5
FE	− 24·9	− 25·7	− 20·5
EF	+ 9·8	+ 8·8	+ 2·8

A comparison of the second and fourth columns shows the appreciable errors, of the order of 20 per cent. in the larger moments, arising from neglect of the true widths of the stanchions.

This is rather an extreme instance since the stanchions have considerable width and the connexions are far from rigid but it shows that the assumptions must be chosen with care if accurate results are to be obtained. It is, unfortunately, impossible to give a complete guide but it can be said that in general when joints are rigid the width of the members can be safely neglected in the collection of design data. For instance, in single bay frames of one, two, three and four storeys made up of 8 in. × 6 in. **I** stanchions, storey height 8 feet with 12 in. × 5 in. **I** beams, 15 feet 3 inches long framing into the stanchion flanges, the errors in the bending moments produced by assuming the members were represented by their neutral axes were found to vary between 2·27 and 3·45 per cent.

In all building frames of practical proportions with rigid or semi-rigid connexions the deformations due to axial force and shear can be neglected, though the existence of these reactions must never be forgotten. The effect of the deformations on frames built up of 8 in. × 6 in. **I** stanchions and 12 in. × 5 in. **I** beams was found to be less than 1 per cent. The effect of the direct thrust in the member on the flexure may be slightly more pronounced but as far as design data are concerned it can be dealt with as shown in Chapter 18.

10.5. The Hybrid Method.—The great merit of the moment distribution method is that the stresses in any structure, no matter how complicated, can be determined by simple arithmetical computation without introducing the simultaneous equations which limited the usefulness of strain energy and slope deflexion analysis. However, it is sometimes possible to simplify moment distribution calculations, particularly where the sway correction is concerned, by making use of what may be termed the hybrid method, which introduces simultaneous equations. The engineer should always be quick to adjust his methods in this way to suit the particular problem in hand. It can be done very easily where moment distribution is used because the actual behaviour of the structure is revealed at every step.

The principle of the hybrid method is to keep the distribution of the moments due to sway separate from that of the moments due to the application of the external loads to the structure prevented from swaying, and then to use the equilibrium equations for the structure to evaluate the magnitudes of the sway moments. It can be illustrated by analysing the two-bay frame shown in Fig. 10.8. The first step is to introduce a stop at the level of the beam to prevent side sway, then to apply the concentrated load of 80 lb. and allow the joints to rotate. The end moments under these conditions have already been calculated in Table 10.5, steps (a) to (g), collected in column (2), Table 10.6 and repeated in column (2), Table 10.15. Now take the unloaded structure, subject it to an arbitrary side sway δ and calculate the moments developed. Since in this example all the stanchions are of the same height and stiffness the moments induced at the ends of the stanchions before the joints are allowed to rotate all have the same value $-\dfrac{6EJ}{h^2}\delta$. Since δ is arbitrary these moments can more conveniently be represented by some such expression as $100x$ in the first line of Table 10.16 where x is a function of δ and $\dfrac{EJ}{h^2}$. Table 10.16 shows the distribution as the joints are allowed to rotate. The total sway moments from this calculation are collected in column 3, Table 10.15.

TABLE 10.15.

BENDING MOMENTS (LB.-IN.) IN MEMBERS OF DOUBLE PORTAL FRAME.
RIGID JOINTS. HYBRID METHOD.

1	2	3	4
Moment	Sway Prevented	Sway	Complete Solution (2) + (3)
QP	+308	+77x	+235
PQ	+614	+54x	+563
SR	−229	+91x	−315
RS	−455	+82x	−532
UT	+ 58	+77x	− 15
TU	+114	+54x	+ 63
PR	−614	−54x	−563
RP	+851	−41x	+890
RT	−397	−41x	−358
TR	−114	−54x	− 63

The total end moments in the free loaded portal, that is in the condition shown in Fig. 10.8, can be represented by the sum of columns (2) and (3), Table 10.15. The value of x must be such that the frame is in equilibrium under these moments. Since there is no horizontal shear across the portal the equilibrium equation is the same as equation (9.22), that is to say the sum of all the stanchion end moments must be zero. Substitution of the values of the total end moments from columns (2) and (3), Table 10.15 in equation (9.22) gives

$$410 + 435x = 0, \quad . \quad . \quad . \quad . \quad . \quad (10.15)$$

so that $x = -0.942$.

Substituting this value of x in the moments of column (3), Table 10.15 and adding to the moments of column (2) gives the complete solution, column (4), which should be compared with column (3), Table 10.6.

TABLE 10.16.

CALCULATION OF END MOMENTS (LB.-IN.) DUE TO SWAY. DOUBLE PORTAL.
RIGID JOINTS. HYBRID METHOD.

1	2	3	4	5	6	7
P	P	R	R	R	T	T
100x	0	0	100x	0	0	100x
− 50x	− 50x	− 33x	− 33x	− 33x	− 50x	− 50x
0	− 16x	− 25x	0	− 25x	− 16x	0
+ 8x	+ 8x	+ 16x	+ 16x	+ 16x	+ 8x	+ 8x
0	+ 8x	+ 4x	0	+ 4x	+ 8x	0
− 4x	− 4x	− 2x	− 2x	− 2x	− 4x	− 4x
0	− x	− 2x	0	− 2x	− x	0
0	0	+ x	+ x	+ x	0	0

Q		S		U
100x		100x		100x
0		0		0
− 25x		− 16x		− 25x
0		0		0
+ 4x		+ 8x		+ 4x
0		0		0
− 2x		− x		− 2x
0		0		0

The same steps are taken when analysing a two-storey frame such as that of Fig. 10.13 (a) in which the second moment of area of the right-hand stanchion DEF is twice that of the other members. The distribution factors at all joints are collected in Table 10.17 ; as before, we first introduce stops at D and E to prevent all sway and then apply the external loads consisting of one ton uniformly distributed on the top beam CD and a one ton eccentric concentrated load on BE. The joints are now allowed to rotate under these loads and the full moment distribution, without sway, is carried through ; the resulting stanchion end bending moments are collected in column 2, Table 10.18. The top storey of the unloaded frame is then given an arbitrary side sway relative to the bottom storey which is prevented from swaying, Fig. 10.13 (b), the fixed-end moments before joint rotation being $100x$ at the ends of BC and $200x$ at the ends of DE, a member which is twice as stiff as BC ; the fixed-end moments on all other members are zero. All

TABLE 10.17.

DISTRIBUTION FACTORS.

TWO-STOREY UNSYMMETRICAL FRAME.

Member	I/l	Distribution factor	Joint
AB	I/15	0·385 ⎫	
BE	I/25	0·230 ⎬	B
BC	I/15	0·385 ⎭	
CB	I/15	0·625 ⎫	C
CD	I/25	0·375 ⎭	
DC	I/25	0·230 ⎫	D
DE	2I/15	0·770 ⎭	
ED	2I/15	0·526 ⎫	
EB	I/25	0·158 ⎬	E
EF	2I/25	0·316 ⎭	

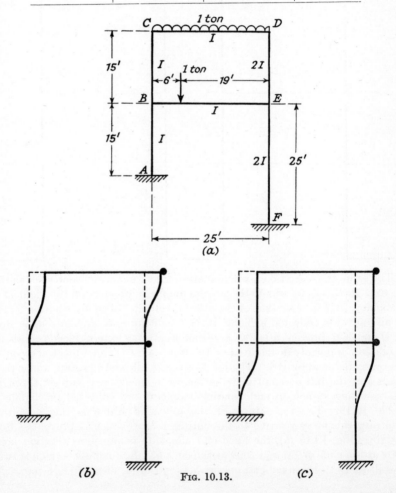

FIG. 10.13.

joints are now allowed to rotate and the full moment distribution is carried through, the resulting stanchion end bending moments being those of column 3, Table 10.18. Finally, sway is introduced into the bottom storey, all joints moving through the same arbitrary horizontal distance, Fig. 10.13 (c). It is convenient to give the fixed-end moments on AB the value $100y$, then because of the differences in stiffness and length of EF the fixed-end moments on it will be $72y$. All joints are now allowed to rotate, the resulting end bending moments being collected in column 4, Table 10.18.

The total end moment at a particular section of the structure loaded as in Fig. 10.13 (a) is the sum of columns (2) to (4), Table 10.18, the values of x and y being such that the structure is in equilibrium. Two equations of equilibrium can be written down for this two-storey frame and it is obviously convenient to have them expressed in terms of end moments only ; this can be done easily by considering the state of horizontal shear across each storey as in equation (9·24) which gives for the top storey,

$$M_{CB}+M_{BC}+M_{DE}+M_{ED}=0 \quad . \quad . \quad . \quad . \quad (10.16)$$

and for the bottom storey

$$25(M_{AB}+M_{BA})+15(M_{EF}+M_{FE})=0. \quad . \quad . \quad (10.17)$$

Substituting the values of the total moments from Table 10.18 these equations become

$$216x-77y+3\cdot8=0$$

and

$$26x-69y-6\cdot2=0,$$

so that

$$x=-0\cdot057$$

and

$$y=-0\cdot111.$$

The final values of the total end moments in the structure can then be written down as in column 5, Table 10.18.

TABLE 10.18.

BENDING MOMENTS (TONS-IN.) IN MEMBERS OF TWO-STOREY UNSYMMETRICAL FRAME. RIGID JOINTS. HYBRID METHOD.

1	2	3	4	5
Moment	Sway prevented	Sway of top storey	Sway of bottom storey	Complete solution (2)+(3)+(4)
AB	$+ 6\cdot9$	$-13x$	$+81y$	$- 1\cdot4$
BA	$+13\cdot7$	$-26x$	$+61y$	$+ 8\cdot4$
BC	$+20\cdot3$	$+54x$	$-33y$	$+20\cdot9$
CB	$+20\cdot1$	$+43x$	$- 8y$	$+18\cdot5$
DE	$-22\cdot7$	$+47x$	$- 6y$	$-24\cdot7$
ED	$-13\cdot9$	$+72x$	$-30y$	$-14\cdot7$
EF	$- 2\cdot2$	$-42x$	$+51y$	$- 5\cdot5$
FE	$- 1\cdot1$	$-21x$	$+61y$	$- 6\cdot7$

It will be seen from these examples that there are as many sway distributions and independent equations of equilibrium as the structure has degrees of freedom. In the frame with a setback, Fig. 10.14 (a) for instance, there will be three, one for the horizontal sway of each storey as in the last example

and a third due to the vertical movement of DE relative to the other stanchions, Fig. 10.14 (b). From this last diagram the fixed-end moments which
will appear in the third sway distribution should be clear. Convenient
equations of equilibrium will be found by considering the shear across each
storey, equation (9.24), and also the equilibrium of the part EFG. From
this last, resolving vertically, the vertical reaction at G must be equal to the
shear in EF. The former can be found in terms of end moments by considering the equilibrium of the whole frame, Fig. 10.14 (a), taking moments
about A, and the latter by considering the equilibrium of the member EF.
The required equation is then

$$(l_1+l_2)[M_{EF}+M_{FE}]-l_2[M_{AB}+M_{GF}]=Wl_2(h_1+h_2)+Pl_2d \quad . \quad . \quad (10.18)$$

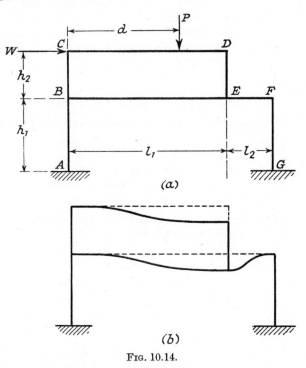

(a)

(b)

FIG. 10.14.

The frame with inclined members shown in Fig. 9.18, is quite easily
analysed by the hybrid method. Table 10.19 gives the moment distribution
under the external load of 5 tons on BC when sway is prevented. The
distribution factors are given in line (a) and the total end moments in line (b).
The unloaded frame is now made to sway but no rotations of the joints B
and C are allowed, Fig. 9.19. The relations existing between the relative
deflexions of the ends of the members have been given in (9.37) and (9.38)
so the ratios of the fixed-end moments, which are proportional to the deflexions and inversely to the squares of the lengths of the members, can
be calculated ; they are $1 : -0.530 : 0.316$ on AB, BC and CD respectively. Table 10.20 gives the details of the sway moment distribution in
which arbitrary fixed-end moments of $+1000x$, $-530x$ and $+316x$ are
distributed. The equilibrium equation (9.42) for the frame has already been
conveniently derived in terms of end moments ; it must be satisfied by the

sums of the end moments from Tables 10.19 and 10.20, giving $x = -0 \cdot 00349$. The final end moments are then found to be $M_{AB} = -1 \cdot 30$, $M_{BA} = +0 \cdot 89$, $M_{CD} = -4 \cdot 17$ and $M_{DC} = -2 \cdot 65$ tons-ft.

TABLE 10.19.

CALCULATION OF MOMENTS (TONS-FT.) DUE TO EXTERNAL LOAD.
FRAME WITH INCLINED MEMBERS. RIGID JOINTS.

1	2		3	4	
0·586	0·414		0·528	0·472	a
B	B		C	C	
0	−4·17		+4·17	0	
+2·44	+1·73		−2·20	−1·97	
0	−1·10		+0·87	0	
+0·64	+0·46		−0·46	−0·41	
0	−0·23		+0·23	0	
+0·13	+0·10		−0·12	−0·11	
0	−0·06		+0·05	0	
+0·03	+0·03		−0·03	−0·02	
0	−0·02		+0·02	0	
+0·01	+0·01		−0·01	−0·01	
+3·25	−3·25		+2·52	−2·52	b

A			D		
0			0		
0			0		
+1·22			−0·99		
0			0		
+0·32			−0·21		
0			0		
+0·07			−0·06		
0			0		
+0·02			−0·01		
0			0		
+1·63			−1·27		b

Another interesting example is provided by the pitched roof portal subjected to any external load system, Fig. 10.15 (*a*). This structure has two degrees of freedom since B will not suffer the same horizontal movement as D. The first step in the calculation is to restrain the portal by means of stops at B and D so that horizontal movement at these joints is prevented; apply the external loads, allow the joints to rotate and carry out the moment distribution. It is then possible to calculate the horizontal forces P_B and P_D, Fig. 10.15 (*b*), applied by the stops to the portal. This is a salutary exercise because it reminds the engineer that, while it is usually permissible in elementary analysis to neglect the strains due to the axial forces in members, the axial forces themselves do exist. Now take the unloaded portal and force the joints B and D through the same horizontal arbitrary distance δ_1 to the right and maintain them there by stops; allow the joints

TABLE 10.20.

CALCULATION OF SWAY MOMENTS.
FRAME WITH INCLINED MEMBERS. RIGID JOINTS.

1	2	3	4	
0·586	0·414	0·528	0·472	a

B	B	C	C
$+1000x$	$-530x$	$-530x$	$+316x$
$-\ 275x$	$-195x$	$+113x$	$+101x$
0	$+\ 57x$	$-\ 98x$	0
$-\ \ 33x$	$-\ 24x$	$+\ 52x$	$+\ 46x$
0	$+\ 26x$	$-\ 12x$	0
$-\ \ 15x$	$-\ 11x$	$+\ \ 6x$	$+\ \ 6x$
0	$+\ \ 3x$	$-\ \ 6x$	0
$-\ \ 2x$	$-\ \ x$	$+\ \ 3x$	$+\ \ 3x$
0	$+\ \ 2x$	$-\ \ x$	0
$-\ \ x$	$-\ \ x$	$+\ \ x$	0
$+\ 674x$	$-674x$	$-472x$	$+472x$

A		D
$+1000x$		$+316x$
0		0
$-\ 138x$		$+\ 51x$
0		0
$-\ \ 17x$		$+\ 23x$
0		0
$-\ \ \ 8x$		$+\ \ 3x$
0		0
$-\ \ \ x$		$+\ \ 2x$
0		0
$+\ 836x$		$+395x$

to rotate and from the moments, which will appear as functions of δ_1, calculate the forces $h_1\delta_1$ and $k_1\delta_1$, Fig. 10.15 (c), developed at the stops. Repeat this whole process but move B and D towards one another by a distance δ_2, Fig. 10.15 (d), and again calculate the forces $h_2\delta_2$ and $k_2\delta_2$ applied by the stops. When the external loads are applied to the unrestrained portal, Fig. 10.15 (a), movements such as δ_1 and δ_2 will take place but no restraining forces will be developed at B and D. Combining Figs. 10.15 (b) to (d), therefore, it will be seen that

$$P_B + h_1\delta_1 + h_2\delta_2 = 0$$

and

$$P_D + k_1\delta_1 + k_2\delta_2 = 0 \qquad \qquad . \quad . \quad . \quad . \quad . \quad . \quad (10.19)$$

From these two equations δ_1 and δ_2 can be found and the final end moments follow as in earlier examples.

10.6. Secondary stresses.—In his original paper Cross suggested the application of the moment distribution method to the determination of secondary stresses and the first worked example appears to be due to

Thompson and Cutler (1932). We cannot do better than set out their calculations. The truss considered is that shown in Fig. 10.16 (*a*), which has been treated by the orthodox methods in " Modern Framed Structures," Part II, Johnson, Bryan and Turneaure, where an exhaustive discussion of

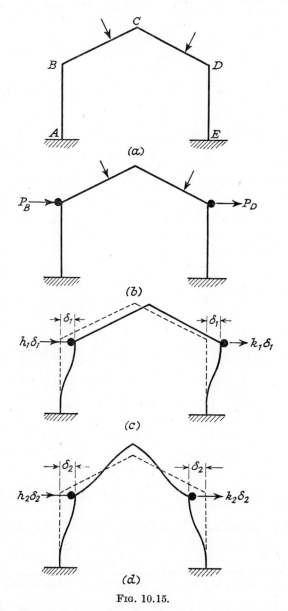

FIG. 10.15.

secondary stresses is given. As in the method already outlined in paragraph 9.6 the deflexions of the nodes of the pin-jointed frame must first be found. The Williot diagram, giving these deflexions, is shown in Fig. 10.16 (*b*) in which D is the displacement δ multiplied by E, the Young's modulus of the material of the truss. The figures in brackets on the line diagram of the

8*

truss are the axial deformations of the members multiplied by E while the other figures are the axial forces in the members in pounds.

The nodes of the actual rigid-jointed frame are first moved into the deflected positions given by the Williot diagram but are not allowed to rotate. Fixed-end moments will, therefore, be developed in the members. These can be calculated from equations (9.46) by putting $\theta_B = \theta_C = 0$ and substituting for I, l and D, the values which are collected in Table 10.21. The sign convention is the usual one originally defined in paragraph 9.3 and the

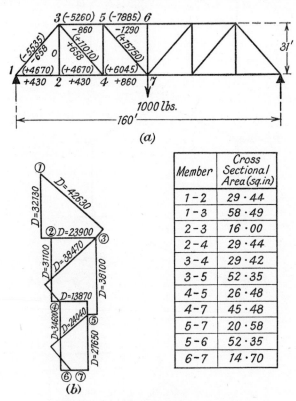

Member	Cross Sectional Area (sq.in)
1 – 2	29 · 44
1 – 3	58 · 49
2 – 3	16 · 00
2 – 4	29 · 44
3 – 4	29 · 42
3 – 5	52 · 35
4 – 5	26 · 48
4 – 7	45 · 48
5 – 7	20 · 58
5 – 6	52 · 35
6 – 7	14 · 70

FIG. 10.16.

arrangement of the calculations, Table 10.22, should be clear from earlier examples.

Consider the member 5–6. It will be seen from the Williot diagram that this member rotates in a clockwise direction and that D=27,650 so that from equation (9.46) the fixed-end moment M_{56} has the value

$$M_{56} = -\frac{6ID}{l^2} = -6 \times \frac{3,978}{(320)^2} \times 27,650 = -6,440 \text{ lb.-in.}$$

This is entered in the first line of the appropriate column (a). In the same way all the other fixed-end moments are calculated and entered. The joints of the truss will not be in equilibrium under these fixed-end moments ; it will be seen for instance that the out-of-balance moment acting on joint (5) is +15,986. When a joint is released, therefore, it will rotate until it reaches a position of equilibrium and balancing moments, proportional to their stiffnesses, will be developed at the ends of the members. As in earlier examples all the joints are released together and the balancing moments are entered in the second line of each column, Table 10.22. The carry-over moments, entered in the third line, throw the joints once more out of balance ; they must therefore be released and balanced again. Five cycles have been carried out in Table 10.22, and the end moments, found by summing each column, are entered in column 6, Table 10.21, where a comparison is

TABLE 10.21.

1	2	3	4	5	6	7
				End moments (lb.-in.)		
					Cross method	
Member	l (inches)	I (inches)^4	D	More exact method	Five cycles	Percentage difference between column 6 and column 5
1–2	320·0	1,218	32,130	+ 230	+ 240	4
2–1	—	—	—	+ 135	+ 151	12
1–3	490·7	4,490	42,630	− 230	− 240	4
3–1	—	—	—	− 527	− 507	4
2–3	372·0	95	23,900	− 53	− 54	2
3–2	—	—	—	− 55	− 56	2
2–4	320·0	1,218	31,100	− 80	− 97	21
4–2	—	—	—	− 141	− 133	6
3–4	490·7	805	38,470	− 307	− 295	4
4–3	—	—	—	− 320	− 301	6
3–5	320·0	3,978	38,100	+ 900	+ 858	5
5–3	—	—	—	+ 495	+ 523	6
4–5	372·0	750	13,870	− 875	− 880	0·5
5–4	—	—	—	− 924	− 927	0
4–7	320·0	1,907	34,600	+1,342	+1,314	2
7–4	—	—	—	+2,602	+2,625	1
5–7	490·7	358	24,040	− 130	− 133	2
7 5	—	—	—	+ 42	+ 45	7
5–6	320·0	3,978	27,650	+ 562	+ 537	4
6–5	—	—	—	+3,544	+3,563	0·5
6–7	372·0	288	0	0	0	0

made (column 7) with the moments calculated by a more exact method (column 5). It will be seen that the moments at the ends of members 2–1 and 2–4 show errors of 12 and 21 per cent. respectively. If greater accuracy is required further cycles of the moment distribution process can be carried out. Had only one more been completed these particular errors would have dropped to 3 and 6 per cent. respectively. From the end moments the end bending stresses, which are the secondary stresses required, are calculated. Thus in member 3–4, which is made up of two 15-inch channels back to back, having a total relevant second moment of area of 805 (in.)^4, the maximum bending stress in the member, due to the end moment −301 lb.-in., Table

TABLE 10.22.

3				5			a	6		
−4,768	− 98	−700	−8,880	−8,880	− 452	−214	−6,440	−6,440	0	+6,440
+5,640·3	+157·2	+986·3	+7,662·0	+7,196·6	+1,169·5	+423·2	+7,196·6	0		0
+2,493·4	+ 74·7	+432·3	+3,598·3	+3,831·0	+ 545·7	0	0	+3,598·3		−3,598·3
−2,576·3	− 71·8	−450·5	−3,499·9	−1,970·3	− 320·2	−115·9	−1,970·3	0		0
−1,389·5	− 34·7	−131·0	− 985·1	−1,749·9	− 165·4	0	0	− 985·1		+ 985·1
+ 991·8	+ 27·6	+173·4	+1,347·4	+ 862·2	+ 140·1	+ 50·7	+ 862·2	0		0
+ 638·0	+ 15·0	+ 54·0	+ 431·1	+ 673·7	+ 68·1	0	0	+ 431·1		− 431·1
− 444·4	− 12·4	− 77·7	− 603·7	− 333·9	− 34·3	− 19·6	− 333·9	0		0
− 254·1	− 6·6	− 22·8	− 166·9	− 301·8	− 28·8	0	0	− 166·9		+ 166·9
+ 175·9	+ 4·9	+ 30·8	+ 238·9	+ 148·8	+ 24·2	+ 8·8	+ 148·8	0		0

1		2			4				7				
−4,768	−2,290	−2,290	− 98·0	−2,214	−2,214	−700	− 452	−3,864	−3,864	−214	0	+214	+3,864
+4,986·9	+2,071·1	+2,226·3	+149·4	+2,226·3	+2,053·4	+864·6	+1,091·5	+3,220·5	0	0		0	0
+2,820·1	+1,113·1	+1,035·5	+ 78·6	+1,026·7	+1,113·1	+493·1	+ 584·7	0	+1,610·2	+211·6		−211·6	−1,610·2
−2,779·1	−1,154·1	−1,035·6	− 69·5	−1,035·6	− 622·2	−262·0	− 330·8	− 975·9	0	0		0	0
−1,288·1	− 517·8	− 577·0	− 35·9	− 311·1	− 517·8	−225·2	− 160·1	0	− 487·9	− 57·9		+ 57·9	+ 487·9
+1,276·0	+ 529·9	+ 447·1	+ 30·0	+ 447·1	+ 256·5	+108·0	+ 136·3	+ 402·3	0	0		0	0
+ 495·9	+ 223·5	+ 264·9	+ 13·8	+ 128·2	+ 223·5	+ 87·7	+ 70·0	0	+ 201·1	+ 25·3		− 25·3	− 201·1
− 508·3	− 211·1	− 196·8	− 13·2	− 196·8	− 108·3	− 45·6	− 57·6	− 169·8	0	0		0	0
− 222·2	− 98·4	− 105·5	− 6·2	− 54·1	− 98·4	− 38·8	− 27·1	0	− 84·9	− 9·8		+ 9·8	+ 84·9
+ 226·5	+ 94·1	+ 80·2	+ 5·4	+ 80·2	+ 46·7	+ 19·6	+ 24·8	+ 73·2	0	0		0	0

10.21, column 6, is of magnitude $\dfrac{301 \times 7 \cdot 5}{805} = 2 \cdot 81$ lb. per square inch.   The primary stress in this member due to the particular arrangement of external load considered is $22 \cdot 43$ lb. per square inch so that the secondary stress is $12 \cdot 6$ per cent. of the primary.

Though it is an effect that can usually be neglected, the end moments do modify the axial forces in the members.   If great accuracy is required in the calculation allowance can be made for the modification by the moment distribution method.   The change in the position of the nodes due to the alterations in the axial forces brought about by the end moments is determined and the process of moving the rigid joints into the new positions, determining the fixed-end moments, releasing the joints and balancing is again carried out.

The moment distribution method also enables the other secondary effects mentioned at the beginning of paragraph 9.6 to be evaluated without difficulty.   If the weights of the members are to be taken into account the bars are considered as beams carrying a distributed load equal to their own weight.   The fixed-end moments are then found from the expressions

$$M_{BC} = -\frac{6ID}{l^2} - \frac{wl^2}{12}$$

and
$$M_{CB} = -\frac{6ID}{l^2} + \frac{wl^2}{12},$$

where w is the intensity of the transverse load representing the weight of the member.   These moments are entered in the first lines of the table of calculations and the releasing and balancing of the joints is carried out as before.

When there is eccentricity in a joint due to the axes of the members not intersecting at one point the stresses arising can be determined by introducing

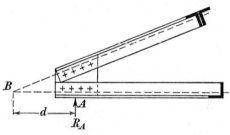

Fig. 10.17.

into the analysis an external moment at the joint equal to the moment produced by the axial primary forces in the bars meeting there.   An example of this type of eccentricity is commonly found at one end of light roof trusses and is shown diagrammatically in Fig. 10.17.   The axes of the members meet at the point B which is a distance d from the support A.   The theoretical joint where the axes meet is therefore subjected to an external moment of magnitude $-d.R_A$ and this must be included in the first balance of the joint. Suppose the truss illustrated in Fig. 10.16 (a) was supported, not at the inter- section of the members 1–3 and 1–2 but at a point 6 inches nearer to joint 2. As far as the development of stresses is concerned this is equivalent to the provision of a support at the point of intersection of the members together with an anti-clockwise moment of magnitude 3,000 lb.-in. acting on the joint. It will be seen from the first two columns of Table 10.22 that the fixed-end moments applied by joint (1) to the members meeting at it are —4,768 and —2,290. The total out-of-balance moment on the joint at the instant when it is released is therefore +4,058 lb.-in. made up of —3,000 arising from the eccentricity of the support together with +4,768 and +2,290 lb.-in., the moments applied by the members. As the joint moves into its equilibrium position this out-of-balance moment is divided between the members in proportion to their stiffnesses so that the first two lines of the appropriate columns of Table 10.22 will appear as in Table 10.23. The

TABLE 10.23.

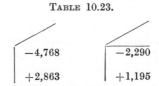

entries in the first two lines of the other columns are unchanged and the subsequent procedure is the same as before.

When, as frequently happens, one end of a truss is firmly fixed to its support so that it cannot rotate, the procedure in the calculations is the same as that used in the case of a continuous beam having one end encastré. If the joint (1) of the truss which has been considered above is firmly bolted to its abutment then the fixed end moments will be as before, Table 10.22, but since the joint cannot rotate no balancing moments appear in the second line of Table 10.24. The subsequent procedure is the same as before except that joint (1) is never released.

TABLE 10.24.

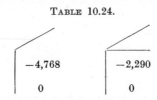

Little more remains to be said about the determination of secondary stresses. The moment distribution method provides the most efficient tool for the work and the principles underlying the method have been described so fully that the reader should be in a position to attack any particular case of secondary stress determination without the help of further illustrative examples. The assumptions used have been set out clearly. They are adequate for most practical problems but, as has been emphasised more than once already, it is impossible to define the limits beyond which they need amplification. Experience alone can do this. One assumption made so far in this chapter is that the effect of the axial force on the flexure of a member is negligible. Manderla, to whom is due the first satisfactory treatment of secondary stresses, gave in 1880 equations which take into account the effect of the axial force. These equations are derived just as equation (9.47) and state the fact that the sum of the end moments in the members meeting at a joint is zero. The expressions for the end moments to be substituted in these equations are, however, not the simple slope deflexion expressions but the more elaborate equations of which those for a member, initially curved, carrying a compressive force have been given in equations (7.42) and (7.43). Those for a member carrying a tensile force can be derived from the expressions of paragraph 8.4. The labour of solving these equations makes the method impracticable for most real trusses and use must again be made of distribution methods which, though exceedingly laborious in this case, are possible.

10.7. Column analogy.—Hardy Cross made another important contribution in the field of stress analysis with his column analogy (1930 (*b*)). This is a more limited method than moment distribution since it applies only to singly connected forms such as rings, single storey, single bay portals or beams, but it is powerful in that members of variable cross-section present little difficulty.

The first step in applying the method is to produce a statically determinate structure, by cutting a section or otherwise, and to find the free moments due to the external load system. Thus in the eccentrically loaded fixed-base

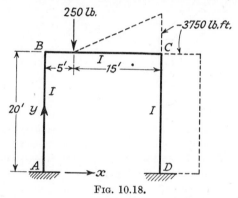

FIG. 10.18.

portal, Fig. 10.18, which is of uniform flexural rigidity EI throughout, the foot A, for instance, would be freed completely and the bending moment, M_s, determined at any point due to the 250 lb. load. The resulting bending moment diagram is shown by the dotted lines in Fig. 10.18. As in some of the earlier methods of analysis it is now necessary to apply at A reactions M_A, H_A and V_A, to bring the foot back to its original encastré condition.

The total bending moment at any point on the portal will then be

$$M = M_s - M_i . \quad . \quad . \quad . \quad . \quad . \quad (10.20)$$

where the statically indeterminate moment is

$$M_i = M_A + V_A x + H_A y. \quad . \quad . \quad . \quad . \quad (10.21)$$

It should be noted that M_i varies linearly across the frame.

The total bending strain energy in the portal is $U = \int \dfrac{M^2}{2EI} ds$ and for the encastré conditions at A,

$$\frac{\partial U}{\partial M_A} = \frac{\partial U}{\partial H_A} = \frac{\partial U}{\partial V_A} = 0,$$

i.e.

$$\int \frac{M}{EI} ds = \int \frac{Mx}{EI} ds = \int \frac{My}{EI} ds = 0.$$

Then, from equation (10.20)

$$\left.\begin{aligned}
\int \frac{M_s}{EI}ds &= \int \frac{M_i}{EI}ds \\[4pt]
\int \frac{M_s}{EI}x\,ds &= \int \frac{M_i}{EI}x\,ds \\[4pt]
\int \frac{M_s}{EI}y\,ds &= \int \frac{M_i}{EI}y\,ds
\end{aligned}\right\} \qquad \cdots \cdots \cdots \quad (10.22)$$

Now imagine a stocky column, Fig. 10.19, with a cross-section in the shape of the centre line of the portal and a width varying inversely as its EI;

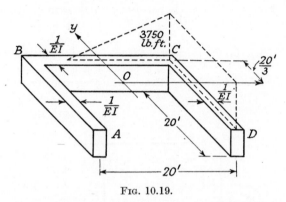

FIG. 10.19.

suppose the top face to carry a vertical load of intensity M_s as in Fig. 10.19. At a cross-section remote from the top face a longitudinal stress p will be developed which like M_i, equation (10.21), varies linearly across the section. The vertical load system M_s, and the stresses p are in equilibrium so that

$$\left.\begin{aligned}
\int \frac{M_s}{EI}ds &= \int \frac{p}{EI}ds \\[4pt]
\int \frac{M_s}{EI}x\,ds &= \int \frac{p}{EI}x\,ds \\[4pt]
\int \frac{M_s}{EI}y\,ds &= \int \frac{p}{EI}y\,ds.
\end{aligned}\right\} \qquad \cdots \cdots \cdots \quad (10.23)$$

A comparison of expressions (10.22) and (10.23) shows the analogy and it is clear that the value of the restraining moment M_i, at any point can be calculated as simply as the longitudinal stress p in the analogous column.

For the portal of Fig. 10.18 the analogous column has a three-sided cross-section because the base to which the feet of the portal are attached is assumed, as usual, to have infinite stiffness and therefore its $\frac{1}{EI}$ is zero. The centroid of the cross-section lies on the axis of symmetry Oy at a distance $\frac{20}{3}$ feet from BC. The area of cross-section and second moments of area are

$$A = \frac{60}{EI}, \quad I_x = \frac{8000}{3EI} \quad \text{and} \quad I_y = \frac{14000}{3EI}$$

The total load, P, on the top surface is $-28,125/EI$ on BC and $-75,000/EI$ on CD, adopting the sign convention that a sagging moment, or one causing tension on the inside surface of a member, is positive. These loads give moments

$$M_x = \frac{62,500}{EI} \text{ and } M_y = -\frac{890,625}{EI}.$$

The total stress at any point in the cross-section is

$$p = \frac{P}{A} + \frac{M_x \cdot y}{I_x} + \frac{M_y \cdot x}{I_y}, \quad \cdots \cdots \quad (10.24)$$

from which

$$p_A = -1718 - 312 + 1908 = -122$$
$$p_B = -1718 + 156 + 1908 = +346$$
$$p_C = \qquad\qquad\qquad = -3472$$
$$p_D = \qquad\qquad\qquad = -3940 \text{ lb.-ft.}$$

These are analogous to the statically indeterminate moments M_i so that the final moments are, from equation (10.20),

$$M_A = 0 - (-122) \qquad = +122$$
$$M_B = 0 - (+346) \qquad = -346$$
$$M_C = -3750 - (-3472) = -278$$
$$M_D = -3750 - (-3940) = +190 \text{ lb.-ft.}$$

For a portal with hinged feet, Fig. 10.20, the only redundant reaction is the thrust H but the steps taken in the analysis are unchanged. First make

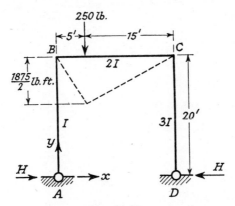

FIG. 10.20.

the portal statically determinate by imagining that the hinge at A is mounted on rollers, thus removing H. The distribution of sagging bending moment M_s due to the external load of 250 lb. is then as shown by the dotted lines in Fig. 10.20. The cross-section of the analogous column is produced as before, Fig. 10.21 ; it should be noted, Fig. 10.20, that in the particular example chosen the portal is not of the same section throughout. Due to the presence in the portal of hinged feet which have no stiffness, the

column cross-section at A and D has, for a short distance, infinite width. This means that the centroid O of the column section must be mid-way

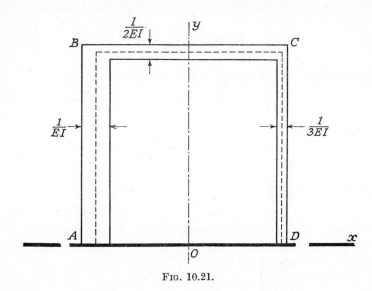

FIG. 10.21.

between A and D and that the stresses, other than those due to bending about the x-axis are negligible.   The second moment of area about AD is

$$I_x = \left(\frac{1}{12} \times \frac{1}{EI} \times 8000 + \frac{20}{EI} \times 100\right) + \left(\frac{1}{2EI} \times 20 \times 400\right)$$
$$+ \left(\frac{1}{12} \times \frac{1}{3EI} \times 8000 + \frac{20}{3EI} \times 100\right)$$
$$= \frac{4000 \times 17}{9EI}$$
$$M_x = \frac{9375 \times 20}{2EI} = \frac{93750}{EI}.$$

The stress at any point is, from equation (10.24),

$$p = \frac{M_x \cdot y}{I_x}$$

so that $$p_A = p_D = 0$$
$$p_B = p_C = 248$$

and from equation (10.20)

$$M_B = M_C = 0 - (248) = -248 \text{ lb.-ft.}$$

Lack of symmetry of the geometrical form of the structure to be analysed involves the calculation of product second moments of area of the cross-section of the analogous column.   The unsymmetrical frame of Fig. 10.22, of uniform section throughout, is encastré at the feet and is subjected to a central concentrated load on BC.   It is first made statically determinate by hinging the feet and mounting one on rollers ; the free bending moment diagram is shown by the dotted lines.

The cross-section of the analogous column has its centroid at O, Fig. 10.22, and geometrical properties

$$A=50/EI, \quad I_x=\frac{1750}{EI}, \quad I_y=\frac{10400}{3EI}$$

and

$$I_{xy}=0+\frac{20}{EI}\times 5\times -2+\frac{20}{EI}\times 8\times -5=-\frac{1000}{EI}.$$

For the statically determinate condition assumed,

$$P=\frac{10,000}{EI}, \quad M_x=\frac{50,000}{EI} \text{ and } M_y=-\frac{20,000}{EI}.$$

The stress at any point of an unsymmetrical column is

$$p=\frac{P}{A}+\frac{(I_yM_x-I_{xy}M_y)}{(I_xI_y-I_{xy}^2)}y+\frac{(I_xM_y-I_{xy}M_x)}{(I_xI_y-I_{xy}^2)}x \quad . \quad . \quad . \quad (10.25)$$

which gives

$$p_A=+13, \ p_B=+316, \ p_C=+385\cdot2 \text{ and } p_D=-221 \text{ lb.-ft.}$$

so that

$$M_A=-13, \ M_B=-316, \ M_C=-385\cdot2 \text{ and } M_D=+221 \text{ lb.-ft.}$$

These examples give all the information required for the calculation of bending moments in any singly-connected structure.

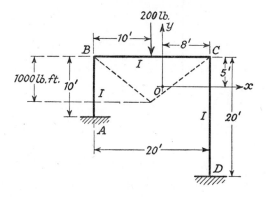

Fig. 10.22.

Column analogy is also of great help when the moment distribution method is being applied to structures with members of varying cross-section whose stiffnesses must be calculated. As will be seen from equations (10.6), (10.7) and (10.8), for the purpose of determining distribution factors the stiffness of a member could have been defined as the moment induced at one end of an encastré member when that end is rotated through a unit angle. This can be calculated by determining the stresses in the analogous column when a unit load is applied to the appropriate end. Thus for the member BC, Fig. 10.1, the analogous column would have a length l_2 and a width $\frac{1}{EI_2}$; when it is loaded with a unit load at the end B the stress there is

$$p_B=\frac{1}{l_2/EI_2}+\frac{(1\times l_2/2)(l_2/2)}{\frac{1}{12}\cdot\frac{l_2^3}{EI_2}}=\frac{EI_2}{l_2}+\frac{3EI_2}{l_2}=\frac{4EI_2}{l_2}$$

so that $M_{BC}=\dfrac{4EI_2}{l_2}$, the result given by equation (10.7) for unit rotation, that is when $\theta_B=1$. When similar calculations have been made for all the other members meeting at a joint the distribution factors follow.

REFERENCES

Cross, H.   1930.   (a) *Proc. Amer. Soc. Civ. Engrs.*, **56**, 919–28.
Cross, H.   1930.   (b) *Ill. Eng. Exp. Stat. Bull.* **215**.
Thompson, S. and Cutler, R. W.   1932.   *Trans. Amer. Soc. Civ. Engrs.*, **96**, 108.

EXERCISES

(These exercises should be solved by the various methods described in Chapters 9 and 10.)

(1) Plot the bending moment diagram for the bent shown in Diagram 10a.   A and D are pinned joints, B and C are rigid.

The flexural rigidity is constant throughout the bent.

(2) The frame ABCD shown at 10b has rigid corners at B and C and is pinned to supports at A and D.   It carries a load W in the position shown.   If the cross-section of the members is the same throughout, plot the bending moment diagram for the whole structure.

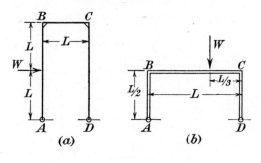

(a)   (b)

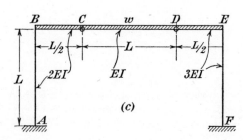

(c)

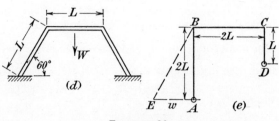

(d)   (e)

DIAGRAM 10.

(3) The frame shown at 10c is built in at A and F; the joints at B and E are rigid and at C and D are pinned.

A uniform load of intensity w is carried on BE.

Calculate the deflexion of the mid-point of BE below its original position. The flexural rigidity of the frame varies as shown in the diagram.

$$\left(\frac{205wL^4}{4,608EI}\right)$$

(4) The stiff-jointed trestle of constant flexural rigidity shown at 10d is encastré at both supports. Plot the bending moment diagram when a concentrated load is placed at the centre of the horizontal member.

(5) A stiff-jointed portal ABCD of constant flexural rigidity is encastré at A and D and carries a uniform load of intensity w on BC. The length AB=CD=L and BC=2L. Find the fixing moments at A and D.

$$\left(\frac{2wL^2}{15}\right)$$

(6) Diagram 10e represents a stiff-jointed frame of constant flexural rigidity pinned at A and D. A load is distributed along AB which varies as shown from an intensity w at A to nothing at B.

Calculate the thrust on the support pin D.

$$\left(\frac{104wL}{345}\right)$$

(7) A horizontal force of 10 lb. is applied at the level of the top beam of a three-storey single-bay frame similar to that shown in Fig. 10.11, but having semi-rigid beam-to-stanchion connections defined by the constants

$$\alpha_1 = 2 \cdot 20 \qquad \beta_1 = 1 \cdot 78$$
$$\alpha_2 = 1 \cdot 46 \qquad \beta_2 = 1 \cdot 77$$
$$\alpha_3 = 1 \cdot 82 \qquad \beta_3 = 1 \cdot 49.$$

Show that the magnitudes of the bending moments at the feet of the stanchions are 295 and 305 lb.-in.

CHAPTER 11

REINFORCED CONCRETE

11.1. Simple composite members.—A structural member may be made of more than one material, the parts being so rigidly connected that when the member is loaded there is no relative movement between them. This is termed a composite member and in modern engineering practice the use of such a method of construction is confined almost entirely to reinforced concrete. It is of interest, however, as an approach to this branch of the theory of structures to consider some simpler cases, although at the present day these may be of little importance.

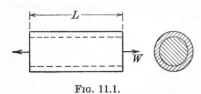

Fig. 11.1.

The most elementary example of a composite member is a tension member made of two different metals. Suppose, for example, that a tube of one metal is shrunk on to a bar of another as shown in Fig. 11.1, so that there is a firm connexion between the two and that this composite member carries an axial tensile load W.

Let A_1 be the cross-sectional area of the tube,
  A_2, the cross-sectional area of the rod,
  L, the length of the composite member,
  f_1, the stress in the tube,
  f_2, the stress in the rod,
  E_1, the value of Young's modulus for the tube
and E_2, the value of Young's modulus for the rod.

Since the two components are rigidly connected the elastic strains in the tube and rod will be equal, *i.e.*

$$\frac{f_1}{E_1} = \frac{f_2}{E_2}.$$

Also the total load carried by the tube and rod is W, so

$$f_1 A_1 + f_2 A_2 = W.$$

From these equations

$$f_1 \left(A_1 + \frac{E_2 A_2}{E_1} \right) = W$$

or

$$f_1 = \frac{W E_1}{E_1 A_1 + E_2 A_2}$$

and

$$f_2 = \frac{W E_2}{E_1 A_1 + E_2 A_2}.$$

The extension of the bar under load is $\dfrac{f_1 L}{E_1} = \dfrac{f_2 L}{E_2}$,

i.e.

$$\text{extension} = \frac{WL}{E_1 A_1 + E_2 A_2}.$$

234

Another simple composite member is the flitched beam as shown in cross-section in Fig. 11.2, which consists of a piece of steel plate bolted firmly between two cheeks of wood. This type of beam was in common use before the introduction of rolled steel joists but is now obsolete.

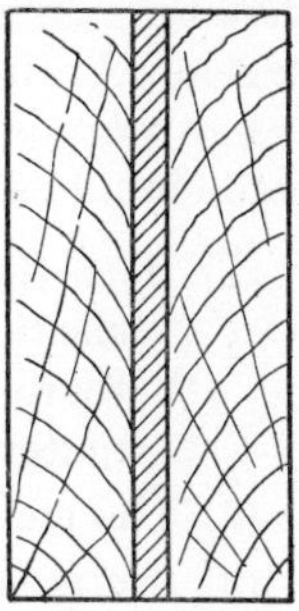

Suppose such a beam, simply supported over a span L, to be bent under the action of a central load W. The strains in the wood and the steel at any point are equal and so at the centre we have

radius of curvature of wood=radius of curvature of steel

or
$$\frac{M_w}{E_w I_w} = \frac{M_s}{E_s I_s}$$

FIG. 11.2.

where M_w is the bending moment resisted by the wood,

M_s is the bending moment resisted by the steel,

E_w, E_s are the values of Young's modulus for wood and steel respectively,

I_w, I_s are the second moments of area of the wood and steel sections respectively

and d is the depth of the beam.

Also
$$M_w + M_s = \frac{WL}{4}.$$

From these equations
$$M_w = \frac{E_w I_w}{E_s I_s} M_s$$

and
$$M_s \left(\frac{E_w I_w + E_s I_s}{E_s I_s} \right) = \frac{WL}{4},$$

which give the values of the bending moments carried by the two components.

The greatest stresses in the steel and wood are then

$$f_s = \frac{M_s d}{2 I_s} \; ; \; f_w = \frac{M_w d}{2 I_w}.$$

11.2. General principles of reinforced concrete.—Concrete consists of a mixture of cement, sand and graded stone or aggregate, which sets after the addition of water into a solid mass which has considerable compressive strength but little resistance to tension. It is very useful for such purposes as foundations, where the loads to be carried are wholly compressive, but it is useless for members subjected to bending since failure would occur at very low loads in regions where tension is developed. This limitation of the material can, however, be overcome and the necessary resistance to tensile stresses can be provided by the insertion of steel rods at appropriate places ; this composite structure is known as reinforced concrete. Such a combination is made practicable by two fortunate circumstances. Steel and concrete have almost identical coefficients of expansion, so that no serious internal stresses are set up by temperature changes, and when concrete sets in air it contracts so that if a steel bar is embedded in a mass of wet concrete it is found to be firmly gripped after set has occurred. The bond between the steel and the concrete is so good that the loads are shared between the two materials in the ideal manner we have assumed in earlier paragraphs for other composite members. In order that calculation of strength can be made it is necessary to know the physical properties of the component materials, *i.e.* the concrete and the steel.   For the present it will be assumed that the necessary information is available and the general theory will be developed ; in later paragraphs the values of the constants to be taken for design purposes will be discussed.   The following general assumptions are made in all calculations on reinforced concrete :—

(1) Both the concrete and the steel reinforcement are assumed to behave elastically and to follow a linear stress-strain law.   As a corollary there is a constant ratio between the moduli of elasticity of the two materials which is known as the modular ratio.

(2) The concrete is assumed to be incapable of resisting tensile stress.

(3) Sections of the members which are plane before straining actions are applied are assumed to remain plane under such actions.

(4) When steel is embedded in concrete the strains produced at any point by forces acting on the combination are the same in both materials.

These assumptions are open to criticism and may be considered as simplifications introduced to make possible a practical theory of the behaviour of reinforced concrete which can be used for design purposes.   The justification for accepting them is to be found in the reasonable agreement in most cases between the calculated and experimental strengths of members designed by their application.

(5) At any section of a structural member the sum of the forces in the steel and concrete in any direction is equal to the resultant action of the external forces at that section in the same direction.

(6) At any section the total moment of the forces in the steel and concrete, *i.e.* the moment of resistance of the section, is equal to the applied bending moment at that section.

The expression of these assumptions and conditions in algebraic form leads to very simple formulas.   These simple results can, however, be cast into various forms which, although more complicated, serve a useful purpose when considerable design work has to be done since they form the basis of curves which, once plotted, can be used rapidly.   The re-casting of the fundamental formulas does not, however, contribute anything to the basic theory and the subject will be considered here in the simplest terms.

The British Standards Institution Council for Codes of Practice are now revising a Code dealing with the structural use of normal reinforced concrete in buildings, CP 114 (1948), which contains much valuable practical data. Specific references to the revised Code will appear throughout this chapter.

11.3. The rectangular reinforced concrete beam with tension reinforcement.—In the first instance the rectangular beam which is reinforced on the tension side only will be considered.   This is not a complete system of reinforcement, since if a shearing force acts at any section of the beam the shearing stresses caused thereby are accompanied by tensile and compressive stresses at angles of 45° to the shear and failure is just as liable to occur on these tension planes as on any others.

Further, in modern reinforced concrete practice it is usual to provide not only tension steel but reinforcement against compressive stresses.   For the present, however, both these points will be ignored and the effect of longitudinal tension reinforcement alone considered.   Fig. 11.3 represents a rectangular beam of width b and depth d from the top of the concrete to the centre of the reinforcing bars.   It is subjected to a pure couple.

Since it is assumed that plane sections in the unstrained beam remain plane when the beam is bent, *efogh* in the figure is a strain diagram, *ef* representing the maximum compressive strain in the concrete, *gh* the strain of the reinforcement and *o* the position of the neutral axis NA.

Let NA be a distance n below the top of the beam.

Also let t be the tensile stress in the steel,

    c, the maximum compressive stress in the concrete,

    E_s, the modulus of elasticity of the steel,

    E_c, the modulus of elasticity of the concrete,

    m, the modular ratio, E_s/E_c

and A_t, the total cross-sectional area of steel in the reinforcement.

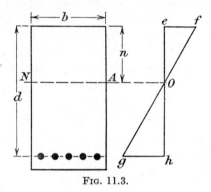

FIG. 11.3.

Then, the maximum strain in the concrete : strain in the steel :: *oe* : *oh*

i.e.
$$\frac{c}{E_c} : \frac{t}{E_s} :: n : d-n$$

or
$$\frac{t}{c} = \left(\frac{d-n}{n}\right)m. \qquad \ldots \ldots \quad (11.1)$$

Again, there is no resultant axial load on the beam and so the total compression in the concrete must be equal to the total tension in the steel. Since the average compressive stress in the concrete is $c/2$ we have

$$\frac{bnc}{2} = A_t t$$

or
$$\frac{t}{c} = \frac{bn}{2A_t}. \qquad \ldots \ldots \quad (11.2)$$

The total compressive force in the concrete at any cross-section is $\dfrac{bnc}{2}$ and this acts at the centre of compression.   Since the strain, and therefore the stress distribution, is linear, the centre of compression is $n/3$ from the top of the beam.   The total tensile force is $A_t t$ acting at the centre of the reinforcement and these equal and opposite forces acting at a distance apart $a = d - n/3$ form a couple which is the moment of resistance of the cross-section.

Hence

$$M_R = \frac{bnc}{2}\left(d-\frac{n}{3}\right) = A_t t \left(d-\frac{n}{3}\right) \qquad \ldots \quad (11.3)$$

and the applied bending moment must not exceed the value given by this expression when either t or c reaches the prescribed limiting value.

If t/c is eliminated from equations (11.1) and (11.2) it is seen that the value of n for a beam of given dimensions depends only on m and the area of the reinforcement. Therefore, if these are specified, the ratio of the stresses developed in the steel and concrete is determined by equation (11.2). Conversely, if the stress ratio is specified the values of A_t and n are determined.

The value of A_t which causes the stresses in both steel and concrete to reach their allowable limits simultaneously is known as the economic area, and the ratio $100A_t/bd$ is called the economic percentage.

To illustrate these results consider a reinforced concrete beam 12 inches wide and $22\frac{1}{2}$ inches deep to the centre of the reinforcement in which the stresses in the concrete and steel are limited to 600 lb. per square inch and 16,000 lb. per square inch respectively, and the modular ratio is 15. It is required to determine the area of steel needed and what uniformly distributed load the beam can carry over a freely supported span of 20 feet.

$$\frac{\text{The strain in the steel}}{\text{Max. strain in the concrete}}=\frac{t/E_s}{c/E_c}=\frac{d-n}{n}$$

i.e.
$$\frac{16,000}{600\times15}=\frac{22\cdot5-n}{n},$$

from which $n=8\cdot1$ inches.

Also the total compression in the concrete=total tension in the steel,

or
$$\frac{bnc}{2}=A_tt$$

i.e.
$$A_t=\frac{bnc}{2t}=\frac{12\times8\cdot1\times600}{32,000}=1\cdot822 \text{ square inches.}$$

The moment of resistance=total tension $\times$ arm of couple
$$=A_tt(d-n/3)$$
$$=1\cdot822\times16,000\times19\cdot8=578,000 \text{ in.-lb.}$$

Let w be the intensity of loading on the beam in lb. per foot so that the total load is $20w$ lb.

The maximum bending moment is then $\dfrac{20w\times240}{8}$ inch-lb.

Equating this to the moment of resistance we have
$$600w=578,000$$
or
$$w=963\cdot3 \text{ lb. per foot.}$$

This includes the weight of the beam itself which, assuming reinforced concrete to weight 150 lb. per cubic foot, is $\dfrac{12\times24\times150}{144}$ lb. per foot, *i.e.* 300 lb. per foot. The extra $1\frac{1}{2}$ inches is added to the effective depth to provide cover for the steel bars.

The additional load which the beam can carry is therefore 663 lb. per foot.

As another example of calculation we will assume that the beam just considered has $2\cdot5$ square inches of reinforcing steel and we will determine the alteration this makes in the strength.

From the equation for the proportionality of strain we now obtain

$$\frac{t}{600 \times 15} = \frac{22 \cdot 5 - n}{n}$$

i.e.
$$t = \frac{9,000(22 \cdot 5 - n)}{n}.$$

From the equation of total compression and tension we have

$$\frac{12 \times n \times 600}{2} = 2 \cdot 5t$$

or
$$t = 1,440n.$$

Equating these two values of t we obtain

$$1,440n^2 = 9,000(22 \cdot 5 - n)$$
or
$$n^2 + 6 \cdot 25n - 140 \cdot 6 = 0,$$
which gives
$$n = 9 \cdot 125 \text{ inches}$$

and so $t = 1,440 \times 9 \cdot 125 = 13,140$ lb. per square inch.

The safe load on this beam is therefore governed by the stress in the concrete.

The moment of resistance $= 2 \cdot 5 \times 13,140 \times 19 \cdot 41$
$$= 638,000 \text{ inch-lb.}$$

Equating this to the bending moment as found in the previous example we have

$$w = \frac{638,000}{600} = 1,063 \cdot 3 \text{ lb. per foot.}$$

Deducting the weight of the beam itself this gives 763 lb. per foot as the safe distributed load on the beam.

The Code quotes simplified formulas which may be used for calculating the moment of resistance of a rectangular beam or slab section reinforced only against tension.

It is assumed that the lever arm $a = d - \dfrac{3A_t t}{4bc}$ where t is the permissible tensile stress in the reinforcement and c is the permissible compressive stress in the concrete in bending. Then the lesser of two values calculated respectively on the basis of the strength of tensile reinforcement and that of the concrete in compression may be taken. The formulas are

$$\left. \begin{aligned} M_R &= A_t t a \\ M_R &= \frac{cbd^2}{4}. \end{aligned} \right\} \qquad \cdots \qquad (11.4)$$

and

11.4. The reinforced concrete T-beam with tension reinforcement.—In a floor made of joists and planks the latter do not contribute to the strength of the structure and the whole load must be carried by the joists. In reinforced concrete construction, however, the floor consists of a slab which is integral with the beams, as shown diagrammatically in Fig. 13.4. It will be seen that the beam member is actually of T section, as shown shaded, but the great difficulty in dealing with this form of construction is to know what width of the floor slab may be safely assumed to act as the compression flange of the beam. In the Code it is laid down that the breadth of slab taken into account in calculation shall be not greater than the least of the following :—

(a) One-third of the effective span of the T-beam,
(b) The distance between the centres of the ribs of the T-beam, L,
(c) The breadth of the rib plus twelve times the thickness of the slab, D.

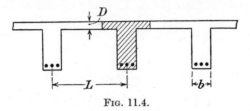

FIG. 11.4.

Suppose Fig. 11.5 represents such a T-beam and that the dimensions are as shown. It will be assumed that the neutral axis is below the bottom of the slab. The principles involved in design are exactly the same as for the rectangular beam, but the formulas are more cumbersome.

Thus, as before,

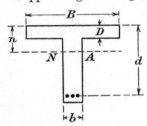

FIG. 11.5.

$$\frac{t}{c}=\left(\frac{d-n}{n}\right)m,$$

as in equation (11.1).

Since the stresses are proportional to the distances from the neutral axis the stress at the underside of the slab is

$$\left(\frac{n-D}{n}\right)c.$$

The mean stress over the slab is $\dfrac{c}{2}\left(\dfrac{2n-D}{n}\right)$ and over the portion of the rib above the neutral axis it is $\dfrac{c}{2}\left(\dfrac{n-D}{n}\right)$.

Hence the total compressive force on the section is

$$\frac{BDc}{2}\left(\frac{2n-D}{n}\right)+\frac{b(n-D)c}{2}\left(\frac{n-D}{n}\right),$$

or

$$\frac{c}{2n}\{BD(2n-D)+b(n-D)^2\}.$$

This must be equal to the total tensile force in the steel, so that

$$\frac{c}{2n}\{BD(2n-D)+b(n-D)^2\}=A_t t$$

or

$$\frac{t}{c}=\frac{BD(2n-D)+b(n-D)^2}{2nA_t}.$$

The remainder of the work closely follows that for a rectangular beam and it is unnecessary to derive the equations since any particular case is more easily solved arithmetically than by substitution in an algebraic equation.

Suppose Fig. 11.6 represents the cross-section of a rectangular beam ; the neutral axis, determined in the way already explained, is NA.

The concrete below NA has been assumed to take no stress and so, as long as sufficient is left to form adequate cover for the steel the remainder can be removed without affecting the strength of the beam, as shown in the figure, and the result is a T-beam.   It is thus evident that any T-beam in which the neutral axis is not below the bottom of the slab can be treated exactly as a rectangular beam of breadth B and effective depth d.   Even when the neutral axis is below the bottom of the slab the error involved by designing on the assumption of a rectangular section is usually very small.   In Fig. 11.7, for example, (a) is the cross-section of a T-beam, the neutral axis for the rectangular

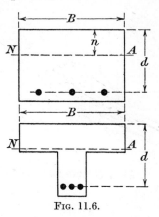

Fig. 11.6.

section shown dotted being NA.   The stress at any point in the compression area is shown in the diagram (b) and if this stress is multiplied by the appropriate width over which it acts, a load intensity curve such as that

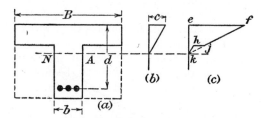

Fig. 11.7.

shown at (c) is obtained.   The sudden break is due to the change of width from B to b.   The area of the triangle efk represents the total compression in the rectangular beam and the area $efjhk$ that in the T-beam.   The difference between these areas, khj, is a measure of the error involved and if NA is not much below the bottom of the slab this error is negligible.   This calculation of the error is not exact since the real position of the neutral axis for the T-section would be displaced slightly from that for the rectangular section but it indicates, in view of the approximate nature of the design data which are generally available, especially with regard to the value to be assigned to B, that for most T-beams the elaborate formulas derived from exact consideration of the geometry are of little importance.

Simplified formulas given in the Code for calculating the moment of resistance of T- or L-beams are

$$M_R = A_t t \left(d - \frac{D}{2} \right)$$

and

$$M_R = Fcbd^2$$

. . . . . . (11.5)

where F has the values in Table 11.1.

As for rectangular beams, the lesser value of the two results should be taken.

TABLE 11.1.

B/b	Values of F for d/D					
	2 or less	3	4	5	6	∞
1	·25	·250	·250	·250	·250	·250
2	·25	·220	·200	·185	·175	·125
4	·25	·200	·170	·150	·140	·062
6	·25	·195	·165	·140	·125	·042
8	·25	·190	·160	·135	·120	·031
∞	·25	·185	·145	·120	·100	·000

11.5. Rectangular beam with compression reinforcement.

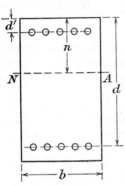

—Since steel is much stronger in compression than concrete it is usual, especially when it is required to keep the overall size of beams as small as possible, to reinforce the compression as well as the tension area. Fig. 11.8 shows a beam of rectangular section which has, in addition to the usual tension reinforcement, a total cross-sectional area of steel A_c in compression at a distance d' from the top of the beam. Other symbols used will be the same as in paragraph 11.3.

Since the same assumptions as to the planarity of sections is made as in the beam with single reinforcement, equation (11.1) is valid.

FIG. 11.8.

Also

$$\frac{\text{the maximum compressive strain}}{\text{in the concrete}} : \frac{\text{compressive strain}}{\text{in steel}} :: n : n-d'$$

or

$$\frac{mc}{f}=\frac{n}{n-d'}$$

so that

$$f=\frac{m(n-d')c}{n}, \qquad \ldots \ldots \quad (11.6)$$

where f is the stress in the compression steel.

The total area of concrete in compression is $bn-A_c$ and the total compressive force in it is $c\left\{\dfrac{bn}{2}-A_c\left(\dfrac{n-d'}{n}\right)\right\}$.

The compressive force in the steel is $A_c f=\dfrac{A_c m(n-d')c}{n}$.

Hence, equating the total compressive force on the cross-section to the total tensile force, we obtain

$$c\left\{\frac{bn}{2}+\frac{A_c(m-1)(n-d')}{n}\right\}=A_t t$$

or

$$\frac{t}{c}=\frac{1}{A_t}\left\{\frac{bn}{2}+\frac{A_c(m-1)(n-d')}{n}\right\}. \qquad \ldots \ldots \quad (11.7)$$

To calculate the moment of resistance of a beam reinforced in this way it is necessary to determine the centre of resistance of the compressive force.

The compressive force in the steel can be written as

$$\frac{A_c(n-d')c}{n}+\frac{A_c(m-1)(n-d')c}{n}.$$

The first term is the amount which would be contributed by the area A_c if the compression area contained no steel and the second term is the extra amount due to the substitution of steel for that area of concrete.

The moment of resistance of the beam is therefore

$$\frac{bnc}{2}\left(\frac{2n}{3}\right)+\frac{A_c(m-1)(n-d')c}{n}(n-d')+A_t t(d-n),$$

i.e.
$$M_R=c\left\{\frac{bn^2}{3}+\frac{A_c(m-1)(n-d')^2}{n}\right\}+A_t t(d-n). \quad . \quad . \quad (11.8)$$

The arm of the moment of resistance is

$$a=\frac{M_R}{A_t t}. \quad . \quad . \quad . \quad . \quad . \quad (11.9)$$

Equations (11.6), (11.7), (11.8) and (11.9) together with equation (11.1) are sufficient for the solution of any problem connected with doubly rein-forced rectangular beams, as will be evident from an example.

Suppose a rectangular beam 10 inches wide and 20 inches deep to the centre of tension reinforcement has 1 square inch of compression steel at a distance of 1 inch from the top of the beam. If the maximum stresses in the concrete and steel are limited to 600 lb. per square inch and 18,000 lb. per square inch respectively, determine the area of tension steel required and the moment of resistance of the beam.

From equation (11.1), taking $m=18$, we have

$$30=\frac{(20-n)}{n}18$$

or
$$n=7\cdot5 \text{ inches.}$$

Then from equation (11.6)

$$f=\frac{18(7\cdot5-1)\times600}{7\cdot5},$$

so the stress in the compression steel is 9,360 lb. per square inch.

From equation (11.7)

$$30=\frac{1}{A_t}\left(\frac{10\times7\cdot5}{2}+\frac{17\times6\cdot5}{7\cdot5}\right)$$

and the area of tension steel required is $1\cdot74$ square inches.

The moment of resistance is then, from equation (11.8),

$$M_R=600\left(\frac{10\times7\cdot5^2}{3}+\frac{17\times6\cdot5^2}{7\cdot5}\right)+1\cdot74\times18,000\times12\cdot5$$

or
$$M_R=561,000 \text{ inch-lb.}$$

The arm of this moment is

$$\frac{561,000}{1\cdot74\times18,000}=18 \text{ inches.}$$

Approximate formulas for the moment of resistance of a doubly-reinforced beam are given in the Code. For rectangular beams

$$M_R=\frac{cbd^2}{4}+A_c f(d-d') \quad . \quad . \quad . \quad . \quad . \quad (11.10)$$

and for T- or L-beams

$$M_R = Fcbd^2 + A_cf(d-d').\qquad\ldots\ \ldots\ \ldots\ (11.11)$$

It is, of course, important that the moment of resistance calculated on the basis of tensile reinforcement should be at least equal to these values.

11.6. Adhesion and bond.—It was indicated in an earlier paragraph that reinforced concrete construction was made possible by the fact that the steel was so firmly gripped by the concrete that the strains in the steel were equal to those in the concrete immediately in contact with it. The resistance which is offered by a rod to withdrawal from a block of concrete in which it is embedded is known as adhesion and the stress between the surface of the steel and the concrete in contact with it is the bond stress. It is clearly vital that the bond stress shall at all points in a structure be kept down to safe limits.

Suppose that in a single reinforced concrete beam the bending moments at two sections separated by a small distance δx are $M + \delta M$ respectively.

Let the distance between the centre of action of the compressive force in the concrete and the centre of the reinforcement be $a = d - n/3$. The total tensions in the steel at the sections under consideration are

$$\frac{M}{a} \text{ and } \frac{M + \delta M}{a}.$$

There is consequently an increase in the tension in the distance δx of $\dfrac{\delta M}{a}$.

This is balanced by the adhesion between the steel and the concrete and if rupture is to be avoided it must be within safe limits.

If the reinforcement consists of n bars each of diameter d the total surface of steel in contact with the concrete is $n\pi d\delta x$ and if the mean bond stress over the short distance δx is s_b we have, for equilibrium,

$$s_b n\pi d\delta x = \frac{\delta M}{a}$$

or

$$s_b = \frac{\delta M}{\delta x}\frac{1}{an\pi d}.$$

In the limit when δx is infinitesimally small $\dfrac{\delta M}{\delta x}$ is the shearing force S at the section considered and if the total perimeter of the bars $n\pi d$ be denoted by o the local bond stress at the point is

$$s_b = \frac{S}{ao}.\qquad\ldots\ \ldots\ \ldots\ (11.12)$$

The allowable values for s_b are given in Table 11.4 ; they vary from 180 to 220 lb. per square inch.

If a bar is embedded in concrete as shown in Fig. 11.9 and subjected to a tensile load, it will be pulled out unless l is sufficient to ensure that the adhesion is not overcome. Such a case occurs where reinforcing bars are not in one length but have to be lapped, e.g. in a circular water tank.

The usual criterion, adopted in the Code, is to make l such that the average bond stress, calculated on the tensile stress in the bar shall not

exceed the safe values, varying from 120 lb./sq. in. to 150 lb./sq. in., given in
Table 11.4. This length l is calculated as follows.

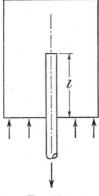

FIG. 11.9.

If t is the permissible tensile stress in the steel the safe strength of one bar
of diameter d is $\dfrac{t\pi d^2}{4}$ and the safe adhesive force, assuming a uniform
distribution along l, is $s_b \pi dl$.

Equating these we have

$$\frac{t\pi d^2}{4} = s_b \pi dl$$

or
$$l = \frac{td}{4s_b}. \quad . \quad . \quad . \quad . \quad . \quad . \quad (11.13)$$

The Code recommends that in no circumstances should this length be less
than $12d$ but allowances may be made for the values of a hook or bent bar.

11.7. Distribution of shear stress in a reinforced concrete beam.—The
distribution of shearing stress across the section of a reinforced concrete
beam can be approximately determined in the same way as for a homogeneous section.

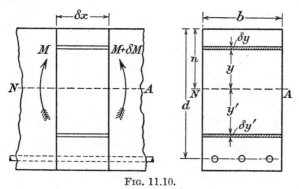

FIG. 11.10.

Fig. 11.10 shows a singly reinforced beam in which two sections at a small
distance δx apart are subjected to bending moments M and M+δM
respectively.

9

Equating the bending moment at any section to the moment of resistance, we have

$$M = a A_t t = \frac{abnc}{2}$$

where t and c are the actual stresses developed in the steel and concrete and a is the moment arm $d - n/3$.

We shall consider first the compressive portion of the beam, *i.e.* the part above the neutral axis. The maximum compressive stresses developed at the top of the beam at the two sections considered are respectively

$$c_1 = \frac{2M}{abn} \text{ and } c_2 = \frac{2(M + \delta M)}{abn}.$$

On any lamina which is y above NA the stresses are y/n times the maximum

i.e. $$\frac{2My}{abn^2} \text{ and } \frac{2(M + \delta M)y}{abn^2}.$$

If the thickness of the lamina is δy the compressive forces on the area $b\delta y$ at the two sections are respectively

$$\frac{2My\delta y}{an^2} \text{ and } \frac{2(M + \delta M)y\delta y}{an^2}$$

and the difference in force on the lamina between the two ends of the length δx is

$$\frac{2\delta My\delta y}{an^2}.$$

The total difference of force on a section of the beam between $y = y_1$ and $y = n$ is

$$\frac{2\delta M}{an^2} \int_{y_1}^{n} y\,dy = \frac{\delta M}{an^2}(n^2 - y_1^2)$$

which is balanced by the shearing force on the horizontal plane of area $b\delta x$ at y_1 above NA so that the average shearing stress is

$$s = \frac{\delta M}{\delta x} \frac{(n^2 - y_1^2)}{abn^2}.$$

In the limit when δx is infinitesimally small $\dfrac{\delta M}{\delta x}$ is the shearing force S at the section and

$$s = \frac{S(n^2 - y_1^2)}{abn^2}.$$

This is a parabola having a maximum value of $\dfrac{S}{ab}$ when $y_1 = 0$, *i.e.* at the neutral axis of the beam, and a zero value when $y_1 = n$, *i.e.* at the top of the beam.

We now consider the portion of the beam below the neutral axis. Since it is assumed that the concrete takes no tension there is no difference of load between the ends of a lamina in the concrete such as that shown at y' in the figure and the shearing stress has the constant value $\dfrac{S}{ab}$ until it is balanced by an equal and opposite shearing stress due to the change in tension in the steel. The difference in tensile stress in the steel between the two ends of the length δx is $\dfrac{\delta M}{aA}$ and the difference in tension is therefore $-\dfrac{\delta M}{a}$ since it is in the opposite direction to the difference in compressions. This may be assumed to be transmitted uniformly to the concrete and the average shearing stress is therefore

$$s = -\frac{\delta M}{\delta x}\frac{1}{ab} = -\frac{S}{ab}$$

which balances the constant shearing stress transmitted through the concrete below the neutral axis.

The distribution curve of shearing stress is shown in Fig. 11.11.

In a beam having double reinforcement the distribution of the shearing stress is modified. It is convenient to treat the total compression as being composed of that upon an area of concrete bn and an extra amount due to the replacement of concrete by steel over the area A_c.

The shearing stress distribution over the concrete area is parabolic as before, but the stress due to the additional term has to be superimposed. This is of constant magnitude and only occurs between the level of the compression steel and the neutral axis ; there is in consequence a discontinuity in the distribution curve at the compression steel.

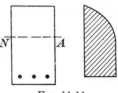

FIG. 11.11.

The additional stress on the area A_c due to the substitution of steel for concrete is, as shown in paragraph 11.5,

$$\frac{(m-1)(n-d')c}{n}$$

and the total compression is

$$c\left\{\frac{bn}{2}+\frac{A_c(m-1)(n-d')}{n}\right\}=cA_0.$$

If c_1 and c_2 are the maximum concrete stresses at the ends of the length δx the change in the total compression over this length is $(c_2-c_1)A_0$.

But this change is also $\dfrac{\delta M}{a}$ where a is the moment arm.

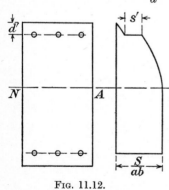

FIG. 11.12.

Hence, the change in the additional compression on the area A_c over the length δx is

$$\frac{A_c(m-1)(n-d')}{n}\frac{\delta M}{aA_0}.$$

Assuming this to be uniformly distributed over the area, the additional shear stress due to steel is

$$s'=\frac{A_c}{A_0}\frac{(m-1)(n-d')}{n}\frac{S}{ab}.$$

Since the change of total compression over the length δx is $\dfrac{\delta M}{a}$ the shearing stress at the neutral axis is $\dfrac{\delta M}{ab\delta x}=\dfrac{S}{ab}$ and the diagram of distribution is as shown in Fig. 11.12.

The value of a may be calculated from equation (11.9).

11.8. Shear reinforcement in beams.—At any point in a beam there is a system of complex stress consisting of the direct tension or compression due to the bending of the beam and complementary shearing stresses calculated as described in the last paragraph. The principal planes through the point will be subjected to pure tensions and compressions and at the neutral axis where there are no bending stresses these principal planes will be at 45° to the direction of shearing stresses and the principal stresses will be of the same intensity as the shearing stresses. Shearing stress is, therefore, accompanied by tension and, in consequence, concrete in shear needs reinforcement. Although in calculations for the main reinforcement of the beam it has been assumed that tensile stresses must all be taken by steel, concrete is in fact capable of resisting some tension and in calculations for shearing resistance it is customary to take this into account. If the shearing stress calculated by the formula $s = \dfrac{S}{ab}$ of the last paragraph does not exceed a specified value, which varies with the quality of concrete from 130 to 100 lb. per square inch, shear reinforcement may be omitted. If it exceeds such a value, however, the Code specifies that sufficient reinforcement should be provided to carry the whole of the shear, *i.e.*, the assumption that there must be no tension in the concrete is again adopted. The Code also lays down that in no case should the shearing stress calculated from the formula $\dfrac{S}{ab}$ exceed four times the permissible shear stress for plain concrete.

Fig. 11.13.

Shear reinforcement is provided in one of three ways or by combination of these. In regions where the bending moment is small and the shearing force is large, some of the longitudinal reinforcing bars are bent to cross the beam diagonally, as shown in Fig. 11.13.

The ends of these bars are carried well into the compression concrete and must be firmly anchored by hooks or otherwise.

The second method of reinforcing against shear is by means of inclined stirrups, as shown in Fig. 11.14. These stirrups are firmly attached to the

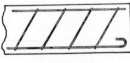

Fig. 11.14.

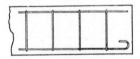

Fig. 11.15.

tension reinforcing bars, carried well into the compression concrete and anchored. If compression steel is provided they should be connected to it to give the necessary anchorage ; if it is not, the ends should be bent.

In the third type of shear reinforcement the inclined stirrups are replaced by vertical stirrups as in Fig. 11.15, the same attention being paid to the question of anchorage.

To understand the action of the inclined rods and stirrups in resisting the shearing force it is convenient to imagine a braced girder in which all the compression members are concrete and all the tension members are steel.

A truss of this type can be constructed in two ways shown in Fig. 11.16. Concrete members are shown section-lined and steel members as single lines. Fig. 11.16 (*a*) shows a concrete top boom and steel rod bottom boom connected by vertical concrete struts. The panels thus formed are braced diagonally by steel members. A is a point of support and when loads are

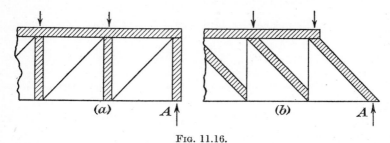

FIG. 11.16.

carried on the top boom it is clear that all the steel is in tension and all the concrete is in compression. An alternative is shown at (*b*) in which steel vertical members are used and the panels braced by concrete bars across the opposite diagonals to those at (*a*). This structure also fulfils the condition that the concrete and steel are in compression and tension respectively. Provided the joints are suitable either of these trusses is a sound theoretical structure and the spaces between the members may be supposed to be filled in with concrete. The result is reinforced concrete beams with inclined and vertical stirrups respectively. The stress distribution is, of course, affected by the concrete filling, and the analogy of the reinforced concrete beam with the trussed girder must not be pushed too far. It does give, however, an idea of the way in which stirrups can resist shearing forces and affords a basis of design for inclined shear reinforcement.

The application of this method to determine the adequacy of shear reinforcement gives results which are conservative and another approach is more generally adopted.

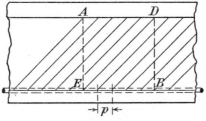

FIG. 11.17.

On the assumption that the concrete takes no tensile stress the shearing stress between the neutral axis and the tension reinforcement has been shown to be constant. The state of stress is therefore one of pure shear which induces a principal tensile stress of the same intensity on planes inclined at 45° to the axis of the beam. Hence if rods are turned through 45° or inclined stirrups are placed at the same angle they will be in the best position to resist this tensile stress. In Fig. 11.17 let AD be the level of the centre of compression and EB the tension reinforcement, so that the distance BD is a, the arm of the moment of resistance. The shear reinforcement is provided by stirrups inclined at 45° and spaced a distance p apart along the line EB.

Consider a length of the beam EB equal to a and let the shearing force transmitted from BD to EA be S.

Since the tensile stress across AB is of the same intensity as the shearing stress on BD, the total pull on AB is $S\sqrt{2}$.

The number of stirrups cut by AB is $\dfrac{2a}{p}$,

so the load taken by each stirrup is $\dfrac{pS\sqrt{2}}{2a}=\dfrac{pS}{a\sqrt{2}}$.

Let A_w be the cross-sectional area of a stirrup and t_w the permissible tensile stress in the material.

Then the maximum shearing force which can be resisted is given when

$$\frac{pS}{a\sqrt{2}}=t_wA_w$$

or
$$S=\frac{t_wA_wa\sqrt{2}}{p} \qquad . \quad . \quad . \quad . \quad . \quad (11.14)$$

If the stirrups are vertical, as in Fig. 11.18, the tensile force on AB which is $S\sqrt{2}$ as before is resisted by a/p stirrups. The vertical component of the force on AB is S and so the load in each stirrup is $\dfrac{Sp}{a}$.

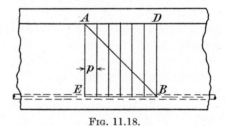

Fig. 11.18.

Then equating as before to obtain the maximum shearing force which can be resisted

$$\frac{Sp}{a}=t_wA_w$$

or
$$S=\frac{t_wA_wa}{p} \qquad . \quad . \quad . \quad . \quad . \quad (11.15)$$

This formula is recommended for design purposes in the Code of Practice.

11.9. Flexural stiffness of reinforced concrete members.—The second moment of area or, as it is often but erroneously called, the moment of inertia of the cross-section, appears in many calculations for homogeneous members and this has led to a confusion of ideas in connexion with reinforced concrete structures. The second moment of area is a purely geometrical conception and has no reference whatever to the material of which a member is made. For example, in calculations of strength for a steel and a wooden beam of the same cross-section the same value of I would be used in both cases. It is therefore somewhat disconcerting to find methods described for calculating the "moment of inertia" which make allowance for the reinforcement. The second moment of area I and Young's modulus E cannot in this connexion be treated as separate parameters; it is their product EI, known as the flexural rigidity, which is significant and if this product is treated as a single term no discrepancy appears in the calculations such as arises from attempts to assess I as a separate term.

In a beam with single reinforcement as shown in Fig. 11.3 the moment of resistance is

$$M_R = \frac{bnc}{2}\left(d - \frac{n}{3}\right) = A_t t\left(d - \frac{n}{3}\right).$$

From the ordinary theory of bending for homogeneous bars,

$$I = \frac{M_R y}{f}$$

where f is the stress at a distance y from the neutral axis and I is the second moment of area.

Applying this to the reinforced concrete beam we obtain two different values for I depending upon whether the calculation is based upon concrete or steel stress. Thus

$$I_c = \frac{\dfrac{bnc}{2}\left(d - \dfrac{n}{3}\right)n}{c} = \frac{bn^2}{2}\left(d - \frac{n}{3}\right)$$

and

$$I_s = \frac{A_t t(d - n/3)(d - n)}{t} = A\left(d - \frac{n}{3}\right)(d - n).$$

So, from (11.1)

$$\frac{I_c}{I_s} = \frac{bn^2}{2A(d-n)} = \frac{t}{c} \cdot \frac{n}{d-n} = m.$$

Thus, $I_c = mI_s$ showing that the term second moment of area is misleading and meaningless in connexion with composite sections.

Substituting for m, however, we have

$$E_c I_c = E_s I_s$$

and we see that the *flexural rigidity* is the same whichever basis of calculation is adopted.

Formulas in which I appears as an isolated term should be viewed with suspicion; they are probably of an empirical character and unless the meaning is explicitly stated considerable ambiguity may arise.

11.10. The axially loaded reinforced concrete column.—The simplest form of reinforcement in a column consists of a number of rods running the whole length and sharing the compression with the concrete. Such simple reinforcement is, however, not sufficient by itself to develop the full strength of the combination and it is necessary to tie the longitudinal reinforcement transversely. The ties may be either separate link pieces spaced at intervals of from 6 to 12 inches throughout the column, or a continuous spiral reinforcement may encircle the main bars. The spirals should be evenly spaced and the ends must be properly anchored. The pitch should be not more than 3 inches or one-sixth of the diameter of the core of concrete included in the spiral, whichever is the smaller, and should be not less than one inch or three times the diameter of the bar of which the spiral is made, whichever is the greater.

Columns with spiral reinforcement should have at least six longitudinal bars and other types of column one bar near each angle of the cross-section.

Spiral reinforcement restricts the lateral expansion of the core when the column is loaded and allows the concrete to be more highly stressed. This extra strength is recognised by an allowance in practical design formulas.

The theoretical strength of a short axially loaded column is easily obtained as follows :

let A be the area of the concrete in the cross-section,

A_c the cross-sectional area of steel in longitudinal bars,

c, the stress *developed* in the concrete,

t, the compressive stress *developed* in the steel

and m, the modular ratio.

Then if the steel and concrete are assumed to strain together, we have

$$\text{strain in concrete} = \text{strain in steel}$$

or $$c/\mathrm{E}_c = t/\mathrm{E}_s$$

i.e. $$t = mc.$$

Also, if the total axial load which the column can carry is P,

$$P = cA + tA_c$$

or $$= c(A + mA_c). \qquad . \quad . \quad . \quad . \quad . \quad (11.16)$$

Actual tests of columns indicate that this simple theory gives low results and the formula specified in the Code is

$$P = cA + c_1 A_c \qquad . \quad . \quad . \quad . \quad . \quad . \quad (11.17)$$

where c and c_1 are stresses which are permissible in the concrete and steel respectively ; they are not related by the expression $t = mc$ derived from the equation of strains.

When spiral reinforcement encircles the longitudinal bars it encloses a core of concrete. Let the total volume of spiral reinforcement in a column of length l be denoted by V and let the radius of the concrete core be r.

If we suppose the whole of the spiral reinforcement to be replaced by a steel tube enclosing the core, the cross-sectional area of this tube is

$$A_b = V/l.$$

Also let A_k=the area of concrete core $= \pi r^2$,

and t_b=permissible stress in the spiral steel.

When a compressive load is applied to the column the spiral does more than bind the longitudinal reinforcement ; it decreases the lateral expansion of the concrete in the core which would accompany the shortening of the column and enables the concrete to resist greater longitudinal stresses. The steel in the spiral, which is thrown into tension, is found to be approximately twice as effective in strengthening the column as an equal amount used as additional longitudinal reinforcement. The Code formula suggested for design purposes is based on this, and the load which the column can carry is given as

$$P = cA_k + c_1 A_c + 27,000 A_b \qquad . \quad . \quad . \quad . \quad (11.18)$$

the units being pounds and inches.

The greater of the two values of P obtained from (11.17) and (11.18) may be used.

If the columns are long the loads calculated from the above formulas must be reduced to allow for the effect of buckling and Table 11.2 taken from the Code gives suitable correcting coefficients calculated from the expression $1 \cdot 5 - \dfrac{l}{30d}$

where l is the effective length

and d is the least lateral dimension of the column.

To obtain the load which the column is capable of carrying, the value of P should be multiplied by the appropriate coefficient.

In spirally reinforced columns dimensions refer to the core of the column.

TABLE 11.2.

Ratio of effective length to least lateral dimension of column	Coefficient
15	1·00
18	0·90
21	0·80
24	0·70
27	0·60
30	0·50
33	0·40
36	0·35
39	0·30
42	0·25
45	0·20
57	0

The effective length of a column depends upon the type of end fixing and its assessment is largely a matter of judgment ; typical examples are given in the Code.

11.11. Reinforced concrete members subjected to combined bending and axial load.—In most cases the beams attached to columns impose a moment as well as an axial load and the stress distribution under such conditions must now be considered.

Let the singly reinforced member shown in Fig. 11.19 carry a load P acting through the neutral axis and a bending moment M.

The condition of strain proportionality has to be satisfied as before and equation (11.1) is valid.

There is now, however, a resultant axial thrust on the member and so

$$\frac{bnc}{2} - A_t = P. \quad . \quad . \quad . \quad . \quad . \quad (11.19)$$

In addition the moment of resistance of the cross-section must be equal to the applied moment M, so that

$$M = \left(\frac{bnc}{2} \times \frac{2n}{3} \right) + A_t t (d-n). \quad . \quad . \quad . \quad (11.20)$$

These two equations and (11.1) are sufficient for the calculation of the strength of any member of this type. Generally, however, members liable to combined thrust and bending have compression as well as tension reinforcement and the equations must be correspondingly modified.

9*

Equations (11.1), (11.4) and (11.6) are all valid and, using the notation of paragraph 11.5 we have in addition, equating forces on the section,

$$c\left\{\frac{bn}{2}+\frac{A_c(m-1)(n-d')}{n}\right\}-A_tt=P. \quad . \quad . \quad . \quad (11.21)$$

It will be observed that the only difference between these equations and those previously used for beams arises from the introduction of the load P ;

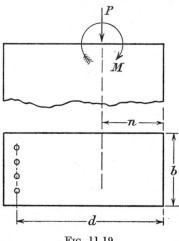

Fɪɢ. 11.19.

the total compressive force must now exceed the tensile force by the amount P to obtain equilibrium of the section. The calculations are similar to those already illustrated but slightly more elaborate.

11.12. Strength of materials and allowable stresses.—Concrete is made of three components ; cement, aggregates and water. The quality of these and the proportions in which they are used will determine the strength of the resulting product. It is essential that the water shall be clean and that the amount used in mixing shall be sufficient, but only sufficient, to give a dense concrete which can be properly placed and compacted. Excess water always results in a loss of strength. The qualities desirable both for aggregates and for cements are laid down by the British Standards Institution and should be complied with wherever possible. B.S.882 is a specification for aggregates and B.S.12, B.S.146 and B.S.915 respectively relate to Portland cement, Portland blast furnace cement and high alumina cement.

The proportions of cement, fine aggregate and coarse aggregate in a mix are nominally specified as a ratio, e.g. 1 : 2 : 4 means that one part by volume of cement is mixed with two parts of fine and four parts of coarse aggregate. This is not, however, the most convenient method of specifying the mix for practical use and the specifications also give the number of cubic feet of aggregates to be mixed with one hundredweight of cement.

The quality of the concrete is controlled by compression tests on 6-in. cubes which are broken when 28 days old except high alumina cement concrete cubes which are tested at 2 days. An alternative test is on a beam 16 in.×4 in.×4 in. aged 7 days. This beam is supported on two 1½ inch diameter steel rollers spaced 12 inches apart and is loaded by a central weight applied through another similar roller. The load should be applied as smoothly as possible at such a rate that failure takes place in about five minutes. The modulus of rupture, My/I, is used as the criterion of strength. For the specified size of test specimen this is $9W/32$ lb. per square inch, if W is in pounds. The compressive strengths and the moduli of rupture for the different mixes are given in Table 11.3. It should be remarked that the

TABLE 11.3.

COMPRESSIVE STRENGTHS AND MODULI OF RUPTURE.

Cement	Nominal mix	Cu. ft. of aggregate per cwt. cement		Cube strength lb./sq. in.		Modulus of rupture lb./sq. in.
		Fine	Coarse	Prelim.	Works	
Portland and blast furnace	1 : 1 : 2	1¼	2½	6000	4500	450
	1 : 1½ : 3	1⅞	3¾	5000	3750	400
	1 : 2 : 4	2½	5	4000	3000	350
High alumina	1 : 2 : 4	2½	5	6000	5000	500

moduli of rupture are measures of the tensile strength of the concrete since in the absence of reinforcement a beam will fail on the tension side long before the compressive stress becomes of importance. The preliminary tests referred to in the Table are those made under laboratory conditions to design the mix ; the Works tests are those made on the site and are solely for check purposes.

The permissible stresses in the concrete due to shear and bond are given in Table 11.4.

TABLE 11.4.

PERMISSIBLE STRESSES IN CONCRETE DUE TO SHEAR AND BOND.

Cement	Nominal mix	Shear stress lb./sq. in.	Bond stress lb./sq. in.	
			Average	Local
Portland and blast furnace	1 : 1 : 2	130	150	220
	1 : 1½ : 3	115	135	200
	1 : 2 : 4	100	120	180
High alumina	1 : 2 : 4	130	150	220

The strength of concrete varies with age and in many instances the full load does not come upon the material in the structure for a long time after it has been placed and set. Table 11.5 gives the factors by which the permissible compressive stresses at 28 days may be increased to allow for this effect but these do not apply to concrete made with high alumina cement for which no age allowance is permissible.

TABLE 11.5.

INCREASE OF PERMISSIBLE STRENGTH WITH AGE.

Age of concrete (months)	Multiplying factor
1	1·00
2	1·10
3	1·16
6	1·20
12	1·24

The weight of reinforced concrete may be taken as 150 lb. per cubic foot unless the reinforcement is more than 2 per cent. in which case special allowance must be made.

The modular ratio may be assumed to be 15 for all mixes.

The quality of reinforcing bars is controlled by B.S.785 and two types are specified, viz., steels with no guaranteed yield stress and those with such guarantee.

For the former the permissible stresses, whether in tension or compression, are 20,000 lb./square inch for bars up to $\frac{3}{4}$ inch diameter, 18,000 lb./square inch for those between $\frac{3}{4}$ inch and $1\frac{3}{8}$ inch and 16,000 lb./square inch for diameters over $1\frac{3}{8}$ inch.

For steels with a guaranteed yield stress the permissible stress in tension is half the guaranteed yield with the proviso that it shall not exceed 30,000 lb./square inch. For compressive stress the permissible value is half the guaranteed yield but with a maximum of 23,000 lb./square inch.

The guaranteed yield stresses given in the British Standard specifications are shown in Table 11.6.

TABLE 11.6.

Diameter of bar	Guaranteed yield stress : lb./sq. in.	
	Medium tensile steel	High tensile steel
Up to and including 1″ . . .	44,000	51,500
Over 1″ up to and including 1½″ . .	41,500	49,500
Over 1½″ ,, ,, 2″ . .	39,000	47,000
,, 2″ ,, ,, 2½″ . .	37,000	45,000
,, 2½″ ,, ,, 3″ . .	37,000	42,500

EXERCISES

(1) A flitched beam is made of two timber joists each 4 inches wide and 12 inches deep with a $12 \times \frac{1}{2}$-inch steel plate firmly fastened between them.

If the stress in the timber is limited to 1,000 lb. per square inch and that in the steel to 10,000 lb. per square inch, calculate the safe uniformly distributed load which the beam can carry when freely supported on a span of 20 feet.

E for steel $= 30 \times 10^6$ lb. per square inch.

E for timber $= 1\cdot5 \times 10^6$ lb. per square inch.

(7,200 lb.)

(2) A reinforced concrete beam is 10 inches wide and 12 inches deep to the centre of reinforcement which consists of a total area of 1 square inch of steel. Calculate the position of the neutral axis of the beam and the stress in the steel when that in the concrete is 600 lb. per square inch. $m=15$.

(n=4·68 inches ; t=14,040 lb. per square inch)

(3) A reinforced concrete floor slab is $4\frac{1}{2}$ inches deep to the centre of reinforcement and is carried on secondary beams 8 feet apart. If a concrete stress of 600 lb. per square inch and a steel stress of 18,000 lb. per square inch are developed simultaneously, calculate the area of steel required per foot width of slab and the load per square foot the floor can carry. $m=15$.

(0·30 square inches ; 225 lb. per square foot)

(4) A reinforced concrete T-beam 40 inches wide and 6 inches deep at the top has 5 square inches of reinforcement at a depth of 20 inches where the width of the beam is 12 inches.

Calculate the uniformly distributed load it can carry on a freely supported span of 20 feet, inclusive of its own weight, if the stresses in the concrete and steel are limited to 600 and 16,000 lb. per square inch respectively.

The modular ratio may be taken as 15.

(1·05 tons per foot)

(5) Take the overall sizes of the beam specified in the last question and calculate the percentage error involved in the moment of resistance determined by the approximate method when the slab thickness is 4 inches.

(3·6 per cent.)

(6) A reinforced concrete beam, rectangular in cross-section, is 8 inches wide and 18 inches effective depth to the centre of the tension reinforcement. It is reinforced on both the tension and compression sides by two $\frac{1}{2}$-inch diameter rods and subjected to a pure bending moment. The compression steel is centred at 1 inch from the top of the beam.

Calculate the position of the neutral axis and the stresses in the steel when the maximum concrete stress is 600 lb. per square inch. $m=15$.

(5·35 inches ; 7,310 lb. per square inch in compression ; 21,350 lb. per square inch in tension)

(7) The moment of resistance of an economically designed reinforced concrete beam may be expressed by the formula

$$M=Rbd^2$$

where M is the moment of resistance, b the breadth of the beam and d the depth to the reinforcement, R being a constant depending on the allowable concrete and steel stresses and the modular ratio.

If the allowable stresses in the concrete and steel are 750 lb. per square inch and 18,000 lb. per square inch respectively and the value of the modular ratio is 18, determine the value of R. Also calculate the economic percentage of steel.

(137·7 ; 0·893 per cent.)

(8) Derive a shear stress distribution curve for a concrete beam of rectangular section reinforced on the tension side only.

A beam of this description is 10 inches wide, 12 inches deep to the centre of reinforcement and 4·8 inches deep to the neutral axis. It is subjected to a maximum shear force of 7,500 lb. Calculate the maximum shear stress in the concrete.

(72 lb. per square inch)

CHAPTER 12

ELASTIC ARCHES AND RINGS

12.1. Action of the arch.—It has been shown that the essential reactive forces for the equilibrium of any system of loads acting upon a plane frame are provided if the structure is supported on a pin at one point and on a frictionless bearing at another ; the reactive forces are then determinate from the equations of static equilibrium for the system. Thus, the curved beam shown in Fig. 12.1 which is pinned to a support at A and rests on rollers at B can carry any system of loads and the reactions will consist of vertical forces at A and B and a horizontal force at A. The elastic straining of the beam will cause the end B to move slightly in a horizontal direction.

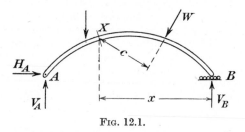

FIG. 12.1.

The resultant actions at a section of the beam, such as X, normal to its centre line will be :—

(a) A thrust equal to the algebraic sum of the forces to the right of X resolved in a direction normal to the section.

(b) A shearing force equal to the algebraic sum of the forces to the right of X resolved in a direction parallel to the section.

(c) A bending moment $M = Wc - V_B x$.

If the free movement of the end B is restricted by the introduction of a horizontal force at B the resultant actions at any section are not modified in type but their magnitudes will be altered by amounts dependent upon the extent to which the point B is restrained. The most important change will be in the magnitude of the bending moment, which may be reduced considerably. The action of the horizontal restraining force upon the structure is known as arch action and its effects are very important since it may considerably reduce the size of a member required to carry a specified load system and so allow spans to be bridged which might otherwise be impossible.

It is usual to restrict the movement of the end completely and the term arch is generally applied to a curved structure in which both supports are fixed in position, although not necessarily in direction.

Arches are constructed of a variety of materials. Steel is commonly used for the purpose and the arch may be either a rolled or plated section when it is termed an arch rib, or a braced structure such as the Sydney Harbour Bridge. Concrete, either plain or reinforced, is also frequently used in

similar structures.   Both steel and concrete arches are characterised by a
homogeneity of structure : they may be considered as units made of a single
material and in this respect differ from arches of brickwork or masonry
where small units, bricks or voussoirs, are held together by cement or mortar
joints.   From the standpoint of theoretical treatment the distinction is of
some importance since a homogeneous structure may reasonably be expected
to behave elastically within the limits set by the material of which it is made,
whereas the same assumption becomes questionable in the case of a structure
made of composite material.

There is, however, good experimental evidence that masonry and brickwork arches behave elastically and obey Hooke's Law.   This will be dealt
with in Chapter 16.

12.2. General types.—The simplest type of arch theoretically is that
known as the three-pinned arch and shown in Fig. 12.2.   It consists of two

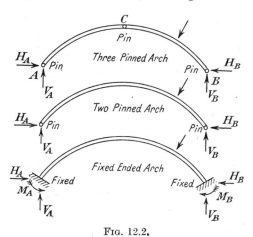

FIG. 12.2.

sections pinned together at the crown C and to pins at A and B so that its
ends are fixed in position but not in direction.

If the central pin is omitted and the member is made continuous between
supports it becomes a two-pinned arch.   In both these types the reactive
forces consist of vertical and horizontal components at A and B.

The ends of the arch may be restrained not only in position but also in
direction in a manner analogous to that of an encastré beam : the arch is
then of the fixed-end type and the reactions consist of vertical and horizontal
forces and fixing moments at each support.   Arches of any of these types
may be either ribs or braced structures and the stress analysis of the various
forms will now be considered.

12.3. The three-pinned arch.—Fig. 12.3 represents a three-pinned arch of
span L, the third pin being midway between A and B.   A load having
vertical and horizontal components Y and X is carried at a horizontal
distance x from the centre, y being the rise of the arch at this point.

AC and BC are essentially two bars connecting the point C to the two fixed
points A and B, and the frame is just stiff ; the arch is therefore statically
determinate.

Let the vertical and horizontal forces at A be V_A and H_A, and at B, V_B and H_B.

The equation of the vertical and horizontal forces on the structure and the equation of moments about A gives

$$V_A + V_B - Y = 0,$$
$$H_A - H_B - X = 0,$$
$$Y\left(\frac{L}{2} + x\right) - Xy - V_B L = 0.$$

If the arch be separated at the crown pin, as shown in the figure, the internal reactions which it provided must be replaced by external forces

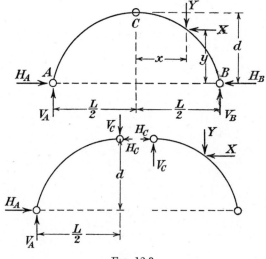

FIG. 12.3.

H_C and V_C for equilibrium of each half to be restored. The equations of equilibrium for the left-hand section are then

$$V_A - V_C = 0,$$
$$H_A - H_C = 0,$$
$$H_C d - V_C \frac{L}{2} = 0.$$

These equations, together with the three above, enable the values H_A, H_B, H_C, V_A, V_B and V_C to be found in any particular example.

Suppose, for instance, an arch of 80 feet span and 10 feet rise carries a load of 10 tons at the quarter span as shown in Fig. 12.4 and it is desired to calculate the reactions. From a consideration of the equilibrium of the whole arch the following equations are obtained :—

$$V_A + V_B - 10 = 0,$$
$$H_A - H_B = 0,$$
$$600 - 80 V_B = 0 ;$$

which give
$$V_B = 7 \cdot 5 \text{ tons},$$
$$V_A = 2 \cdot 5 \text{ tons},$$
and
$$H_A = H_B.$$

For equilibrium of the left-hand section of the arch the following equations must be satisfied :—

$$V_A - V_C = 0,$$
$$H_A - H_C = 0,$$
$$10H_C - 40V_C = 0 ;$$

from which

$$H_C = 4V_C = 4V_A,$$
$$H_A = H_C,$$

and so

$$V_A = 2 \cdot 5 \text{ tons,}$$
$$V_B = 7 \cdot 5 \text{ tons,}$$
$$H_A = H_B = 10 \text{ tons.}$$

In many three-pinned arches the results can be obtained more simply. In the example just worked, for instance, it should be noticed that since C is a pin-joint there can be no bending moment there and the line of action of the resultant of all the forces on the left-hand section must, therefore, pass through it. Hence, if AC in Fig. 12.4 be joined, the reaction at A is directed along AC. Also, since the reaction at A, the reaction at B and the

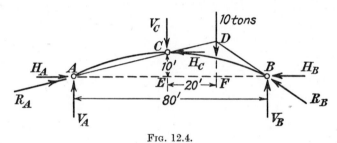

FIG. 12.4.

external load are in equilibrium their lines of action must meet at a point. If AC be produced to meet the load line at D therefore, the resultant of the forces at B must act along the line BD. Hence the directions of the reactions at A and B are known and their components are readily obtained. Thus, R_A is directed along AC, and CE and AE represent the values of V_A and H_A to the same scale that AC represents R_A.

Therefore $H_A = 4V_A.$

Similarly R_B is directed along BD and so BF and FD represent to scale the values of H_B and V_B.

Since FD = 15 and FB = 20

$$H_B = \tfrac{4}{3}V_B.$$

By taking moments about A, V_B is found to be $7 \cdot 5$ tons and V_A to be $2 \cdot 5$ tons and so

$$H_A = H_B = 10 \text{ tons as before.}$$

If both sides of the arch are loaded the solution can be found in a similar way. The load system is divided into two, so that the right- and left-hand portion respectively is unloaded. These are solved separately and the results superposed.

12.4. Bending moments in a three-pinned arch.—Having found the horizontal thrust, the bending moment at any point is readily calculated.

In Fig. 12.5 if K is any point on an arch carrying vertical loads only, the bending moment there is

$$M_K = \Sigma Wc - V_B x + H_B y$$

where the summation sign denotes that all loads to the right of the section must be included.

Since V_B is unaffected by horizontal forces acting at A and B its value would be unaltered if AB were spanned by a horizontal beam instead of by an arch. The terms $\Sigma Wc - V_B x$ give the bending moment at any point for the hypothetical beam AB and the bending moment for this is readily plotted. As there are no horizontal loads on the arch $H_A = H_B = H$ say, and the term Hy can be represented for all values of x by the line of the arch itself. Remembering that there can be no bending moment at the pin C the complete bending moment diagram is readily drawn as follows. The curve of the arch is first set out. If the rise is actually represented by a inches on the diagram this dimension represents Hd tons-feet, the value of Hy at the centre. The bending moments represented by this line are positive and the values of the " beam " bending moment which are essentially negative must

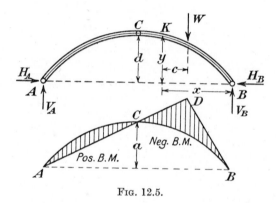

Fig. 12.5.

be deducted to obtain the true moments. The bending moment diagram for the beam in the case shown is a triangle with its apex on the line of action of the load. Hence, if the line ACD is drawn to meet the load line at D, and D and B are joined, ADB is the beam diagram and the bending moment at any point on the arch is the intercept between the two diagrams.

It will be seen that whatever the shape of the arch, the centre line will always represent the Hy term of the bending moment to an appropriate scale and the beam bending moment diagram has then only to be drawn to pass through the points A, B and C in order to complete the construction. If the arch carries horizontal as well as vertical loads the diagram cannot be plotted quite so simply. H_A will not then be equal to H_B and the curve of the arch no longer represents Hy. There is, however, no difficulty since the reactive forces can be calculated with no more trouble than before. In the special case of a three-pinned arch carrying a uniformly distributed load of intensity w over its whole span the bending moment diagram for the pin-jointed beam of the same span is a parabola. If the centre line of the arch is also a parabola the Hy curve and the load curve coincide at all points and there is no bending moment anywhere in the rib.

12.5. The segmental-arc cantilever.—Fig. 12.6 represents a segmental cantilever rib, encastré at A and carrying a single vertical load P at θ from the radius OC. The angle AOC is ϕ and the rib carries at the free end C a moment M_0, a tangential force H_0 and a radial force V_0 acting as shown. These are independent actions and the displacements of C can be determined by strain energy methods.

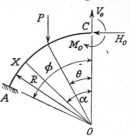

At any point X on the rib at an angular distance α from OC the bending moment and tangential force are

FIG. 12.6.

$$M=M_0-H_0R(1-\cos \alpha)-V_0R \sin \alpha+[PR(\sin \alpha-\sin \theta)]$$

and
$$T=H_0 \cos \alpha-V_0 \sin \alpha+[P \sin \alpha].$$

$$(12.1)$$

The terms in P only occur between $\alpha=\phi$ and $\alpha=\theta$; the others between $\alpha=\phi$ and $\alpha=0$.

If the effects of radial shearing forces are neglected as being inappreciable, the angular displacement, μ_0, and the component displacements, h_0 and v_0, of C are

$$\mu_0=\frac{\partial U}{\partial M_0}, \; h_0=\frac{\partial U}{\partial H_0} \text{ and } v_0=\frac{\partial U}{\partial V_0},$$

where U is the strain energy of the rib due to bending moments and tangential forces.

Then

$$\mu_0=\frac{1}{EI}\int M\frac{\partial M}{\partial M_0}ds+\frac{1}{AE}\int T\frac{\partial T}{\partial M_0}ds,$$

$$h_0=\frac{1}{EI}\int M\frac{\partial M}{\partial H_0}ds+\frac{1}{AE}\int T\frac{\partial T}{\partial H_0}ds,$$

and
$$v_0=\frac{1}{EI}\int M\frac{\partial M}{\partial V_0}ds+\frac{1}{AE}\int T\frac{\partial T}{\partial V_0}ds,$$

where EI is the constant flexural rigidity of the rib and AE is its constant extensional rigidity.

If the values of the derivatives for bending moment and tangential force taken from equation (12.1) are substituted in the above they become

$$\mu_0=\frac{R}{EI}\int Md\alpha,$$

$$h_0=-\frac{R^2}{EI}\int M(1-\cos \alpha)d\alpha+\frac{R}{AE}\int T \cos \alpha d\alpha=$$

$$-R\mu_0+\frac{R^2}{EI}\int M \cos \alpha d\alpha+\frac{R}{AE}\int T \cos \alpha d\alpha,$$

$$-v_0=\frac{R^2}{EI}\int M \sin \alpha d\alpha+\frac{R}{AE}\int T \sin \alpha d\alpha.$$

$$(12.2)$$

Then

$$\mu_0 = \frac{R}{EI}\left[\int_0^{\phi}\{M_0 - H_0R(1-\cos\alpha) - V_0R\sin\alpha\}d\alpha + \int_{\theta}^{\phi}PR(\sin\alpha - \sin\theta)d\alpha\right],$$

which gives

$$\frac{EI\mu_0}{R^2} = \frac{M_0\phi}{R} - H_0(\phi - \sin\phi) - V_0(1 - \cos\phi)$$

$$+P\{\cos\theta - \cos\phi - (\phi - \theta)\sin\theta\} ; \quad . \quad (12.3)$$

also

$$h_0 = -R\mu_0 + \frac{R^2}{EI}\left[\int_0^{\phi}\{M_0 - H_0R(1-\cos\alpha) - V_0R\sin\alpha\}\cos\alpha\,d\alpha\right.$$

$$\left. + \int_{\theta}^{\phi}PR(\sin\alpha - \sin\theta)\cos\alpha\,d\alpha\right]$$

$$+ \frac{R}{AE}\left[\int_0^{\phi}(H_0\cos\alpha - V_0\sin\alpha)\cos\alpha\,d\alpha + \int_{\theta}^{\phi}P\sin\alpha\cos\alpha\,d\alpha\right],$$

which gives

$$\frac{4AEh_0}{R} = -4AE\mu_0 + \beta\left\{\frac{4M_0\sin\phi}{R} + H_0(2\phi + \sin 2\phi - 4\sin\phi) - V_0(1 - \cos 2\phi)\right.$$

$$\left. + 2P(\sin\phi - \sin\theta)^2\right\}$$

$$+ H_0(2\phi + \sin 2\phi) - V_0(1 - \cos 2\phi) + P(\cos 2\theta - \cos 2\phi), \quad (12.4)$$

where $\beta = R^2/k^2$; k being the radius of gyration of the cross-section of the rib about the axis of bending.

And finally,

$$-v_0 = \frac{R^2}{EI}\left[\int_0^{\phi}\{M_0 - H_0R(1-\cos\alpha) - V_0R\sin\alpha\}\sin\alpha\,d\alpha\right.$$

$$\left. + \int_{\theta}^{\phi}PR(\sin\alpha - \sin\theta)\sin\alpha\,d\alpha\right]$$

$$+ \frac{R}{AE}\left[\int_0^{\phi}(H_0\cos\alpha - V_0\sin\alpha)\sin\alpha\,d\alpha + \int_{\theta}^{\phi}P\sin^2\alpha\,d\alpha\right],$$

which gives

$$-\frac{4AEv_0}{R} = \beta\left[\frac{4M_0(1-\cos\phi)}{R} - 2H_0(1-\cos\phi)^2 - V_0(2\phi - \sin 2\phi)\right.$$

$$\left. + P\{2(\phi - \theta) - \sin 2\phi - \sin 2\theta + 4\sin\theta\cos\phi\}\right]$$

$$+ H_0(1 - \cos 2\phi) - V_0(2\phi - \sin 2\phi) + P(2\theta' - \sin 2\phi + \sin 2\theta), \quad (12.5)$$

where θ' is written for $\phi - \theta$.

This completes the solution for the cantilever carrying a concentrated vertical load P and terminal actions, but the cases where the point load is replaced by a distributed load need consideration.

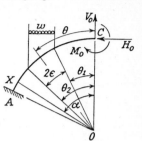

FIG. 12.7.

Fig. 12.7 shows a segmental rib as before but it now carries a distributed vertical load of intensity w which is uniform on a horizontal projection. This load covers the arc between θ_1 and θ_2.

In the first place the values of the bending moment and tangential force at any point α due to w must be determined. Let ψ be any angle between θ_1 and θ_2; then the vertical load acting on the element of length $R\,d\psi$ is $wR\cos\psi\,d\psi$. The bending moment and tangential force at α due to w are

$$m=wR^2\int_{\theta_1}^{\alpha}\cos\psi(\sin\alpha-\sin\psi)d\psi \quad \text{and} \quad t=wR\int_{\theta_1}^{\alpha}\cos\psi\sin\alpha\,d\psi$$

for all values of α between θ_1 and θ_2, and by the same expressions integrated between the limits $\psi=\theta_1$ and $\psi=\theta_2$ for all values of α greater than θ_2.

These expressions give, when α lies between θ_1 and θ_2,

$$m=\frac{wR^2}{2}(\sin\alpha-\sin\theta_1)^2$$

and

$$t=wR\sin\alpha(\sin\alpha-\sin\theta_1),$$

$$\left.\begin{array}{l} \\ \\ \end{array}\right\} \quad . \quad . \quad . \quad . \quad (12.6)$$

and when α lies between θ_2 and ϕ,

$$m=\frac{wR^2}{2}(\sin\theta_2-\sin\theta_1)(2\sin\alpha-\sin\theta_2-\sin\theta_1)$$

and

$$t=wR\sin\alpha(\sin\theta_2-\sin\theta_1).$$

$$\left.\begin{array}{l} \\ \\ \end{array}\right\} \quad . \quad . \quad (12.7)$$

These terms replace those in P in the equation (12.1) and, since those in M_0, H_0 and V_0 are unaltered, attention may be directed solely to the alterations in μ_0, h_0 and v_0 caused by the replacement.

The load term in the expression for μ_0 becomes

$$\mu_w=\frac{wR^3}{2EI}\left[\int_{\theta_1}^{\theta_2}(\sin\alpha-\sin\theta_1)^2d\alpha+(\sin\theta_2-\sin\theta_1)\int_{\theta_2}^{\phi}(2\sin\alpha-\sin\theta_2-\sin\theta_1)d\alpha\right]$$

and the corresponding terms in the expressions for h_0 and v_0 are

$$h_w=\frac{wR^4}{2EI}\left[\int_{\theta_1}^{\theta_2}(\sin\alpha-\sin\theta_1)^2\cos\alpha\,d\alpha\right.$$

$$\left.+(\sin\theta_2-\sin\theta_1)\int_{\theta_2}^{\phi}(2\sin\alpha-\sin\theta_2-\sin\theta_1)\cos\alpha\,d\alpha\right]$$

$$+\frac{wR^2}{AE}\left[\int_{\theta_1}^{\theta_2}(\sin\alpha-\sin\theta_1)\sin\alpha\cos\alpha\,d\alpha+(\sin\theta_2-\sin\theta_1)\int_{\theta_2}^{\phi}\sin\alpha\cos\alpha\,d\alpha\right]$$

and

$$-v_w=\frac{wR^4}{2EI}\left[\int_{\theta_1}^{\theta_2}(\sin\alpha-\sin\theta_1)^2\sin\alpha\,d\alpha\right.$$

$$\left.+(\sin\theta_2-\sin\theta_1)\int_{\theta_2}^{\phi}(2\sin\alpha-\sin\theta_2-\sin\theta_1)\sin\alpha\,d\alpha\right]$$

$$+\frac{wR^2}{AE}\left[\int_{\theta_1}^{\theta_2}(\sin\alpha-\sin\theta_1)\sin^2\alpha\,d\alpha+(\sin\theta_2-\sin\theta_1)\int_{\theta_2}^{\phi}\sin\alpha^2d\alpha\right].$$

The results are simplified by putting $\theta_1+\theta_2=2\theta$ and $\theta_2-\theta_1=2\varepsilon$ and when the above expressions are integrated and these substitutions made, the equations for μ_0, h_0 and v_0 are

$$\frac{EI\mu_0}{R^2}=\frac{M_0\phi}{R}-H_0(\phi-\sin\phi)-V_0(1-\cos\phi)$$

$$+\frac{wR}{4}\{2\varepsilon(2-\cos 2\varepsilon\cos 2\theta)-2\theta'\sin 2\varepsilon\sin 2\theta$$

$$-8\sin\varepsilon\cos\theta\cos\phi+3\sin 2\varepsilon\cos 2\theta\},$$

$$\frac{4AEh_0}{R}=-4AE\mu_0+\beta\left[\frac{4M_0\sin\phi}{R}+H_0(2\phi+\sin 2\phi-4\sin\phi)\right.$$

$$-V_0(1-\cos 2\phi)+wR\{(3-2\cos 2\phi)\sin\varepsilon\cos\theta$$

$$\left.-\tfrac{1}{3}\sin 3\varepsilon\cos 3\theta-2\sin 2\varepsilon\sin 2\theta\sin\phi\}\right]+H_0(2\phi+\sin 2\phi)$$

$$-V_0(1-\cos 2\phi)+wR\{(1-2\cos 2\phi)\sin\varepsilon\cos\theta$$

$$+\tfrac{1}{3}\sin 3\varepsilon\cos 3\theta\},$$

$$-\frac{4AEv_0}{R}=\beta\left[\frac{4M_0(1-\cos\phi)}{R}-2H_0(1-\cos\phi)^2-V_0(2\phi-\sin 2\phi)\right.$$

$$+wR\{\sin\theta(3\sin\varepsilon-4\varepsilon\cos\varepsilon)-\tfrac{1}{3}\sin 3\varepsilon\sin 3\theta$$

$$\left.+2(2\theta'-\sin 2\phi)\sin\varepsilon\cos\theta+2\sin 2\varepsilon\sin 2\theta\cos\phi\}\right]$$

$$+H_0(1-\cos 2\phi)-V_0(2\phi-\sin 2\phi)$$

$$+wR\{\sin\theta(5\sin\varepsilon-4\varepsilon\cos\varepsilon)+\tfrac{1}{3}\sin 3\varepsilon\sin 3\theta$$

$$+2(2\theta'-\sin 2\phi)\sin\varepsilon\cos\theta\}.$$

(12.8)

In the limit when 2ε is very small the vertical load carried is $2wR\varepsilon\cos\theta$ and the above equations then reduce to the corresponding ones for a point load of this magnitude.

If a load P acts horizontally instead of vertically as in Fig. 12.8, the equations for bending moment and tangential force at any point are

$$M=M_0-V_0R\sin\alpha-H_0R(1-\cos\alpha)+[PR(\cos\theta-\cos\alpha)]$$

and $$T=H_0\cos\alpha-V_0\sin\alpha-[P\cos\alpha].$$

(12.9)

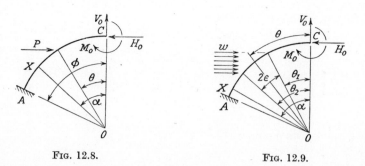

FIG. 12.8.   FIG. 12.9.

These expressions, except for the terms in P are the same as before and therefore only the last term need be considered.

Thus,

$$\mu_P = \frac{PR^2}{EI}\int_\theta^\phi (\cos\theta - \cos\alpha)d\alpha,$$

$$h_P = \frac{PR^3}{EI}\int_\theta^\phi (\cos\theta - \cos\alpha)\cos\alpha\,d\alpha - \frac{PR}{AE}\int_\theta^\phi \cos^2\alpha\,d\alpha$$

and

$$-v_P = \frac{PR^3}{EI}\int_\theta^\phi (\cos\theta - \cos\alpha)\sin\alpha\,d\alpha - \frac{PR}{AE}\int_\theta^\phi \cos\alpha\sin\alpha\,d\alpha,$$

and on reduction these give the following equations for the displacements of the end C of the cantilever :

$$\frac{EI\mu_0}{R^2} = \frac{M_0\phi}{R} - H_0(\phi - \sin\phi) - V_0(1-\cos\phi) + P(\sin\theta - \sin\phi + \theta'\cos\theta).$$

$$\frac{4AEh_0}{R} = -4AE\mu_0 + \beta\left[\frac{4M_0\sin\phi}{R} + H_0(2\phi + \sin 2\phi - 4\sin\phi)\right.$$
$$-V_0(1-\cos 2\phi) - P\{2\theta' + \sin 2\phi + \sin 2\theta$$
$$\left.-4\cos\theta\sin\phi\}\right] + H_0(2\phi + \sin 2\phi) - V_0(1-\cos 2\phi)$$
$$-P(2\theta' + \sin 2\phi - \sin 2\theta),$$

$$-\frac{4AEv_0}{R} = \beta\left[\frac{4M_0(1-\cos\phi)}{R} - 2H_0(1-\cos\phi)^2 - V_0(2\phi - \sin 2\phi)\right.$$
$$\left.+2P(\cos\theta - \cos\phi)^2\right] + H_0(1-\cos 2\phi) - V_0(2\phi - \sin 2\phi)$$
$$-P(\cos 2\theta - \cos 2\phi).$$

$$(12.10)$$

If the load is distributed over the portion of the rib between θ_1 and θ_2, as shown in Fig. 12.9, the terms in M_0, H_0 and V_0 are the same as before but alterations must be made in those for P.

As in the argument for the distributed vertical loading, an element of the rib at ψ from OC carries a horizontal load $wR\sin\psi\,d\psi$ and the bending moment and tangential force due to the distributed load at any section of the rib which is α from OC are given by

$$m = wR^2\int_{\theta_1}^\alpha \sin\psi(\cos\psi - \cos\alpha)d\psi$$

and

$$t = -wR\int_{\theta_1}^\alpha \sin\psi\cos\alpha\,d\psi$$

when α is between θ_1 and θ_2, and by the same expressions integrated between θ_1 and θ_2 when α is greater than θ_2. Thus, when α lies between θ_1 and θ_2,

$$m = \frac{wR^2}{2}(\cos\theta_1 - \cos\alpha)^2$$

and

$$t = -wR\cos\alpha(\cos\theta_1 - \cos\alpha),$$

$$(12.11)$$

and when α lies between θ_2 and ϕ,

$$m = \frac{wR^2}{2}(\cos\theta_1 - \cos\theta_2)(\cos\theta_1 + \cos\theta_2 - 2\cos\alpha)$$

and

$$t = -wR\cos\alpha(\cos\theta_1 - \cos\theta_2).$$

$$(12.12)$$

These terms replace those in P in equations (12.9) and the contributions of w to μ_0, h_0 and v_0 are given by

$$\mu_w = \frac{wR^3}{2EI}\left[\int_{\theta_1}^{\theta_2}(\cos\theta_1-\cos\theta_2)^2 d\alpha\right.$$
$$\left. +(\cos\theta_1-\cos\theta_2)\int_{\theta_2}^{\phi}(\cos\theta_1+\cos\theta_2-2\cos\alpha)d\alpha\right],$$

$$h_w = \frac{wR^4}{2EI}\left[\int_{\theta_1}^{\theta_2}(\cos\theta_1-\cos\alpha)^2\cos\alpha d\alpha\right.$$
$$\left. +(\cos\theta_1-\cos\theta_2)\int_{\theta_2}^{\phi}(\cos\theta_1+\cos\theta_2-2\cos\alpha)\cos\alpha d\alpha\right]$$
$$-\frac{wR^2}{AE}\left[\int_{\theta_1}^{\theta_2}(\cos\theta_1-\cos\alpha)\cos^2\alpha d\alpha+(\cos\theta_1-\cos\theta_2)\int_{\theta_2}^{\phi}\cos^2\alpha d\alpha\right],$$

$$-v_w = \frac{wR^4}{2EI}\left[\int_{\theta_1}^{\theta_2}(\cos\theta_1-\cos\alpha)^2\sin\alpha d\alpha\right.$$
$$\left. +(\cos\theta_1-\cos\theta_2)\int_{\theta_2}^{\phi}(\cos\theta_1+\cos\theta_2-2\cos\alpha)\sin\alpha d\alpha\right]$$
$$-\frac{wR^2}{AE}\left[\int_{\theta_1}^{\theta_2}(\cos\theta_1-\cos\alpha)\cos\alpha\sin\alpha d\alpha\right.$$
$$\left. +(\cos\theta_1-\cos\theta_2)\int_{\theta_2}^{\phi}\cos\alpha\sin\alpha d\alpha\right].$$

As for vertical distributed load we put $\theta_1+\theta_2=2\theta$ and $\theta_2-\theta_1=2\varepsilon$, and with these substituted in the integrated expressions above the displacements of C are given by

$$\left.\begin{aligned}
\frac{EI\mu_0}{R^2} &= \frac{M_0\phi}{R}-H_0(\phi-\sin\phi)-V_0(1-\cos\phi) \\
&\quad +\frac{wR}{4}\{2\varepsilon(2+\cos 2\varepsilon\cos 2\theta)+2\theta'\sin 2\varepsilon\sin 2\theta \\
&\qquad\qquad -8\sin\varepsilon\sin\theta\sin\phi-3\sin 2\varepsilon\cos 2\theta\}, \\[4pt]
\frac{4AEh_0}{R} &= -4AE\mu_0+\beta\left[\frac{4M_0\sin\phi}{R}+H_0(2\phi+\sin 2\phi-4\sin\phi)\right. \\
&\quad -V_0(1-\cos 2\phi)+wR\{\cos\theta(3\sin\varepsilon-4\varepsilon\cos\varepsilon) \\
&\quad +\tfrac{1}{3}\sin 3\varepsilon\cos 3\theta-2(2\theta'+\sin 2\phi)\sin\varepsilon\sin\theta \\
&\quad \left. +2\sin 2\varepsilon\sin 2\theta\sin\phi\}\right]+H_0(2\phi+\sin 2\phi) \\
&\quad -V_0(1-\cos 2\phi)+wR\{\cos\theta(5\sin\varepsilon-4\varepsilon\cos\varepsilon) \\
&\qquad\qquad -\tfrac{1}{3}\sin 3\varepsilon\cos 3\theta-2(2\theta'+\sin 2\phi)\sin\varepsilon\sin\theta\}, \\[4pt]
-\frac{4AEv_0}{R} &= \beta\left[\frac{4M_0(1-\cos\phi)}{R}-2H_0(1-\cos\phi)^2-V_0(2\phi-\sin 2\phi)\right. \\
&\quad +wR\{(3+2\cos 2\phi)\sin\varepsilon\sin\theta+\tfrac{1}{3}\sin 3\varepsilon\sin 3\theta \\
&\quad \left. -2\sin 2\varepsilon\sin 2\theta\cos\phi\}\right]+H_0(1-\cos 2\phi) \\
&\quad -V_0(2\phi-\sin 2\phi)+wR\{(1+2\cos 2\phi)\sin\varepsilon\sin\theta \\
&\qquad\qquad -\tfrac{1}{3}\sin 3\varepsilon\sin 3\theta\}.
\end{aligned}\right\} \quad (12.13)$$

In the limit when 2ε is very small the horizontal point load acting at θ is $2wR\varepsilon\sin\theta$ and the above equations give the same results as (12.10).

12.6. The encastré segmental arch rib with a concentrated load.—The results of the last paragraph will now be used to determine the resultant actions in an encastré arch rib carrying concentrated loads acting in any directions at specified positions.   All such loads can be resolved into vertical and horizontal components and so general solutions for a single vertical and horizontal load respectively enable the complete resultant actions to be determined by superposition.

Further, a single load can be represented, as shown in Fig. 12.10, by a pair of symmetrically disposed loads superposed on a pair of skew-symmetrical loads.   Thus the reactions at A and B for the loading shown at (a) can be found by superposing the reactions at these points due to the symmetrical system (b) and the skew-symmetrical system (c).

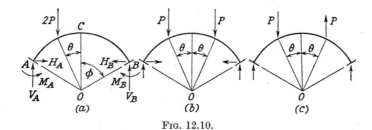

FIG. 12.10.

Vertical load on arch rib.   Considering first the symmetrical system (b) of Fig. 12.10, the resultant actions at C consist of a couple M_0 and a thrust H_0, as shown in Fig. 12.6.   From considerations of symmetry, V_0 is zero and the only displacement of section C is in a vertical direction.   Hence, the conditions at C are

$$V_0=0 \; ; \; \mu_0=0 \; ; \; h_0=0.$$

Substituting these conditions in equations (12.3) and (12.4), simultaneous equations are obtained to determine H_0 and M_0.   These are

$$\frac{M_0\phi}{R}-H_0(\phi-\sin\phi)+P(\cos\theta-\cos\phi-\theta'\sin\theta)=0,$$

$$\frac{4\beta M_0\sin\phi}{R}+H_0\{\beta(2\phi+\sin 2\phi-4\sin\phi)+2\phi+\sin 2\phi\}$$
$$+P\{2\beta(\sin\phi-\sin\theta)^2+\cos 2\theta-\cos 2\phi\}=0,$$

and their solution gives

$$\left.\begin{array}{l}\dfrac{H_0}{2P}=\dfrac{\beta\{\phi(\cos 2\phi+\cos 2\theta-2)+4\sin\phi(\theta\sin\theta-\cos\phi+\cos\theta)\}}{2\beta\{2\phi^2+\phi\sin 2\phi-4\sin^2\phi\}+2\phi(2\phi+\sin 2\phi)}, \\[4mm] \dfrac{M_0}{R}=\dfrac{1}{\phi}[H_0(\phi-\sin\phi)-P(\cos\theta-\cos\phi-\theta'\sin\theta)].\end{array}\right\} \quad (12.14)$$

Under the skew-symmetrical loading of Fig. 12.10 (c) the conditions to be satisfied at C are

$$M_0=0 \; ; \; H_0=0 \; ; \; v_0=0 \; ;$$

and so from equation (12.5),

$$\beta[-V_0(2\phi-\sin 2\phi)+P(2\theta'-\sin 2\phi-\sin 2\theta+4\sin\theta\cos\phi)]$$
$$-V_0(2\phi-\sin 2\phi)+P(2\theta'-\sin 2\phi+\sin 2\theta)=0,$$

which gives

$$\frac{V_0}{2P}=\frac{\beta\{2\theta'-\sin 2\phi-\sin 2\theta+4\sin\theta\cos\phi\}+2\theta'-\sin 2\phi+\sin 2\theta}{2(1+\beta)(2\phi-\sin 2\phi)} \quad . \quad . \quad (12.15)$$

Since H_0 and M_0 are zero for skew-symmetrical loading and V_0 is zero for symmetrical loading, the expressions in (12.14) and (12.15) give the complete resultant actions at the centre of the arch rib under the asymmetrical loading of Fig. 12.10 (a).

It will be observed that all actions contain terms which involve β and also terms which are independent of it. Since β is always very large it is, in the great majority of cases, only necessary to take account of the terms which are multiplied by this factor. The terms which are independent of β arise from the compressive strains caused by the thrust in the rib and are often referred to as the effects of rib-shortening.

If the rib-shortening is neglected, the results of (12.14) and (12.15) are simplified as follows :

$$\left.\begin{aligned}
\frac{H_0}{2P}&=\frac{\phi(\cos 2\phi+\cos 2\theta-2)+4\sin\phi(\theta\sin\theta-\cos\phi+\cos\theta)}{2\phi^2+\phi\sin 2\phi-4\sin^2\phi}, \\[2mm]
\frac{M_0}{R}&=\frac{1}{\phi}[H_0(\phi-\sin\phi)-P(\cos\theta-\cos\phi-\theta'\sin\theta)], \\[2mm]
\frac{V_0}{2P}&=\frac{2\theta'-\sin 2\phi-\sin 2\theta+4\sin\theta\cos\phi}{2(2\phi-\sin 2\phi)}.
\end{aligned}\right\} \quad (12.16)$$

The reactions at A and B in the directions shown in Fig. 12.10 (a) are then

$$\left.\begin{aligned}
M_A&=M_0-H_0R(1-\cos\phi)-V_0R\sin\phi+2PR(\sin\phi-\sin\theta), \\
M_B&=M_0-H_0R(1-\cos\phi)+V_0R\sin\phi, \\
H_A&=H_B=H_0, \\
V_A&=2P-V_0, \\
V_B&=V_0,
\end{aligned}\right\} \quad (12.17)$$

and the resultant bending moments at any point in the loaded and unloaded segments of the rib are obtainable from the equations

$$\left.\begin{aligned}
&M=M_0-H_0R(1-\cos\alpha)-V_0R\sin\alpha+[2PR(\sin\alpha-\sin\theta)] \\
\text{and} \qquad &M=M_0-H_0R(1-\cos\alpha)+V_0R\sin\alpha.
\end{aligned}\right\} \quad (12.18)$$

Horizontal load on arch rib. The single horizontal load 2P shown in Fig. 12.11(a) can also be split into symmetrical and skew-symmetrical systems as shown at (b) and (c) in the same figure. The conditions to be

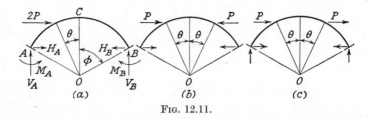

Fig. 12.11.

satisfied at the centre of the rib are the same as for vertical loading, *i.e.* $V_0=0$, $\mu_0=0$ and $h_0=0$ for the symmetrical system and $M_0=0$, $H_0=0$ and $v_0=0$ for the skew-symmetrical system.

Substituting these conditions in equations (12.10),

$$\frac{H_0}{2P}=\frac{\beta[\phi(2\theta'+\sin 2\phi+\sin 2\theta)-4\sin\phi(\sin\phi-\sin\theta+\theta\cos\theta)]+\phi(2\theta'+\sin 2\phi-\sin 2\theta)}{2\beta(2\phi^2+\phi\sin 2\phi-4\sin^2\phi)+2\phi(2\phi+\sin 2\phi)},$$

$$\frac{M_0}{R}=\frac{1}{\phi}[H_0(\phi-\sin\phi)-P(\sin\theta-\sin\phi+\theta'\cos\theta)], \qquad (12.19)$$

$$\frac{V_0}{2P}=\frac{(\cos\theta-\cos\phi)\{\beta(\cos\theta-\cos\phi)-(\cos\theta+\cos\phi)\}}{(\beta+1)(2\phi-\sin 2\phi)}.$$

If the rib-shortening is neglected these become

$$\frac{H_0}{2P}=\frac{\phi(2\theta'+\sin 2\phi+\sin 2\theta)-4\sin\phi(\sin\phi-\sin\theta+\theta\cos\theta)}{2(2\phi^2+\phi\sin 2\phi-4\sin^2\phi)},$$

$$\frac{M_0}{R}=\frac{1}{\phi}[H_0(\phi-\sin\phi)-P(\sin\theta-\sin\phi+\theta'\cos\theta)], \qquad (12.20)$$

$$\frac{V_0}{2P}=\frac{(\cos\theta-\cos\phi)^2}{2\phi-\sin 2\phi}.$$

The reactions at the supports are then

$$\begin{aligned}
M_A&=M_0-H_0R(1-\cos\phi)-V_0R\sin\phi+2PR(\cos\theta-\cos\phi),\\
M_B&=M_0-H_0R(1-\cos\phi)+V_0R\sin\phi,\\
H_A&=H_0-2P,\\
H_B&=H_0,\\
-V_A&=V_B=V_0.
\end{aligned} \qquad (12.21)$$

12.7. The encastré segmental arch rib with distributed load.—When the arch carries a load distributed over a portion of its span, the same method as that used in the last paragraph gives a solution and the two cases of vertical and horizontal loading will be adequate for any load combination.

Uniformly distributed vertical load over part of span.—Fig. 12.12 (a) shows the loading to be considered, which can be split into symmetrical and skew-symmetrical systems as at (b) and (c). The superposition of the separate solutions then provides the complete data for (a).

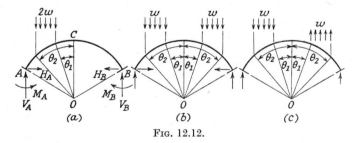

FIG. 12.12.

As before, the conditions to be satisfied at the centre of the arch when the loading is symmetrical are $V_0=\mu_0=h_0=0$; and when the loading is skew-symmetrical, $M_0=H_0=v_0=0$. These conditions substituted in equations (12.8) give the pair of simultaneous equations to determine M_0 and H_0 and the single equation for V_0. Since M_0 and H_0 only appear in symmetrical and V_0 only in skew-symmetrical loading, these are the complete values for the asymmetrical loading shown at (a).

The equations derived thus are

$$\frac{M_0\phi}{R} - H_0(\phi - \sin\phi) + \frac{wR}{4}\{2\varepsilon(2 - \cos 2\varepsilon \cos 2\theta) - 2\theta' \sin 2\varepsilon \sin 2\theta$$
$$- 8\sin\varepsilon\cos\theta\cos\phi + 3\sin 2\varepsilon\cos 2\theta\} = 0,$$

$$\beta\left[\frac{4M_0\sin\phi}{R} + H_0(2\phi + \sin 2\phi - 4\sin\phi) + wR\{(3 - 2\cos 2\phi)\sin\varepsilon\cos\theta\right.$$
$$\left. - \tfrac{1}{3}\sin 3\varepsilon\cos 3\theta - 2\sin 2\varepsilon\sin 2\theta\sin\phi\}\right] + H_0(2\phi + \sin 2\phi)$$
$$+ wR\{(1 - 2\cos 2\phi)\sin\varepsilon\cos\theta + \tfrac{1}{3}\sin 3\varepsilon\cos 3\theta\} = 0,$$

$$(\beta + 1)V_0(2\phi - \sin 2\phi) - wR\beta\{\sin\theta(3\sin\varepsilon - 4\varepsilon\cos\varepsilon) - \tfrac{1}{3}\sin 3\varepsilon\sin 3\theta$$
$$+ 2(2\theta' - \sin 2\phi)\sin\varepsilon\cos\theta + 2\sin 2\varepsilon\sin 2\theta\cos\phi\}$$
$$- wR\{\sin\theta(5\sin\varepsilon - 4\varepsilon\cos\varepsilon) + \tfrac{1}{3}\sin 3\varepsilon\sin 3\theta + 2(2\theta' - \sin 2\phi)\sin\varepsilon\cos\theta\} = 0.$$

The solution of these is

$$\frac{H_0}{2wR} = \cfrac{\begin{cases}\beta[\sin\phi\{2\varepsilon(2 - \cos 2\varepsilon\cos 2\theta) + 2\theta\sin 2\varepsilon\sin 2\theta \\ \qquad\qquad - 8\sin\varepsilon\cos\theta\cos\phi + 3\sin 2\varepsilon\cos 2\theta\} \\ - \phi\{(3 - 2\cos 2\phi)\sin\varepsilon\cos\theta - \tfrac{1}{3}\sin 3\varepsilon\cos 3\theta\}] \\ - \phi\{(1 - 2\cos 2\phi)\sin\varepsilon\cos\theta + \tfrac{1}{3}\sin 3\varepsilon\cos 3\theta\}\end{cases}}{2\beta(2\phi^2 + \phi\sin 2\phi - 4\sin^2\phi) + 2\phi(2\phi + \sin 2\phi)},$$

$$\frac{M_0}{R} = \frac{1}{\phi}\left[H_0(\phi - \sin\phi) - \frac{wR}{4}\{2\varepsilon(2 - \cos 2\varepsilon\cos 2\theta) - 2\theta'\sin 2\varepsilon\sin 2\theta\right.$$
$$\left. - 8\sin\varepsilon\cos\theta\cos\phi + 3\sin 2\varepsilon\cos 2\theta\}\right], \tag{12.22}$$

$$\frac{V_0}{2wR} = \cfrac{\begin{cases}\beta[\sin\theta(3\sin\varepsilon - 4\varepsilon\cos\varepsilon) - \tfrac{1}{3}\sin 3\varepsilon\sin 3\theta \\ \qquad + 2(2\theta' - \sin 2\phi)\sin\varepsilon\cos\theta + 2\sin 2\varepsilon\sin 2\theta\cos\phi] \\ + \sin\theta(5\sin\varepsilon - 4\varepsilon\cos\varepsilon) + \tfrac{1}{3}\sin 3\varepsilon\sin 3\theta \\ \qquad\qquad\qquad + 2(2\theta' - \sin 2\phi)\sin\varepsilon\cos\theta\end{cases}}{2(\beta + 1)(2\phi - \sin 2\phi)}.$$

If rib-shortening is neglected these are

$$\frac{H_0}{2wR} = \cfrac{\begin{cases}\sin\phi\{2\varepsilon(2 - \cos 2\theta) + 2\theta\sin 2\varepsilon\sin 2\theta \\ \qquad\qquad - 8\sin\varepsilon\cos\theta\cos\phi + 3\sin 2\varepsilon\cos 2\theta\} \\ - \phi\{(3 - 2\cos 2\phi)\sin\varepsilon\cos\theta - \tfrac{1}{3}\sin 3\varepsilon\cos 3\theta\}\end{cases}}{2(2\phi^2 + \phi\sin 2\phi - 4\sin^2\phi)},$$

$$\frac{M_0}{R} = \frac{1}{\phi}\left[H_0(\phi - \sin\phi) - \frac{wR}{4}\{2\varepsilon(2 - \cos 2\varepsilon\cos 2\theta) - 2\theta'\sin 2\varepsilon\sin 2\theta\right.$$
$$\left. - 8\sin\varepsilon\cos\theta\cos\phi + 3\sin 2\varepsilon\cos 2\theta\}\right], \tag{12.23}$$

$$\frac{V_0}{2wR} = \cfrac{\sin\theta(3\sin\varepsilon - 4\varepsilon\cos\varepsilon) - \tfrac{1}{3}\sin 3\varepsilon\sin 3\theta \atop + 2(2\theta' - \sin 2\phi)\sin\varepsilon\cos\theta + 2\sin 2\varepsilon\sin 2\theta\cos\phi}{2(2\phi - \sin 2\phi)}.$$

The results of (12.22) and (12.23) agree with those of (12.14), (12.15) and (12.16) if 2ε is made very small and $2wR\varepsilon\cos\theta$ is replaced by P.

Uniformly distributed horizontal load over part of span.   In Fig. 12.13 the loading $2w$ over the arc between θ_1 and θ_2 is split into symmetrical and skew-symmetrical systems.   The conditions to be satisfied at the centre of the rib are the same as before, and when substituted in (12.13) give the three following equations to determine M_0, H_0 and V_0 :

$$\frac{M_0\phi}{R}-H_0(\phi-\sin\,\phi)+\frac{wR}{4}\{2\varepsilon(2+\cos\,2\varepsilon\,\cos\,2\theta)+2\theta'\sin\,2\varepsilon\,\sin\,2\theta$$

$$-8\sin\,\varepsilon\,\sin\,\theta\,\sin\,\phi-3\sin\,2\varepsilon\,\cos\,2\theta\}=0,$$

$$\beta\left[\frac{4M_0\sin\,\phi}{R}+H_0(2\phi+\sin\,2\phi-4\,\sin\,\phi)+wR\{\cos\,\theta(3\,\sin\,\varepsilon-4\varepsilon\,\cos\,\varepsilon)\right.$$

$$\left.+\tfrac{1}{3}\sin\,3\varepsilon\,\cos\,3\theta-2(2\theta'+\sin\,2\phi)\sin\,\varepsilon\,\sin\,\theta+2\,\sin\,2\varepsilon\,\sin\,2\theta\,\sin\,\phi\}\right]$$

$$+H_0(2\phi+\sin\,2\phi)+wR\{\cos\,\theta(5\,\sin\,\varepsilon-4\varepsilon\,\cos\,\varepsilon)-\tfrac{1}{3}\sin\,3\varepsilon\,\cos\,3\theta$$

$$-2(2\theta'+\sin\,2\phi)\sin\,\varepsilon\,\sin\,\theta\}=0,$$

$$(\beta+1)V_0(2\phi-\sin\,2\phi)-wR\beta\{(3+2\,\cos\,2\phi)\sin\,\varepsilon\,\sin\,\theta+\tfrac{1}{3}\sin\,3\varepsilon\,\sin\,3\theta$$

$$-2\,\sin\,2\varepsilon\,\sin\,2\theta\,\cos\,\phi\}-wR\{(1+2\,\cos\,2\phi)\sin\,\varepsilon\,\sin\,\theta-\tfrac{1}{3}\sin\,3\varepsilon\,\sin\,3\theta\}=0.$$

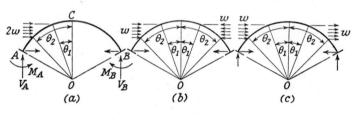

FIG. 12.13.

The solution of these is

$$\frac{H_0}{2wR}=\frac{\left\{\begin{array}{l}\beta[\sin\,\phi\{2\varepsilon(2+\cos\,2\varepsilon\,\cos\,2\theta)-2\theta\,\sin\,2\varepsilon\,\sin\,2\theta\\-8\sin\,\varepsilon\,\sin\,\theta\,\sin\,\phi-3\,\sin\,2\varepsilon\,\cos\,2\theta\}-\phi\{\cos\,\theta(3\,\sin\,\varepsilon\\-4\varepsilon\,\cos\,\varepsilon)+\tfrac{1}{3}\sin\,3\varepsilon\,\cos\,3\theta-2(2\theta'+\sin\,2\phi)\sin\,\varepsilon\,\sin\,\theta\}]\\-\phi\{\cos\,\theta(5\,\sin\,\varepsilon-4\varepsilon\,\cos\,\varepsilon)-\tfrac{1}{3}\sin\,3\varepsilon\,\cos\,3\theta\\-2(2\theta'+\sin\,2\phi)\sin\,\varepsilon\,\sin\,\theta\}\end{array}\right\}}{2\beta(2\phi^2+\phi\,\sin\,2\phi-4\,\sin^2\,\phi)+2\phi(2\phi+\sin\,2\phi)},$$

$$\frac{M_0}{R}=\frac{1}{\phi}\left[H_0(\phi-\sin\,\phi)-\frac{wR}{4}\{2\varepsilon(2+\cos\,2\varepsilon\,\cos\,2\theta)\right.$$

$$\left.+2\theta'\sin\,2\varepsilon\,\sin\,2\theta-8\,\sin\,\varepsilon\,\sin\,\theta\,\sin\,\phi-3\,\sin\,2\varepsilon\,\cos\,2\theta\}\right],$$

$$\frac{V_0}{2wR}=\frac{\left\{\begin{array}{l}\beta[(3+2\,\cos\,2\phi)\sin\,\varepsilon\,\sin\,\theta+\tfrac{1}{3}\sin\,3\varepsilon\,\sin\,3\theta\\-2\,\sin\,2\varepsilon\,\sin\,2\theta\,\cos\,\phi]+(1+2\,\cos\,2\phi)\sin\,\varepsilon\,\sin\,\theta\\-\tfrac{1}{3}\sin\,3\varepsilon\,\sin\,3\theta\end{array}\right\}}{2(\beta+1)(2\phi-\sin\,2\phi)}.$$

(12.24)

If the rib-shortening is neglected these become

$$\frac{H_0}{2wR} = \frac{\left\{\begin{array}{l}\sin\phi\{2\varepsilon(2+\cos 2\varepsilon\cos 2\theta)-2\theta\sin 2\varepsilon\sin 2\theta\\ -8\sin\varepsilon\sin\theta\sin\phi-3\sin 2\varepsilon\cos 2\theta\}-\phi\{\cos\theta(3\sin\varepsilon\\ -4\varepsilon\cos\varepsilon)+\tfrac{1}{3}\sin 3\varepsilon\cos 3\theta-2(2\theta'+\sin 2\phi)\sin\varepsilon\sin\theta\}\end{array}\right\}}{2(2\phi^2+\phi\sin 2\phi-4\sin^2\phi)},$$

$$\frac{M_0}{R} = \frac{1}{\phi}\left[\, H_0(\phi-\sin\phi)-\frac{wR}{4}\{2\varepsilon(2+\cos 2\varepsilon\cos 2\theta)\right.$$
$$\left. +2\theta'\sin 2\varepsilon\sin 2\theta-8\sin\varepsilon\sin\theta\sin\phi-3\sin 2\varepsilon\cos 2\theta\}\,\right],$$

$$\frac{V_0}{2wR} = \frac{\begin{array}{c}(3+2\cos 2\phi)\sin\varepsilon\sin\theta+\tfrac{1}{3}\sin 3\varepsilon\sin 3\theta\\ -2\sin 2\varepsilon\sin 2\theta\cos\phi\end{array}}{2(2\phi-\sin 2\phi)}.$$

$$\left.\begin{array}{r}\\ \\ \\ \\ \\ \\ \\ \\ \\ \\ \\ \end{array}\right\}(12.25)$$

Segmental arch rib loaded on half span. If the arch carries a uniformly distributed load over one-half of the span, $2\theta=2\varepsilon=\phi$ and these values must be substituted in the results previously obtained.

If the load acts vertically, equations (12.23) give

$$\frac{H_0}{2wR} = \frac{\sin\phi\{2\phi(2+\cos 2\phi)-3\sin 2\phi\}}{12(2\phi^2+\phi\sin 2\phi-4\sin^2\phi)},$$

$$\frac{M_0}{R} = \frac{1}{\phi}\{H_0(\phi-\sin\phi)-\frac{wR}{8}(2\phi-\sin 2\phi)\},$$

$$\frac{V_0}{2wR} = \frac{(2+\cos\phi)(1-\cos\phi)^2}{3(2\phi-\sin 2\phi)}.$$

$$\left.\begin{array}{r}\\ \\ \\ \\ \end{array}\right\}\quad .\quad .\quad .\quad (12.26)$$

If the load acts horizontally, equations (12.25) give

$$\frac{H_0}{2wR} = \frac{1}{2}-\frac{\sin\phi\{2\phi(2+\cos 2\phi)-3\sin 2\phi\}}{12(2\phi^2+\phi\sin 2\phi-4\sin^2\phi)},$$

$$\frac{M_0}{R} = \frac{1}{\phi}\left[\, H_0(\phi-\sin\phi)-\frac{wR}{8}(6\phi-8\sin\phi+\sin 2\phi)\right],$$

$$\frac{V_0}{2wR} = \frac{(1-\cos\phi)^3}{3(2\phi-\sin 2\phi)}.$$

$$\left.\begin{array}{r}\\ \\ \\ \\ \end{array}\right\}\quad .\quad (12.27)$$

12.8. The two-pinned segmental arch rib with a concentrated load.—If the arch rib shown in Fig. 12.10, carrying a vertical load 2P at θ from OC, is pinned to supports at A and B there is only one redundant element, which may conveniently be taken as the horizontal thrust, H_A, at a pin. The skew-symmetrical component of the load system, shown at (c) in the figure, gives no thrust and so H_A is found from the strain energy equation for the symmetrical arrangement (b) ; *i.e.*

$$\frac{dU}{dH_A} = \frac{2R}{EI}\int_0^\phi M\frac{dM}{dH_A}d\alpha+\frac{2R}{AE}\int_0^\phi T\frac{dT}{dH_A}d\alpha=0,$$

where α is measured from OC.

$$M=H_A R(\cos\alpha-\cos\phi)-PR(\sin\phi-\sin\alpha)+[PR(\sin\theta-\sin\alpha)]$$

and
$$T=H_A\cos\alpha+[P\sin\alpha].$$

The term in square brackets in M only occurs when $\alpha < \theta$, and that in T only when $\alpha > \theta$.

The solution of this equation gives

$$\frac{H_A}{2P} = \frac{\beta[4\cos\phi(\cos\theta + \theta\sin\theta - \cos\phi - \phi\sin\phi) + \cos 2\theta - \cos 2\phi] - \cos 2\theta + \cos 2\phi}{2\beta[4\phi - 3\sin 2\phi + 2\phi\cos 2\phi] + 2(2\phi + \sin 2\phi)} \quad . \quad (12.28)$$

If the rib-shortening due to the compression terms is neglected

$$\frac{H_A}{2P} = \frac{4\cos\phi(\cos\theta + \theta\sin\theta - \cos\phi - \phi\sin\phi) + \cos 2\theta - \cos 2\phi}{2(4\phi - 3\sin 2\phi + 2\phi\cos 2\phi)} \quad . \quad (12.29)$$

The vertical reactions, obtained from the sum of those arising from the systems (b) and (c) are

$$V_A = P(1 + \sin\theta\operatorname{cosec}\phi) ; \quad V_B = P(1 - \sin\theta\operatorname{cosec}\phi) \quad . \quad . \quad (12.30)$$

If the two-pinned rib carries a horizontal load 2P at θ from OC as shown in Fig. 12.11 the reactions are again found by superposition. From system (c) by taking moments about A,

$$V_B'' = -V_A'' = P(\cos\theta - \cos\phi)\operatorname{cosec}\phi,$$

and
$$-H_A'' = H_B'' = P.$$

Under the symmetrical loading of (b), there are no vertical reactions and the thrust H_A' is given by the strain energy equation of the vertical load case but with

$$M = H_A'R(\cos\alpha - \cos\phi) + [PR(\cos\alpha - \cos\theta)]$$

and $T = (P + H_A')\cos\alpha$ between 0 and θ, and $H_A'\cos\alpha$ between θ and ϕ. This leads to

$$\left.\begin{array}{l}\dfrac{H_A'}{2P} = -\dfrac{\beta[2\theta - \sin 2\theta + 4\cos\phi(\theta\cos\theta - \sin\theta)] + 2\theta + \sin 2\theta}{2\beta[4\phi - 3\sin 2\phi + 2\phi\cos 2\phi] + 2(2\phi + \sin 2\phi)}\\[1em]\text{or, when rib-shortening is neglected,}\\[0.5em]\dfrac{H_A'}{2P} = -\dfrac{2\theta - \sin 2\theta + 4\cos\phi(\theta\cos\theta - \sin\theta)}{2[4\phi - 3\sin 2\phi + 2\phi\cos 2\phi]}.\end{array}\right\} \quad . \quad . \quad (12.31)$$

Then, superposing the results from (b) and (c), the reactions are

$$\left.\begin{array}{l}\dfrac{H_A}{2P} = -\left[\dfrac{1}{2} + \dfrac{\beta[2\theta - \sin 2\theta + 4\cos\phi(\theta\cos\theta - \sin\theta)] + 2\theta + \sin 2\theta}{2\beta[4\phi - 3\sin 2\phi + 2\phi\cos 2\phi] + 2(2\phi + \sin 2\phi)}\right],\\[1em]\dfrac{H_B}{2P} = \dfrac{1}{2} - \dfrac{\beta[2\theta - \sin 2\theta + 4\cos\phi(\theta\cos\theta - \sin\theta)] + 2\theta + \sin 2\theta}{2\beta[4\phi - 3\sin 2\phi + 2\phi\cos 2\phi] + 2(2\phi + \sin 2\phi)},\\[1em]-\dfrac{V_A}{2P} = \dfrac{V_B}{2P} = \dfrac{1}{2}(\cos\theta - \cos\phi)\operatorname{cosec}\phi,\end{array}\right\} \quad (12.32)$$

with corresponding results when rib-shortening is neglected.

12.9. The two-pinned segmental arch rib with distributed load.—When the rib carries a uniformly distributed load over part of the span the value of H_A may either be found directly from the strain energy equations, as already illustrated in the treatment of the encastré rib, or more simply by integrating the value of H_A found for a point load in the previous paragraph over the range of the distributed load.

Rib with uniform load acting vertically.—As shown in Fig. 12.12 a load of intensity $2w$ acts over the section of the rib between θ_1 and θ_2 on one side only and this is split into symmetrical and skew-symmetrical systems. The supports A and B in Fig. 12.12 are now considered to be pinned instead of encastré.

At any point ψ from OC, where ψ lies between θ_1 and θ_2, the element of load acting vertically for cases (b) and (c) is $wR \cos \psi \delta\psi$, and the element of thrust, due to (b) only, is $\delta H_A = 2wR k_1 \cos \psi \delta\psi$, where k_1 represents the right-hand side of either equation (12.28) or (12.29) with ψ in place of θ throughout.

Then
$$H_A = 2wR \int_{\theta_1}^{\theta_2} k_1 \cos \psi \, d\psi$$

and this leads to

$$\frac{H_A}{2wR} = \frac{\left.\begin{array}{l}\beta[\tfrac{1}{3} \cos 3\theta \sin 3\varepsilon - \cos \theta \sin \varepsilon(3 + 6 \cos 2\phi + 4\phi \sin 2\phi) \\ + \cos \phi(3 \cos 2\theta \sin 2\varepsilon + 2\theta \sin 2\theta \sin 2\varepsilon - 2\varepsilon \cos 2\theta \cos 2\varepsilon \\ + 4\varepsilon)] - [\tfrac{1}{3} \cos 3\theta \sin 3\varepsilon + \cos \theta \sin \varepsilon(1 - \cos 2\phi)],\end{array}\right\}}{2\beta[4\phi - 3 \sin 2\phi + 2\phi \cos 2\phi] + 2(2\phi + \sin 2\phi)} \quad \text{. (12.33)}$$

also
$$\frac{V_A}{V_B} = 2wR \cos \theta \sin \varepsilon(1 \pm \sin \theta \cos \varepsilon \operatorname{cosec} \phi)$$

where, as in previous results, $2\theta = \theta_2 + \theta_1$ and $2\varepsilon = \theta_2 - \theta_1$. The total load on the rib is $4wR \cos \theta \sin \varepsilon$. In the limit when 2ε is made very small the result reduces to that for the point load.

Rib with uniform load acting horizontally.—This is shown in Fig. 12.13 for the encastré rib. The elementary load acting horizontally at ψ from OC for load cases (b) and (c) is now $wR \sin \psi \delta\psi$ and for load case (b), $\delta H_A' = 2wR k_2 \sin \psi \delta\psi$, where k_2 is the right-hand side of (12.31) with θ replaced by ψ.

Then
$$H_A' = 2wR \int_{\theta_1}^{\theta_2} k_2 \sin \psi \, d\psi,$$

which gives

$$\frac{H_A'}{2wR} = -\frac{\begin{array}{l}\beta[\tfrac{1}{3} \cos 3\theta \sin 3\varepsilon + 3 \cos \theta \sin \varepsilon + 4\theta \sin \theta \sin \varepsilon - 4\varepsilon \cos \theta \cos \varepsilon \\ + \cos \phi(3 \cos 2\theta \sin 2\varepsilon + 2\theta \sin 2\theta \sin 2\varepsilon - 2\varepsilon \cos 2\theta \cos 2\varepsilon - 4\varepsilon)] \\ + [-\tfrac{1}{3} \cos 3\theta \sin 3\varepsilon + 5 \cos \theta \sin \varepsilon + 4\theta \sin \theta \sin \varepsilon - 4\varepsilon \cos \theta \cos \varepsilon]\end{array}}{2\beta[4\phi - 3 \sin 2\phi + 2\phi \cos 2\phi] + 2[2\phi + \sin 2\phi]} \text{(12.34)}$$

There are no vertical reactions in the symmetrical loading case. For skew-symmetrical loading the horizontal reactions at A and B are each equal to the total load on one side of the arch, *i.e.* $2wR \sin \theta \sin \varepsilon$. The vertical reactions are found by taking moments about A, which gives

$$V_B'' = wR \operatorname{cosec} \phi \int_{\theta_1}^{\theta_2} (\cos \psi - \cos \phi) \sin \psi \, d\psi,$$

i.e.
$$V_B'' = 2wR \sin \theta \sin \varepsilon(\cos \theta \cos \varepsilon - \cos \phi) \operatorname{cosec} \phi.$$

The complete reactions are thus :

$$\left.\begin{array}{l}H_A = H_A' - 2wR \sin \theta \sin \varepsilon, \\ H_B = H_A' + 2wR \sin \theta \sin \varepsilon, \\ -V_A = V_B = 2wR \sin \theta \sin \varepsilon(\cos \theta \cos \varepsilon - \cos \phi) \operatorname{cosec} \phi.\end{array}\right\} \quad \text{. . (12.35)}$$

12.10. The parabolic-arc cantilever.—Fig. 12.14 represents a constant section, parabolic-arc cantilever, encastré at A, carrying in the first place a concentrated vertical load P at l from the free end and actions M_0, H_0 and V_0 as shown. The span AC is L and the rise of C above A is a. If axes are taken through C, x being measured horizontally from C towards A and y vertically downward as shown, the shape of the rib is given by

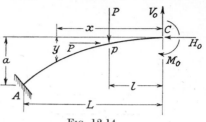

FIG. 12.14.

$$y = \frac{ax^2}{L^2}.$$

The bending moment at x from C is

$$M = M_0 - H_0 y - V_0 x + [P(x-l)],$$

the term in P being included only when $x-l$ is positive. The displacements of the end C are given as for the segmental-arc cantilever by

$$\mu_0 = \frac{\partial U}{\partial M_0} = \frac{1}{EI} \int M \frac{\partial M}{\partial M_0} ds,$$

$$v_0 = \frac{\partial U}{\partial V_0} = \frac{1}{EI} \int M \frac{\partial M}{\partial V_0} ds,$$

$$h_0 = \frac{\partial U}{\partial H_0} = \frac{1}{EI} \int M \frac{\partial M}{\partial H_0} ds,$$

if the terms due to rib-shortening are neglected. The integration of these expressions is cumbersome, but if it is assumed that the second moment of area of the rib varies according to the relation $I_x = I \frac{\delta s}{\delta x}$ where I is the value at C and $\frac{\delta s}{\delta x}$ in the limit is the secant of the angle of slope of the rib at any point x, the error introduced is very small for ribs of the usual proportion of rise to span and the integrations are considerably easier : this assumption will be adopted throughout the analysis which follows. Then

$$EI\mu_0 = \int_0^L \left(M_0 - \frac{H_0 ax^2}{L^2} - V_0 x \right) dx + P \int_l^L (x-l)dx,$$

$$EIv_0 = -\int_0^L \left(M_0 - \frac{H_0 ax^2}{L^2} - V_0 x \right) xdx - P \int_l^L (x-l)xdx,$$

$$\frac{EIL^2}{a} h_0 = -\int_0^L \left(M_0 - \frac{H_0 ax^2}{L^2} - V_0 x \right) x^2 dx - P \int_l^L (x-l)x^2 dx.$$

On integration these give

$$6EI\mu_0 = L(6M_0 - 2H_0 a - 3V_0 L) + 3P(L-l)^2,$$

$$-12EIv_0 = L^2(6M_0 - 3H_0 a - 4V_0 L) + 2P(L-l)^2(2L+l),$$

$$-\frac{60EIL^2 h_0}{a} = L^3(20M_0 - 12H_0 a - 15V_0 L) + 5P(L-l)^2(3L^2 + 2Ll + l^2).$$

(12.36)

10

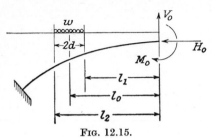

If the load is distributed over a section of the cantilever instead of concentrated, the terms in M_0, H_0 and V_0 in the above are unaltered but those in P must be modified. Suppose the cantilever carries a vertical load of intensity w uniformly distributed over the section between $x=l_1$ and $x=l_2$, as shown in Fig. 12.15, then at a distance x from C, between l_1 and l_2, the elementary load acting is $w\delta x$ and the contribution of this to the expression for $6EI\mu_0$ is $3w(L-x)^2\delta x$.

FIG. 12.15.

Hence the total contribution of the distributed load is $3w\int_{l_1}^{l_2}(L-x)^2dx$ and this replaces the term in P.

Similarly, the terms in P for the expressions defining v and h in (12.36) are replaced respectively by

$$2w\int_{l_1}^{l_2}(L-x)^2(2L+x)dx \quad \text{and} \quad 5w\int_{l_1}^{l_2}(L-x)^2(3L^2+2Lx+x^2)dx.$$

The displacements at the end of the cantilever under the actions of M_0, H_0, V_0 and the vertical load are then

$$\left.\begin{array}{l} 6EI\mu_0 = L(6M_0-2H_0a-3V_0L)+2wd\{3(L-l_0)^2+d^2\}, \\ -12EIv_0 = L^2(6M_0-3H_0a-4V_0L)+4wd\{(L-l_0)^2(2L+l_0)+d^2l_0\}, \\ -\dfrac{60EIL^2h_0}{a} = L^3(20M_0-12H_0a-15V_0L)+2wd\{5(L-l_0)^2(3L^2 \\ \qquad\qquad\qquad\qquad\qquad\qquad\qquad +2Ll_0+l_0^2)+d^2(10l_0^2+d^2)\}. \end{array}\right\} \quad (12.37)$$

In these expressions, $2l_0=l_1+l_2$ and $2d=l_2-l_1$, i.e. l_0 is the distance of the centre of the load from C and $2d$ is the length over which it acts.

The concentrated load P shown in Fig. 12.14 will now be supposed to act horizontally instead of vertically. The terms in M_0, H_0 and V_0 in the bending moment expression will be the same as before but that in P is $\dfrac{Pa}{L^2}(x^2-l^2)$. The expressions for the displacements of C are then

$$\left.\begin{array}{l} 6EI\mu_0 = L(6M_0-2H_0a-3V_0L)+\dfrac{2Pa}{L^2}(L-l)^2(L+2l), \\[2mm] -12EIv_0 = L^2(6M_0-3H_0a-4V_0L)+\dfrac{3Pa}{L^2}(L^2-l^2)^2, \\[2mm] -\dfrac{60EIL^2h_0}{a} = L^3(20M_0-12H_0a-15V_0L)+\dfrac{4Pa}{L^2}(L-l)^2(3L^3 \\ \qquad\qquad\qquad\qquad\qquad\qquad\qquad +6L^2l+4Ll^2+2l^3). \end{array}\right\} \quad (12.38)$$

If a horizontal load of intensity w acts in the same direction as P on the portion of the rib between $x=l_1$ and $x=l_2$ the elementary load at x from C is $w\delta y$ or $\dfrac{2awx}{L^2}\delta x$. The terms to replace those in P in equations (12.38) are therefore

$$\frac{4a^2w}{L^4}\int_{l_1}^{l_2}(L-x)^2(L+2x)xdx,$$

$$\frac{6a^2w}{L^4}\int_{l_1}^{l_2}(L^2-x^2)^2xdx \text{ and } \frac{8a^2w}{L^4}\int_{l_1}^{l_2}(L-x)^2(3L^3+6L^2x+4Lx^2+2x^3)xdx.$$

Integrating these and substituting l_0 and d as before,

$$\left.\begin{aligned}
6EI\mu_0&=L(6M_0-2H_0a-3V_0L)+\frac{8a^2wd}{L^4}\{l_0(L-l_0)^2(L+2l_0)\\
&\qquad\qquad -d^2(3Ll_0-4l_0^2-\tfrac{2}{5}d^2)\},\\
-12EIv_0&=L^2(6M_0-3H_0a-4V_0L)+\frac{4a^2wdl_0}{L^4}\{3(L^2-l_0^2)^2\\
&\qquad\qquad -d^2(6L^2-10l_0^2-3d^2)\},\\
-\frac{60EIL^2h_0}{a}&=L^3(20M_0-12H_0a-15V_0L)+\frac{16a^2wd}{L^4}\{l_0(L-l_0)^2(3L^3\\
&\quad +6L^2l_0+4Ll_0^2+2l_0^3)-d^2(5L^3l_0-10l_0^4-6l_0^2d^2-\tfrac{2}{7}d^4)\}.
\end{aligned}\right\} \quad (12.39)$$

The total load of intensity w is

$$\frac{2aw}{L^2}\int_{l_1}^{l_2}xdx=\frac{4awl_0d}{L^2}.$$

12.11. The encastré parabolic arch rib.—The results of the last paragraph may be used to obtain the general solutions for an encastré parabolic arch rib in the same way as for the segmental arch dealt with in paragraph 12.6.

Parabolic arch with vertical concentrated load.—When the arch rib of Fig. 12.10 is parabolic instead of segmental, the conditions under the symmetrical load system (b) are $\mu_0=0$, $h_0=0$ and $V_0=0$ and the first and last of equations (12.36) become

$$(6M_0-2H_0a)L+3P(L-l)^2=0,$$
$$4(5M_0-3H_0a)L^3+5P(L-l)^2(3L^2+2Ll+l^2)=0.$$

For the skew-symmetrical loading shown at (c) the conditions are $M_0=0$, $H_0=0$ and $v_0=0$ and the second equation of (12.36) becomes

$$4V_0L^3=2P(L-l)^2(2L+l).$$

The solution of these equations gives the resultant actions at the crown of the arch for a vertical load of $2P$ on the left half at l from the centre;

$$\left.\begin{aligned}
\frac{H_0}{2P}&=\frac{15(L^2-l^2)^2}{32aL^3},\\
\frac{M_0}{4PL}&=\frac{(L-l)^2(3L^2-10Ll-5l^2)}{64L^4},\\
\frac{V_0}{2P}&=\frac{(L-l)^2(2L+l)}{4L^3}.
\end{aligned}\right\} \quad . \quad . \quad . \quad . \quad (12.40)$$

In the special case of a parabolic rib carrying a central load $2P=W$, the span being $2L=S$, these results become

$$\frac{H_0}{W}=\frac{15}{64}\left(\frac{S}{a}\right) \; ; \; \frac{M_0}{WS}=-\frac{3}{64} \; ; \; \frac{V_0}{W}=\frac{1}{2}. \quad . \quad . \quad (12.41)$$

Parabolic arch with horizontal concentrated load.—This loading for the segmental arch is shown in Fig. 12.11. The conditions at the crown both for the symmetrical loading (b) and skew-symmetrical loading (c) are the same as for the previous case and substitution of these conditions in (12.38) gives the resultant actions at the crown for a horizontal load 2P on the left half at l from the centre,

$$\left.\begin{aligned}
\frac{H_0}{2P} &= \frac{(L-l)^2(2L^3+4L^2l+6Ll^2+3l^3)}{4L^5}, \\[2mm]
\frac{M_0}{4PL} &= \frac{a(L-l)^2(2L+l)l^2}{8L^6}, \\[2mm]
\frac{V_0}{2P} &= \frac{3a(L^2-l^2)^2}{8L^5}.
\end{aligned}\right\} \quad . \quad . \quad . \quad (12.42)$$

Parabolic arch with distributed vertical load.—The same conditions, when substituted in (12.37), give the resultant actions at the crown for a distributed load of intensity $2w$ acting over a distance $2d$ on the left half of the arch,

$$\left.\begin{aligned}
\frac{H_0}{4wd} &= \frac{15(L^2-l_0^2)^2-d^2(10L^2-30l_0^2-3d^2)}{32aL^3}, \\[2mm]
-\frac{M_0}{8wdL} &= \frac{(L-l_0)^2(3L^2-10Ll_0-5l_0^2)+d^2(6L^2-10l_0^2-d^2)}{64L^4}, \\[2mm]
\frac{V_0}{4wd} &= \frac{(L-l_0)^2(2L+l_0)+d^2l_0}{4L^3}.
\end{aligned}\right\} \quad . \quad (12.43)$$

In the limit when $l_0=l$, $d=0$ and $4wd=2P$ these reduce to the values for a vertical concentrated load given by equations (12.40).

If the arch carries a uniform vertical load of intensity w over the whole span, V_0 is zero and the other resultant actions at the crown are the same as if the arch carried a load of intensity $2w$ over one-half the span. Putting $2d=2l_0=L$ in the above equations, therefore, we obtain for the uniformly loaded parabolic rib $\dfrac{H_0}{2wL}=\dfrac{S}{8a}$ and $M_0=0$ which are well known results.

Parabolic arch with distributed horizontal load.—Using equations (12.39) and the same conditions at the crown as for other loadings, the resultant actions for a horizontal load of intensity $2w$ distributed over a part of the rib are

$$\left.\begin{aligned}
\frac{L^2H_0}{8awl_0d} &= \frac{1}{4l_0L^5}\left[l_0(L-l_0)^2(2L^3+4L^2l_0+6Ll_0^2+3l_0^3)\right. \\
&\qquad\qquad\left. -d^2l_0^2(10L^2-15l_0^2-9d^2)-d^4(L^2-\tfrac{3}{7}d^2)\right], \\[2mm]
\frac{LM_0}{16awl_0d} &= \frac{a}{8l_0L^6}\left[l_0^3(L-l_0)^2(2L+l_0)+d^2l_0(2L^3-6L^2l_0+5l_0^3)\right. \\
&\qquad\qquad\left. +d^4(3l_0^2-\tfrac{3}{5}L^2+\tfrac{1}{7}d^2)\right], \\[2mm]
\frac{L^2V_0}{8awl_0d} &= \frac{a}{8L^5}\left[3(L^2-l_0^2)^2-d^2(6L^2-10l_0^2-3d^2)\right].
\end{aligned}\right\} \quad (12.44)$$

The total horizontal load on the arch due to the distributed load of intensity $2w$ is $\dfrac{8awl_0d}{L^2}$ and putting this equal to 2P with $l_0=l$ and $d=0$ these equations reduce to those of (12.42).

12.12. Two-pinned parabolic arch rib.—It is convenient to make H_A, the thrust at the left-hand pin, the redundant element instead of the thrust at the crown, H_0, as has been done so far. Keeping the notation of the previous paragraph, the values of H_A for different load systems are readily found from the symmetrical load system by using the strain energy equation, and the vertical reactions at the supports from statical considerations.

Two-pinned arch with concentrated vertical load.—The corresponding case is shown in Fig. 12.10 for a segmental encastré arch. The value of H_A is obtained from $\dfrac{dU}{dH_A}=0$ for loading (b) where U is the strain energy of half the rib since the loading is symmetrical. The bending moment at x from the crown is

$$M=\frac{H_A a}{L^2}(L^2-x^2)-P(L-x)+[P(l-x)],$$

where the last term only appears when positive. The strain energy and static equations give

$$\left.\begin{aligned}
\frac{H_A}{2P}&=\frac{H_B}{2P}=\frac{5}{64aL^3}(5L^2-l^2)(L^2-l^2),\\
\frac{V_A}{2P}&=\frac{L+l}{2L}\;;\;\frac{V_B}{2P}=\frac{L-l}{2L}.
\end{aligned}\right\} \quad . \quad . \quad . \quad (12.45)$$

When the load 2P=W is at the centre of the span 2L=S, the vertical reactions are each $\dfrac{W}{2}$ and $\dfrac{H_A}{W}=\dfrac{25}{128}\left(\dfrac{S}{a}\right)$.

Two-pinned arch with concentrated horizontal load.—In this case, shown for the encastré segmental arch in Fig. 12.11, if H is the thrust at A or B for the symmetrical load system (b) we have

$$M=\frac{a}{L^2}\left\{H(L^2-x^2)+P(l^2-x^2)\right\}$$

and the same procedure as for the vertical load gives

$$\left.\begin{aligned}
\frac{H_A}{2P}&=-\frac{1}{2}\left\{1+\frac{l^3}{4L^5}(5L^2-l^2)\right\},\\
\frac{H_B}{2P}&=\frac{1}{2}\left\{1-\frac{l^3}{4L^5}(5L^2-l^2)\right\},\\
-\frac{V_A}{2P}&=\frac{V_B}{2P}=\frac{a(L^2-l^2)}{2L^3}.
\end{aligned}\right\} \quad . \quad . \quad . \quad (12.46)$$

Two-pinned arch with uniform vertical load on part of span.—This is shown for the encastré segmental arch in Fig. 12.12. If x is the distance of an elementary load $w\delta x$ from the crown, the value of H_A for the symmetrical load system is, from (12.45),

$$H_A=\frac{5w}{32aL^3}\int_{l_1}^{l_2}(5L^2-x^2)(L^2-x^2)dx.$$

On integration this gives

$$\frac{H_A}{4wd} = \frac{H_B}{4wd} = \frac{5}{64aL^3}\{(L^2-l_0^2)(5L^2-l_0^2)-d^2(2L^2-2l_0^2-\tfrac{1}{5}d^2)\}$$

also

$$\frac{V_A}{4wd} = \frac{L+l_0}{2L}\ ; \quad \frac{V_B}{4wd} = \frac{L-l_0}{2L}.$$

$$\left.\begin{array}{c}\end{array}\right\} \quad . \quad (12.47)$$

In the limit when $4wd=2P$, $d=0$ and $l_0=l$ this gives the same value as (12.45) for a vertical point load. If the arch carries a load of intensity $2w$ over one-half the span $l_0=d=L/2$ and H_A from the above equation is $\dfrac{wL^2}{2a}$ which is also the value of H_A when a uniform load of intensity w covers the whole span.

Two-pinned arch with uniform horizontal load on part of span.—For the symmetrical load system the elementary load at x from the crown is, as on p. 278, $\dfrac{2awx\delta x}{L^2}$ and so H_A for the whole load is, from (12.46),

$$H_A = -\frac{2aw}{L^2}\int_{l_1}^{l_2}\left\{1+\frac{x^3}{4L^5}(5L^2-x^2)\right\}xdx.$$

Hence

$$\frac{H_A L^2}{8awl_0 d} = -\frac{1}{2}\left[1+\frac{1}{4L^5 l_0}\left\{L^2(5l_0^4+10l_0^2 d^2+d^4)-(l_0^6+5l_0^4 d^2\right.\right.$$
$$\left.\left.+3l_0^2 d^4+\tfrac{1}{7}d^6)\right\}\right],$$

$$\frac{H_B L^2}{8awl_0 d} = \frac{1}{2}\left[1-\frac{1}{4L^5 l_0}\left\{L^2(5l_0^4+10l_0^2 d^2+d^4)-(l_0^6+5l_0^4 d^2\right.\right.$$
$$\left.\left.+3l_0^2 d^4+\tfrac{1}{7}d^6)\right\}\right],$$

$$-\frac{V_A}{8awl_0 d} = \frac{V_B}{8awl_0 d} = \frac{a}{2L^3}(L^2-l_0^2-d^2).$$

$$\left.\begin{array}{c}\end{array}\right\} \quad . \quad (12.48)$$

In the limit when d approaches zero, $\dfrac{8awl_0 d}{L^2}=2P$ and the results agree with those of (12.46).

12.13. Analysis of arch from strain equations.—Suppose Fig. 12.16 represents the centre line of a curved bar subjected to any system of bending moments. Let the bending on a small element of length δs at C turn this element through a small angle δi and cause the chord CB to move to CD.

If CF is the perpendicular from C to the chord AB

$$BCF = BDE = \alpha$$

where BE and ED are the component movements of B normal and parallel to AB.

Then

$$DE = BD\cos\alpha = \delta i BC\cos\alpha = y\delta i.$$

Also, applying the theory of bending for initially straight beams which is sufficiently accurate for the case of the arch rib,

$$\frac{\delta i}{\delta s} = \frac{M}{EI}$$

where M is the bending moment at C and EI is the flexural rigidity of the element δs.

Hence
$$DE = y\,\delta i = \frac{M}{EI}y\,\delta s$$

or, in the limit when δs is made infinitesimal, the total horizontal movement of B due to the bending of AB is
$$\int_A^B \frac{M}{EI_x}y\,ds.$$

In the two-pinned arch the total movement of B along AB is zero and so
$$\int \frac{My}{I_x}ds = 0.$$

But y is $\dfrac{dM}{dH}$ and the equation is identical with that obtained from considerations of strain energy.

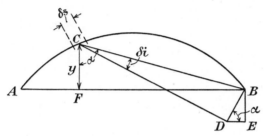

FIG. 12.16.

The vertical movement of B due to the rotation of a small element δs is
$$BE = BD \sin \alpha = \delta i BC \sin \alpha = x\,\delta i$$

and the argument follows exactly as for the horizontal component leading to the equation
$$\int \frac{M_x}{I_x}x\,ds = 0.$$

The third condition to be satisfied is that the change of slope at B must be zero.

The change of slope at B due to the rotation of the element δs is δi.

But
$$\delta i = \frac{M_x}{EI_x}\,\delta s,$$

therefore the total change of slope $= \displaystyle\int \frac{M_x}{EI_x}ds$

and since this is zero, we obtain the third equation
$$\int \frac{M_x}{I_x}ds = 0.$$

These are the same equations as obtained by an application of the strain energy method.

12.14. Two-pinned arch ; graphical solution of equations.—If the arch is of such a shape that the equations cannot readily be integrated, a graphical treatment is of general applicability. Suppose the arch shown in Fig. 12.17 is subjected to any system of loads indicated by W_1, W_2 and W_3 which act at distances a, b and c respectively from A. Let X be any point on the arch rib at a horizontal distance x from A and let the rise of the arch at this point be y.

Then the condition for the determination of H is

$$\frac{d\text{U}}{d\text{H}}=\frac{1}{\text{E}}\int\frac{\text{M}_x d\text{M}_x}{\text{I}_x d\text{H}}ds=0$$

where I_x is the second moment of area about the axis of bending at X and M_x is the bending moment at X.

Now $\text{M}_x=\text{H}y-\text{V}_\text{A}x+\text{W}_1(x-a)+\text{W}_2(x-b)+\text{W}_3(x-c)$, where the terms in brackets are only included if they are positive.

Also
$$\frac{d\text{M}_x}{d\text{H}}=y$$

and the equation for H takes the form

$$\int\left\{\frac{\text{H}y^2}{\text{I}_x}-\frac{\text{V}_\text{A}xy}{\text{I}_x}+\frac{\text{W}_1(x-a)y}{\text{I}_x}+\frac{\text{W}_2(x-b)y}{\text{I}_x}+\frac{\text{W}_3(x-c)y}{\text{I}_x}\right\}ds=0,$$

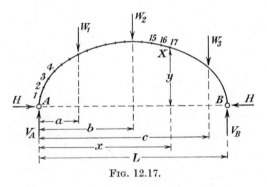

FIG. 12.17.

the limits of integration being from $x=0$ to $x=\text{L}$ for the terms in H and V_A and from $x=a$, b and c to $x=\text{L}$ for W_1, W_2 and W_3 respectively. Generally, direct integration will be impossible and we proceed as follows.

Divide the centre line of the rib into a number of parts ; it is preferable but not essential to make them equal. The greater the number the more accurate will be the final result. Let the length of any part be δs.

At each point obtained by this division, numbered 1, 2, etc., in the figure, measure the values of I_x, x and y and calculate the terms $\dfrac{y^2}{\text{I}_x}$, $\dfrac{xy}{\text{I}_x}$, $\dfrac{(x-a)y}{\text{I}_x}$, $\dfrac{(x-b)y}{\text{I}_x}$ and $\dfrac{(x-c)y}{\text{I}_x}$. Plot these values upon a base representing s at the appropriate distances from the origin. The area of the resulting curves will give the coefficients of H, V_A, W_1, W_2 and W_3 in the equation for H and if these areas are denoted by A_1, A_2 ... A_5, the equation is

$$\text{HA}_1-\text{V}_\text{A}\text{A}_2+\text{W}_1\text{A}_3+\text{W}_2\text{A}_4+\text{W}_3\text{A}_5=0.$$

Since V_A can be calculated from the moment equation about B the equation is soluble for H.

As an example this method will be applied to a segmental arch which can also be solved analytically.

Fig. 12.18 shows the centre line of the rib divided into 13 equal parts, the load acting between points 9 and 10. Since the second moment of area of the rib is constant it can be omitted from the equation.

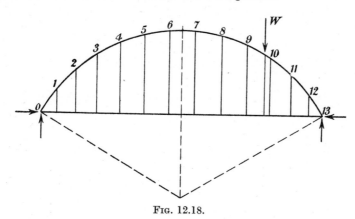

FIG. 12.18.

The values of x and y for each point and the terms calculated from them are given in Table 12.1. The scales used are immaterial provided they are the same throughout.

TABLE 12.1.

Point	x	y	y^2	xy	$(x-a)y$
0	0	0	0	0	—
1	7·2	11·2	123	80·5	—
2	17·0	21·0	441	357	—
3	28·0	29·0	841	812	—
4	40·0	35·5	1,260	1,420	—
5	52·5	40·0	1,600	2,100	—
6	66·0	42·0	1,764	2,772	—
7	79·5	42·0	1,764	3,340	—
8	92·6	40·0	1,600	3,704	—
9	105·6	35·5	1,260	3,750	—
9·78	115·0	31·0	961	3,565	0
10	117·5	29·0	841	3,410	72·5
11	128·6	21·0	441	2,700	286·0
12	138·0	11·2	123	1,530	257·5
13	146·0	0	0	0	0

The load does not come exactly at one of the divisions but at the point $x=115$, $y=31$. This is entered in the Table as 9·78, i.e. it is $9\cdot78\delta s$ from the origin.

The curves of y^2, xy and $(x-a)y$ are plotted on a base s in Fig. 12.19 and the proportional areas of these curves as measured are

$$A_1 = \int y^2 ds \quad = 6\cdot12,$$
$$A_2 = \int xy ds \quad = 13\cdot36,$$
$$A_3 = \int (x-a)y ds = 0\cdot35.$$

Hence

$$6\cdot12H - 13\cdot36V_A + \cdot35W = 0,$$

10*

and by taking moments about B we find

$$146V_A = 31W$$

or
$$V_A = \cdot 212W$$

$$\therefore \qquad 6 \cdot 12H - 2 \cdot 84W + \cdot 35W = 0$$

and
$$\frac{H}{W} = \cdot 406$$

which agrees with the value found by direct analysis.

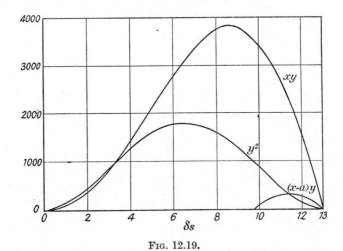

FIG. 12.19.

12.15. Resultant actions in two-pinned arch.—Having calculated the value of the horizontal thrust as shown in previous paragraphs, the bending moment, normal thrust and transverse shearing force can be found for all points on the arch rib.

Fig. 12.20 represents a two-pinned arch carrying loads W_1 and W_2 tons at points C and D which are at distances a and b respectively from A.

The bending moment at X, which is x from A, is

$$M_x = Hy - \{V_A x - W_1(x-a) - W_2(x-b)\},$$

where the terms $(x-a)$, $(x-b)$ only appear when $x > a$ and $x > b$ respectively.

Hy represents the bending moment due to H and the remainder of the expression that upon a beam of span AB loaded identically with the rib. The curve of Hy is, to an appropriate scale, the centre line of the rib : thus, if the true rise of the arch at the centre is d inches and the scale of the drawing of the rib is $\frac{1}{n}$ then Hd inch-tons is represented by $\frac{d}{n}$ inches and the drawing of the rib is the Hy curve to a scale of 1 inch $= Hn$ inch-tons. The " beam " bending moment diagram $acdb$ is plotted to the same scale, as shown in Fig. 12.20 and the bending moment at any point on the rib is then given by the intercept between the two curves.

If the arch had been made in the shape of the beam bending moment diagram, in this case if the centre line had followed the line $acdb$, there would clearly be no bending moment at any point in the arch. $acdb$ is known as the linear arch.

The normal thrust and transverse shearing force at any point in the rib may be found by resolving the forces to the right or left of the section in directions along and normal to the tangent to the rib at that point. Thus, at X, in Fig. 12.20, if the tangent makes an angle α to the horizontal,

the resultant vertical shearing force at $X = V_B - W_2$
and the resultant horizontal force $\quad = H.$

Resolving along and normal to the tangent we obtain

normal thrust at X $\quad\quad\quad = (V_B - W_2) \sin \alpha + H \cos \alpha$
and transverse shearing force $\quad = (V_B - W_2) \cos \alpha - H \sin \alpha.$

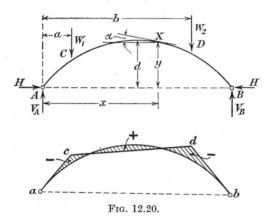

Fig. 12.20.

The linear arch may be considered from another point of view. If the loads on the arch were reversed in direction and carried on a flexible cable, this cable would take the form of the linear arch provided the constant horizontal tension in it were equal to H. Such a cable would be stable since every section would be in tension. Theoretically therefore when the loads act in their original directions, struts ac, cd and db pinned together at their ends would support the loads; the resulting arrangement would, however, obviously be unstable. For every load system there are an unlimited number of possible linear arches depending on the polar distance used in drawing the funicular polygon, $i.e.$ on the value of H. The correct linear arch is that having the true value of H for the real arch. Having obtained the correct linear arch we know the direction, point of application and magnitude of the thrust at any section of the true arch. Its distance from the centre line of the real arch is the eccentricity of loading at that section and the bending moment there is the product of this eccentricity and the thrust.

The linear arch, or line of thrust as it is often called, is much used in the design and analysis of masonry arches.

12.16. The braced arch.—The arches considered so far have been of the rib type, but most large arches are braced. They may be three-pinned, two-pinned or fixed ended.

The three-pinned arch shown in Fig. 12.21 is statically determinate as regards reactive forces and can be dealt with in the way described for the arch rib. Thus, for a load W acting as shown the reactions can be found by joining BC and producing the line to cut the line of action of W at D and then drawing DA. The vertical components of the reactions at A and B are known from the equation of moments about A, and since AD and BC give the lines of their action, R_A and R_B are readily calculated from the geometry of the figure as in paragraph 12.3.

The arch can now be treated like any other framed structure and the forces in all the bars found by means of a stress diagram, by the method of sections or by means of tension coefficients.

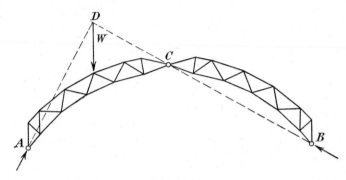

FIG. 12.21.

The two-pinned braced arch has one degree of redundancy due to its method of support; the redundant element may conveniently be taken to be the horizontal thrust at one pin.

In Fig. 12.22 is shown a two-pinned spandrel-braced arch. If the pin at B were replaced by a frictionless bearing the structure would be a just-stiff braced girder and could be analysed for any system of loads by the usual

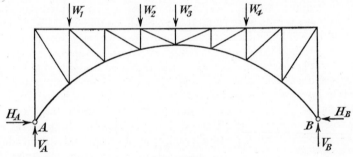

FIG. 12.22.

methods. The introduction of the pin at B, however, gives a horizontal constraint H_B and the stress analysis requires strain energy or other equivalent methods. H_B may be considered either as an internal redundancy, in which case the method of minimum strain energy demands that $\dfrac{dU}{dH_B}=0$, or as an external force which prevents movement of the pin in a horizontal direction : the first theorem of Castigliano then gives the same equation.

The forces in all the bars of the arch must first be found in terms of the known external loads $W_1 \ldots W_4$ and the unknown H_B.

This is best done by drawing one stress diagram for the external load system and another for H_B.

The force in any member is then of the form

$$P_0 = f(W) + \alpha H_B$$

where $f(W)$ is the force arising from the loads $W_1 \ldots W_4$ and αH_B is that from H_B.   If u is the strain energy in that bar, then

$$\frac{du}{dH_B} = \frac{P_0 L}{AE} \frac{dP_0}{dH_B}$$

where L is the length of the bar and A its cross-sectional area,

and
$$\frac{dU}{dH_B} = \sum \frac{P_0 L}{AE} \frac{dP_0}{dH_B} = 0.$$

The various terms in this equation should be tabulated as previously explained in Chapter 6 and the resulting equation solved for H_B.   Substitution of the value of H_B in the expressions for P_0 then gives the stresses in all members of the arch.

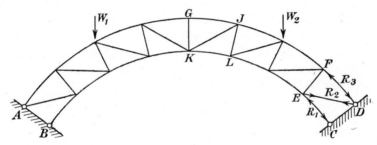

FIG. 12.23.

Fig. 12.23 shows a braced arch which is fixed to pins at A, B, C and D. If the bars EC, ED and FD are removed the structure remaining is a cantilever which can be analysed without difficulty.

If the forces in the three bars specified above are denoted by R_1, R_2 and R_3 respectively the following conditions must be satisfied :

$$\frac{\partial U}{\partial R_1} = \sum \frac{P_0 L}{AE} \frac{\partial P_0}{\partial R_1} = 0,$$

$$\frac{\partial U}{\partial R_2} = \sum \frac{P_0 L}{AE} \frac{\partial P_0}{\partial R_2} = 0,$$

$$\frac{\partial U}{\partial R_3} = \sum \frac{P_0 L}{AE} \frac{\partial P_0}{\partial R_3} = 0.$$

A stress diagram is drawn for the external loads acting together, and one for each of the redundancies R_1, R_2 and R_3 acting separately.   The equations derived from the above conditions can then be formed and their simultaneous solution gives the values of R_1, R_2 and R_3.

If it is more convenient, any three members such as GJ, JK and KL may be treated as redundancies ; the arch is then divided into two cantilever portions and each requires the separate diagrams for external loads, R_1, R_2 and R_3 to be drawn.   The three equations corresponding to the above conditions are then formed as before.

12.17. Temperature stresses in an arch.—The effect of a change of temperature upon any structure is to cause alterations in the lengths of the members composing it. If the structure, even when redundant, is made of the same material throughout and has just the essential number of reactive forces, such changes in length result only in a slight change in the geometry of the truss without the introduction of extra stresses. If, however, the structure has redundant reactive forces which restrain free movement the temperature change causes extra stresses in the bars of the truss.

Consider, for example, the effect of a rise in temperature on a curved beam pinned at one end and resting on a frictionless roller at the other. The dimensions of the member increase and since it is free to move on the roller the result is merely a proportional increase in all dimensions of the beam. If, however, it is fixed to pins at both ends, movement is prevented and the resulting thrust from the pins induces stresses throughout the member.

The result is the same as if free movement were allowed and the end of the rib then forced back into its original position by a horizontal force.

Suppose a two-pinned arch rib of span L is subjected to a temperature rise $t°$.

Then, if it were free to expand, the new span would be $L(1+\beta t)$ where β is the coefficient of expansion of the material. Now assume that a horizontal force H is applied to the free end of sufficient amount to force it back through the distance $L\beta t$.

The first theorem of Castigliano gives

$$\text{movement of H horizontally} = \frac{dU}{dH} = L\beta t$$

or, if we neglect all effects except bending of the rib,

$$\int \frac{M}{EI} \frac{dM}{dH} ds = L\beta t.$$

But $M = Hy$ so

$$\int \frac{Hy^2}{EI} ds = L\beta t,$$

the integration extending round the whole rib.

This equation can be solved by one of the methods already described and H evaluated.

Example.—In a two-pinned parabolic arch rib the second moment of area at any section is $I_0 \sec \alpha$ where I_0 is the value at the crown and α is the slope of the rib at the section. Find the increase in the horizontal thrust per degree rise of temperature.

Let span $= L$,
rise of rib at centre $= d$,
coefficient of expansion $= \beta$.

If one pin were released the increase in span due to a unit rise of temperature would be $L\beta$.

If the origin be taken at the centre of the span the rise of the arch at x from the origin is

$$y = d\left(1 - \frac{4x^2}{L^2}\right)$$

and

$$M_x = Hd\left(1 - \frac{4x^2}{L^2}\right)$$

also
$$\frac{d\mathrm{M}_x}{d\mathrm{H}}=d\left(1-\frac{4x^2}{\mathrm{L}^2}\right)$$

$\therefore$
$$\frac{d\mathrm{U}}{d\mathrm{H}}=\frac{2}{\mathrm{E}}\int_{x=0}^{x=\frac{\mathrm{L}}{2}}\frac{\mathrm{H}d^2}{\mathrm{I}_x}\left(1-\frac{4x^2}{\mathrm{L}^2}\right)^2ds=\mathrm{L}\beta.$$

But
$$\mathrm{I}_x=\mathrm{I}_0\frac{ds}{dx}$$

$\therefore$
$$\frac{2\mathrm{H}d^2}{\mathrm{EI}_0}\int_0^{\frac{\mathrm{L}}{2}}\left(1-\frac{4x^2}{\mathrm{L}^2}\right)^2dx=\mathrm{L}\beta$$

which gives
$$\mathrm{H}=\frac{15\mathrm{EI}_0\beta}{8d^2}.$$

12.18. The circular ring.—The circular ring is a common unit in engineering construction. It may occur as a simple link, a connexion for a number of load-carrying members, or as the rim of a wheel, and the analysis of the stresses to which it is subjected under any system of loading is a matter of importance. Usually a knowledge of the exact distribution of stress across any section is not necessary and this is fortunate since the problem is one of considerable complexity, but it is essential to be able to calculate the resultant actions at any section and from them obtain reasonable estimates of the maximum stresses. This is relatively simple, an application of strain energy methods being sufficient in the simpler cases for the first step and Winkler's theory of the bending of curved bars adequate for the calculation of stresses.

If a ring under any system of loads is cut at one section it will still be able to carry the loads, provided the material is not overstressed, and the resultant actions at any other section can be calculated straightforwardly. To restore the ring to its original condition of stress, however, it is necessary to apply a moment and a force to each side of the cut section, and these, together with the inclination of the force to the section are statically indeterminate and must be calculated by reference to the elastic properties of the ring. It is convenient to replace the unknown force and its line of action by two component and independent forces which are usually taken as tangential and radial to the ring. These and the moment then constitute the three redundant actions to be determined by strain energy analysis or an equivalent method. The first example is that of a ring of uniform cross-section in equilibrium under the action of three parallel forces as shown in Fig. 12.24.

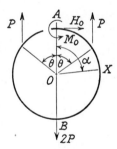

Fig. 12.24.

Two forces each of magnitude P act at θ on either side of the axis AB of the ring and are equilibrated by 2P at B. If the ring is supposed to be cut at A, the resultant actions necessary to restore the original conditions are the moment M_0 and the tangential thrust H_0. Considerations of symmetry show that the radial shearing force at A is zero.

At any point X on the ring at an angular distance α from OA the bending moment is

$$\mathrm{M}=\mathrm{M}_0-\mathrm{H}_0\mathrm{R}(1-\cos\alpha)-[\mathrm{PR}(\sin\alpha-\sin\theta)],$$

the term in P only occurring when α is greater than θ. If the effects of tangential compressive stresses and radial shearing stresses are neglected and the strain energy of a curved bar is assumed to be the same as for a straight one, the equations for the determination of M_0 and H_0 are

$$\frac{\partial U}{\partial M_0} = \frac{2}{EI} \int_0^\pi M \frac{\partial M}{\partial M_0} ds = 0,$$

$$\frac{\partial U}{\partial H_0} = \frac{2}{EI} \int_0^\pi M \frac{\partial M}{\partial H_0} ds = 0,$$

where U is the total strain energy in the ring.

On substituting for M and its derivatives these equations become

$$\int_0^\pi \{M_0 - H_0 R(1 - \cos \alpha)\} d\alpha - PR \int_\theta^\pi (\sin \alpha - \sin \theta) d\alpha = 0$$

$$\int_0^\pi \{M_0 - H_0 R(1 - \cos \alpha)\}(1 - \cos \alpha) d\alpha - PR \int_\theta^\pi (\sin \alpha - \sin \theta)(1 - \cos \alpha) d\alpha = 0.$$

It should be noted that the first of these equations may be subtracted from the second so that the terms from the bending moment equation in the latter need only be multiplied by $\cos \alpha$ instead of $(1 - \cos \alpha)$ with a consequent reduction of work. The resulting equations are

$$\pi(M_0 - RH_0) - PR\{1 + \cos \theta - (\pi - \theta) \sin \theta\} = 0$$

$$2\pi RH_0 - PR(1 - \cos 2\theta) = 0.$$

From these

$$\left. \begin{array}{l} H_0 = \dfrac{P}{\pi} \sin^2 \theta \\[3mm] M_0 = \dfrac{PR}{\pi}\{\sin^2 \theta + f_1(\theta)\} \end{array} \right\} \quad . \quad . \quad . \quad . \quad (12.49)$$

and

where

$$f_1(\theta) = 1 + \cos \theta - (\pi - \theta) \sin \theta. \quad . \quad . \quad . \quad (12.50)$$

When $\theta = 0$, *i.e.* when the ring is subjected to a diametral pull 2P, these become

$$\left. \begin{array}{l} H_0 = 0 \\ M_0 = 2PR/\pi. \end{array} \right\} \quad . \quad . \quad . \quad . \quad (12.51)$$

In Fig. 12.25 the vertical forces of this example are replaced by a pair of horizontal forces, each equal to P and acting at θ on either side of the axis of symmetry.

The bending moment at X is now

$$M = M_0 - H_0 R(1 - \cos \alpha) - [PR(\cos \theta - \cos \alpha)]$$

and the strain energy equations $\dfrac{\partial U}{\partial M_0} = \dfrac{\partial U}{\partial H_0} = 0$ lead to

$$\int_0^\pi \{M_0 - H_0 R(1 - \cos \alpha)\} d\alpha - PR \int_\theta^\pi (\cos \theta - \cos \alpha) d\alpha = 0$$

$$\int_0^\pi \{M_0 - H_0 R(1 - \cos \alpha)\} \cos \alpha \, d\alpha - PR \int_\theta^\pi (\cos \theta - \cos \alpha) \cos \alpha \, d\alpha = 0$$

which on integration and solution give

$$H_0 = -\frac{P}{\pi}f_2(\theta)$$

$$M_0 = -\frac{PR}{\pi}\{f_2(\theta) - f_3(\theta)\}$$
. . . . (12.52)

where $\qquad f_2(\theta) = \pi - \theta + \tfrac{1}{2}\sin 2\theta$

and $\qquad f_3(\theta) = \sin \theta + (\pi - \theta)\cos \theta.$
. . . . (12.53)

Since any force can be resolved into vertical and horizontal components the foregoing results provide solutions for any symmetrical load system. Each load is resolved and the contributions made by the components to the values of M_0 and H_0 are calculated separately. These are then added to obtain the effect of each pair of loads. If there are a number of symmetrically disposed pairs of loads acting on the ring the algebraic sum of the values of M_0 and H_0 for each separate pair gives the total resultant actions at A.

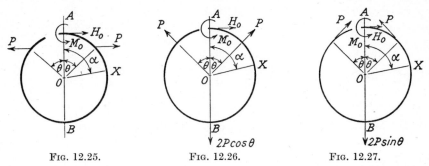

FIG. 12.25.   FIG. 12.26.   FIG. 12.27.

It is sometimes convenient to resolve the loads radially and tangentially and Fig. 12.26 shows a ring loaded with a pair of radial loads each of magnitude P, acting at θ from the axis of symmetry. These are balanced by a vertical load at the point B.

The bending moment at α from OA is

$$M = M_0 - H_0 R(1 - \cos \alpha) - [PR \sin (\alpha - \theta)]$$

and the equations derived from $\dfrac{\partial U}{\partial M_0} = \dfrac{\partial U}{\partial H_0} = 0$ are

$$\int_0^\pi \{M_0 - H_0 R(1 - \cos \alpha)\}d\alpha - PR\int_\theta^\pi \sin (\alpha - \theta)d\alpha = 0$$

$$\int_0^\pi \{M_0 - H_0 R(1 - \cos \alpha)\} \cos \alpha d\alpha - PR\int_\theta^\pi \sin (\alpha - \theta)\cos \alpha d\alpha = 0$$

which on integration and solution give

$$H_0 = -\frac{P}{\pi}(\pi - \theta)\sin \theta$$

$$M_0 = \frac{PR}{\pi}f_1(\theta).$$
. . . . . (12.54)

If the radial loads of this case are replaced by tangential loads as shown in Fig. 12.27, the bending moment at α from OA is

$$M = M_0 - H_0 R(1 - \cos \alpha) + [PR\{1 - \cos (\alpha - \theta)\}],$$

and the strain energy equations give

$$\int_0^\pi \{M_0 - H_0 R(1 - \cos \alpha)\}d\alpha + PR\int_\theta^\pi \{1 - \cos (\alpha - \theta)\}d\alpha = 0$$

$$\int_0^\pi \{M_0 - H_0 R(1 - \cos \alpha)\} \cos \alpha d\alpha + PR\int_\theta^\pi \{1 - \cos (\alpha - \theta)\} \cos \alpha d\alpha = 0$$

which lead to

$$\left.\begin{aligned} H_0 &= \frac{P}{\pi}f_3(\theta) \\ M_0 &= \frac{PR}{\pi}\{f_3(\theta) + \sin \theta - (\pi - \theta)\}. \end{aligned}\right\} \qquad \ldots \quad (12.55)$$

Alternatively the forces P in Fig. 12.26 can be resolved into components $P \cos \theta$ and $P \sin \theta$ acting parallel to and at right angles to the axis of symmetry, while the forces of Fig. 12.27 have resolved components $P \sin \theta$ and $-P \cos \theta$ parallel to and at right angles to the same axes. The resultant actions at A for the separate components can in either case be calculated

from equations (12.49) and (12.52) and superposed to obtain the results given in (12.54) and (12.55).

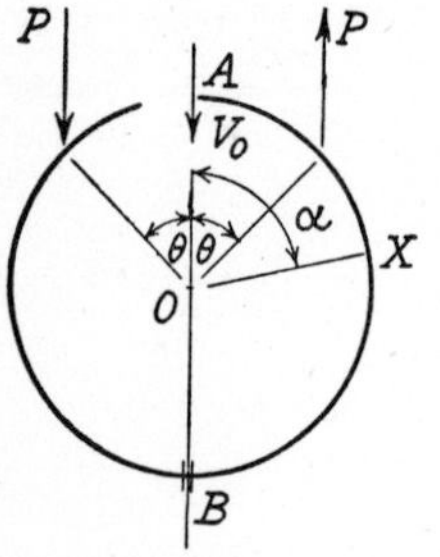

The loadings so far considered have been symmetrical about one axis of the ring. It is desirable to derive the corresponding expressions for skew-symmetrical loading since the superposition of appropriate symmetrical and skew-symmetrical systems enables any type of loading to be dealt with readily.

Fig 12.28 shows loads P acting at θ from the axis of symmetry and parallel to that axis, but the loads now

FIG. 12.28.

act in opposite directions, producing a couple on the ring which is assumed to be held rigidly at section B. From the conditions of skew-symmetry it is clear that there will be neither a bending moment nor a tangential force in the ring at A, but there will be a radial shearing force V_0 the magnitude of which can be found from the equation $\dfrac{dU}{dV_0} = 0$.

The bending moment at α from OA is

$$M = V_0 R \sin \alpha - [PR(\sin \alpha - \sin \theta)]$$

and

$$\frac{1}{2}\frac{dU}{dV_0} = \frac{V_0 R^3}{EI}\int_0^\pi \sin^2 \alpha d\alpha - \frac{PR^3}{EI}\int_\theta^\pi (\sin \alpha - \sin \theta) \sin \alpha d\alpha = 0$$

which gives, on reduction,

$$V_0 = \frac{P}{\pi}f_4(\theta) \quad . \quad . \quad . \quad . \quad . \quad . \quad (12.56)$$

where $\qquad f_4(\theta) = \pi - \theta - \sin \theta(2 + \cos \theta)$.

If the loads are perpendicular to the axis of symmetry as shown in Fig. 12.29, the bending moment and thrust at A are again zero.

The bending moment at α from OA is

$$M = V_0 R \sin \alpha - [PR(\cos \theta - \cos \alpha)]$$

and

$$\frac{1}{2}\frac{dU}{dV_0}=\frac{V_0R^3}{EI}\int_0^{\pi}\sin^2\alpha d\alpha-\frac{PR^3}{EI}\int_{\theta}^{\pi}(\cos\theta-\cos\alpha)\sin\alpha d\alpha=0.$$

From this equation

$$V_0=\frac{P}{\pi}(1+\cos\theta)^2. \quad . \quad . \quad . \quad . \quad . \quad (12.57)$$

The case of skew-symmetrical radial loading is shown in Fig. 12.30 and again V_0 is the only internal action at A.

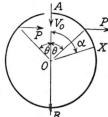  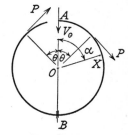

FIG. 12.29.　　　　　　FIG. 12.30.　　　　　　FIG. 12.31.

The bending moment at α from OA is

$$M=V_0R\sin\alpha-[PR\sin(\alpha-\theta)]$$

and

$$\frac{1}{2}\frac{dU}{dV_0}=\frac{V_0R^3}{EI}\int_0^{\pi}\sin^2\alpha d\alpha-\frac{PR^3}{EI}\int_{\theta}^{\pi}\sin(\alpha-\theta)\sin\alpha d\alpha=0$$

which gives, on reduction,

$$V_0=\frac{P}{\pi}\{(\pi-\theta)\cos\theta+\sin\theta\}=\frac{P}{\pi}f_3(\theta) \quad . \quad . \quad . \quad (12.58)$$

Tangential loading of skew-symmetrical type is shown in Fig. 12.31. As in the other cases there is neither bending moment nor thrust at A and so

$$M=V_0R\sin\alpha-[PR\{1-\cos(\alpha-\theta)\}]$$

while

$$\frac{1}{2}\frac{dU}{dV_0}=\frac{V_0R^3}{EI}\int_0^{\pi}\sin^2\alpha d\alpha-\frac{PR^3}{EI}\int_{\theta}^{\pi}\{1-\cos(\alpha-\theta)\}\sin\alpha d\alpha=0$$

which gives, on reduction,

$$V_0=\frac{P}{\pi}\{2(1+\cos\theta)-(\pi-\theta)\sin\theta\} \quad . \quad . \quad . \quad (12.59)$$

$$=\frac{P}{\pi}\{1+\cos\theta+f_1(\theta)\}.$$

As with symmetrical loading, (12.58) and (12.59) may also be obtained by resolving the radial and tangential forces into components acting parallel to and at right angles to the axis of skew-symmetry, and superposing the results obtained from equations (12.56) and (12.57).

For ease of reference the values of the resultant actions for all loadings are presented in Table 12.2, and the values of the functions $f_1(\theta)$, etc., are given in Table 12.3 on page 297. By suitable superposition of these results the resultant actions for any load system can be obtained.

TABLE 12.2.

INTERNAL ACTIONS IN LOADED RING.

Loading	$\pi H_0/P$	$\pi M_0/PR$	$\pi V_0/P$
Symmetrical, vertical	$\sin^2\theta$	$\sin^2\theta + f_1(\theta)$	—
Symmetrical, horizontal	$-f_2(\theta)$	$f_3(\theta) - f_2(\theta)$	—
Symmetrical, radial	$-(\pi-\theta)\sin\theta$	$f_1(\theta)$	—
Symmetrical, tangential	$f_3(\theta)$	$f_3(\theta) + \sin\theta - (\pi-\theta)$	—
Skew-symmetrical, vertical	—	—	$f_4(\theta)$
Skew-symmetrical, horizontal	—	—	$(1+\cos\theta)^2$
Skew-symmetrical, radial	—	—	$f_3(\theta)$
Skew-symmetrical, tangential	—	—	$1+\cos\theta + f_1(\theta)$

As an example, consider the ring shown in Fig. 12.32 (*a*) which is in equilibrium under the three loads $2P_1$, $2P_2$ and $2P_3$. The last two are tangential to the ring but $2P_1$ is assumed to act in any direction. It is convenient to take an axis AOB parallel to the line of action of $2P_1$, but this is not essential since any load can be resolved either radially and tangentially or along and perpendicular to any arbitrarily chosen axis.

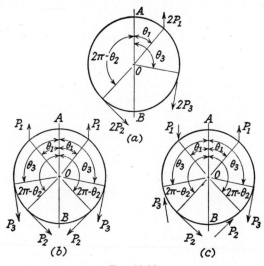

FIG. 12.32.

The load $2P_1$ is replaced by the symmetrical loads in Fig. 12.32 (*b*) and the skew-symmetrical loads P_1 shown at (*c*). Similarly, $2P_2$ and $2P_3$ are split into symmetrical and skew-symmetrical components as shown at (*b*) and (*c*). When the load system (*b*) is superposed on (*c*) we obtain the specified load on the ring. M_0 and H_0 are calculated from the appropriate expressions in Table 12.2 for the symmetrical loadings P_1, P_2 and P_3 and their sums give the total values of the internal bending moment and thrust respectively at A. V_0 is calculated for each skew-symmetrical loading from the expression in the same Table and the results added to obtain the total value of the radial shearing force at A.

The bending moment, tangential thrust and radial shearing force at any point in the ring are then obtained quite simply.

TABLE 12.3.—FUNCTIONS FOR LOADED RINGS

$f_1(\theta)=1+\cos\theta-(\pi-\theta)\sin\theta$ $\qquad$ $f_3(\theta)=\sin\theta+(\pi-\theta)\cos\theta$
$f_2(\theta)=\pi-\theta+\frac{1}{2}\sin 2\theta$ $\qquad$ $f_4(\theta)=\pi-\theta-(2+\cos\theta)\sin\theta$

$\theta°$	$f_1(\theta)$	$f_2(\theta)$	$f_3(\theta)$	$f_4(\theta)$	$\theta°$	$f_1(\theta)$	$f_2(\theta)$	$f_3(\theta)$	$f_4(\theta)$
0	2·0	3·1416	3·1416	3·1416	92	−0·5699	1·5010	0·9458	−0·4280
2	1·8910	3·1416	3·1397	3·0020	94	−0·5671	1·4314	0·8929	−0·4246
4	1·7833	3·1414	3·1340	2·8627	96	−0·5626	1·3621	0·8413	−0·4190
6	1·6771	3·1408	3·1248	2·7239	98	−0·5564	1·2934	0·7911	−0·4115
8	1·5725	3·1398	3·1119	2·5858	100	−0·5487	1·2253	0·7423	−0·4023
10	1·4696	3·1381	3·0956	2·4488	102	−0·5395	1·1580	0·6951	−0·3916
12	1·3685	3·1355	3·0760	2·3130	104	−0·5290	1·0917	0·6494	−0·3794
14	1·2694	3·1320	3·0531	2·1787	106	−0·5171	1·0266	0·6053	−0·3660
16	1·1723	3·1273	3·0271	2·0461	108	−0·5041	0·9627	0·5627	−0·3516
18	1·0773	3·1213	2·9981	1·9155	110	−0·4901	0·9003	0·5218	−0·3363
20	0·9846	3·1139	2·9661	1·7871	112	−0·4750	0·8395	0·4826	−0·3202
22	0·8942	3·1049	2·9314	1·6611	114	−0·4591	0·7803	0·4450	−0·3036
24	0·8061	3·0943	2·8941	1·5377	116	−0·4423	0·7230	0·4091	−0·2866
26	0·7205	3·0818	2·8542	1·4171	118	−0·4249	0·6676	0·3749	−0·2693
28	0·6375	3·0674	2·8118	1·2994	120	−0·4069	0·6142	0·3424	−0·2518
30	0·5570	3·0510	2·7673	1·1850	122	−0·3884	0·5629	0·3116	−0·2344
32	0·4792	3·0325	2·7205	1·0739	124	−0·3695	0·5138	0·2825	−0·2171
34	0·4041	3·0118	2·6717	0·9662	126	−0·3503	0·4670	0·2550	−0·2000
36	0·3318	2·9888	2·6211	0·8622	128	−0·3308	0·4224	0·2293	−0·1833
38	0·2622	2·9635	2·5686	0·7619	130	−0·3113	0·3803	0·2051	−0·1670
40	0·1954	2·9359	2·5146	0·6655	132	−0·2917	0·3405	0·1826	−0·1513
42	0·1315	2·9058	2·4590	0·5730	134	−0·2722	0·3032	0·1616	−0·1361
44	0·0705	2·8733	2·4021	0·4846	136	−0·2528	0·2682	0·1422	−0·1217
46	0·0123	2·8384	2·3440	0·4004	138	−0·2336	0·2358	0·1244	−0·1080
48	−0·0430	2·8011	2·2847	0·3203	140	−0·2148	0·2057	0·1080	−0·0950
50	−0·0953	2·7614	2·2245	0·2444	142	−0·1963	0·1781	0·0930	−0·0830
52	−0·1448	2·7192	2·1634	0·1729	144	−0·1783	0·1528	0·0795	−0·0717
54	−0·1913	2·6746	2·1016	0·1056	146	−0·1609	0·1298	0·0672	−0·0614
56	−0·2350	2·6278	2·0392	0·0425	148	−0·1440	0·1091	0·0563	−0·0519
58	−0·2758	2·5787	1·9764	−0·0162	150	−0·1278	0·0906	0·0466	−0·0434
60	−0·3138	2·5274	1·9132	−0·0707	152	−0·1124	0·0742	0·0380	−0·0357
62	−0·3489	2·4740	1·8498	−0·1209	154	−0·0977	0·0598	0·0305	−0·0290
64	−0·3813	2·4186	1·7863	−0·1670	156	−0·0839	0·0473	0·0241	−0·0230
66	−0·4109	2·3612	1·7228	−0·2090	158	−0·0710	0·0366	0·0188	−0·0179
68	−0·4378	2·3021	1·6595	−0·2469	160	−0·0591	0·0277	0·0140	−0·0136
70	−0·4621	2·2413	1·5963	−0·2809	162	−0·0481	0·0203	0·0102	−0·0100
72	−0·4837	2·1788	1·5335	−0·3111	164	−0·0382	0·0143	0·0072	−0·0071
74	−0·5027	2·1150	1·4712	−0·3374	166	−0·0294	0·0096	0·0048	−0·0048
76	−0·5193	2·0499	1·4094	−0·3602	168	−0·0217	0·0061	0·0031	−0·0030
78	−0·5334	1·9836	1·3483	−0·3794	170	−0·0151	0·0035	0·0018	−0·0018
80	−0·5452	1·9163	1·2879	−0·3953	172	−0·0097	0·0018	0·0009	−0·0009
82	−0·5546	1·8482	1·2283	−0·4079	174	−0·0055	0·0008	0·0004	−0·0004
84	−0·5618	1·7795	1·1697	−0·4175	176	−0·0024	0·0002	0·0001	−0·0001
86	−0·5669	1·7102	1·1120	−0·4241	178	−0·0006	0	0	0
88	−0·5698	1·6406	1·0554	−0·4280	180	0	0	0	0
90	−0·5708	1·5708	1·0	−0·4292					

In finding the expressions of Table 12.2 it was assumed that each pair of forces, whether disposed symmetrically or skew-symmetrically, were balanced as required at B. The sum of these reactions for the whole system $2P_1$, $2P_2$ and $2P_3$ will be zero since the three applied forces are in equilibrium.

Ring with distributed loading.—The results obtained for the resultant reactions of a ring under any system of point loads may be used to calculate the effects of distributed loads. Thus, if a distributed load of intensity $2w$ acts upwards parallel to OA on an arc of the ring between $\alpha=\theta_2$ and $\alpha=\theta_1$, it can be split into symmetrical and skew-symmetrical systems of intensity w and the results superposed to obtain the contribution made by $2w$ to the values of H_0, V_0 and M_0.

If α is any angle between θ_1 and θ_2 the element of load acting parallel to OA at that point is $w\mathrm{R}\cos\alpha d\alpha$ if $\alpha<\pi/2$ and $-w\mathrm{R}\cos\alpha d\alpha$ if $\alpha>\pi/2$. The values of the actions at A due to this can be calculated from the results for a point load by putting $P=\pm w\mathrm{R}\cos\alpha d\alpha$ as appropriate.

The total values of these actions due to the whole load $2w$ are then

$$H_0'=\frac{w\mathrm{R}}{\mathrm{P}}\int_{\theta_1}^{\theta_2}H_0\cos\alpha d\alpha \; ; \quad V_0'=\frac{w\mathrm{R}}{\mathrm{P}}\int_{\theta_1}^{\theta_2}V_0\cos\alpha d\alpha \; ; \quad M_0'=\frac{w\mathrm{R}}{\mathrm{P}}\int_{\theta_1}^{\theta_2}M_0\cos\alpha d\alpha,$$

where H_0, V_0 and M_0 are the corresponding actions under a load $2P$ acting parallel to OA at α.

If the distributed load acts at right angles to the axis OA the point load is replaced by symmetrical and skew-symmetrical components $w\mathrm{R}\sin\alpha d\alpha$ and the contributions of $2w$ to the resultant actions at A are

$$H_0'=\frac{w\mathrm{R}}{\mathrm{P}}\int_{\theta_1}^{\theta_2}H_0\sin\alpha d\alpha \; ; \quad V_0'=\frac{w\mathrm{R}}{\mathrm{P}}\int_{\theta_1}^{\theta_2}V_0\sin\alpha d\alpha \; ; \quad M_0'=\frac{w\mathrm{R}}{\mathrm{P}}\int_{\theta_1}^{\theta_2}M_0\sin\alpha d\alpha,$$

where H_0, V_0 and M_0 are the actions due to $2P$ acting at right angles to OA at α.

As an example, suppose a circular culvert carries a uniform load of intensity w acting vertically downwards and that this load produces a similarly distributed upward reaction from the ground upon which it rests.

The conditions of loading being symmetrical there is no vertical action V_0 at A. Due to w acting downward between 0 and $\pi/2$, using (12.49),

$$H_0'=-\frac{w\mathrm{R}}{\pi}\int_0^{\pi/2}\sin^2\alpha\,\cos\alpha d\alpha,$$

$$M_0'=-\frac{w\mathrm{R}^2}{\pi}\int_0^{\pi/2}\{\sin^2\alpha+1+\cos\alpha-(\pi-\alpha)\sin\alpha\}\cos\alpha d\alpha,$$

and due to w acting upward between $\pi/2$ and π,

$$H_0'=-\frac{w\mathrm{R}}{\pi}\int_{\pi/2}^{\pi}\sin^2\alpha\,\cos\alpha d\alpha,$$

$$M_0'=-\frac{w\mathrm{R}^2}{\pi}\int_{\pi/2}^{\pi}\{\sin^2\alpha+1+\cos\alpha-(\pi-\alpha)\sin\alpha\}\cos\alpha d\alpha.$$

These give $H_0'=0$; $M_0'=-\dfrac{w\mathrm{R}^2}{4}$; results which can also be obtained by direct integration as follows :—

The bending moment at α from OA is, with the conventions hitherto used,

$$M_x=M_0-H_0\mathrm{R}(1-\cos\alpha)+\frac{w\mathrm{R}^2\sin^2\alpha}{2}$$

and the conditions $\quad \dfrac{\partial U}{\partial M_0}=\dfrac{\partial U}{\partial H_0}=0$ give

$$\int_0^\pi \left(M_0 - H_0 R(1-\cos\alpha) + \frac{wR^2}{2}\sin^2\alpha \right) dx = 0$$

$$\int_0^\pi \left\{ M_0 - H_0 R(1-\cos\alpha) + \frac{wR^2}{2}\sin^2\alpha \right\} (1-\cos\alpha) dx = 0.$$

These lead to the results

$$H_0 = 0$$

$$M_0 = -\frac{wR^2}{4},$$

which are the same as before.

12.19. Stresses in a braced ring.—In certain forms of construction braced rings have been used. These may present problems of great difficulty and no attempt will be made here to treat the general case. The ring in such a

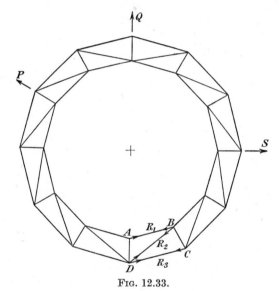

FIG. 12.33.

structure is usually a polygon and the bracing may be of a variety of types. Fig. 12.33 shows a simple form of braced polygon carrying three loads P, Q and S which are in equilibrium. This frame has three degrees of redundancy and presents no difficulty in solution. If any three members such as AB, BD and CD are replaced by unknown forces R_1, R_2 and R_3 the frame can be considered to be held at points A and D and the forces in all the bars determined as functions of R_1, R_2, R_3, P, Q and S just as in the case of the braced arch described in paragraph 12.16. Then by the method of minimum strain energy,

$$\frac{\partial U}{\partial R_1} = \frac{\partial U}{\partial R_2} = \frac{\partial U}{\partial R_3} = 0,$$

where U is the total strain energy of the ring including that in the three members AB, BD and CD. These equations enable the unknown forces to be determined and hence the forces in all members of the structure. Many rings of this type, however, may have redundant bars in addition to the three due to the continuity of the ring, *e.g.* the one shown in Fig. 12.33 might have been provided with counter-bracing members in each panel. Each such redundancy introduces an extra equation and the problem, although theoretically soluble, may present such arithmetical complexity that an exact solution will be impracticable.

Should the panels have counterbracing wires not stressed initially, those which would be called upon by the load system to carry compression will become slack. A difficulty then arises in determining which are the operative wires, and several solutions may have to be obtained before the correct one is found.

EXERCISES

(1) An arch span is 50 feet, its centre line being the segment of a circle subtending 120° at the centre. It is pinned at the supports and at the crown, and carries a load of 10 tons at 12 feet 6 inches measured horizontally from the left-hand support. Calculate the magnitude and direction of the reactions at the supports and the force on the central pin.

(Left support : $5\sqrt{3}$ tons at 60° to horizontal.
Right support : 5 tons at 30° to horizontal.

Centre pin : shear$=2\frac{1}{2}$ tons ; thrust$=\dfrac{5\sqrt{3}}{2}$ tons.)

2) A semi-circular arch of 40 feet span is pinned at the supports and at the crown. ¡carries a uniform load of 2 tons per foot (horizontal projection) over the left-hand half of the span. Calculate the magnitudes and directions of the reactions on the end pins and sketch carefully the bending moment diagram for the arch.

(Left-hand pin : $31 \cdot 62$ tons at $\tan^{-1} 3$ to horizontal.
Right-hand pin : $14 \cdot 14$ tons at 45° to horizontal.)

(3) A parabolic arch rib of uniform section with pinned ends is 80 feet span and has a rise of 10 feet at the centre. It carries a concentrated load of 10 tons at the crown. Plot the approximate bending moment diagram for the rib.

(4) A rolled steel joist $24 \times 7\frac{1}{2}$ inches having a second moment of area of 2,200-inch units is used to make a two-pinned segmental arch of 40 feet span and 5 feet rise.

Calculate what central load this arch can carry if the bending stress in the material is limited to 8 tons per square inch.

(53·5 tons.)

(5) A two-hinged segmental arch rib of 120 feet span and 12 feet rise experiences a change of temperature of 50° F.

Calculate the alteration which this makes in the horizontal thrust.

$E=13{,}000$ tons per square inch.

$I=90$ inch units.

Coefficient of expansion for steel$=6 \times 10^{-6}$ per 1° F.

(0·035 tons.)

(6) Find the value of the horizontal force and end fixing moment for an encastré segmental arch of radius R carrying a central load W, when the ratio of rise to span is 1 to 4.

(H$=0 \cdot 926$ W ; M$=0 \cdot 059$ WR.)

(7) A stiff-jointed frame in the form of a regular hexagon with a length of side L carries two equal and opposite loads of W applied radially at opposite corners.

Calculate the bending moments at the loaded points.

$$\left(\frac{WL}{2\sqrt{3}} . \right)$$

(8) A steel ring made of 1-inch square material is 8 inches mean diameter.   A steel rod 0·1 square inches in cross-sectional area connects two points at the ends of a diameter and the ring is compressed by equal and opposite loads W acting at right angles to the rod.   Calculate the tension in the rod.

$$(0 \cdot 54W.)$$

(9) A ring of radius R and flexural rigidity EI is radially braced by three equally-spaced spokes, of cross-sectional area a and Young's modulus E, which are pinned to a small centre hub and to the ring.   If the hub, which is rigid, is held fixed show that the loads in the spokes when a load W acts radially inwards at a spoke point are

$$\frac{W}{3}\left(\frac{I}{I + \cdot 016R^2a}\right); \quad \frac{W}{3}\left(\frac{I}{I + \cdot 016R^2a}\right); \quad -\frac{2W}{3}\left(\frac{I + \cdot 024R^2a}{I + \cdot 016R^2a}\right).$$

CHAPTER 13

THE SUSPENSION BRIDGE

13.1. The hanging cable.—When a flexible cable suspended from two supports carries loads which are large compared with the weight of the cable the shape it assumes can be obtained by means of a funicular polygon, provided that a third point through which the cable must pass, or alternatively the horizontal reaction at one point of support, is specified. The methods used are given in books on mechanics and need not be dealt with here.

When a uniform cable hangs freely under its own weight it assumes a shape known as the catenary and the chains of a suspension bridge would take this form if otherwise unloaded. The weight of the platform, suspension rods, etc., tend to modify this curve.

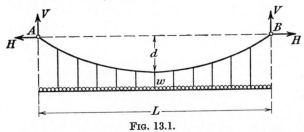

Fig. 13.1.

Suppose a cable of negligible weight carries, by means of suspension rods, a flexible platform upon which there is a uniformly distributed load of intensity w, as shown in Fig. 13.1.

The reactions at A and B consist of vertical forces $V = \dfrac{wL}{2}$ and horizontal forces H which have to be determined. H is the constant horizontal component of the tension in the cable since there are no external horizontal loads. Take the lowest point on the cable as origin and consider the equilibrium of a portion OC where C is a distance x horizontally from O and a distance y vertically above it, as in Fig. 13.2. The only forces acting on OC are the tensions H and T

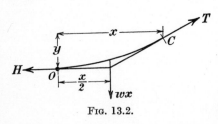

Fig. 13.2.

at O and C respectively and the load wx acting at $x/2$ from O.

By taking moments about C we have

$$Hy = \frac{wx^2}{2},$$

or
$$y = \frac{wx^2}{2H},$$

and the cable assumes a parabolic form.

302

When $x=L/2$, $y=d$ and

$$d=\frac{wL^2}{8H},$$

so that

$$H=\frac{wL^2}{8d}. \quad . \quad . \quad . \quad . \quad . \quad . \quad (13.1)$$

The uniformly distributed dead load of the platform thus causes the cables to distort from the catenary and the result is a curve which is neither catenary nor parabola. For the small ratios of d/L which occur in actual bridges, however, the difference between the curves is very slight and it is always assumed that when carrying its dead load the cable of a bridge takes the parabolic form.

If the origin of this parabola be taken at O, the lowest point, its equation is

$$y=\frac{4dx^2}{L^2}. \quad . \quad . \quad . \quad . \quad . \quad . \quad (13.2)$$

It is often convenient, however, to take the origin at A and the equation is then

$$y=\frac{4d}{L^2}x(L-x). \quad . \quad . \quad . \quad . \quad . \quad (13.3)$$

At any point in the cable the tension T is $H\dfrac{ds}{dx}$,

and since

$$\frac{ds}{dx}=\sqrt{1+\left(\frac{dy}{dx}\right)^2},$$

we have

$$T=H\sqrt{1+\left(\frac{dy}{dx}\right)^2}.$$

From equation (13.2), when the origin is at O, this is

$$T=H\sqrt{1+\frac{64d^2x^2}{L^4}}. \quad . \quad . \quad . \quad . \quad (13.4)$$

When $x=L/2$, T is a maximum and

$$T_{max}=H\sqrt{1+\frac{16d^2}{L^2}}. \quad . \quad . \quad . \quad . \quad (13.5)$$

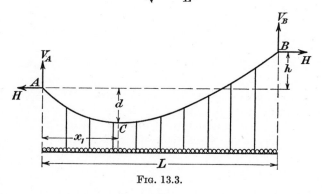

FIG. 13.3.

If a cable is supported at two points which are at different levels and carries a uniformly distributed load along a horizontal line as shown in Fig. 13.3, it hangs in the parabola ACB where C is the lowest point of the curve. Let the support B be a distance h above the support A and the maximum dip of the cable at C be d below A and let C be x_1 from A.

Then, since the horizontal component of the tension in the cable is constant, we have

$$H = \frac{wx_1^2}{2d} = \frac{w(L-x_1)^2}{2(h+d)}$$

or

$$\frac{x_1^2}{d} = \frac{(L-x_1)^2}{h+d}.$$

From which

$$x_1 = \frac{L}{h}\{\sqrt{d(d+h)} - d\}. \quad . \quad . \quad . \quad . \quad . \quad (13.6)$$

13.2. Stiffened suspension bridges.—Owing to the tendency to change its configuration under different load systems the simple suspension cable does not make a satisfactory bridge except for the lightest traffic, and to overcome this disadvantage stiffening girders are used in conjunction with the cable. Such girders are suitably supported at the bridge piers and suspension rods connect them with the cables. Loads on the bridge are distributed through the stiffening girders to the suspension rods and so to the cables.

A reasonably simple approach to the problem of stress distribution in a stiffened suspension bridge is only possible by the introduction of drastic simplifications as follows.

(1) It is assumed that the suspension rods are so adjusted that under the dead weight of the bridge the cable assumes a parabolic shape and that the whole of the dead weight is carried direct to the cables through the suspension rods. The stiffening girders are thus relieved of all stress arising from the dead weight of the bridge.

(2) It is assumed that the cable retains a parabolic shape under all conditions of live loading.

Since, as was shown in the previous paragraph, the parabolic shape can only be maintained by a loading which is uniformly distributed along the horizontal projection, the second assumption implies that any live load on the bridge causes a uniform pull in all the suspension rods.

The stiffening girder may be supported in various ways : if the bridge is a single span, the girder will normally be pinned or hinged to the piers. If there are stiffened side spans, the girder may be either continuous over the piers or pinned as before. Pinned girders only will be considered in this book.

The suspension cable acting alone is a sufficient and statically determinate means of carrying loads, and when a beam which is itself also statically determinate is connected to it the resultant structure is redundant. Hence a suspension bridge with a stiffening girder simply supported at the piers exhibits one degree of redundancy. If, however, the girder is provided with an additional pinned joint or hinge somewhere in its span the bridge stiffened by such a three-pinned girder is statically soluble and will be considered first.

13.3. Suspension bridge with three-pinned stiffening girder.—Fig. 13.4 represents a suspension cable of span L and central dip d, stiffened by a girder pinned to supports at A and B and having a hinge at C. The hinge is shown in the diagram at the centre of the span but this is not necessary and the following argument is quite general.   The reactive forces from the cable loads will consist of horizontal and vertical components as shown, and since the assumption is made that however the bridge is loaded the pulls from the suspension rods will always give a uniformly distributed load on the cable, the reactive forces will be the same at each pier.

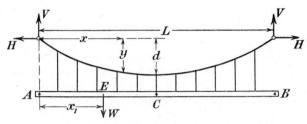

FIG. 13.4.

If the total dead weight of the bridge is equivalent to a uniform horizontally distributed load of intensity w_0, the horizontal component of tension in the cable due to this will be

$$H_0 = \frac{w_0 L^2}{8d} \qquad \cdots \qquad \cdots \qquad (13.7)$$

and the tension in each suspension rod will be

$$t_0 = \frac{w_0 L}{N}, \qquad \cdots \qquad \cdots \qquad (13.8)$$

where N is the number of rods.

When a load W is placed on the bridge at a distance x_1 from A it produces a uniform tension in the suspension rods equivalent to that produced by a horizontally distributed load of intensity w, to be determined, and the conditions of loading of the cable and girder are shown in Fig. 13.5.

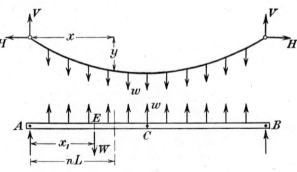

FIG. 13.5.

The girder is subjected to bending from the downward concentrated load W and the uniformly distributed upward load of intensity w, so that at any point nL from A the bending moment is

$$M = W\{-n(L-x_1)+[nL-x_1]\}+wnL^2(1-n)/2, \qquad \cdots \qquad (13.9)$$

the term in square brackets only appearing when it is positive.   If the hinge C is at $n_1 L$ from A and $n_1 L$ is greater than x_1 the bending moment at C is

$$M_C = 0 = Wx_1(n_1-1)+wn_1 L^2(1-n_1)/2,$$

and so
$$w = \frac{2Wx_1}{n_1 L^2}. \qquad \cdot \quad \cdot \quad \cdot \quad \cdot \quad \cdot \quad \cdot \quad (13.10)$$

If, as shown in Fig. 13.4, the hinge is at the centre of the span, $n_1 = \frac{1}{2}$,

$$\left.\begin{array}{l} w = \dfrac{4Wx_1}{L^2} \\[2ex] \text{and} \qquad H = \dfrac{wL^2}{8d} = \dfrac{Wx_1}{2d}. \end{array}\right\} \quad \cdot \quad \cdot \quad \cdot \quad \cdot \quad \cdot \quad (13.11)$$

In all the subsequent work in this Chapter it will be assumed that the pin is at the centre of the stiffening girder. It is clearly unnecessary to deal with more than one-half of the girder and so the load will be taken to act always on the left-hand half of the span as shown in the figure and as assumed in the derivation of (13.10), i.e. $x_1 < L/2$.

The bending moment expression (13.9) is made up of a term in W and one in w. The first represents the sagging moments caused by the concentrated load W on a freely supported beam AB and is shown by the triangle ADB in Fig. 13.6. The second term is the parabola AFB which represents the hogging moments due to the uniformly distributed upward load of the suspension rods.

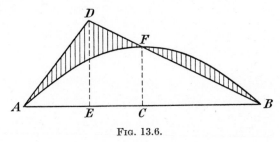

Fig. 13.6.

Having calculated w from (13.11) the shearing force diagrams for the girder can be plotted, since the shearing force at any section is the algebraic sum of the forces due to W and w. The load W as in Fig. 13.4 acts at x_1 from A and we shall calculate the shearing forces at any point nL from A.

If $nL < x_1$

$$F = -\left(\frac{L - x_1}{L}\right)W - wnL + \frac{wL}{2}$$

and substituting the value of w from equation (13.11) we find

$$F = \frac{W}{L}(3x_1 - L - 4nx_1) \quad \cdot \quad \cdot \quad \cdot \quad \cdot \quad (13.12)$$

which is a straight line in n.

When $n = 0$
$$F_A = \frac{W}{L}(3x_1 - L),$$

and when $nL = x_1$
$$F_W = \frac{W}{L}\left(3x_1 - L - \frac{4x_1^2}{L}\right).$$

If $nL > x_1$
$$F = \frac{W}{L}(3x_1 - 4nx_1). \quad \cdot \quad \cdot \quad \cdot \quad \cdot \quad (13.13)$$

which is also a straight line in n.

When $nL = x_1$ $$F_W = \frac{W}{L}\left(3x_1 - \frac{4x_1^2}{L}\right)$$

and when $n = 1$ $$F_B = -\frac{Wx_1}{L}.$$

The shearing force diagram will vary according as $x_1 < L/3$ or $x_1 > L/3$ as shown in Fig. 13.7.

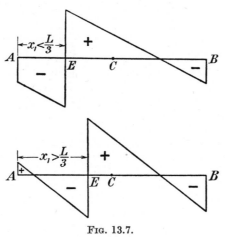

FIG. 13.7.

The negative shearing force to the left of E is clearly always **greater** numerically than that at A. Hence, the maximum negative shearing force will occur either to the left of E or at B.

The numerical value at E is greater than that at B if

$$-3x_1 + L + \frac{4x_1^2}{L} > x_1$$

i.e. if $$(L - 2x_1)^2 > 0$$

which is always true.

Hence the maximum negative shearing force occurs just to the left of the load and the maximum positive shearing force just to the right of the load.

The equations to the curves of maximum positive and negative shearing forces as a load W rolls across the bridge are respectively

$$\left.\begin{aligned} F_M &= \frac{W}{L}\left(3x_1 - \frac{4x_1^2}{L}\right) \\ F_M &= \frac{W}{L}\left(3x_1 - \frac{4x_1^2}{L} - L\right). \end{aligned}\right\} \quad \cdots \quad (13.14)$$

and

The positions of the absolute maximum values are found by putting $\frac{dF_M}{dx_1} = 0$

which leads in each instance to

$$x_1 = \tfrac{3}{8}L. \quad \cdots \quad \cdots \quad (13.15)$$

The values of the absolute maximum shearing forces are then

$$\left.\begin{aligned} +F_M &= \tfrac{9}{16}W \\ -F_M &= \tfrac{7}{16}W \end{aligned}\right\} \cdots \quad \cdots \quad (13.16)$$

So for a single concentrated load on the bridge the maximum shearing forces are obtained when the load is at $\frac{3}{8}$ of the span from the end and they are $\frac{9}{16}W$ and $-\frac{7}{16}W$ respectively, occurring to the right and left of the load.

From the bending moment diagram of Fig. 13.6 it is clear that the maximum negative bending moment occurs at E and is

$$-M_M = \frac{W}{L}x_1(L-x_1) - \frac{w}{2}x_1(L-x_1).$$

Substitution for w gives

$$-M_M = \frac{W}{L^2}x_1(L-x_1)(L-2x_1). \quad . \quad . \quad . \quad . \quad (13.17)$$

Differentiating this expression and equating to zero we find that the position of maximum negative bending moment is given by

$$6x_1^2 - 6x_1L + L^2 = 0,$$

or when $\qquad\qquad\qquad x_1 = \cdot 211L.$

The value of the bending moment is then $-\cdot 096WL$. The maximum positive bending moment occurs midway between C and B and is

$$M_M = -\frac{Wx_1}{L} \cdot \frac{L}{4} + \frac{3wL^2}{32}.$$

On substitution for w this becomes

$$M_M = \frac{Wx_1}{8} \quad . \quad . \quad . \quad . \quad . \quad . \quad (13.18)$$

which has its absolute maximum value of $\frac{WL}{16}$ when x_1 has its maximum value of $L/2$.

Hence the greatest negative bending moment due to a concentrated load occurs at the load point when the load is $\cdot 211L$ from one end, its value being $-\cdot 096WL$. The greatest positive bending moment $\frac{WL}{16}$ occurs at the quarter-span points when the load is at the centre of the span.

13.4. Influence lines for bridge with three-pinned stiffening girder.—The effect of a distributed load upon a suspension bridge is best studied by the use of influence diagrams which will now be obtained (see Chapter 14).

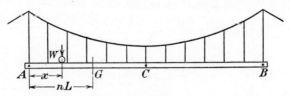

FIG. 13.8.

Suppose a load W rolls across the bridge as shown in Fig. 13.8 ; influence lines are to be drawn for the point G which is at a distance nL from A. n will be always restricted to the range of $0 < n < \frac{1}{2}$: if G is on the other half of the girder the influence lines will be obtained directly from those for the corresponding position on AC.

In the first place we shall consider the variation in shearing force at G as x increases from zero to L.

If $x < nL$

$$F_G = -W\left(\frac{L-x}{L}\right) + W - wnL + \frac{wL}{2}$$

and substituting for w from equation (13.11) this reduces to

$$F_G = \frac{Wx}{L}(3 - 4n) \quad . \quad . \quad . \quad . \quad . \quad (13.19)$$

which is a straight line having zero value at A and a maximum ordinate $Wn(3-4n)$ at G.

If $nL < x < \dfrac{L}{2}$

$$F_G = \frac{Wx}{L}(3 - 4n) - W \quad . \quad . \quad . \quad . \quad (13.20)$$

which is also a straight line having an ordinate $W(3n - 4n^2 - 1)$ at $x = nL$ and an ordinate $\dfrac{W}{2}(1 - 4n)$ at $x = L/2$.

If $x > \dfrac{L}{2}$ the value for w given in equation (13.11) is not valid, but since loads at x and $L-x$ from A will be symmetrically placed about C they will produce the same effect and therefore when $x > L/2$ it is only necessary to replace x by $L-x$ to obtain w,

i.e.
$$w = \frac{4W(L-x)}{L^2}. \quad . \quad . \quad . \quad . \quad . \quad . \quad (13.21)$$

As before
$$F_G = -W\left(\frac{L-x}{L}\right) - wnL + \frac{wL}{2}$$

and substituting the value of w from (13.21) this reduces to

$$F_G = -W\left(\frac{L-x}{L}\right)(4n - 1) \quad . \quad . \quad . \quad . \quad (13.22)$$

which is also a straight line giving $F_G = 0$ when $x = L$

and
$$F_G = -\frac{W}{2}(4n - 1) \text{ when } x = \frac{L}{2}.$$

From this last value for the shearing force when the load is at the centre of the girder it is seen that when $n < \frac{1}{4}$, F_G is positive and when $n > \frac{1}{4}$, F_G is negative. If $n = \frac{1}{4}$ there is no shearing force at the point G when the load has passed the centre of the span. The three influence lines are shown in Fig. 13.9.

We will now consider the influence line of bending moments for the same point G.

Equation (13.9) is true for all positions of the load and, paying due attention to the terms in square brackets, we can re-write it as follows :
When the load is between A and G, *i.e.* when $x < nL$,

$$M = -(1 - n)(Wx - wnL^2/2),$$

and when the load has passed G, *i.e.* when $x > nL$, it is

$$M = -Wn(L - x) + wnL^2(1 - n)/2.$$

As long as the load is on the left-hand section of the girder the value of w is given by equation (13.11) but if it passes the pin at C, equation (13.21) must be used.

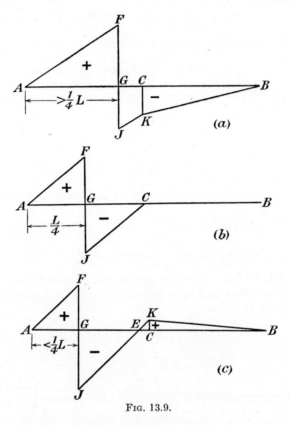

FIG. 13.9.

There are therefore three separate parts of the diagram to be considered for each of which the moment equation is different ; these equations are, after substitution of the appropriate values of w,

when $x < nL < L/2$

$$M = -Wx(1-n)(1-2n) ; \qquad \qquad (13.23)$$

when $nL < x < L/2$

$$M = Wn\{x(3-2n) - L\} ; \qquad \qquad (13.24)$$

when $x > L/2$

$$M = Wn(L-x)(1-2n). \qquad \qquad (13.25)$$

These are all straight lines and can be plotted from the following points.

In (13.23) when $x = 0$, $M = 0$,
and when $x = nL$, $M = -WnL(1-n)(1-2n)$.

In (13.24) when $x = nL$, $M = -WnL(1-n)(1-2n)$,
and when $x = L/2$, $M = \frac{1}{2}WnL(1-2n)$.

In (13.25) when $x = L/2$, $M = \frac{1}{2}WnL(1-2n)$,
and when $x = L$, $M = 0$.

The influence line of bending moments is then as shown in Fig. 13.10.

The maximum numerical bending moment occurs either when the load is at G or C.

The B.M. for the load at G is greater than the B.M. for the load at C if

$$Ln(1-n)(1-2n)>\frac{Ln}{2}(1-2n),$$

i.e. if
$$2(1-n)>1.$$

Since $n<\tfrac{1}{2}$ this is always true and the maximum numerical bending moment therefore occurs when the load is over the point considered and it is negative in sign. Its value is

$$-M_M=WnL(1-n)(1-2n). \quad . \quad . \quad . \quad (13.26)$$

This is an absolute maximum when $\frac{dM}{dn}=0,$

i.e. when
$$6n^2-6n+1=0$$

or when
$$n=\cdot211.$$

Hence the maximum negative bending moment occurs under the load when the load is $\cdot211L$ from either end and its value is $-\cdot096WL$ as found previously from the bending moment diagram.

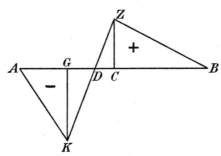

FIG. 13.10.

The maximum positive bending moment is

$$M_M=\tfrac{1}{2}WLn(1-2n). \quad . \quad . \quad . \quad . \quad (13.27)$$

The absolute maximum occurs when $\frac{dM}{dn}=0,$

i.e. when
$$1-4n=0$$

or
$$n=\tfrac{1}{4}.$$

Its value is then $\frac{WL}{16}.$

So the greatest positive bending moment occurs when the load is at the centre of the span. Its position is at the quarter-span points and its value is $\frac{WL}{16}$ as previously determined from the bending moment diagram.

13.5. Effect of uniform load on three-pinned stiffening girders.—By the use of the influence lines obtained in the preceding paragraph we can determine the maximum bending moments and shearing forces in the stiffening girder when a uniformly distributed load of intensity p crosses the bridge.

From the influence lines for shearing force given in Fig. 13.9 it will be seen that the maximum positive shearing force at G will occur either when AG in line (a) is covered by the rolling load or when AG and EB in line (c) are simultaneously covered.

Consider (a), for which n lies between $\frac{1}{4}$ and $\frac{1}{2}$.

The value of the positive shearing force at G is

$$F_G = p(\text{area AFG})$$

$$= \frac{p}{2} \cdot nL \cdot n(3-4n)$$

$$= \frac{pL}{2} n^2(3-4n). \quad . \quad . \quad . \quad . \quad . \quad (13.28)$$

This is a maximum when $\dfrac{dF}{dn} = 0$,

i.e. when $\qquad\qquad 6n - 12n^2 = 0$

or when $\qquad\qquad n = \frac{1}{2}.$

Its value is then $\qquad\qquad F_G = \dfrac{pL}{8}.$

When $n < \frac{1}{4}$ the line (c) is applicable and AG and EB must be simultaneously covered to obtain the maximum positive shearing force at G.

Now $\qquad\qquad \dfrac{EC}{EG} = \dfrac{KC}{JG} = \dfrac{1-4n}{-2(3n-4n^2-1)}.$

$\therefore \qquad\qquad \dfrac{EC}{EC+EG} = \dfrac{1-4n}{8n^2-10n+3}$

or $\qquad\qquad EC = \dfrac{(1-4n)(1-2n)L}{2(8n^2-10n+3)}$

$$= \left(\frac{1-4n}{3-4n}\right)\frac{L}{2}$$

$\therefore \qquad\qquad EB = 2L\left(\dfrac{1-2n}{3-4n}\right).$

Then $\qquad\qquad F_G = p(\text{area AGF} + \text{area EKB}),$

or $\qquad F_G = \dfrac{pL}{2}\left\{ n^2(3-4n) + \dfrac{(1-4n)(1-2n)}{3-4n} \right\} \quad . \quad . \quad (13.29$

This value decreases steadily as n increases from 0 to $\frac{1}{4}$, and the maximum value is therefore $\dfrac{pL}{6}$ when $n = 0$.

Hence, the maximum positive shearing force $\dfrac{pL}{6}$ occurs at the support A when the loaded length is $EB = 2/3L$.

The maximum negative shearing force at G occurs either when GB in Fig. 13.9 (a) is covered by the load or when GE in Fig. 13.9 (c) is so covered.

When GB is covered the shearing force is

$$F_G = \frac{p}{2}\left[\{(3n-4n^2-1) + \tfrac{1}{2}(1-4n)\}\left(\frac{L}{2}-nL\right) + \frac{L}{4}(1-4n) \right]$$

or
$$F_G = \frac{pL}{8}(16n^3 - 12n^2) \quad . \quad . \quad . \quad . \quad . \quad . \quad (13.30)$$

which is a maximum when $\dfrac{dF_G}{dn} = 0$,

i.e. when $\qquad\qquad\qquad n = \frac{1}{2}$;

its value is then $-\dfrac{pL}{8}$.

When EG is covered the negative shearing force is

$$F_G = \frac{p}{2}\left[\left\{(L - nL) - 2L\left(\frac{1 - 2n}{3 - 4n}\right)\right\}(3n - 4n^2 - 1)\right]$$

or $\qquad F_G = -\dfrac{pL}{2}\dfrac{(4n^2 - 3n + 1)^2}{(3 - 4n)} \quad . \quad . \quad . \quad . \quad . \quad . \quad . \quad (13.31)$

This is a maximum when $n = 0$ and the value is then $-\dfrac{pL}{6}$, the covered length being $L/3$. Hence the maximum negative shearing force $-\dfrac{pL}{6}$ also occurs at A when the loaded length EG is $L/3$.

Considering now the bending moments due to a uniformly distributed load, it is clear from the influence line of Fig. 13.10 that the maximum negative bending moment at G will occur when the length AD is covered by the load. This length can be found by putting the expression for M equal to zero,

i.e. $\qquad\qquad\qquad Wn\{x(3 - 2n) - L\} = 0$

or $\qquad\qquad\qquad x = AD = \dfrac{L}{3 - 2n}. \quad . \quad . \quad . \quad . \quad . \quad . \quad (13.32)$

The value of the maximum negative bending moment at G is then

$$M_M = p(\text{area AKD})$$

$$= -\frac{p}{2}\left(\frac{L}{3 - 2n}\right)Ln(1 - n)(1 - 2n)$$

or $\qquad M_M = -\dfrac{pL^2 n(1 - n)(1 - 2n)}{2(3 - 2n)}. \quad . \quad . \quad . \quad . \quad . \quad (13.33)$

To find the position of G for which the negative bending moment has the greatest possible value we put

$$\frac{dM_M}{dn} = \frac{pL^2}{2}\left\{\frac{(3 - 2n)(1 - 6n + 6n^2) + 2n(1 - 3n + 2n^2)}{(3 - 2n)^2}\right\} = 0$$

or $\qquad\qquad\qquad 8n^3 - 24n^2 + 18n - 3 = 0 \; ;$

from which $\qquad\qquad\qquad n = 0\cdot234.$

Substituting this value of n in equation (13.33) we find that the greatest negative bending moment in the girder is $-0\cdot01883pL^2$ which occurs at a distance of $\cdot234L$ from the end of the girder. The loaded length to produce this maximum bending moment is found from equation (13.32) to be $\cdot395L$.

The maximum positive bending moment at G occurs when the length DB is covered by the load.

Now
$$DB = L - \left(\frac{L}{3-2n}\right)$$

or
$$DB = \frac{2(1-n)L}{3-2n}. \quad . \quad . \quad . \quad . \quad . \quad . \quad (13.34)$$

The bending moment at G is then

$$M_M = \frac{p}{2} \cdot \frac{2(1-n)L}{3-2n} \cdot \frac{nL(1-2n)}{2}$$

$$= \frac{pL^2 n(1-n)(1-2n)}{2(3-2n)}. \quad . \quad . \quad . \quad . \quad (13.35)$$

This is the same expression as that for the negative bending moment at G given in equation (13.33). Hence the greatest possible positive bending moment also occurs at ·234L from one support when the bridge is loaded for a distance of ·605L from the other support. The magnitude of this maximum value is $0 \cdot 01883 pL^2$.

13.6. Suspension bridge with two-pinned stiffening girder.—The analysis of this type of bridge is complicated by the fact that the structure is redundant and also because a flexible cable does not follow a linear load-deflexion relation. The principle of superposition cannot be applied and the effects of a live load are not calculable separately from those due to the dead load as would be the case if the structure obeyed a linear law. The methods of strain energy are not, therefore, really applicable to the problem but are used to obtain an approximate solution. The assumptions underlying this treatment must, however, be borne clearly in mind. As stated in paragraph 13.2 the initial shape of the cable is assumed to be a parabola and under all subsequent loads it is assumed to retain this shape. This is equivalent to saying that the cable will always behave as an inverted elastic parabolic arch under a load uniformly distributed along the horizontal projection. The resultant actions in it will be only axial tensions and transverse shearing forces ; there will be no bending moments.

This theory of the suspension bridge is sometimes known as the elastic theory to distinguish it from the more general and accurate treatment which takes into account the deflexion of the girder and cable under live loading.

The horizontal component of cable tension will be taken as the redundant force for the analysis by strain energy methods.

Then
$$\frac{dU}{dH} = 0.$$

If in Fig. 13.5 moments are taken about any point in the cable at nL from the left-hand end, since there can be no resultant moment in the cable, we have

$$M = 0 = Hy + wn^2 L^2/2 - VnL$$

and, on substituting for V, this reduces to

$$Hy = wnL^2(1-n)/2. \quad . \quad . \quad . \quad . \quad . \quad (13.36)$$

The second term in equation (13.9) can therefore be replaced by Hy. This equation is equally valid for the two-pinned girder and so the bending moment in the girder shown in Fig. 13.11 is

$$M = -\frac{W}{L}(L-x_1)x + W[x-x_1] + Hy, \quad . \quad . \quad . \quad (13.37)$$

x being the distance of any point in the girder from A. The term in square brackets only appears when it is positive, *i.e.* when $x > x_1$.

Then for the girder,

$$\frac{dU}{dH} = \int \frac{M}{EI} \frac{dM}{dH} dx = \frac{1}{EI} \int M y \, dx.$$

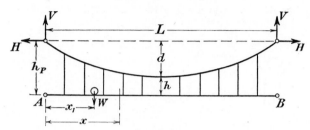

FIG. 13.11.

Taking the equation of the cable to be

$$y = \frac{4d}{L^2} x (L - x)$$

and substituting for M and y we have

$$\frac{dU}{dH} = \frac{W}{EI} \left[-\frac{4d}{L^3}(L - x_1) \int_0^L x^2 (L - x) dx + \frac{4d}{L^2} \int_{x_1}^L x(x - x_1)(L - x) dx \right]$$

$$+ \frac{H}{EI} \left[\frac{16 d^2}{L^4} \int_0^L x^2 (L - x)^2 dx \right],$$

which reduces to

$$\frac{dU}{dH} = \frac{W x_1 d}{3 EI} \left[-L + \frac{x_1^2}{L^2}(2L - x_1) \right] + \frac{8 H L d^2}{15 EI} \quad . \quad . \quad . \quad . \quad (13.38)$$

For the cable it is convenient to take the origin at the mid-point and to write the equation in the form

$$y = \frac{4 x^2 d}{L^2}.$$

Then

$$\frac{dU}{dH} = \frac{1}{AE} \int T \frac{dT}{dH} ds$$

where A is the cross-sectional area of the cable.

At any point in the cable

$$T = H \frac{ds}{dx}$$

and

$$\frac{dT}{dH} = \frac{ds}{dx}.$$

Hence

$$\frac{U d}{dH} = \frac{2H}{AE} \int_{x=0}^{x=\frac{L}{2}} \left(\frac{ds}{dx} \right)^2 ds.$$

Now

$$\frac{dy}{dx} = \frac{8 x d}{L^2}$$

and
$$\left(\frac{ds}{dx}\right)^2 = 1 + \left(\frac{dy}{dx}\right)^2 = 1 + \frac{64x^2d^2}{L^4};$$

$$\therefore \frac{dU}{dH} = \frac{2H}{AE}\int_0^{\frac{L}{2}}\left(1 + \frac{64x^2d^2}{L^4}\right)^{3/2} dx.$$

Substituting B for $\frac{8d}{L^2}$ and putting $Bx = \tan\theta$ this becomes

$$\frac{dU}{dH} = \frac{2H}{BAE}\int_0^{\tan^{-1}\frac{4d}{L}} \sec^5\theta\, d\theta$$

i.e.
$$\frac{dU}{dH} = \frac{2H}{BAE}\left[\frac{1}{4}\tan\theta\sec^3\theta + \frac{3}{8}\tan\theta\sec\theta + \frac{3}{8}\log_e(\tan\theta + \sec\theta)\right]_0^{\tan^{-1}\frac{4d}{L}}$$

or, for the cable,
$$\frac{dU}{dH} = \frac{HL}{AE}\left[\frac{1}{4}\left(\frac{5}{2} + \frac{16d^2}{L^2}\right)\left(1 + \frac{16d^2}{L^2}\right)^{1/2} + \frac{3}{32}\frac{L}{d}\log_e\left\{\frac{4d}{L} + \left(1 + \frac{16d^2}{L^2}\right)^{1/2}\right\}\right]. \quad (13.39)$$

Writing K for the product of L and the terms in the square brackets
$$\frac{dU}{dH} = \frac{KH}{AE}.$$

It is convenient to assume that the suspension rods are replaced by a continuous connexion between the cable and stiffening girder, this being only able to transmit stress vertically.

If there are N rods each having a cross-sectional area a_r, the thickness of this continuous connecting " plate " is
$$\Delta = \frac{Na_r}{L}.$$

At x from the centre of the span the vertical distance between the girder and the cable is
$$l = h + \frac{4x^2d}{L^2}$$

where h is the distance at the centre as shown in Fig. 13.11.

The load on an element of the plate δx in length is $w\delta x$ where w is the uniform intensity of load caused by the weight W. The strain energy of this element is
$$\delta U = \frac{(w\delta x)^2\left(h + \frac{4x^2d}{L^2}\right)}{2\Delta\delta x E_r}$$

where E_r is the modulus of elasticity of the plate and therefore of the rods.

Then
$$U = \frac{w^2}{\Delta E_r}\int_0^{\frac{L}{2}}\left(h + \frac{4x^2d}{L^2}\right)dx.$$

But
$$w = \frac{8Hd}{L^2}$$

$$\therefore \qquad U = \frac{64H^2d^2}{\Delta E_r L^4}\int_0^{\frac{L}{2}}\left(h + \frac{4x^2d}{L^2}\right)dx$$

and
$$\frac{dU}{dH} = \frac{64d^2H}{L^3\Delta E_r}\left(h + \frac{d}{3}\right).$$

Substituting for Δ we obtain for the rods the expression

$$\frac{d\mathrm{U}}{d\mathrm{H}}=\frac{64d^2\mathrm{H}}{\mathrm{N}a_r\mathrm{E}_r\mathrm{L}^2}(h+d/3). \quad . \quad . \quad . \quad . \quad (13.40)$$

The effect of the piers is small but may be included as follows :

Let the equivalent area of the pier be $\mathrm{A_P}$ and its height h_P. The compression in the pier will be V, the vertical component of the cable tension at the pier,

i.e. $$\mathrm{V}=\mathrm{H}\frac{dy}{dx}.$$

From the equation for the cable, with the origin at the centre, we have

$$\frac{dy}{dx}=\frac{8xd}{\mathrm{L}^2}$$

and when $x=\mathrm{L}/2$, i.e. at the pier,

$$\frac{dy}{dx}=\frac{4d}{\mathrm{L}}$$

therefore $$\mathrm{V}=\frac{4\mathrm{H}d}{\mathrm{L}} \text{ and } \frac{d\mathrm{V}}{d\mathrm{H}}=\frac{4d}{\mathrm{L}}.$$

Then $$\frac{d\mathrm{U}}{d\mathrm{H}}=\frac{1}{\mathrm{A_P}\mathrm{E_P}}\int_0^h{}_\mathrm{P}\mathrm{V}\frac{d\mathrm{V}}{d\mathrm{H}}dx=\frac{16d^2h_\mathrm{P}\mathrm{H}}{\mathrm{A_P}\mathrm{E_P}\mathrm{L}^2}.$$

For the two piers therefore

$$\frac{d\mathrm{U}}{d\mathrm{H}}=\frac{32d^2h_\mathrm{P}\mathrm{H}}{\mathrm{A_P}\mathrm{E_P}\mathrm{L}^2} . \quad . \quad . \quad . \quad . \quad . \quad (13.41)$$

Adding the terms from equations (13.38) to (13.41) and equating to zero the total value of $\frac{d\mathrm{U}}{d\mathrm{H}}$ thus found, we obtain

$$\mathrm{H}=\frac{\dfrac{\mathrm{W}x_1d}{3\mathrm{EI}}\left\{\mathrm{L}-\dfrac{x_1^2}{\mathrm{L}^2}(2\mathrm{L}-x_1)\right\}}{\dfrac{8\mathrm{L}d^2}{15\mathrm{EI}}+\dfrac{\mathrm{K}}{\mathrm{AE}}+\dfrac{64d^2}{\mathrm{N}a_r\mathrm{E}_r\mathrm{L}^2}\left(h+\dfrac{d}{3}\right)+\dfrac{32d^2h_\mathrm{P}}{\mathrm{A_P}\mathrm{E_P}\mathrm{L}^2}} \quad . \quad . \quad (13.42)$$

If the effect of the suspension rods and the piers is neglected this reduces to

$$\mathrm{H}=\frac{\dfrac{\mathrm{W}x_1d}{3\mathrm{EI}}\left\{\mathrm{L}-\dfrac{x_1^2}{\mathrm{L}^2}(2\mathrm{L}-x_1)\right\}}{\dfrac{8\mathrm{L}d^2}{15\mathrm{EI}}+\dfrac{\mathrm{K}}{\mathrm{AE}}}. \quad . \quad . \quad . \quad (13.43)$$

The part of this equation affected by the load position is

$$x_1\left\{\mathrm{L}-\frac{x_1^2}{\mathrm{L}^2}(2\mathrm{L}-x_1)\right\}$$

so that H varies with this expression.

Differentiating with respect to x_1 and equating to zero, we find that for a maximum value of H

$$\mathrm{L}-\frac{6x_1^2}{\mathrm{L}}+\frac{4x_1^3}{\mathrm{L}^2}=0$$

or $$x_1=\mathrm{L}/2.$$

11*

The value is then

$$H_{max} = \frac{\dfrac{5WL^2d}{48EI}}{\dfrac{8Ld^2}{15EI} + \dfrac{K}{AE}} \quad . \quad . \quad . \quad . \quad . \quad (13.44)$$

The bending moment can be plotted from equation (13.37) after H has been calculated

If in equation (13.36) n is $\frac{1}{2}$, $y=d$ and we find

$$w = \frac{8Hd}{L^2}. \quad . \quad . \quad . \quad . \quad . \quad (13.45)$$

So, when H has been calculated the value of w is found from this equation, and the shearing force curve for the girder can be plotted as the algebraic sum of the two curves for the concentrated load W and the uniformly distributed load w.

13.7. Influence line of bending moment for two-pinned girder.—Let G in Fig. 13.12 (a) be the point for which the influence line of bending moment is to be drawn and let it be nL from A.

If the load is at x_1 from A, the bending moment at G is as given in equation (13.9) which can, after substituting Hy for the last term, be rewritten

$$M = \left[\frac{W}{y}\{ -n(L-x_1) + [nL-x_1] \} + H \right] y = \left[\frac{\mu}{y} + H \right] y \text{ say } . \quad (13.46)$$

where y, the dip of the cable at $x=nL$, is, from equation (13.3), $4nd(1-n)$.

The term $\dfrac{\mu}{y}$, in equation (13.46), defines a triangle with zero values when $x_1=0$ and L and with its apex at G.   The ordinate at G is

$$\left[\frac{\mu}{y} \right]_G = \frac{-nL(1-n)}{4nd(1-n)} = -\frac{L}{4d}$$

which is independent of the position of G.

For the load in any one position on the beam the value of H is the same throughout the cable and so the influence line of H is the same for all points and is simply the curve obtained from equation (13.42).

Hence to draw the influence line of M/y, the procedure is as follows :

Re-write equation (13.42) as

$$H = CWx_1 \left\{ L - \frac{x_1^2}{L^2}(2L - x_1) \right\}. \quad . \quad . \quad . \quad (13.47)$$

and having calculated C, which depends only on known dimensions of the bridge and its constituents, plot the curve of H when W is made equal to unity for all values of x_1 from 0 to L, as shown in Fig. 13.12 (b).

Draw a line parallel to AB at a distance $\dfrac{L}{4d}$ from it.   This line will be the locus of the apices of the triangles representing μ/y.   If at any point such as G a perpendicular GD is set up to cut this locus, ADB will be the required plot of μ/y and the influence line of M/y will be as shown shaded in the figure.

The bending moment at G for the load at F will then be the ordinate EJ multiplied by y, i.e. by $4dn(1-n)$.

The maximum negative bending moment at G under a distributed load occurs when AK is covered and the maximum positive bending moment when KB is covered.

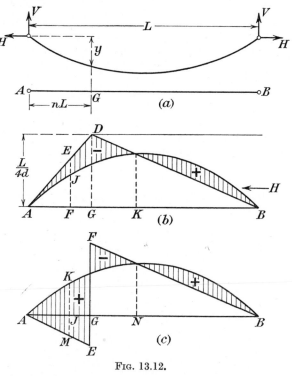

FIG. 13.12.

General expressions such as were obtained for the three-pinned girder are not practicable, but for any particular case the results are quickly found by plotting the influence diagrams as shown.

13.8. Influence line of shearing force for two-pinned girder.—At any point on the girder which is x from A the bending moment is, from equation (13.37),

$$M = W\left\{-\left(\frac{L-x_1}{L}\right)x + [x-x_1]\right\} + Hy,$$

and the shearing force is

$$S.F = \frac{dM}{dx} = W\left\{-\left(\frac{L-x_1}{L}\right) + [1]\right\} + H\frac{dy}{dx} \quad . \quad . \quad . \quad (13.48)$$

As before we shall consider the shearing force at G, which is nL from A. The value of $\frac{dy}{dx}$ here is $\frac{4d}{L}(1-2n)$ from equation (13.3).

If F is the shearing force at G for a unit load anywhere on the girder, we have from the above expression

$$F = \frac{x_1}{L} + H'\frac{4d(1-2n)}{L} \quad \text{when } x_1 \text{ lies between 0 and } nL$$

and $$F = -\left(\frac{L-x_1}{L}\right) + H'\frac{4d(1-2n)}{L} \quad \text{when } x_1 \text{ lies between } nL \text{ and } L,$$

where H' is the value of H from (13.47) when W is unity.

These expressions can be re-written as

$$F=\left[\frac{x_1}{4d(1-2n)}+H'\right]\frac{4d(1-2n)}{L} \text{ for load on section AG}$$

$$\text{and} \quad F=\left[-\frac{L-x_1}{4d(1-2n)}+H'\right]\frac{4d(1-2n)}{L} \text{ for load on section GB.} \tag{13.49}$$

The variable parts of these are included in the square brackets and it is therefore only necessary to plot the influence line for such portions.

As for the bending moment, the influence line for H is the curve of H with W put equal to unity. This is plotted in Fig. 13.12 (c). To balance the moment at G due to H an upward reaction will always be required at B and so the shearing force at G due to H will always be positive.

Upon this curve must be superimposed the other expressions in the square brackets. These define the influence line for a simple beam multiplied by the constant $\dfrac{L}{4d(1-2n)}$.

When the load is just to the left of G the ordinate GE is

$$\frac{nL}{4d(1-2n)},$$

and when the load is just to the right of G the ordinate GF is

$$-\frac{(1-n)L}{4d(1-2n)}.$$

The influence line for the complete expression is then as shown in Fig. 13.12 (c) and to obtain the shearing force at G for a load of unity at J, for example, the ordinate KM must be multiplied by $\dfrac{4d(1-2n)}{L}$.

The maximum positive shearing force at G for a uniformly distributed load will occur when AG and NB are covered by the load, and the maximum negative shearing force when GN is so covered.

13.9. Length of a suspension cable.—The length of a cable hanging in a parabolic arc can be calculated as follows :

Since

$$\frac{ds}{dx}=\sqrt{1+\left(\frac{dy}{dx}\right)^2}$$

we have

$$\int ds=\int\left\{1+\left(\frac{dy}{dx}\right)^2\right\}^{\frac{1}{2}}dx$$

and from equation (13.2) we obtain

$$\frac{dy}{dx}=\frac{8xd}{L^2}$$

so that the total length of the cable is

$$s=2\int_0^{L/2}\left(1+\frac{64x^2d^2}{L^4}\right)^{\frac{1}{2}}dx$$

$$\text{or} \quad s=\frac{L}{2}\left(1+\frac{16d^2}{L^2}\right)^{\frac{1}{2}}+\frac{L^2}{8d}\log_e\left\{\frac{4d}{L}+\left(1+\frac{16d^2}{L^2}\right)^{\frac{1}{2}}\right\}. \quad . \quad . \quad (13.50)$$

By expanding the expression to be integrated a solution in series can be obtained and a result sufficiently accurate for most purposes found in a simpler form.

Thus
$$s=2\int_0^{L/2}\left(1+\frac{32x^2d^2}{L^4}-\frac{512x^4d^4}{L^8}+\ .\ .\ .\ .\ .\ .\ \right)dx$$

$$=2\left[x+\frac{32x^3d^2}{3L^4}-\frac{512x^5d^4}{5L^8}+\ .\ .\ .\ .\ .\ .\ \right]_0^{L/2}$$

$$=\left[L+\frac{8}{3}\frac{d^2}{L}-\frac{32d^4}{5L^3}+\ .\ .\ .\ .\ .\ .\ \right]$$

or
$$s=L\left[1+\frac{8}{3}\left(\frac{d}{L}\right)^2-\frac{32}{5}\left(\frac{d}{L}\right)^4+\ .\ .\ .\ .\ .\ .\ \right]\quad .\ \ .\ \ .\quad (13.51)$$

For small d/L ratios it is sufficient for many purposes to take the first two terms only and write

$$s=L\left\{1+\frac{8}{3}\left(\frac{d}{L}\right)^2\right\}\quad .\ \ .\ \ .\ \ .\ \ .\ \ .\quad (13.52)$$

13.10. Deflexion theory of suspension bridges.—In the elastic theory, upon which the results so far obtained in this chapter are based, it is assumed that the cable maintains the same parabolic curve under all loading systems. This assumption is not accurate since under the action of any load on the girder the cables will deflect and the bending moments in the stiffening girder will be modified. The effect of the deflexion is to reduce the bending moments, and in long span bridges the neglect of this reduction results in unnecessarily large girders. The first treatment of the problem of the suspension bridge taking account of the deflexion terms was given by J. Melan (1888) and since then the theory has been successively extended (Timoshenko, 1930, 1934 ; Steinmann, 1935 ; Atkinson and Southwell, 1938). Space does not permit anything but a short statement of the general principles to be given here. For a full treatment reference should be made to more specialised works (e.g. Johnson, Bryan and Turneaure) and the original papers.

Under the action of the dead weight of the bridge let the dip of the cable at any point be y and the horizontal tension in it be H_w. Suppose now that additional load is placed on the bridge and that this is, as previously assumed, distributed uniformly between the hangers. Let this cause the horizontal tension to be increased to H_w+H. In the elastic theory the dip of the cable is assumed to be unaltered and the bending moment at any point is

$$M=\mu+Hy,$$

where μ represents the terms due to the additional loads on the girder. The effect of the extra load is to increase the dip of the cable to $y+\eta$ and the bending moment in the girder is relieved by the amount $(H_w+H)\eta$.

Then
$$M=\mu+Hy+(H_w+H)\eta.\quad .\ \ .\ \ .\ \ .\ \ .\quad (13.53)$$

If it is assumed that the hangers are inextensible, the deflexion of the stiffening girder at any point will be the same as that of the cable, and the equation connecting bending moment and deflexion in the girder is therefore

$$\frac{d^2\eta}{dx^2}=\frac{M}{EI}.\quad .\ \ .\ \ .\ \ .\ \ .\ \ .\quad (13.54)$$

Substituting the value of M in (13.53) and putting

$$c^2=\frac{H_w+H}{EI}$$

this becomes

$$\frac{d^2\eta}{dx^2}=c^2\eta+\frac{c^2(\mu+Hy)}{H_w+H}. \qquad \cdot \quad \cdot \quad \cdot \quad \cdot \quad \cdot \qquad (13.55)$$

The solution of this equation is

$$\eta=\frac{H}{H_w+H}\left\{C_1e^{cx}+C_2e^{-cx}-\left(\frac{\mu}{H}+y\right)-\frac{1}{c^2}\left(\frac{1}{H}\frac{d^2\mu}{dx^2}+\frac{8d}{L^2}\right)\right\} \quad (13.56)$$

where d and L, as before, are respectively the centre dip and span of the cable.

Substituting this expression in (13.53) we obtain

$$M=H\left\{C_1e^{cx}+C_2e^{-cx}-\frac{1}{c^2}\left(\frac{1}{H}\frac{d^2\mu}{dx^2}+\frac{8d}{L^2}\right)\right\} \qquad \cdot \quad \cdot \quad \cdot \quad (13.57)$$

and differentiating this, the shearing force is

$$S=Hc\{C_1e^{cx}-C_2e^{-cx}\}. \qquad \cdot \quad \cdot \quad \cdot \quad \cdot \quad \cdot \qquad (13.58)$$

Since c contains the term H_w it is evident from equations (13.56) (13.57) and (13.58) that the deflexion, bending moment and shearing force are not proportional to the additional load placed on the bridge and so it is not possible to draw influence lines for these quantities.

If the deformations are small the value of H found from the elastic theory may be used in the equations. A more exact value is given by Johnson, Bryan and Turneaure.

The constants of integration C_1 and C_2 depend on the conditions of loading. As an example of their evaluation suppose the bridge to carry a uniformly distributed load of intensity w along its span.

Then in equation (13.57), $\dfrac{d^2\mu}{dx^2}=w$ and $M=0$ when $x=0$ and when $x=L$.

Substitution of these values gives

$$C_1+C_2-\frac{1}{c^2}\left(\frac{w}{H}+\frac{8d}{L^2}\right)=0$$

and

$$C_1e^{cL}+C_2e^{-cL}-\frac{1}{c^2}\left(\frac{w}{H}+\frac{8d}{L^2}\right)=0$$

and the solution of these simultaneous equations is

$$C_1=\frac{1}{c^2(e^{cL}+1)}\left(\frac{w}{H}+\frac{8d}{L^2}\right)$$

and

$$C_2=C_1e^{cL}.$$

If the loading is not uniform there will be different values of the constants for each section of the bridge carrying a different load intensity and their values may be found by equating the bending moments and shearing forces respectively at points on the girder where the loading changes.

The theory has been extended to include allowance for the elasticity of the hangers (Timoshenko, 1930 and 1934).

13.11. Stresses in an extensible suspension cable.—Cables may be used to form the main supporting members in certain types of structures. They will usually be very light compared with the loads which they support and will be initially stretched as tightly as possible so that when the loads are applied the sag will be reduced to the minimum. In such cases serious errors will be introduced if the cables are assumed to be inextensible (Pippard and Chitty, 1942).

Fig. 13.13 shows a cable of negligible weight in comparison with the loads which it carries, supported at points A and B which are separated by a horizontal distance L and a vertical distance D.

Assume the loads on the cable to be $W_1, W_2, \ldots W_q, \ldots W_{n-1}$, acting at distances $l_1, l_2, \ldots l_q \ldots l_{n-1}$ from A, measured horizontally to their final lines of action, and let the reactions at A and B due these loads to be $R_A + H\alpha$ and $R_B - H\alpha$ vertically and H horizontally, where H is the constant horizontal component of tension in the cable and α is written for $\dfrac{D}{L}$.

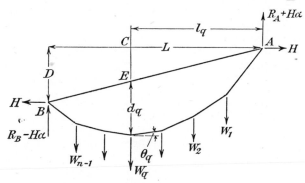

FIG. 13.13.

Let S be the original length of the cable before it is placed in position between the supports A and B ;

d_q, the dip at the qth load point when the cable is loaded, measured from the line AB ;

θ_q, the angle between the cable in the qth bay and the horizontal ;

A, the cross-sectional area of the cable ;

E, Young's modulus for the material of the cable ;

M_q, the bending moment at the qth load due to the force system if H is assumed to be zero ;

F_q, the vertical shearing force in the qth bay on the same assumption.

Then taking moments about Q gives
$$(d_q + EC)H - H\alpha l_q - M_q = 0,$$
and since $EC = \alpha l_q$,
$$d_q = \frac{M_q}{H}. \qquad \ldots \ldots \ldots (13.59)$$

Also $\tan \theta_q = \dfrac{(d_q + \alpha l_q) - (d_{q-1} + \alpha l_{q-1})}{l_q - l_{q-1}} = \dfrac{M_q - M_{q-1}}{H(l_q - l_{q-1})} + \alpha$;

but $\dfrac{M_q - M_{q-1}}{l_q - l_{q-1}} = F_q$

and so $\tan \theta_q = \dfrac{F_q}{H} + \alpha. \qquad \ldots \ldots \ldots (13.60)$

Then, if θ_q is not too large,
$$\sec \theta_q = 1 + \tfrac{1}{2}\left(\frac{F_q}{H} + \alpha\right)^2 \qquad \ldots \ldots (13.61)$$

Subsequent results are based upon this approximation for sec θ_q, and are, therefore, only applicable when the maximum slope of the loaded cable is comparatively small. Table 13.1 gives the error involved for different values of θ ; even when $\theta=30$ degrees it is only about 1 per cent., but it increases rapidly for larger values and the results become increasingly inaccurate. The useful range is, however, considerable and probably covers most cables used for structural purposes.

TABLE 13.1.

θ	Tan θ	Sec θ		Error : per cent.
		Accurate	Approximate	
0	0	1	1	0
10	0·1763	1·0154	1·0155	0·01
20	0·3639	1·0642	1·0662	0·19
30	0·5773	1·1547	1·1667	1·04
45	1·0	1·4142	1·5000	6·07
60	1·7320	2·0	2·5	25·0

The strained length of the cable in the qth bay is (l_q-l_{q-1}) sec θ_q, and so the total length of the cable is

$$\sum_1^n(l_q-l_{q-1})\left\{1+\tfrac{1}{2}\left(\frac{F_q}{H}+\alpha\right)^2\right\}$$

$$=(1+\tfrac{1}{2}\alpha^2)\sum_1^n(l_q-l_{q-1})+\frac{1}{2H^2}\sum_1^n(l_q-l_{q-1})F_q{}^2+\frac{\alpha}{H}\sum_1^n(l_q-l_{q-1})F_q.$$

Now from equation (13.60)

$$\sum_1^n(l_q-l_{q-1})\tan\theta_q=\frac{1}{H}\sum_1^n(l_q-l_{q-1})F_q+\alpha\sum_1^n(l_q-l_{q-1})$$

or

$$D=\frac{1}{H}\sum_1^n(l_q-l_{q-1})F_q+D\ ;$$

so

$$\sum_1^n(l_q-l_{q-1})F_q=0.$$

The total strained length of the cable is therefore

$$L(1+\tfrac{1}{2}\alpha^2)+\frac{Z}{2H^2}\qquad .\quad .\quad .\quad .\quad .\quad .\quad (13.62)$$

where

$$Z=\sum_1^n(l_q-l_{q-1})F_q{}^2.$$

Now if T_q is the tension in the cable in the qth bay, the increase in its length in this bay is

$$\frac{T_q(l_q-l_{q-1})\text{ sec }\theta_q}{AE},$$

and since $T_q=H$ sec θ_q the total increase in the length of the cable is

$$\frac{H}{AE}\sum_1^n(l_q-l_{q-1})\text{ sec}^2\theta_q$$

and the strained length is, using equation (13.61),

$$S+\frac{H}{AE}\left[L(1+\alpha^2)+\frac{Z}{H^2}\right]. \qquad \cdots \qquad (13.63)$$

Equating (13.62) and (13.63) we obtain

$$2H^3L(1+\alpha^2)+2H^2AE\{S-L(1+\tfrac{1}{2}\alpha^2)\}+Z(2H-AE)=0.$$

Since AE is very large in comparison with H this is, very nearly,

$$2H^3L(1+\alpha^2)+2H^2AE\{S-L(1+\tfrac{1}{2}\alpha^2)\}-ZAE=0, \qquad \cdots \qquad (13.64)$$

which determines H for any specified length of cable and distribution of load.

If the cable is erected with an initial tension whose horizontal component is H_0 we have

$$L(1+\tfrac{1}{2}\alpha^2)=S\left\{1+\frac{H_0(1+\tfrac{1}{2}\alpha^2)}{AE}\right\}$$

and on substituting the value obtained for S from this, equation (13.64) becomes

$$2L(1+\alpha^2)(H^3-H^2H_0)-ZAE=0 \qquad \cdots \qquad (13.65)$$

where H is the final tension under load.

If the cable may be assumed to be initially straight, but has no initial tension, $S=L(1+\tfrac{1}{2}\alpha^2)$, and equation (13.64) gives

$$H^3=\frac{ZAE}{2L(1+\alpha^2)}. \qquad \cdots \qquad (13.66)$$

Some particular forms of this result may be noted.

(a) If the loads are unequal, but are spaced equally along the span, that is if $l_q-l_{q-1}=l$,

$$H^3=\frac{AE}{2n(1+\alpha^2)}\sum_1^n F_q^2 \qquad \cdots \qquad (13.67)$$

where n denotes the number of equal bays in the cable.

(b) If the loads and spacings are both equal, that is, if $l_q-l_{q-1}=l$ and $W_1=\ldots=W_q=\ldots=W_{n-1}=W$,

$$\sum_1^n F_q^2=\frac{W^2n(n^2-1)}{12}$$

and

$$H^3=\frac{AEW^2(n^2-1)}{24(1+\alpha^2)}. \qquad \cdots \qquad (13.68)$$

(c) If the loads and spacings are both equal and A and B are at the same level, that is if $D=0$,

$$H^3=\frac{AEW^2(n^2-1)}{24} \qquad \cdots \qquad (13.69)$$

(d) If the loading is continuous and of uniform intensity w along AB, the shearing force at a distance x from A is $w(\tfrac{1}{2}L-x)(1+\tfrac{1}{2}\alpha^2)$.

Then

$$Z=w^2(1+\alpha^2)\int_0^L(\tfrac{1}{2}L-x)^2dx=\frac{w^2L^3(1+\alpha^2)}{12}$$

and

$$H^3=\frac{AEw^2L^2}{24}. \qquad \cdots \qquad (13.70)$$

When H has been calculated, the dips may be found from equation (13.59) and the loaded shape of the cable thus determined.

As an example consider a cable stretched tightly between two points A and B which are 100 feet apart horizontally, A being 10 feet above B so that $\alpha = 0 \cdot 1$. The loads are 2 tons, 1 ton, $\frac{1}{2}$ ton, $\frac{1}{2}$ ton and 1 ton acting at distances of 20 feet, 30 feet, 50 feet, 80 feet and 90 feet respectively from A. The value of AE is 6,000 tons.

The vertical reaction at A is $2 \cdot 75$ tons. The shearing forces and bending moments at the load points, neglecting H, are calculated and entered in columns (3) and (6) of Table 13.2. The values of $l_q - l_{q-1}$ are entered in column (2), and calculated values of F_q^2 and $(l_q - l_{q-1})F_q^2$ in columns (4) and (5). The sum of the values in column (5) gives $Z = 241$ foot-tons², and H is then found from equation (8) to be $19 \cdot 3$ tons. The dips are found by dividing the bending moments in column (6) by H, and are given in column (7) :

TABLE 13.2.

1	2	3	4	5	6	7
Point	$l_q - l_{q-1}$	F_q	F_q^2	$(l_q - l_{q-1})F_q^2$	M_q	d_q
A					0	0
	20	$2 \cdot 75$	$7 \cdot 56$	$151 \cdot 2$		
C					55	$2 \cdot 85$
	10	$0 \cdot 75$	$0 \cdot 56$	$5 \cdot 6$		
D					$62 \cdot 5$	$3 \cdot 24$
	20	$-0 \cdot 25$	$0 \cdot 06$	$1 \cdot 2$		
E					$57 \cdot 5$	$2 \cdot 98$
	30	$-0 \cdot 75$	$0 \cdot 56$	$16 \cdot 8$		
F					$35 \cdot 0$	$1 \cdot 81$
	10	$-1 \cdot 25$	$1 \cdot 56$	$15 \cdot 6$		
G					$22 \cdot 5$	$1 \cdot 17$
	10	$-2 \cdot 25$	$5 \cdot 06$	$50 \cdot 6$		
B					0	0

REFERENCES

Melan, J. 1888 and 1906. *Eiserne Bogenbrucken und Hangenbrucken.*
Timoshenko, S. 1930. *Trans. Amer. Soc. Civ. Engrs.*, **94**, 377.
Timoshenko, S. 1934. *International Assoc. Bridges & Struc. Eng.*, **2**.
Steinmann, D. B. 1935. *Trans. Amer. Soc. Civ. Engrs.*, **100**, 1133.
Atkinson, R. J. and Southwell, R. V. 1938. *J. Instn. Civ. Engrs.*, **11**, 289–326.
Pippard, A. J. S. and Chitty, L. 1942. *J. Instn. Civ. Engrs.*, **18**, 322–333.
Johnson, Bryan and Turneaure. "Modern Framed Structures." Wiley.

EXERCISES

(1) A suspension cable is 700 feet span and 70 feet dip. Calculate the length of the cable.

(718·6 feet.)

(2) A thin uniform flexible cable of weight w per unit length connects two points which are at the same level.

Treating the dip d as small compared with the span prove that the difference between the greatest and least tension is wd, and that the difference between the length of the cable and the span is given approximately by $\dfrac{8}{3}\dfrac{d^2}{l}$.

The span of such a cable is 200 feet, and the dip is 10 feet at a certain temperature. The coefficient of expansion for the cable is 12×10^{-6} per degree Centigrade. Neglecting change of length due to change of stress, calculate the percentage increase in the maximum tension due to a fall in temperature of 30° C.

(2·74 per cent.)

(3) A suspension bridge of 700 feet span has a dip of 70 feet. It carries a uniformly distributed load of 500 tons. If the chains are made of steel, the allowable stress on which is 5 tons per square inch, calculate the required cross-sectional area of the chains.
The anchor chains make an angle of 45° with the piers.
Calculate the load in one anchor chain and the overturning force on a pier

(a) when the chains run over a pulley device,

(b) when the chains are attached to a saddle resting on rollers at the top of the pier.

> [*67·3 square inches.*
> (a) *336·5 tons ; 74·4 tons.*
> (b) *442·0 tons ; none.*]

(4) A cable is suspended from two points separated horizontally by a distance of 60 feet and vertically by a distance of 10 feet. The maximum dip of the cable when hanging freely is 5 feet below the lower point of suspension. It is stiffened by a girder which is hinged at both ends and also at a point vertically below the lowest point of the cable.
Calculate the maximum tension in the cable when the girder carries a uniformly distributed load of 1 ton per foot over the whole span and sketch the bending moment diagram for the girder when a load of 10 tons is placed at the hinge point between the supports.

(61·4 tons.)

(5) A suspension bridge with a three-hinged stiffening girder has a span of 350 feet, a central dip of 35 feet and weighs 350 tons. It is to be designed to carry a super-imposed rolling load of 1 ton per foot of span equally divided between the two sets of chains. This load may cover all or any part of the span.
Using a working stress of 8 tons per square inch calculate :

(a) the cross-sectional area of one suspension cable,

(b) the necessary modulus of section of the stiffening girder.

> [(a) *59 square inches.*
> (b) *1,731 inches³.*]

CHAPTER 14

INFLUENCE LINES FOR STATICALLY DETERMINATE STRUCTURES : ROLLING LOADS.

14.1. Definition.—A diagram which represents the variation of any resultant action, force, deflexion or slope at a particular point in a structure as a *unit* load rolls across the structure is known as an influence line. Thus the influence line of bending moment for any point X on a beam shows how the bending moment at X changes as a load of unity traverses the beam : the ordinate to the curve at any point Y is the bending moment at X when the unit load is at Y. Influence lines are of considerable value in studying the effect of rolling loads on structures and in the present chapter their use for statically determinate beams and trusses will be described.

14.2. Influence lines for a simply supported beam.—Let AB in Fig. 14.1 represent a simply supported beam to be crossed by a rolling load W which

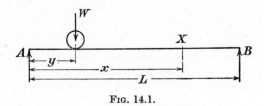

FIG. 14.1.

at any instant is a distance y from A. It is desired to draw a diagram which will represent the variation of bending moment at a fixed point X, which is at a distance x from A, as the load rolls from A to B.

The bending moment at X is

$$M_x = -R_B(L-x) + [W(y-x)]$$

where R_B is the reaction at B and the term in square brackets only appears when it is positive, *i.e.* when $y > x$.

Since

$$R_B = \frac{yW}{L},$$

$$M_x = W\left\{ -\frac{y(L-x)}{L} + [y-x] \right\}.$$

This represents two straight lines covering the ranges A to X and X to B respectively.

When $\quad\quad\quad\quad\quad y=0, \quad M_x=0,$

when $\quad\quad\quad\quad\quad y=x, \quad M_x=-\dfrac{Wx(L-x)}{L},$

when $\quad\quad\quad\quad\quad y=L, \quad M_x=0.$

328

If we now make W=unity, the influence line of bending moments for X is as shown in Fig. 14.2. The bending moment at X when the unit load is at C is represented by the ordinate CD.

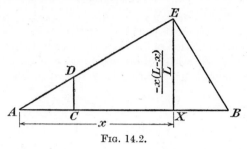

FIG. 14.2.

Again, the shearing force at X is

$$S_x = R_B - [W]$$

the second term only occurring when $y > x$.

i.e.
$$S_x = W \left\{ \frac{y}{L} - [1] \right\}.$$

This again represents two straight lines covering the ranges A—X and X—B respectively.

When $y = 0$ or L, $S_x = 0$,

when $y = x$, $S_x = \dfrac{Wx}{L}$ or $-\dfrac{W}{L}(L-x)$

dependent upon the point being immediately to the left or immediately to the right of X.

The influence line of shearing force for X is therefore as shown in Fig. 14.3, when W is unity. Since XE : XF : : AX : XB, the lines AE and BF are

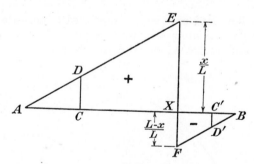

FIG. 14.3.

parallel. When the unit load is between A and X the shearing force at X is positive ; when it is between X and B the shearing force at X is negative. It is in either case represented by ordinates such as CD or C′D′ drawn to the influence line from the load point.

From these influence lines the bending moment or shearing force at X can be found for any system of loads upon the beam. For example, let loads W_1, W_2 . . . W_n act at points 1, 2, . . . n, and let the ordinates to the influence lines of bending moment and shearing force at these points be

$m_1, m_2 \ldots m_n$ and $s_1, s_2 \ldots s_n$ respectively. Then the bending moment and shearing force at X due to this loading are respectively

$$\left.\begin{array}{l} M_x = W_1 m_1 + W_2 m_2 + \ldots + W_n m_n \\ S_x = W_1 s_1 + W_2 s_2 + \ldots + W_n s_n. \end{array}\right\} \quad \ldots \quad (14.1)$$

and

The bending moment and shearing force at the point X due to a uniformly distributed load on any section of the beam can also be found readily from the influence lines. Suppose a load of intensity w covers a length c as indicated on the influence diagram for shearing force drawn in Fig. 14.4. The load

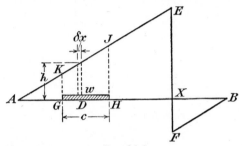

FIG. 14.4.

on a small element of length δx at D is $w\delta x$ and if the ordinate at D is h the shearing force at X due to this element of load is $hw\delta x$. Hence the total shearing force at X due to the whole load cw is $w\int h dx$.

But $\int h dx$ is the area between the length c and the influence line, *i.e.* GHJK, and the shearing force at X is therefore $w \times$ (area of the influence diagram covered by the load). The same argument is applicable to bending moments or any other property for which an influence line can be drawn.

Influence lines will now be used to obtain curves of maximum bending moment and shearing force in a beam when certain systems of rolling loads cross it.

14.3. Single rolling load on a simply supported beam.—Reference to Fig. 14.2 shows that the maximum bending moment at X as a load rolls from A to B occurs when it reaches X, its value then being

$$M_{max} = -\frac{Wx(L-x)}{L}.$$

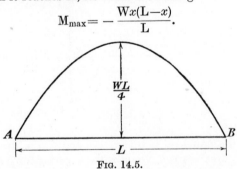

FIG. 14.5.

Since x can have any value between 0 and L the curve of maximum bending moment for any point on the beam is given by this expression, which represents a parabola with a maximum ordinate $\dfrac{WL}{4}$ at the centre of the span. This maximum bending moment diagram is shown in Fig. 14.5,

The influence line for shearing force in Fig. 14.3 shows that the maximum positive shearing force at X occurs when the load reaches X from the left but has not crossed that section.   Its value is

$$S_{max} = \frac{Wx}{L}.$$

Similarly the maximum negative shearing force at X occurs when the load has just crossed the section X, its value being

$$S'_{max} = - \frac{W(L-x)}{L}.$$

These expressions both represent straight lines and are true for all values of x between 0 and L.   Hence the curves of maximum positive and negative shearing forces at all points of the beam are given by Fig. 14.6.

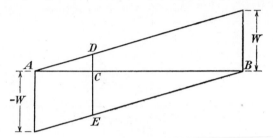

FIG. 14.6.

The two values at any point occur under different load conditions : at C for example the shearing force when the load just reaches C is represented by CD.   As the load crosses the section C it changes from CD to CE which is the maximum negative value at C and occurs when the load acts immediately to the right of that point.

14.4. Distributed rolling load on a simply supported beam.—Two conditions must be considered ; first when the distance covered by the load is greater than the span of the beam and secondly, when it is less than the span.

Load covering a greater length than the span.—Since the bending moment at X, Fig. 14.2, is represented by the area between the load and the influence

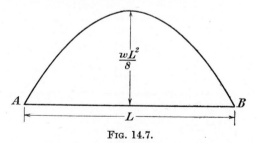

FIG. 14.7.

line, it is clear that the maximum bending moment will occur when the whole span is covered since then the area over the load has the greatest possible value, so

$$M_{max} = -\frac{wL}{2} \times \frac{x(L-x)}{L} = -\frac{wx(L-x)}{2}.$$

This represents the value of the maximum bending moment for any value of x between 0 and L and is a parabola with a maximum ordinate $\dfrac{wL^2}{8}$ at the centre, as shown in Fig. 14.7.

From Fig. 14.3 it is clear that the maximum positive and negative shearing force at X occur when AX and XB respectively are covered by the load, since the positive and negative areas are then the greatest possible.

Hence
$$S_{max} = \frac{wx}{2} \cdot \frac{x}{L} = \frac{wx^2}{2L},$$

and
$$S'_{max} = -\frac{w(L-x)}{2} \cdot \frac{(L-x)}{L} = -\frac{w(L-x)^2}{2L}.$$

These equations hold for all values of x and are parabolas with maximum ordinates of $\dfrac{wL}{2}$ and $-\dfrac{wL}{2}$ when $x=L$ and $x=0$ respectively. The curves are shown in Fig. 14.8.

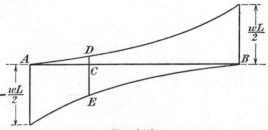

FIG. 14.8.

The two values of the maximum shearing force at C, represented by CD and CE, occur when AC and CB respectively are covered by the load.

Load covering a shorter length than the span.—Let a rolling load of uniform intensity w cover a distance c which is less than L.

It is clear from the influence line that the maximum bending moment at X will occur when the load covers a length FG, part of which lies to the left and part to the right of X as in Fig. 14.9. The area FCEHG must have the greatest possible value.

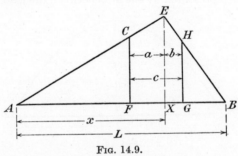

FIG. 14.9.

Suppose XF$=a$ and XG$=b$ so that $a+b=c$.

The mean ordinate between F and X is $\dfrac{(2x-a)(L-x)}{2L}$ and that between G and X is $\dfrac{\{2(L-x)-b\}x}{2L}$.

The area FCEHG=area FCEX+area GHEX,

or
$$A=\frac{(2x-a)(L-x)a}{2L}+\frac{(2L-2x-b)xb}{2L}$$

$$=\frac{1}{2L}\{(2xL-2x^2)c-a^2(L-x)-(c-a)^2x\}.$$

For this to be a maximum $\dfrac{dA}{da}=0$.

Therefore
$$-2a(L-x)+2(c-a)x=0,$$

or
$$\frac{x}{L-x}=\frac{a}{c-a}$$

i.e.
$$\frac{x}{L}=\frac{a}{c},$$

so the bending moment at X is a maximum when the point X divides the load and the span in the same ratio.

The bending moment is then wA and, putting a equal to $\dfrac{cx}{L}$ in the above expression for A, we obtain

$$M_x=\frac{cwx(L-x)}{L}\left(1-\frac{c}{2L}\right).$$

This is a parabola having the maximum ordinate $\dfrac{cwL}{4}\left(1-\dfrac{c}{2L}\right)$ at the centre.

From Fig. 14.3 it is clear that the maximum positive shearing force at X occurs when the load is on the part AX of the beam and the right-hand end of it is at X.

The ordinate at the mid-point of the load is then

$$\frac{x-\dfrac{c}{2}}{x}\times\frac{x}{L}=\frac{2x-c}{2L}$$

and the maximum positive shearing force is

$$S_{max}=\frac{cw(2x-c)}{2L}.$$

This is a straight line in x but it only holds as long as the whole load is on the beam, i.e. when $x\gtreqqless c$.

For values of x less than c the curve will be the parabola of Fig. 14.8.

To plot the complete curve it is convenient to draw the straight line defined by the points

$$x=\left(L+\frac{c}{2}\right),\qquad S=cw.$$

$$x=\frac{c}{2},\qquad\qquad S=0.$$

This gives the maximum positive shearing force between $x=c$ and $x=L$. The diagram is completed by drawing the parabola of Fig. 14.8 between $x=0$ and $x=c$ as shown in Fig. 14.10.

The maximum negative shearing force at X occurs when the load is on the section XB of the beam (Fig. 14.3) with the left-hand end of the load at X.

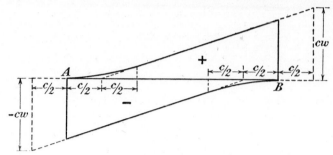

FIG. 14.10.

The ordinate at the mid-point of the load is

$$\frac{L-x-\dfrac{c}{2}}{L-x}\times\frac{L-x}{L}=\frac{2L-2x-c}{2L}$$

and the maximum negative shearing force is

$$S'_{max}=-\frac{cw(2L-2x-c)}{2L}.$$

This is a straight line between $x=0$ and $x=L-c$ and a parabola between $x=L-c$ and $x=L$. Convenient points on the straight line for plotting the diagram are

$$x=\left(L-\frac{c}{2}\right),\quad S'=0.$$

$$x=-\frac{c}{2},\quad S'=-cw.$$

The complete maximum shearing force diagram is then as shown in Fig. 14.10.

14.5. Two concentrated loads on a simply supported beam.—Suppose two loads W_1 and W_2 separated by a distance a, as in Fig. 14.11, to roll across a simply supported beam. Let P, the resultant of these loads, act at c from W_1 and b from W_2 so that $P=W_1+W_2$ and $a=c+b$.

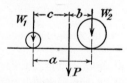

FIG. 14.11.

From a consideration of the bending moment diagram for the loads in any position on the beam it is clear that the maximum value of the bending moment will always occur under one of the loads. Hence the maximum value of the bending moment at a point X will occur when one of the loads is at this point.

In the first place suppose W_2 is at X. The total bending moment at X due to the two loads is then, from the influence line of Fig. 14.2,

$$M_2=-\frac{W_2x(L-x)}{L}-\frac{W_1(x-a)(L-x)}{L}$$

$$=-\frac{(L-x)}{L}\{W_2x+W_1(x-a)\}.$$

The term in brackets is the moment of the loads about the left-hand support of the beam and is therefore equal to the moment of their resultant about the same point, *i.e.*

$$M_2 = -\frac{P(L-x)(x-b)}{L}.$$

Now suppose W_1 to be at X ; the bending moment at X is

$$M_1 = -\frac{W_1x(L-x)}{L} - \frac{W_2x(L-x-a)}{L}$$

$$= -\frac{x}{L}\{W_1(L-x)+W_2(L-x-a)\}.$$

Substituting the moment of P about the right-hand support of the beam for the term in brackets we have

$$M_1 = -\frac{Px(L-x-c)}{L}.$$

M_2 will be numerically greater than M_1 if

$$(L-x)(x-b) > x(L-x-c)$$

i.e. if $$Lx - Lb - x^2 + bx > Lx - x^2 - cx$$

or $$-Lb > -(b+c)x.$$

Substituting $a=b+c$, this leads to the condition

$$ax > Lb.$$

Hence, M_2 will be numerically greater than M_1 if $\dfrac{x}{L} > \dfrac{b}{a}$,

i.e. if $$\frac{x}{L} > \frac{W_1}{W_1+W_2}.$$

To plot the diagram of maximum bending moments on the beam it is convenient to draw the curves for M_1 and M_2 separately.

Thus $$M_2 = -\frac{P}{L}(L-x)(x-b)$$

which is a parabola having its maximum ordinate where

$$L-x = x-b,$$

i.e. at $$x = \tfrac{1}{2}(L+b).$$

The value of the maximum ordinate is $\dfrac{P(L-b)^2}{4L}$.

M_2 is zero at $x=L$ and $x=b$ and the parabola is shown in Fig. 14.12.

Again $$M_1 = -\frac{Px}{L}(L-x-c)$$

which is another parabola with its maximum ordinate at $x=\tfrac{1}{2}(L-c)$, the bending moment there being $\dfrac{P(L-c)^2}{4L}$.

Zero values occur at $x=0$ and at $x=L-c$ and this parabola is also plotted in Fig. 14.12.

The parabolas are correct only as long as both the loads are on the beam, *i.e.* M_1 holds from $x=0$ to $x=L-a$ and M_2 from $x=a$ to $x=L$. Between

$x=L-a$ and $x=L$, M_1 must be drawn for the single load W_1 on the beam and between $x=0$ and $x=a$, M_2 must be drawn for the single load W_2 on the beam. These curves are both parts of parabolas and are shown in the diagram. The curve of maximum bending moment for the beam is indicated by a full line : the point of intersection of the parabolas occurs at $x=\dfrac{W_1L}{W_1+W_2}$ which in Fig. 14.12 coincides accidentally with $x=a$.

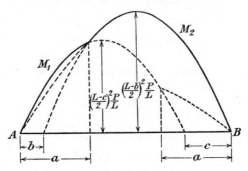

$$\left(\tfrac{L-c}{2}\right)^2\tfrac{P}{L} \qquad \left(\tfrac{L-b}{2}\right)^2\tfrac{P}{L}$$

FIG. 14.12.

Reference to the influence line of Fig. 14.3 shows that the maximum positive and negative shearing forces on the beam occur when W_2 and W_1 are respectively at X, their values being obtained directly from the influence line. Thus the maximum positive value is

$$S_{\max}=\frac{xW_2}{L}+\left(\frac{x-a}{x}\right)\frac{xW_1}{L}=\frac{1}{L}\{W_2x+W_1(x-a)\}$$

or, substituting as before,

$$S_{\max}=\frac{P}{L}(x-b).$$

Similarly, the maximum negative value is

$$S'_{\max}=\left(\frac{L-x}{L}\right)W_1+\left(\frac{L-x-a}{L-x}\right)\left(\frac{L-x}{L}\right)W_2=\frac{P}{L}(L-x-c).$$

The expression for $S_{\max}$ is a straight line between $x=a$ and $x=L$. When x is less than a, W_2 only is on the beam and the curve is the appropriate one for a single load, *i.e.* another straight line, as shown in Fig. 14.6.

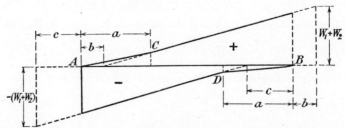

FIG. 14.13.

It should be noticed that the formula above gives $S_{\max}=0$ when $x=b$ and $S_{\max}=P$ when $x=L+b$. The straight line representing $S_{\max}$ is conveniently plotted from these two points as shown in Fig. 14.13.   The diagram is completed by joining AC to represent the effect of the single load W_2 between $x=0$ and $x=a$.

Similarly, S'_{max} is plotted from the two points

$$x=L-c, \quad S'_{max}=0,$$
and
$$x=-c, \quad S'_{max}=P.$$

Then BD, completing the diagram, represents the effect of the single load W_1 between $x=L-a$ and $x=L$.

14.6. Any number of loads on a beam.—When a train of loads crosses a simply supported beam the construction of the maximum bending moment and shearing force diagrams is much more difficult than those already considered.   At any point on the beam the maximum bending moment will occur when one of the loads is over that point but the particular load will vary with the position of the point.   A criterion to determine the disposition of the train to produce the maximum effect may be obtained as follows.

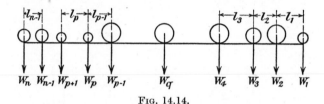

FIG. 14.14.

Let Fig. 14.14 represent a train of loads which passes over a span L, and consider the bending moment at a point X, which is x from A, as shown in Fig. 14.1.

When the load W_p is at X, the negative bending moment at X is, from the influence line,

$$M_p=\frac{L-x}{L}[W_px+W_{p+1}(x-l_p)+W_{p+2}(x-l_p-l_{p+1})+ \cdots$$
$$+W_n(x-l_p-l_{p+1}- \cdots -l_{n-1})]$$
$$+\frac{x}{L}[W_{p-1}(L-x-l_{p-1})+W_{p-2}(L-x-l_{p-1}-l_{p-2})+ \cdots$$
$$+W_1(L-x-l_{p-1}-l_{p-2}- \cdots -l_1)]$$

Similarly when W_{p+1} is at X, the negative bending moment at X is

$$M_{p+1}=\frac{L-x}{L}[W_{p+1}x+W_{p+2}(x-l_{p+1})+ \cdots$$
$$+W_n(x-l_{p+1}-l_{p+2}- \cdots -l_{n-1})]$$
$$+\frac{x}{L}[W_p(L-x-l_p)+W_{p-1}(L-x-l_p-l_{p-1})+ \cdots$$
$$+W_1(L-x-l_p-l_{p-1}- \cdots -l_1)]$$

M_{p+1} will be greater than M_p if

$$M_{p+1}-M_p>0.$$

From the expressions just obtained for the bending moments, this is true if

$$(L-x)[W_{p+1}+W_{p+2}+ \cdots +W_n]-x[W_p+W_{p-1}+ \cdots +W_1]>0,$$

i.e. if $L[W_{p+1}+W_{p+2}+ \ldots +W_n]-x[W_1+W_2+ \ldots +W_n]>0,$

or if $\dfrac{\text{Sum of loads to left of X}}{\text{Total load}} > \dfrac{x}{L}$ . . . .   (14.2)

Suppose for example a particular load of the train, say, W_q, is crossing X. Just before W_q reaches X the sum of the loads to the left of X is $W_q+ \ldots +W_n$ and just after W_q has passed X the sum of the loads to the left of X is $W_{q+1}+ \ldots +W_n.$

If $\dfrac{W_q+ \ldots +W_n}{\overset{n}{\underset{1}{\Sigma}}W} > \dfrac{x}{L}$

but $\dfrac{W_{q+1}+ \ldots +W_n}{\overset{n}{\underset{1}{\Sigma}}W} < \dfrac{x}{L}$

the maximum bending moment at X occurs when W_q is at X.

To illustrate this suppose the train of loads shown in Fig. 14.15 crosses a girder.

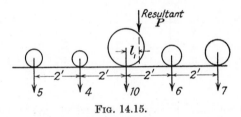

FIG. 14.15.

The maximum bending moment at a point one-third of the span from the left-hand support will occur when the 10-ton load is at the point, since

$$\frac{10+4+5}{32} > \frac{1}{3}$$

and $\dfrac{4+5}{32} < \dfrac{1}{3}.$

The maximum bending moment at a point two-thirds of the span from the left-hand support will occur when the 6-ton load is at that point, since

$$\frac{6+10+4+5}{32} > \frac{2}{3}$$

and $\dfrac{10+4+5}{32} < \dfrac{2}{3}$

In this analysis it is assumed that all the loads are on the beam. At points where this is not true only those loads which are acting should be considered, *e.g.* when the 7-ton load has passed the right-hand support the criterion should be applied for the remaining four loads only.

The maximum bending moment which can occur under any particular load as the train crosses the girder can be determined as follows. Let AB in Fig. 14.16 represent a beam which is traversed by a train of loads and let W_p, the load we are considering, have just reached the point X. The total load is P, which acts through the centre of gravity of the system, a distance

l_1 from X.   Let P_L be the resultant of all the loads on the section AX of the beam, acting at a distance l_2 from X.   The bending moment at X is then

$$M_x = -R_A x + P_L l_2 = -\frac{Px}{L}(L - x + l_1) + P_L l_2$$

which will reach a maximum value at the point where

$$\frac{dM_x}{dx} = 0,$$

i.e. when

$$L - 2x + l_1 = 0.$$

or

$$x = \frac{L}{2} + \frac{l_1}{2} \quad . \quad . \quad . \quad . \quad . \quad (14.3)$$

Thus, the maximum bending moment under any load occurs when the centre of the beam C bisects the distance between the centre of gravity of the load system and the load under consideration.

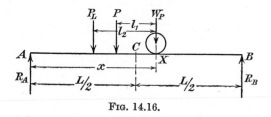

FIG. 14.16.

Once the position of the load has been determined the bending moment at X can be calculated.   The maximum possible bending moment on the beam will occur under one of the loads and by applying the criterion just obtained to all loads in turn and calculating the maximum bending moment under each, the absolute maximum can be found.   This is, however, a long process if there are a number of loads and it is generally possible by the help of the criterion given in equation (14.2) to deduce the load under which the absolute maximum will occur, remembering that such maximum will be almost invariably near the centre of the span.

As an example, consider the train of loads shown in Fig. 14.15.   The load of 10 tons in crossing any section changes the ratio of loads to the left of the section to the total load from $\frac{19}{32}$ to $\frac{9}{32}$.   Hence from equation (14.2) it is evident that between points $\frac{9}{32}$ and $\frac{19}{32}$ of the span of the beam measured from the left-hand support the maximum bending moment will occur under the 10-ton load.   Since this range covers the centre of the beam, it may be deduced that the absolute maximum occurs under this load, and from (14.3) its position will be such that P, the resultant load, and the 10-ton load are each a distance $l_1/2$ from the centre of the beam.   Should this disposition in any particular case place the 10-ton load outside the range over which it governs the position of maximum bending moment, the same procedure should be applied to the load on the other side of the resultant.

Maximum shearing force.—When a train of loads crosses a beam the maximum shearing force at any point X will occur when ΣWs in equation (14.1) is a maximum.   In general, therefore, as will be seen from the influence line in Fig. 14.3, the maximum positive shearing force will occur when the load at one end of the train is at X and all the other loads are on the section

AX. Similarly, the maximum negative shearing force will occur when the other end load is at X and all the other loads are on the section XB. This is generally but not invariably true and conditions may arise in which the maximum occurs when part of the load has crossed X. An instance of this is afforded if the end load is small compared with the next or is separated from it by a considerable distance. It is therefore useful to determine a criterion for load position giving maximum values.

Consider the train of loads represented in Fig. 14.14 and suppose the load W_p has just reached X. Then the loads $W_p \ldots W_n$ contribute positive shearing forces and the loads $W_{p-1} \ldots W_1$ contribute negative shearing forces to the total at X.

The total shearing force at X is then, from the influence line,

$$S_p = \left[\frac{W_p x}{L} + \frac{W_{p+1}(x-l_p)}{L} + \frac{W_{p+2}(x-l_p-l_{p+1})}{L} + \ldots \right.$$
$$\left. + \frac{W_n(x-l_p- \ldots -l_{n-1})}{L}\right]$$
$$- \left[\frac{W_{p-1}(L-x-l_{p-1})}{L} + \frac{W_{p-2}(L-x-l_{p-1}-l_{p-2})}{L} + \ldots \right.$$
$$\left. + \frac{W_1(L-x-l_{p-1}-l_{p-2} \ldots -l_1)}{L}\right]$$

or

$$S_p = \frac{1}{L}\left[x\overset{n}{\underset{1}{\Sigma}}W - \{W_{p+1}l_p + W_{p+2}(l_p+l_{p+1}) + \ldots +W_n(l_p+l_{p+1}+\ldots+l_{n-1})\}\right.$$
$$- \{W_{p-1}(L-l_{p-1}) + W_{p-2}(L-l_{p-1}-l_{p-2}) + \ldots$$
$$\left. + W_1(L-l_{p-1}-l_{p-2} \ldots -l_1)\}\right].$$

Now suppose the train to have moved forward so that W_{p+1} is at X; the shearing force at X is then

$$S_{p+1} = \frac{1}{L}\left[x\overset{n}{\underset{1}{\Sigma}}W - \{W_{p+2}l_{p+1} + W_{p+3}(l_{p+1}+l_{p+2}) + \ldots \right.$$
$$+ W_n(l_{p+1}+l_{p+2} \ldots +l_{n-1})\} - \{W_p(L-l_p) + W_{p-1}(L-l_p-l_{p-1})$$
$$\left. + \ldots +W_1(L-l_p-l_{p-1} \ldots -l_1)\}\right]$$

S_p will be greater than S_{p+1} if

$$S_p - S_{p+1} > 0.$$

From the above expressions this is found to be true if

$$W_p L - l_p \overset{n}{\underset{1}{\Sigma}}W > 0$$

i.e. if
$$\frac{W_p}{l_p} > \frac{\overset{n}{\underset{1}{\Sigma}}W}{L}. \quad \ldots \quad \ldots \quad (14.4)$$

In the above analysis the load W_p is supposed to have just reached X and to contribute a positive shearing force to the total at X.

If it had just passed X its contribution would be negative and the results for S_p and S_{p+1} would be modified by deducting W_p and W_{p+1} respectively.

The criterion then becomes

$$S_p > S_{p+1}$$

if
$$\frac{W_{p+1}}{l_p} > \frac{\overset{n}{\underset{1}{\Sigma W}}}{L} \quad . \quad . \quad . \quad . \quad . \quad (14.5)$$

In the determination of maximum positive shearing forces equation (14.4) must be used : for maximum negative shearing forces, equation (14.5).

The two results can be combined in a single criterion if it is assumed when considering positive shearing forces that the load system moves from left to right and when considering negative shearing forces that it moves from right to left.

Let w_q' be the intensity of loading obtained by uniformly distributing any load W_q of the train over the distance between that load and the following load, and let w be the intensity of loading obtained by similarly distributing the total load over the span of the girder.

Then if $w_q' > w$, the shearing force when the leading load is at any point is *numerically* greater than when the following load is that point. If $w_q' = w$ it signifies that the shearing force at the section will be the same whether the leading or the following load is placed there.

If the section of the beam under consideration is so close to the support that some of the loads are not on the beam, w must be calculated from the total operative load and not from the total of the train of loads.

As an example, the train of loads shown in Fig. 14.17 will be assumed to cross beams of different spans.

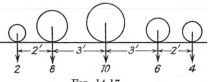

FIG. 14.17.

First, let the span be 60 feet. Since the total load is 30 tons, $w = \frac{1}{2}$ ton per foot. For positive shearing forces the load is considered to move from left to right, *i.e.* the 4-ton load leads.

Then for the 4-ton load

$$w_4' = \tfrac{4}{2} = 2 \text{ tons per foot.}$$

Similarly

$$w_6' = \tfrac{6}{3} = 2 \text{ tons per foot,}$$
$$w_{10}' = \tfrac{10}{3} = 3 \cdot 33 \text{ tons per foot}$$

and
$$w_8' = \tfrac{8}{2} = 4 \text{ tons per foot.}$$

Since these are all greater than w we have

$$S_4 > S_6 > S_{10} > S_8$$

and the maximum positive shearing force at any section occurs when the 4-ton load is at that section.

For negative shearing forces the train is supposed to move over the beam in the opposite direction, *i.e.* with the 2-ton load leading.

Then,
$$w_2' = \tfrac{2}{2} = 1 \text{ ton per foot,}$$
$$w_8' = \tfrac{8}{3} = 2 \cdot 67 \text{ tons per foot,}$$
$$w_{10}' = \tfrac{10}{3} = 3 \cdot 33 \text{ tons per foot,}$$

and
$$w_6' = \tfrac{6}{2} = 3 \cdot 0 \text{ tons per foot.}$$

Here also, since all of these are greater than w, the maximum negative shearing force at any section occurs when the 2-ton load is at that section.

12

Now let the span of the beam be 30 feet, so that $w=1$ ton per foot. As before the maximum positive shear will occur when the 4-ton load is at any section, but since for negative shearing forces $w_2'=w$, the shearing force at any section will be the same whether the 2-ton load or the 8-ton load be placed at that section.

This can be verified by considering any section and, as an example, the mid-section of the beam will be taken. When the 2-ton load just reaches this section the negative shearing force there will be minus the reaction R_A, i.e. $-\frac{148}{15}$ tons, and when the 8-ton load reaches the section the shearing force there will be $-R_A+2$ or $-\frac{148}{15}$ tons.

Finally, let the span of the beam be 24 feet, so that $w=1\cdot25$.

For negative shearing forces, w_2' is less than w and the greatest negative shearing force at any section will occur when the 8-ton load is at that section.

Again verifying this by reference to the mid-section of the beam, the respective shearing forces when the 2-ton and 8-ton loads reach that section are $-\frac{103}{12}$ tons and $-\frac{109}{12}$ tons.

14.7. Influence lines for framed structures.—Influence lines may be drawn to show changes of the force in any member of a framed structure as a load rolls across the truss. They are important in bridge design and the method

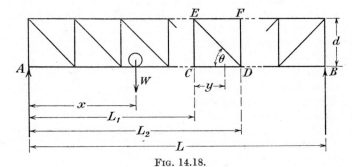

FIG. 14.18.

of drawing them is best illustrated by examples. In the first place we shall find the influence line for the force in a diagonal bracing member of the truss shown in Fig. 14.18 as a load rolls along the bottom chord. Let the total span of the truss be L, and the distances of any adjacent panel points C and D from A be L_1 and L_2 respectively.

If a load W is at a distance x from A and x is less than L_1, the vertical shearing force across the panel ED is

$$S_{ED}=\frac{xW}{L}$$

and the force in the member ED is

$$F_{ED}=-\frac{xW}{L}\ \mathrm{cosec}\ \theta,$$

the negative sign denoting a compression.

If x is greater than L_2

$$S_{ED}=-\left(\frac{L-x}{L}\right)W$$

and

$$F_{ED}=\left(\frac{L-x}{L}\right)W\ \mathrm{cosec}\ \theta.$$

When the load is between two panel points the chord between these points acts as a beam and distributes the load to them.   It is generally assumed that the truss is pin-jointed so that the load is divided in the inverse ratio of its distances from the panel points.   If the load is between A and C or between D and B the total shear, and so the force in ED, is unaffected whether we assume this distribution to have taken place or not.   If, however, the load is on the length CD the distribution affects the shearing force.

Suppose then the load to be at y from C, *i.e.* at L_1+y from A, where y is less than L_2-L_1.   The proportion of the load transferred to D is $\dfrac{yW}{L_2-L_1}$ and the shearing force across the panel ED is $R_B-\dfrac{yW}{L_2-L_1}$

or
$$S_{ED}=\left(\frac{L_1+y}{L}-\frac{y}{L_2-L_1}\right)W$$

and
$$F_{ED}=-\left(\frac{L_1+y}{L}-\frac{y}{L_2-L_1}\right)W\ \text{cosec}\ \theta.$$

These equations for F_{ED} all represent straight lines in x or y and if W is unity they define the influence line for the force in ED.

When the load is at C, both relevant equations give $F_{ED}=-\dfrac{L_1}{L}\ \text{cosec}\ \theta$

and when the load is at D, both relevant equations give $F_{ED}=\dfrac{L-L_2}{L}\ \text{cosec}\ \theta.$

The influence diagram thus consists of three straight lines as is usual in a pin-jointed truss ; sometimes, as will be seen later, two of these lines merge into one.

The first two sections of the diagram are defined by the co-ordinates $(0, 0)$, $(L, -\text{cosec}\ \theta)$ and $(0, \text{cosec}\ \theta)$, $(L, 0)$ respectively.   They are parallel

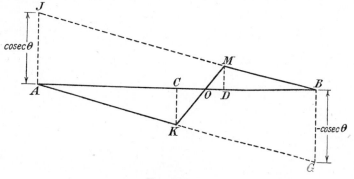

FIG. 14.19.

lines as shown at AG and BJ in Fig. 14.19.   If C and D represent any two adjacent panel points and CK and DM are drawn perpendicular to AB to cut AG and BJ at K and M, these ordinates are the values of F_{ED} at C and D respectively.   K and M are joined by a straight line to form the third section of the diagram and AKMB represents the influence line of force in ED.

The lines AG and BJ are common to all influence lines for diagonal members of the truss ; differences in diagrams depend only on the position of the panel under consideration.   In Fig. 14.19 the left side of the diagram is negative, indicating a compression in the diagonal member when the load is on that section of the truss. The sign depends on the direction of the diagonal : if the panel ED had been braced across the opposite diagonal the force in the bracing member would have been reversed, *i.e.* tensile when the load was on the left-hand portion of the truss and compressive when it was on the right-hand side.

To find a general expression for the force in a chord member such as EF, the method of sections may be used : thus by taking moments about point D we have, when $x < L_2$,

$$F_{EF} = -\frac{R_B(L-L_2)}{d} = -\frac{x(L-L_2)W}{Ld},$$

and when $x > L_2$,

$$F_{EF} = -\frac{x(L-L_2)W}{Ld} + \frac{(x-L_2)W}{d} = -\frac{WL_2}{Ld}(L-x),$$

the negative sign as before denoting that the force is compressive.

When the load is between C and D the portion transferred to D has no moment about that point and these equations are sufficient for the influence diagram, which consists of two straight lines instead of the three for the

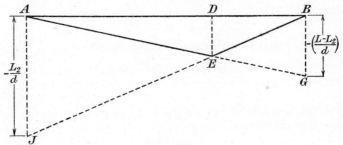

FIG. 14.20.

diagonal member. Making W equal to unity, convenient co-ordinates for plotting the equations are $(0, 0)$ and $\left(L, -\frac{L-L_2}{d}\right)$, $\left(0, -\frac{L_2}{d}\right)$ and $(L, 0)$ respectively. These lines are AG and BJ in Fig. 14.20 : they intersect at E vertically below D and the influence line is AEB.

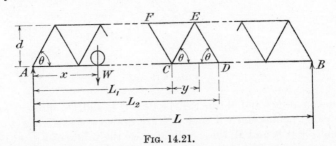

FIG. 14.21.

The influence line may be drawn similarly for a member of the bottom chord. For this particular truss the influence lines for any member are the same whether the load is on the top or the bottom chord but in many structures they are different.

The Warren truss shown in Fig. 14.21 will next be considered and in the first place it will be assumed that the load is on the bottom chord.

When $x < L_1$, the shearing force across CE is $\dfrac{x}{L} W$

and
$$F_{CE} = \frac{x}{L} W \text{ cosec } \theta.$$

When $x > L_2$, $F_{CE} = -\left(\dfrac{L-x}{L}\right) W \text{ cosec } \theta.$

When W is between L_1 and L_2 so that $x = L_1 + y$
$$F_{CE} = \left\{ \left(\frac{L_1 + y}{L}\right) - \left(\frac{y}{L_2 - L_1}\right) \right\} W \text{ cosec } \theta.$$

As before, these equations represent three straight lines and the influence diagram is as shown in Fig. 14.22, which is drawn as for the first example.

The force in CD can be found by the method of sections for any position of the load and since the distances of E from A and B are respectively $\frac{1}{2}(L_1 + L_2)$ and $\frac{1}{2}(2L - L_1 - L_2)$ the following results are obtained.

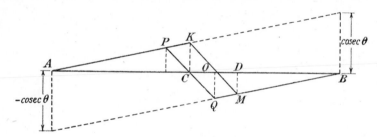

FIG. 14.22.

When $x < L_1$, $F_{CD} = \dfrac{R_B(2L - L_1 - L_2)}{2d} = \dfrac{W}{2Ld} x(2L - L_1 - L_2).$

This is a straight line with values for F_{CD} of 0 and $\dfrac{WL_1}{2Ld}(2L - L_1 - L_2)$ when x is 0 and L_1 respectively.

When $x > L_2$, $F_{CD} = \dfrac{R_A(L_1 + L_2)}{2d} = \dfrac{W}{2Ld}(L - x)(L_1 + L_2)$

which is also a straight line, F_{CD} being $\dfrac{W}{2Ld}(L - L_2)(L_1 + L_2)$ and 0 when x is L_2 and L respectively.

When x lies between L_1 and L_2,
$$F_{CD} = \frac{R_B}{2d}(2L - L_1 - L_2) - \left(\frac{x - L_1}{L_2 - L_1}\right)\left(\frac{L_2 - L_1}{2}\right)\frac{W}{d}$$
$$= \frac{W}{2Ld}\{x(L - L_1 - L_2) + LL_1\}.$$

This is again a straight line, the values of F_{CD} when x is L_1 and L_2 being $\dfrac{WL_1}{2Ld}(2L - L_1 - L_2)$ and $\dfrac{W}{2Ld}(L - L_2)(L_1 + L_2)$ as obtained for the same points from the other two equations.

If W is made equal to unity these three lines define the influence diagram. The first two equations may be plotted from the co-ordinates $(0, 0)$, $\left(L, \dfrac{2L-L_1-L_2}{2d}\right)$ and $\left(0, \dfrac{L_1+L_2}{2d}\right)$, $(L, 0)$ respectively and are shown in Fig. 14.23. If from C and D perpendiculars are drawn to cut these lines at G and H and these points are joined, the complete influence diagram is AGHB.

When the top chord is loaded the diagrams obtained will be of the same general shape but since the nodes of the top chord are not vertically above those of the bottom chord the three lines forming the diagrams will not terminate at the same points as when the bottom chord is loaded, *e.g.* the influence diagram for the force in CE will be APQB in Fig. 14.22 instead of AKMB as before.

From these diagrams it is easy to determine the worst position of a uniformly distributed load for any particular member. From Fig. 14.20 or 14.23, for example, it is clear that the worst load in any chord member will

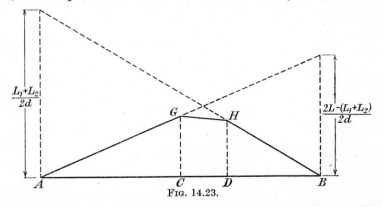

Fig. 14.23.

occur when the whole truss is loaded. If the load is of such length that the whole span cannot be covered by it, it must be arranged in such a way that the area of the diagram over the load is a maximum. For a truss in which the influence diagram is formed of two lines, as in Fig. 14.20, this is done as in paragraph 14.4, the result obtained there being directly applicable. When the diagram consists of three lines as in Fig. 14.23, the disposition of load will depend on its length relative to a bay of the truss and a general solution is cumbersome.

The maximum load in a diagonal member will occur either when AO or OB (Fig. 14.19) is completely covered. In the first instance the load will be the maximum compression and in the second the maximum tension. The position of O is found thus :—

From the similar triangles OCK and ODM,

$$\frac{OC}{OD}=\frac{CK}{MD}.$$

Since BJ and AG are parallel, the triangles AKC, BMD are similar and

$$\frac{CK}{MD}=\frac{AC}{BD}$$

hence

$$\frac{OC}{OD}=\frac{AC}{DB}=\frac{L_1}{L-L_2}.$$

If the load is not long enough to cover these lengths its positions to obtain the maximum areas under the influence line may be found as in paragraph 14.4.

14.8. Influence lines for three-pinned arch.—ACB in Fig. 14.24 is a three-pinned arch of any shape.

The load W is at y from A, y being less than L_1.   The line of action of

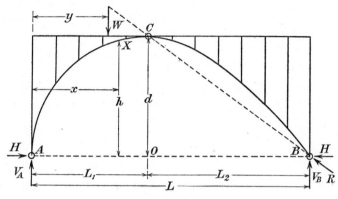

Fig. 14.24.

the resultant reaction at B must pass through C and the sides BO, OC and BC of the triangle BOC represent to scale the forces H, V_B and R.

Then
$$H=\left(\frac{OB}{OC}\right)V_B=\frac{L_2yW}{Ld}$$

where $L=L_1+L_2$.

This is a straight line and is the influence line for H for positions of the load between A and C when W is unity.   Its maximum value is $\dfrac{L_1L_2}{Ld}$, when $y=L_1$.

A corresponding line is obtained for the load between B and C, taking the origin at B and measuring y to the left.

The influence diagram ADB is shown in Fig. 14.25, the two lines being plotted from the co-ordinates $(0, 0)$, $\left(L,\dfrac{L_2}{d}\right)$ and $\left(0,\dfrac{L_1}{d}\right)$, $(L, 0)$.

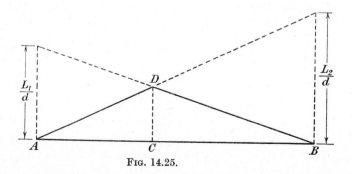

Fig. 14.25.

To obtain the influence line of bending moments it is necessary to consider the load in three regions.

If X is any point between A and C at a distance x from A we have when $y < x$,

$$M_x = Hh - V_B(L-x)$$

$$= \frac{L_2yWh}{Ld} - \frac{yW}{L}(L-x)$$

$$= \frac{Wy}{L}\left\{\frac{L_2h}{d} - (L-x)\right\}.$$

When y lies between x and L_1

$$M_x = Hh - V_Ax,$$

$$= \frac{L_2yWh}{Ld} - \frac{x(L-y)W}{L}$$

$$= \frac{W}{L}\left\{\frac{L_2hy}{d} - x(L-y)\right\}.$$

When $y > L_1$,

$$H = \frac{L_1(L-y)W}{Ld}$$

and

$$M_x = Hh - V_Ax$$

$$= \frac{L_1(L-y)Wh}{Ld} - \frac{x(L-y)W}{L}$$

$$= \frac{W(L-y)}{L}\left\{\frac{L_1h}{d} - x\right\}.$$

These three linear equations define the influence diagram of bending moments, when W is unity.

Then when $y = x$, the first two give

$$M_x = \frac{x}{L}\left\{\frac{L_2h}{d} - (L-x)\right\},$$

which is always negative.

When $y = L_1$, the second two give

$$M_x = \frac{L_2}{L}\left\{\frac{L_1h}{d} - x\right\},$$

which is always positive.

When $y = 0$ and L, $M_x = 0$.

The bending moment at X when the load is at X will be *numerically* greater than when it is at C if

$$x\left\{\frac{L_2h}{d} - (L-x)\right\} + L_2\left\{\frac{L_1h}{d} - x\right\} \qquad \text{is negative,}$$

i.e. if

$$\frac{xL_2h}{d} - x(L-x) + \left(\frac{L_1L_2h}{d} - xL_2\right) < 0,$$

or

$$\frac{L_2h}{d}(x+L_1) - x(L_2+L-x) < 0,$$

i.e. if

$$\left(\frac{L_2h}{d} + x\right)(x+L_1) < 2xL.$$

This condition is not always satisfied and the maximum bending moment at X may occur either when the load is at X or at C.   The influence diagram

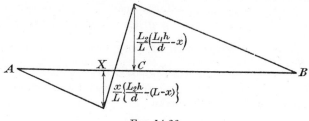

FIG. 14.26.

is shown in Fig. 14.26 and the curve of maximum negative bending moments can be found from the first equation for M_x.

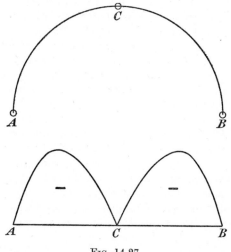

FIG. 14.27.

As an illustration consider the semi-circular arch with a central pin as shown in Fig. 14.27.

Now
$$L_1 = L_2 = L/2,$$

$$\frac{h}{d} = \frac{2\sqrt{x(L-x)}}{L}$$

and
$$M_x = \frac{x}{L}\{\sqrt{x(L-x)} - (L-x)\}.$$

This is zero both at $x=0$ and at $x=\frac{L}{2}$, and the curve of maximum negative bending moments is shown in Fig. 14.27.

14.9. Conventional load systems.—The exact calculation of the maximum bending moments and shearing forces at all sections of a bridge as a train of loads passes across it is very laborious and the uncertainties introduced by the dynamic effects of the system travelling at high speed are such that extreme accuracy in calculation is not justified. It is usual therefore in design to adopt conventional systems of load to simplify the procedure.

One method assumes that the effect of a train of wheels can be reproduced by an equivalent uniformly distributed load. It has already been shown that when a single load traverses a girder the curve of maximum bending moments is a parabola having a maximum ordinate $\dfrac{WL}{4}$ at the centre of the span : if the concentrated load is supposed to be replaced by a uniformly distributed load of intensity w it is necessary, if the maximum bending moments are to be the same, to make

$$\frac{wL^2}{8} = \frac{WL}{4}$$

i.e.
$$w = \frac{2W}{L}.$$

The bending moments at all points when this equivalent load w covers the span will be the same as those under the concentrated load W as it traverses the girder. The maximum shearing forces caused by both systems will also be the same at the ends of the beam but for no other points, since for the concentrated load the curves of maximum shearing force are straight lines whilst for the uniformly distributed load they are parabolas.

When the train consists of a number of concentrated loads the curve of maximum bending moments can be enveloped by a curve which approximates to a parabola but which is rather flatter at midspan and steeper at the ends than a true parabola. It is thus impossible to obtain exact agreement at all points when a uniformly distributed load is substituted for the train. If a parabola is drawn which has the same area as the true curve the ordinates of the two curves are equal at about the quarter-point of the span, and one approximate method of determining the effect of a train of loads is to calculate the maximum bending moment they produce at the quarter-point and to make the equivalent uniformly distributed load of such magnitude that it gives the same value at that point.

The bending moment at the quarter-point of the span under a uniformly distributed load of intensity w is $\dfrac{3wL^2}{32}$ and if the calculated maximum bending moment at the same point due to the actual load system is M' the equivalent load is

$$w = \frac{32M'}{3L^2}.$$

This equivalent load gives a bending moment at the centre of the span rather greater and near the ends rather less than the correct values. Agreement between the true bending moment and that due to a uniformly distributed load may be obtained for any point other than the quarter span by using a different value of w, and if a number of bridges have to be designed for the same rolling load system it is worth while to determine the values of w appropriate to a number of points along the span. Once tables or curves embodying these data have been obtained they can be applied very simply to the design of any bridge subjected to the particular load system, but unless the number to be designed is considerable the time involved in obtaining the data will not be justified.

In general, if M′ is the true bending moment caused at the $\frac{1}{n}$th point of the bridge by the actual load system and w the equivalent distributed load which produces the same bending moment at this point we make

$$M' = \frac{w}{2}\left(\frac{n-1}{n^2}\right)L^2$$

or

$$w = \frac{2n^2 M'}{(n-1)L^2}.$$

In American railway practice use is made of a number of conventional load systems proposed by Theodore Cooper in 1894, so designed that any two of them are connected by a constant multiplier.   The system consists

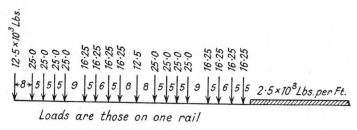

Loads are those on one rail

FIG. 14.28.

of two engines followed by a train.   An example, which represents the E.50 loading on one line of rail, is shown in Fig. 14.28.

When a system such as this is in general use the method of calculation by the use of equivalent distributed loads varying for different points on the span is very satisfactory since curves giving these equivalent loads can be standardised (Johnson, Bryan and Turneaure).

The shearing force across a panel cannot be calculated directly from the equivalent loads for bending moments but a simple device enables the same data to be used for this purpose.

Fig. 14.29 shows a truss and the influence line of shearing force for the panel CD.   The panels are of equal length l.   Suppose that any system of loads is placed on the section AO of the truss and let P_L and P_R be the resultants of the loads to the left and right of C respectively.

These resultants act respectively at a from A and b from C.   It is evident from the geometry of the diagram that

$$OC = \frac{nl}{N-1} \; ; \quad AO = \frac{Nnl}{N-1}$$

and C is the $\frac{1}{N}$th point of the length AO.

Suppose the length AO to be a simply supported beam, then the bending moment at C, due to the load system, is

$$M_C = -R_0 . CO + P_R . b$$

where R_0 is the reaction at O,

i.e.

$$M_C = -CO\left\{\frac{aP_L}{AO} + \left(\frac{AC+b}{AO}\right)P_R\right\} + P_R b.$$

On substituting for the lengths this becomes

$$M_C = -\frac{1}{N}\{aP_L + (nl+b)P_R - NbP_R\}.$$

Now consider the complete span AB.
The shearing force across the panel CD is

$$S_{CD} = R_B - \frac{b}{l}P_R$$

which gives, on substitution for R_B,

$$S_{CD} = \frac{1}{Nl}\{aP_L + (nl+b)P_R - NbP_R\},$$

i.e. for any system of loads on AO,

$$M_C = lS_{CD} \text{ numerically.}$$

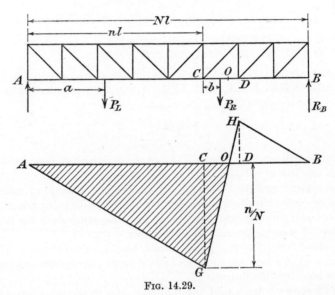

Fig. 14.29.

Now let w_s be the uniformly distributed load which will give the same maximum shearing force across the panel CD as the actual load system considered. This will occur when the length AO is covered and then

$$S_{CD} = w_s(\text{area AOG})$$

$$= w_s \times \frac{n}{N} \times \frac{Nnl}{2(N-1)}$$

or

$$S_{CD} = \frac{w_s n^2 l}{2(N-1)}.$$

Hence, the true bending moment at C on a span of length AO is, from the previous equation

$$M_C = \frac{w_s n^2 l^2}{2(N-1)}.$$

Now the influence line of bending moments for point C on the span AO is a triangle similar to AOG, the ordinate CG being given by $\dfrac{\text{AC.CO}}{\text{AO}}$, *i.e.* by $\dfrac{nl}{N}$.

From the tables or curves of equivalent loading already prepared we determine the value appropriate to the $\frac{1}{N}$th point of a span of length AO. If this is w, the correct bending moment at C is, from the influence line,

$$\frac{w}{2} \times AO \times \frac{nl}{N}$$

or
$$M_C = \frac{wn^2l^2}{2(N-1)}.$$

Equating the two expressions for M_C we obtain $w_s = w$.

Hence, to determine the true value of the shearing force across the panel CD, we assume AO to carry the uniform load which produces the correct bending moment at the $\frac{1}{N}$th point on a span AO.

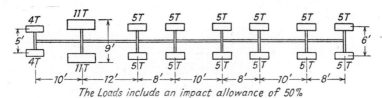

The Loads include an impact allowance of 50%

FIG. 14.30.

Another method of conventional design is illustrated by reference to the requirements for highway bridges which were introduced by the Ministry of Transport in 1932. Fig. 14.30 shows the standard train of loads which was assumed to cross the bridge, but for the purposes of calculation the effect of this was reduced to an equivalent distributed load, which varied with the loaded length of the bridge as shown in Fig. 14.31, together with a single concentrated load. The figures from which this diagram is plotted are given in Table 14.1.

The "loaded length" was defined as that length of the bridge which, when loaded, produced the worst effect at any particular section and is found in general from the influence diagrams. In a freely supported girder it is the full span for the calculation of bending moments, and the portion between one support and the section under consideration for the calculation of shearing forces.

An additional concentrated load of 2,700 lb. per foot width of the bridge was assumed to act at the section where it would produce most effect, e.g. for calculating the bending moment at midspan it was placed at the midspan point and for shearing force at the section under consideration.

In 1954, a new British Standard Specification (B.S.153, Part 3A) replaced the curves of Fig. 14.31 by others based on equivalent loadings per lineal foot of the bridge on each standard traffic lane of 10 feet width. The basis of this specification has been discussed in detail by Henderson (1954).

14.10. Dynamical loads on bridges.—It has long been recognised that the stresses in a bridge are not due simply to the static effects of the loads which traverse it : dynamical effects play a very important part and a structure designed without due consideration of these might have a carrying capacity very much below that estimated.

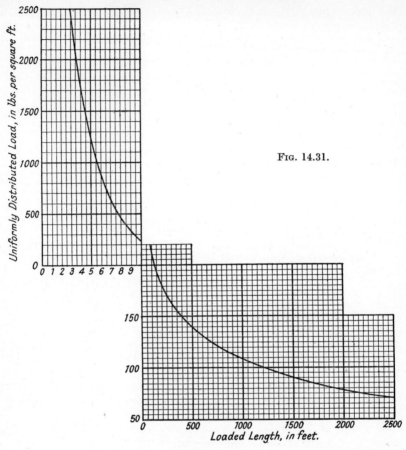

Fig. 14.31.

TABLE 14.1.

Loaded length		lb./sq. ft.	Loaded length	lb./sq. ft.	Loaded length	lb./sq. ft.
feet	inches		feet		feet	
3	0	2,420	100	208	1,200	100
3	6	2,020	150	192	1,300	97
4	0	1,700	200	180	1,400	94
4	6	1,445	250	170	1,500	90
5	0	1,225	300	163	1,600	88
5	6	1,033	350	156	1,700	85
6	0	872	400	150	1,800	82
6	6	735	450	145	1,900	79
7	0	625	500	140	2,000	77
7	6	525	600	132	2,100	76
8	0	444	700	125	2,200	74
8	6	374	800	119	2,300	73
9	0	314	900	114	2,400	72
9	6	265	1,000	108	2,500 and over	70
10 0 to 75 0		220	1,100	104	—	—

The customary method of dealing with this problem prior to 1928 was by the introduction of an impact factor : the live loads were multiplied by this factor and the stresses calculated on the assumption that these increased loads actually traversed the bridge. The impact factor was usually calculated from an empirical formula, the most widely used up to 1920 being the Pencoyd formula, according to which the actual loads were multiplied by the term $\left(1+\dfrac{300}{300+l}\right)$, where l was the span of the bridge in feet : in 1920 this formula was modified by the Ministry of Transport to $\left(1+\dfrac{120}{90+1\cdot5l}\right)$. The impact factor was thus assumed to be merely a function of the span and this assumption was common to the many other formulas proposed for the purpose of calculating impact allowances.

In 1923 a Committee of the Department of Scientific and Industrial Research, under the Chairmanship of Sir Alfred Ewing, was set up to investigate the whole problem of impact on railway bridges and a comprehensive report was published (Bridge Stress Committee, 1928). This report was amplified in a paper to the Institution of Civil Engineers (Inglis, 1931) and in a book (Inglis, 1934). These three publications placed a difficult problem upon a scientific basis and close approximations to the dynamical effects of a train upon a bridge can now be made.

When a train crosses a bridge there is a certain amount of vibration due to the sudden application of the load ; irregularities in the track and the presence of rail joints also cause impact effects which are irregular and incalculable. These, however, are completely overwhelmed by another cause of vibration. The driving-wheels of a locomotive are balanced for the inertia effects of the reciprocating parts and the centrifugal effect of these revolving balance weights causes the pressure of the wheel on the rail to undergo a periodic variation ; this is known as hammer-blow and the peak value of the pressure, which occurs at intervals of distance equal to the circumference of the driving-wheel, may be very high. This hammer-blow is the main cause of the vibrations in a bridge, and since it is periodic it can be investigated mathematically. Experimental data obtained by the Bridge Stress Committee from tests on actual bridges showed that applications of the mathematical analysis lead to very accurate estimates of the true stresses produced by vibration.

The analysis is too long to be reproduced here and reference should be made to the original work, but the general principles underlying the problem will be outlined.

A locomotive is supported on springs whose effect is considerable : if it crosses a bridge at low speeds the vibrations set up are so small that the springs do not come into operation and the locomotive acts as if it were non-spring-borne. At higher speeds, since the hammer-blow varies in intensity as the square of the speed, the vibrations are greater and may reach an amplitude which brings the springs into action. This results in a damping of the oscillations, since the spring-borne part of the mass is out of phase with the non-spring-borne portion. The two cases corresponding to non-spring-borne and spring-borne loads both produce distinct resonance ; the second is that which must be considered in bridges of moderate span.

In its unloaded state a bridge has a natural frequency which is decreased by the addition of a mass at any point ; as the locomotive passes across it, therefore, the natural frequency of the loaded bridge changes. This natural frequency depends on whether the loads are spring-borne or not ; if they are, the frequency may even be raised above that for the unloaded bridge.

This variation of natural frequency tends to increase safety for, unless the speed of the locomotive is so adjusted that the peak values of the hammer-blow synchronise with the natural frequency at every point, the dangers of resonance are reduced.

Other factors which limit the cumulative effects of hammer-blow are the restriction imposed by the length of span upon the number of impulses given to the bridge and the damping exercised by the imperfect elasticity of the bridge, ballast, piers, etc.

In view of this it is evident that it is impossible to specify a single critical speed for a given engine on a given bridge. Since, however, the worst effect will be produced when the centre of gravity of the engine is at the centre of the bridge in its most heavily loaded state, the Bridge Stress Committee defined critical speed as that engine speed at which the frequency of the hammer-blow coincides with the natural frequency of the loaded structure at the instant when the load is over the middle of the bridge.

The frequency of a long bridge is less than that of a short one and the Committee classified bridges according to the following scheme :—

Long spans.—In these the maximum effects occur at speeds such that the locomotive can be considered as non-spring borne, *i.e.* at the lower critical speed.

Medium spans.—In these the maximum effects are produced at the higher critical speed, *i.e.* when the oscillations are sufficient to bring the springs of the locomotive into action.

Short spans.—In these the frequency is so great that no attainable frequency of hammer-blow can produce resonance.

This classification cannot be interpreted merely in terms of the actual length of a bridge, since the frequency is affected both by the depth of the girders through its influence on the second moment of area of the cross-section and also by the mass of the structure.

When a bridge oscillates due to the passage of a locomotive the stresses caused in the members arise from three separate causes :—

(1) From the statical effects of the mass of the locomotive.

(2) From the hammer-blow which varies periodically as the locomotive crosses the span.

(3) From the forces due to the acceleration of the masses composing the bridge as it oscillates.

Inglis showed that for long and medium span bridges the last can be represented by additional loads on the bridge and that little error is caused if these are assumed to include the effect of hammer blow.

The practical way to allow for impact effects on a bridge is therefore to superimpose the effects of equivalent loads upon those caused by the statical loads of the train as it crosses the bridge. The methods of calculating these equivalent loads will be considered in the next paragraph.

14.11. Calculation of impact allowance on railway bridges.—In the following treatment (Inglis, 1934), it is assumed that the bridge is of uniform section and mass freely supported at the ends and that the locomotive consists of a mass which is spring supported on a single pair of wheels and axle.   In an actual bridge the section and mass vary along the span but little error is introduced by assuming an idealised uniform bridge having a constant second moment of area equal to that at the mid cross-section and the average mass per unit length.

Let M_G be the total mass of the bridge in tons,
l, the span in feet,
m, the mass per unit length,
I, the second moment of area of the cross-section in feet units,
M, the total mass of the locomotive (excluding tender) in tons,
M_S, the spring-borne mass of the locomotive,
M_U, the non-spring-borne mass of the locomotive,
n_s, the frequency for free vertical oscillations of M_S on its springs,
F, the total frictional force resisting spring movement,
N, the revolutions per second of the driving wheels,
v, the speed of the locomotive,

$$n = \frac{v}{2l},$$

$P \sin 2\pi Nt$, the hammer-blow at N revolutions per second in tons,
$P_1 N^2 = P$, the intensity of the hammer-blow at N revolutions per second,

and   E, the modulus of elasticity of the material of the bridge in tons-inch units.

These constitute the data for a solution of the problem and are supposed to be known or calculable with sufficient accuracy.   Then the fundamental frequency of the unloaded bridge is given by

$$n_0 = 10 \cdot 83 \frac{\pi^2}{l^2} \sqrt{\frac{EIl}{M_G}} \quad \cdot \quad \cdot \quad \cdot \quad \cdot \quad (14.6)$$

where M_G, I and l are in tons and feet units and E is in tons per square inch.
If the bridge carries extra masses M_1, M_2 ... etc., at distances of a_1, a_2 ... etc., from one end of the span, this frequency is reduced to

$$n_0 \sqrt{\frac{M_G}{M_G + 2\left(M_1 \sin^2 \frac{\pi a_1}{l} + M_2 \sin^2 \frac{\pi a_2}{l} + \ldots\right)}} \quad \cdot \quad \cdot \quad (14.7)$$

The central deflexion of the bridge in feet under a static load of P tons at the centre of the span is

$$D_P = \frac{Pg}{2\pi^2 n_0^2 M_G} \cdot \quad \cdot \quad \cdot \quad \cdot \quad \cdot \quad (14.8)$$

For an alternating force of $P \sin 2\pi Nt$ acting at a section which is a distance a from the end of the span, the central deflexion is

$$D_P \frac{\sin (2\pi Nt - \alpha) \sin \frac{\pi a}{l}}{\left\{\left(1 - \frac{N^2}{n_0^2}\right)^2 + \left(\frac{2Nn_b}{n_0^2}\right)^2\right\}^{\frac{1}{2}}}, \quad \cdot \quad \cdot \quad (14.9)$$

where $$\tan \alpha = \frac{2Nn_b}{n_0^2 - N^2}$$

and n_b is the damping coefficient of the bridge, the ratio of successive deflexions of the bridge when the oscillating force is removed being $e^{-2\pi\frac{n_b}{n_0}}$. A formula for n_b for spans between 80 and 300 feet has been deduced from the experimental results obtained by the Bridge Stress Committee as follows :

$$n_b = \frac{l}{M_G}\left(0\cdot12 + \frac{0\cdot63\times10^6}{l^3}\right) \quad . \quad . \quad . \quad . \quad (14.10)$$

The magnitude of the hammer-blow varies considerably : in the Report of the Bridge Stress Committee, data are given relating to 173 engines and an analysis of this list shows that

in 27 cases it lay between the values				0	and	$\cdot138N^2$	tons.
,, 44 ,,	,,	,,	,,	$\cdot138N^2$	,,	$\cdot278N^2$	,,
,, 59 ,,	,,	,,	,,	$\cdot278N^2$	,,	$\cdot417N^2$	,,
,, 31 ,,	,,	,,	,,	$\cdot417N^2$	,,	$\cdot556N^2$	,,
,, 8 ,,	,,	,,	,,	$\cdot556N^2$	,,	$\cdot694N^2$	,,
,, 4 ,,	,,	,,	,,	$\cdot694N^2$	,,	$\cdot833N^2$	,,

Since the bridge is affected so vitally by this factor it is evident that correct data relating to the particular classes of locomotives which will use it should be obtained prior to design : otherwise a very large value must of necessity be assumed to ensure the safety of the structure.

The study of long, medium and short span bridges must be dealt with separately, since the conditions controlling their oscillations are different, as explained in the previous paragraph. The oscillations are greatest when the locomotive is not followed by a train, the presence of which tends to damp them, and four separate loadings are considered as follows :

(1) Single locomotive on a single track bridge.
(2) Two similar locomotives separated by a distance d on a single track bridge.
(3) Two similar locomotives arriving simultaneously at the centre of a double track bridge.
(4) Two similar locomotives as in (2) on each track of a double track bridge.

Long span bridges.—In this class are included all bridges in which the oscillations are not sufficient to overcome the friction of the springs on the locomotive. If $\delta \sin 2\pi N t$ is the maximum vertical displacement of the wheels, the springs will remain locked if

$$\delta < \frac{Fg}{4\pi^2N^2M_S} \quad . \quad . \quad . \quad . \quad . \quad . \quad (14.11)$$

and this is the criterion as to whether a particular bridge falls into the category of long span.

The formulas for use in calculating the impact allowance for long span bridges are given in Table 14.2 and the procedure is as follows. First determine n_0 from equation (14.6) or (14.7) : N, the speed of the driving wheels which produces the maximum dynamical deflexion is then found from the formula in column 2 of the table.

The coefficient of damping, n_b, is calculated from equation (14.10) and column 3 enables n_b' to be found.

TABLE 14.2.

FORMULAS FOR LONG SPAN BRIDGES.

No.	Condition		N/n₀	n_b'/n_b	Dynamic increment of central deflexion δ_0 feet	Uniformly distributed load for dynamic bending moments (tons)	Allowance for dynamic shear at a from far end of span (tons)
	No. of tracks	No. of locos.					
	1		2	3	4	5	6
1	One.	One.	$\sqrt{\dfrac{M_G}{M_G + 2M}}$	$\left(\dfrac{N}{n_0}\right)^2$	$\dfrac{D_P}{2}\dfrac{N}{\sqrt{n^2 + n_b'^2}}$	$\left(M_G + \dfrac{\pi^2 M}{4}\right)\delta_0 N^2$	$\dfrac{\pi}{8}\left[-M_G\cos\dfrac{\pi a}{l} + M\dfrac{\pi a}{l}\sin\dfrac{\pi a}{l}\right]\delta_0 N^2$
2	One.	Two. Separated by distance d.	$\sqrt{\dfrac{M_G}{M_G + 4M\cos^2\frac{\pi d}{2l}}}$	$\left(\dfrac{N}{n_0}\right)^2$	$D_P\cos\dfrac{\pi d}{2l}\dfrac{N}{\sqrt{n^2 + n_b'^2}}$	$\left(M_G + \dfrac{\pi^2 M}{2}\dfrac{(l-d)}{l}\cos\dfrac{\pi d}{2l}\right)\delta_0 N^2$	$\dfrac{\pi}{8}\left[-M_G\cos\dfrac{\pi a}{l} + M\dfrac{\pi a}{l}\sin\dfrac{\pi a}{l} + M\dfrac{\pi(a-d)}{l}\sin\dfrac{\pi(a-d)}{l}\right]\delta_0 N^2$
3	Two.	One on each track, reaching centre of span simultaneously.	$\sqrt{\dfrac{M_G}{M_G + 4M}}$	$\left(\dfrac{N}{n_0}\right)^2$	$D_P\dfrac{N}{\sqrt{n^2 + n_b'^2}}$	$\left(M_G + \dfrac{\pi^2 M}{2}\right)\delta_0 N^2$	$\dfrac{\pi}{8}\left[-M_G\cos\dfrac{\pi a}{l} + 2M\dfrac{\pi a}{l}\sin\dfrac{\pi a}{l}\right]\delta_0 N^2$
4	Two.	Two. Separated by distance d on each track.	$\sqrt{\dfrac{M_G}{M_G + 8M\cos^2\frac{\pi d}{2l}}}$	$\left(\dfrac{N}{n_0}\right)^2$	$2D_P\cos\dfrac{\pi d}{2l}\dfrac{N}{\sqrt{n^2 + n_b'^2}}$	$\left(M_G + \dfrac{\pi^2 M(l-d)}{l}\cos\dfrac{\pi d}{2l}\right)\delta_0 N^2$	$\dfrac{\pi}{8}\left[-M_G\cos\dfrac{\pi a}{l} + 2M\dfrac{\pi a}{l}\sin\dfrac{\pi a}{l} + 2M\dfrac{\pi(a-d)}{l}\sin\dfrac{\pi(a-d)}{l}\right]\delta_0 N^2$

The dynamic increment of central deflexion, δ_0, is then obtainable from the formula in column 4 and on substituting this in the formula of column 5 we find the total load which must be distributed uniformly along the span to allow for the extra bending moments produced by the oscillation of the bridge. The allowance for dynamic shearing force is calculated from the formula in column 6 which gives the maximum shearing force produced at a distance a from the farther end of the span.

Medium span bridges.—The greatest dynamical effect on bridges in this category is found by considering the locomotive to be stationary at the centre of the bridge while its wheels skid at a constant speed N. If there are two locomotives they are spaced equally about the centre. The first step, as in the case of long span bridges, is to calculate the fundamental frequency n_0 from equation (14.6) or (14.7). This done, the value of N for which the bridge oscillations are greatest is found from the equation

$$N^4 - N^2 n_1^2 \left(1 + \frac{n_s^2}{n_2^2}\right) + n_1^2 n_s^2 = 0. \quad \ldots \quad (14.12)$$

This is solved as a quadratic in N^2, the greater of the two roots being that required. The values of n_1^2 and n_2^2 are given in Table 14.3.

TABLE 14.3.

Condition	$\dfrac{n_1{}^2}{n_0{}^2}$	$\dfrac{n_2{}^2}{n_0{}^2}$
1	$\dfrac{M_G}{M_G + 2M_U}$	$\dfrac{M_G}{M_G + 2M}$
2	$\dfrac{M_G}{M_G + 4M_U \cos^2 \dfrac{\pi d}{2l}}$	$\dfrac{M_G}{M_G + 4M \cos^2 \dfrac{\pi d}{2l}}$
3	$\dfrac{M_G}{M_G + 4M_U}$	$\dfrac{M_G}{M_G + 4M}$
4	$\dfrac{M_G}{M_G + 8M_U \cos^2 \dfrac{\pi d}{2l}}$	$\dfrac{M_G}{M_G + 8M \cos^2 \dfrac{\pi d}{2l}}$

The value of n_s is given approximately by the formula

$$n_s = \frac{1}{2\pi} \sqrt{\frac{\mu_1 + \mu_2 + \ldots + \mu_n}{M_S} g} \quad \ldots \quad (14.13)$$

in which $\mu_1 \ldots \mu_n$ are the stiffnesses of the different axle springs of the locomotive, *i.e.* the loads required to produce unit deflexions measured in tons per foot. This formula assumes that the values of μ for all the axle springs are appreciably the same, so that if a load were applied to the centre of gravity of the spring-borne mass of the locomotive this mass would sink without any angular movement. An average value for n_s found by the Bridge Stress Committee was 3.

The value of N found from equation (14.12), which will be denoted by N_2, may be greater than the permissible speed, which may be taken as 6. The subsequent calculation will depend on whether N_2 is less than or greater than this limiting value.

If it is less than the limiting value the formulas in Table 14.4, column 2, are used to determine the central dynamic deflexion δ_0 : if greater, the appropriate equation of column 4 is first solved for n_d, the functions of N in these equations being

$$\phi(N) = \frac{N^4}{n_1^2} - N^2 \left(1 + \frac{4n_b n_d}{n_0^2} + \frac{n_s^2}{n_2^2} \right) + n_s^2$$

and

$$\psi(N) = 2N \left(n_d \frac{n_2^2 - N^2}{n_2^2} + n_b \frac{n_s^2 - N^2}{n_0^2} \right)$$

where n_1^2 and n_2^2 are given in Table 14.3.

The formulas in column 3 of Table 14.4 then enable the value of δ_0 to be calculated.

The formulas giving the allowances for dynamic bending moment are given in column 2 of Table 14.5 : as for long span bridges the load obtained in this way is assumed to be distributed uniformly over the span.

To calculate the maximum dynamic shearing forces at a distance a from the farther end of the bridge the values of S_1 and S_2 are found from the formulas of columns 3 and 4 in Table 14.5. The shearing force required is then $(S_1^2 + S_2^2)^{\frac{1}{2}}$ but this may, near the centre of the span, fall below a mini-mum permissible value given by the formulas of column 5 ; then the value obtained from column 5 should be used. In this formula N_F is the frequency at which spring friction just breaks down, calculated from equation (14.11), and $P_1 N_F^2$ is the hammer-blow at this frequency.

Short span bridges.—In short span bridges the period of vibration is too rapid for resonance to occur.

The value of the hammer-blows should be calculated for the maximum permissible speed and treated as statical loads added to the corresponding axle loads.

14.12. Influence lines of deflexion.—So far in this chapter the use of influence lines has been confined to the representation of bending moments and shearing forces. Influence lines can, however, be drawn to represent the way in which the deflexion at any point on a girder or braced structure changes during the passage of a unit load and such diagrams are used exten-sively in the analysis of redundant structures. In the present chapter statically determinate structures alone will be dealt with, leaving the consideration of redundant structures to a later stage.

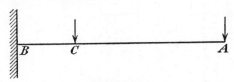

FIG. 14.32.

The simplest method of drawing an influence line of deflexion for a beam is by the use of Clerk Maxwell's reciprocal theorem (paragraph 4.10). For example, to take a very elementary case, suppose that the influence line of deflexions is required for A, the free end of the cantilever AB shown in Fig. 14.32. If a unit load is placed at any point C on the cantilever, we know

TABLE 14.4.

1	2	3	4
Condition	N₂ < Limiting Value	N₂ = Limiting Value	
	Central dynamical deflexion, δ_0 feet	Central dynamical deflexion, δ_0 feet	Equation to determine n_d
1	$D_P \dfrac{n_0^2}{2N_2 n_b}\left[1 - \dfrac{4F}{\pi P}\dfrac{N_2^2}{N_2^2 - n_s^2}\right]$	$D_P \dfrac{F}{\pi P}\dfrac{M_G}{M_S}\dfrac{n_0^2\{(N^2 - n_s^2)^2 + (2Nn_d)^2\}^{\frac{1}{4}}}{N^3 n_d}$	$\left[\dfrac{2\pi^3 N^3 M_S D_P}{Fg}\right]^2 n_d^2 = [\phi(N)]^2 + [\psi(N)]^2$
2	$2D_P \cos\dfrac{\pi d}{2l}\dfrac{n_0^2}{2N_2 n_b}\left[1 - \dfrac{4F}{\pi P}\dfrac{N_2^2}{N_2^2 - n_s^2}\right]$	$D_P \dfrac{F}{\pi P \cos\frac{\pi d}{2l}}\dfrac{M_G}{M_S}\dfrac{n_0^2\{(N^2 - n_s^2)^2 + (2Nn_d)^2\}^{\frac{1}{2}}}{N^3 n_d}$	$\left[\dfrac{4\pi^3 N^3 M_S D_P \cos^2\frac{\pi d}{2l}}{Fg}\right]^2 n_d^2 = [\phi(N)]^2 + [\psi(N)]^2$
3	Twice the value for 1	As for 1	$\left[\dfrac{4\pi^3 N^3 M_S D_P}{Fg}\right]^2 n_d^2 = [\phi(N)]^2 + [\psi(N)]^2$
4	Twice the value for 2	As for 2	$\left[\dfrac{8\pi^3 N^3 M_S D_P \cos^2\frac{\pi d}{2l}}{Fg}\right]^2 n_d^2 = [\phi(N)]^2 + [\psi(N)]^2$

TABLE 14.5.

1	2	3	4	5
Condition	Allowance for dynamic bending moment. Total load uniformly distributed (tons)	Maximum dynamic shearing force $=(S_1^2+S_2^2)^{\frac{1}{2}}$		Minimum permissible shearing force near centre
		S_1	S_2	
1	$M_G\left[N_2^2+\dfrac{\pi^2}{8}(n_0^2-N_2^2)\right]\delta_0$	$\dfrac{\pi M_G\delta_0}{32}\left[-4N_2^2\cos\dfrac{\pi a}{l}+\pi(n_0^2-N_2^2)\right]$	$\dfrac{\pi M_G\delta_0}{32}2N_2 n_b\left(4\cos\dfrac{\pi a}{l}+\pi\right)$	$\dfrac{1}{2}\left(P_1 N_F^2+\dfrac{M}{M_S}F\right)$
2	$M_G\left[N_2^2+\dfrac{\pi^2}{8}\dfrac{l-d}{l}\dfrac{1}{\cos\dfrac{\pi d}{2l}}(n_0^2-N_2^2)\right]\delta_0$	$\dfrac{\pi M_G\delta_0}{32}\left[-4N_2^2\cos\dfrac{\pi a}{l}+\dfrac{\pi}{\cos\dfrac{\pi d}{2l}}(n_0^2-N_2^2)\right]$	$\dfrac{\pi M_G\delta_0}{32}2N_2 n_b\left(4\cos\dfrac{\pi a}{l}+\dfrac{\pi}{\cos\dfrac{\pi d}{2l}}\right)$	Twice the value for 1
3	As in 1	As in 1	As in 1	Twice the value for 1
4	As in 2	As in 2	As in 2	Four times the value for 1

from the reciprocal theorem that the vertical deflexion at A when the load is at C is the same as the vertical deflexion at C when the load is at A. The deflexion at A when the load is at C gives a point on the influence diagram and therefore the influence diagram will be the same as the deflexion curve for the cantilever AB when a load of unity is placed at A. Hence, for a beam, the influence diagram of deflexions for any point is found by placing a unit load at that point and determining the deflected form of the beam. This curve is the influence line required.

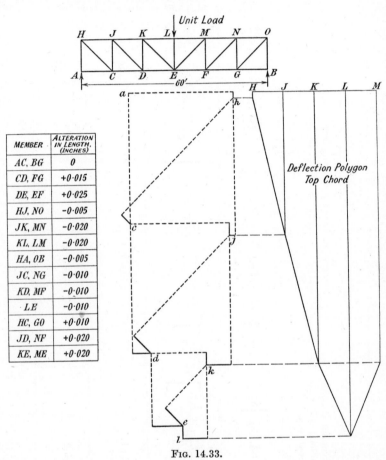

MEMBER	ALTERATION IN LENGTH. (INCHES)
AC, BG	0
CD, FG	+0·015
DE, EF	+0·025
HJ, NO	−0·005
JK, MN	−0·020
KL, LM	−0·020
HA, OB	−0·005
JC, NG	−0·010
KD, MF	−0·010
LE	−0·010
HC, GO	+0·010
JD, NF	+0·020
KE, ME	+0·020

FIG. 14.33.

This is equally true for a frame, but usually it is not so easy to obtain the deflected form of such a structure as it is for a beam. The simplest method is by the use of the Williot-Mohr diagram. An example will make the procedure clear : Fig. 14.33 shows a Pratt truss with 6 equal bays and we shall determine the influence line for the point L as a unit load traverses the top boom of the girder. As before, when the load is at any point such as J, the deflexion at L will be the same as the deflexion at J when the load is placed at L and so we must determine the deflexion polygon for the top chord of the girder under the action of a unit load at L. The table given in Fig. 14.33 shows the alteration in length of the various members when a unit load is placed at L.   Since the structure is assumed to be symmetrical about the centre line we take L as the reference point and LE as the datum line and avoid the necessity for drawing a Mohr diagram, since this line will not rotate.   The Williot diagram for one-half of the truss, drawn as described in paragraph 5.8, is shown in the figure.   The point A is fixed and so the vertical distances below A of the various joints taken from the Williot diagram give the true vertical deflexions.   If a is projected horizontally as shown and the line HJKLM is set out to represent the top boom of the girder, the deflexions of the various joints on this top boom are obtained by projecting h, j, k and l as shown in the diagram.   The deflexion polygon for the top chord is thus found and is the influence line of deflexions for the point L as a load traverses the top boom.

REFERENCES

Johnson, Bryan and Turneaure.   " Modern Framed Structures."   Wiley.

Bridge Stress Committee.   1928.   *Report*.   London.   H.M.S.O.

Inglis, C. E.   1931.   *Proc. Instn. Civ. Engrs.*, **234**.

Inglis, C. E.   1934.   " Mathematical Treatment of Vibrations in Railway Bridges."   Camb. Univ. Press.

Henderson, W.   1954.   *Proc. Instn. Civ. Engrs.*, **3**, Part II.   325–350.

EXERCISES

(1) A bridge of 56 feet span has simply supported ends.   It is crossed by a four-wheeled lorry which imposes a load of 2 tons through the two front wheels and a load of 3 tons through the two rear wheels.   The wheel base of the lorry is 14 feet.

Draw the bending moment and shearing force diagrams for the mid-point of the bridge for all positions of the load.   (*These may be plotted directly from the influence lines for the mid-point of the bridge.*)

(2) A bridge truss of 150 feet span is crossed by a uniformly distributed load of $\frac{1}{2}$ ton per foot and of length 40 feet.   Plot the diagrams of maximum bending moment and shearing force for the truss.

(3) A span of 300 feet is crossed from left to right by a train of six loads, A, B, C, D, E and F, their magnitudes being 10, 15, 15, 25, 15 and 10 tons respectively.   The distances between them are AB = 6 feet, BC = 8 feet, CD = 8 feet, DE = 10 feet, and EF = 12 feet.   A is the leading load.

Calculate the maximum bending moment and shearing forces at a point 100 feet from the left-hand support and the magnitude and position of the maximum bending moment.

(5,560 tons-feet ; 52·7 tons
6,280 tons-feet when D is 151·17 feet from right-hand support.)

(4) A Pratt (N) truss has a span of 200 feet, a depth of 16 feet and is divided into ten equal panels.   Draw the influence lines for the loads in the top boom of the eighth panel from the left-hand support and for the diagonal in the sixth panel from the same support when the bottom chord is loaded.

(5) A five-panel Warren truss is formed of equilateral triangles and is loaded on the bottom chord.

Draw the influence lines for the diagonal member and the top chord member immediately to the left of the centre point of the truss.

(6) A three-pinned segmental arch in which the rise is one quarter of the span is crossed by a rolling load.   Plot the influence line of horizontal thrust and also the influence line of bending moment at a quarter-span point.

(7) A beam ABC is pinned to supports A and B a distance of 15 feet apart.   The overhang BC is 5 feet.

Draw the influence line of deflexion for the mid-point of AB.

CHAPTER 15

INFLUENCE LINES FOR STATICALLY INDETERMINATE STRUCTURES

15.1. Use of influence lines.—It was shown in the concluding paragraph of the last chapter that the curve of deflexion for any structure under a unit load placed at any point is the influence line of deflexion for that point. For beams this curve is easily found by the methods described in Chapter 3 and for trusses by means of a Williot-Mohr diagram and deflexion polygon for the loaded chord as described in paragraph 5.8.

Influence lines of deflexion are not often needed for statically determinate structures since, except in special circumstances, knowledge of the deflected form of the girder or truss is not an essential step in the design. When the structure is redundant, however, whether the redundancy is due either to the provision of more than the essential number of reactive forces or more internal members than are statically necessary, the stress analysis involves the elastic properties of the structure. Calculations of deflexions in some form or another thus become imperative and the use of deflexion influence lines often enables the analysis of the structure to be made with the minimum labour. This chapter therefore will deal with some of the applications of influence lines to problems connected with statically indeterminate structures. The simpler examples only are considered ; reference should be made to specialised works for more elaborate extensions of these principles.

15.2. Müller-Breslau's theorem.—A simple theorem due to Müller-Breslau enables the influence line of deflexions to be used for the calculation of redundant reactions in a beam or truss.

The truss shown in Fig. 15.1 is supported at the three points A, D and F and these supports are assumed to be rigid. Let the support D be removed : the structure is now statically soluble, and if a unit load acts vertically downwards at D the deflexion polygon for the bottom chord can be drawn using a Williot-Mohr diagram. This diagram, *abcdef*, is also the influence line of deflexion for the point D on the simply supported truss AF and so, if a unit load acts vertically at any panel point of the bottom chord the ordinate to the polygon represents the deflexion produced at D ; a unit load at C, for example, will produce a deflexion δ_{CD} at D.

To move the point D through a distance δ_{DD} a unit force must be applied at D and, since the structure is assumed to follow a linear load-displacement law, a force of $\dfrac{\delta_{CD}}{\delta_{DD}}$ applied at D will move it through a distance δ_{CD}. If the support D were in position, therefore, the force on it due to a unit force at C would be $\dfrac{\delta_{CD}}{\delta_{DD}}$ and similarly for a load at any other panel point. Thus, if the ordinates of the polygon are divided by δ_{DD} the resulting diagram is the influence line of reactions at D.

In general terms the ordinates of the influence line for the force in any redundant element of a structure are equal to those of the deflexion curve drawn for the structure when a unit load replaces the redundancy, the scale being so chosen that the deflexion at the point of application of the unit load represents unity.

This is Müller-Breslau's theorem.   It may also be deduced by an application of the first theorem of Castigliano, for if D is replaced by a downward

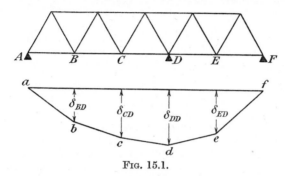

FIG. 15.1.

load Q and another load P acts at E, the load in any member of the truss can be expressed in the form

$$P_0 = \alpha Q + \beta P.$$

The deflexion of D is $\qquad \dfrac{\partial U}{\partial Q} = \sum \dfrac{\alpha(\alpha Q + \beta P)L}{AE}$

and that of E is $\qquad \dfrac{\partial U}{\partial P} = \sum \dfrac{\beta(\alpha Q + \beta P)L}{AE}.$

If P is now made equal to zero and Q equal to unity, the deflexion of D is

$$\Delta_D = \sum \frac{\alpha^2 L}{AE}$$

and the deflexion of E is

$$\Delta_E = \sum \frac{\alpha \beta L}{AE}.$$

If P is made equal to unity and a force R is applied upwards to the point D, R being sufficient to maintain the support at its original level, the load in any member is $-\alpha R + \beta$ and

$$\frac{\partial U}{\partial R} = \sum \frac{\alpha(\alpha R - \beta)L}{AE} = 0.$$

This equation gives the reaction at D when a unit load acts at E.

Hence $\qquad R \sum \dfrac{\alpha^2 L}{AE} = \sum \dfrac{\alpha \beta L}{AE}$

or $\qquad R\Delta_D = \Delta_E$

i.e. $\qquad R = \dfrac{\text{deflexion at E when a unit load acts at D}}{\text{deflexion at D when a unit load acts at D}},$

which proves the theorem.

The theorem applies to any elastic body and can be used either for beams or trusses : the deflected shape of the former can be found by the usual methods and will be considered in the next paragraph.

15.3. Influence lines of reaction for continuous girders.—The following treatment is due to F. C. Lea (1910).

Let Fig. 15.2 represent a girder resting on supports A and C and continuous over a third support B. The spans AB and BC are L_1 and L_2 respectively

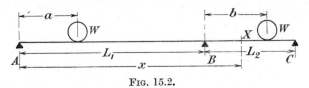

FIG. 15.2.

and the variation of the reactions as a load W rolls across the girder is to be found.

Suppose the load W is on the span AB at a from A and let X be any point on the girder at x from A. Then the bending moment at X is

$$EI\frac{d^2y}{dx^2}=-R_Ax+W[x-a]-R_B[x-L_1]$$

where the terms in brackets only appear when they are positive.

Integrating this expression twice we obtain

$$EI\frac{dy}{dx}=-\frac{R_Ax^2}{2}+\frac{W}{2}[x-a]^2-\frac{R_B}{2}[x-L_1]^2+A$$

and

$$EIy=-\frac{R_Ax^3}{6}+\frac{W}{6}[x-a]^3-\frac{R_B}{6}[x-L_1]^3+Ax+B,$$

where A and B are constants of integration.

Since $y=0$ when $x=0$ or L_1

$$B=0$$

and

$$A=\frac{R_AL_1^2}{6}-\frac{W(L_1-a)^3}{6L_1}.$$

Again since $y=0$ when $x=L_1+L_2$

$$R_AL_2(L_1+L_2)(2L_1+L_2)-W\left[(L_1+L_2-a)^3-\frac{(L_1-a)^3(L_1+L_2)}{L_1}\right]$$
$$+R_BL_2^3=0. \quad . \quad . \quad . \quad (15.1)$$

Now

$$R_A+R_B+R_C=W \quad . \quad . \quad . \quad . \quad . \quad (15.2)$$

and by taking moments about B,

$$R_CL_2+W(L_1-a)-R_AL_1=0. \quad . \quad . \quad . \quad (15.3)$$

The solution of these three equations, when W is equal to unity, is

$$R_A=\frac{L_1^2+L_1L_2-aL_2-\frac{3}{2}aL_1+\frac{a^3}{2L_1}}{L_1(L_1+L_2)} \quad . \quad . \quad . \quad (15.4)$$

When the load is on the span BC the general equations for slope and deflexion are the same but the term L_1-a is negative and the value of the constant A is modified.   Putting $y=0$ when $x=L_1$ we have

$$A=\frac{R_AL_1^2}{6}.$$

When $x=L_1+L_2$, $y=0$ and equation (15.1) becomes

$$R_AL_2(L_1+L_2)(2L_1+L_2)-W(L_1+L_2-a)^3+R_BL_2^3=0.$$

The result is simplified by measuring the distance of the load from the support B so we shall put $a=L_1+b$.   The above equation then becomes

$$R_AL_2(L_1+L_2)(2L_1+L_2)-W(L_2-b)^3+R_BL_2^3=0. \quad . \quad . \quad (15.5)$$

Equation (15.2) is unaltered but equation (15.3) becomes

$$R_CL_2-Wb-R_AL_1=0. \quad . \quad . \quad . \quad . \quad . \quad (15.6)$$

The solution of (15.2), (15.5) and (15.6) is, for W equal to unity,

$$R_A=-\frac{bL_2-\frac{3b^2}{2}+\frac{b^3}{2L_2}}{L_1(L_1+L_2)} \quad . \quad . \quad . \quad . \quad (15.7)$$

Equations (15.4) and (15.7) are the equations of the influence line of reaction at A and may be plotted as follows.

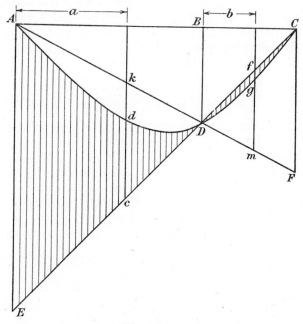

Fig. 15.3.

From B in Fig. 15.3 draw BD perpendicular to AC representing the product L_1L_2 to a convenient scale.   Join CD and produce CD to meet the perpendicular from A at E.

Then $AE=L_1(L_1+L_2)$, the slope of ED is $-L_1$ and the equation of the line ED is

$$y=L_1^2+L_1L_2-aL_1.$$

A curve plotted from the equation

$$y = \frac{1}{2}aL_1 + aL_2 - \frac{a^3}{2L_1}$$

will pass through the points A and D ; let it cut the ordinate from a at the point d. Then

$$dc = (L_1^2 + L_1 L_2 - aL_1) - \left(\frac{1}{2}aL_1 + aL_2 - \frac{a^3}{2L_1}\right)$$

$$= L_1^2 + L_1 L_2 - aL_2 - \frac{3}{2}aL_1 + \frac{a^3}{2L_1},$$

i.e. dc represents the numerator of R_A in equation (15.4) and since AE is the denominator of this equation to the same scale, the value of R_A is given by the ordinate dc if AE be taken to be unity. AED is thus the influence diagram for R_A for all positions of the load between A and B.

If the numerator of equation (15.7) is written in the form

$$-\left(bL_2 - \frac{3b^2}{2} + \frac{b^3}{2L_2} + L_1 L_2 - bL_1\right) + (L_1 L_2 - bL_1),$$

the second term is the ordinate to the line CE when $a = L_1 + b$ and the first term represents a curve DgC passing through the points D and C. Hence, when the load is at any point between B and C the reaction at A is measured by the distance gf to the scale for which AE is unity ; gf is negative and so for a load between A and B the reaction at A is positive while for a load between B and C it is negative. The complete influence diagram for R_A is therefore as shown shaded in Fig. 15.3.

From equations (15.3) and (15.4) we have

$$R_C = -\frac{\left(\frac{1}{2}aL_1 - \frac{a^3}{2L_1} + aL_2\right) - aL_2}{L_2(L_1 + L_2)}.$$

The first term in the numerator is the equation of the curve AdD and the second is that of the straight line ADF. Hence, for loads between A and B, the distance kd represents the reaction at C to the scale for which CF is unity. Similarly, gm represents the reaction at C for load positions between B and C and so the complete influence diagram for R_C is obtained.

The foregoing results may also be obtained by an application of Müller-Breslau's theorem. Suppose the support at A to be removed and a load W applied downwards at that point. The reaction at B is found by taking moments about C to be

$$R_B = \frac{W(L_1 + L_2)}{L_2},$$

and we have

$$EI\frac{d^2y}{dx^2} = Wx - \frac{W(L_1 + L_2)}{L_2}[x - L_1],$$

the term in square brackets only occurring when it is positive.

Integrating twice,

$$EI\frac{dy}{dx} = \frac{Wx^2}{2} - \frac{W(L_1 + L_2)}{2L_2}[x - L_1]^2 + A$$

and
$$EIy = \frac{Wx^3}{6} - \frac{W(L_1 + L_2)}{6L_2}[x - L_1]^3 + Ax + B.$$

From the conditions $y=0$ when $x=L_1$ and $x=L_1+L_2$ we obtain

$$A=-\frac{WL_1}{6}(3L_1+2L_2)$$

and

$$B=\frac{WL_1^2}{3}(L_1+L_2).$$

The curve of deflexions for the span AB is then

$$y=\frac{W}{6EI}\{x^3-3L_1^2x-2L_1L_2x+2L_1^3+2L_1^2L_2\},$$

while the deflexion of the point A is

$$y_A=\frac{WL_1^2}{3EI}(L_1+L_2).$$

Hence, the influence line of reaction at A is, from Müller-Breslau's theorem,

$$\frac{y}{y_A}=\frac{1}{L_1(L_1+L_2)}\left\{\frac{x^3}{2L_1}-\frac{3}{2}L_1x-L_2x+L_1{}^2+L_1L_2\right\} \quad . \quad . \quad (15.8)$$

which is the same result as given in equation (15.4) when a is written instead of x.

For the span BC, putting $x=L_1+b$, we find

$$y=\frac{W}{6EI}\frac{L_1}{L_2}\{-2bL_2^2-b^3+3b^2L_2\}$$

and

$$\frac{y}{y_A}=-\frac{1}{L_1(L_1+L_2)}\left\{bL_2-\frac{3}{2}b^2+\frac{b^3}{2L_2}\right\}, \quad . \quad . \quad . \quad (15.9)$$

which is the result given in equation (15.7).

The influence line for the centre reaction may be found from equation (15.2) since expressions for R_A and R_C have been determined, but as a further example of the use of Müller-Breslau's theorem we will obtain it directly. The support at B is removed and an upward load W placed at that point : then, if x is measured from A,

$$EI\frac{d^2y}{dx^2}=W\left(\frac{L_2}{L_1+L_2}\right)x-W[x-L_1]$$

the term in square brackets only occurring when it is positive.

Integrating twice,

$$EI\frac{dy}{dx}=\frac{W}{2}\left(\frac{L_2}{L_1+L_2}\right)x^2-\frac{W}{2}[x-L_1]^2+A$$

and

$$EIy=\frac{W}{6}\left(\frac{L_2}{L_1+L_2}\right)x^3-\frac{W}{6}[x-L_1]^3+Ax+B.$$

y is zero when $x=0$ and $x=L_1+L_2$ and so

$$B=0$$

and

$$A=-\frac{WL_1L_2(L_1+2L_2)}{6(L_1+L_2)}.$$

In span L_1 the substitution of these values gives

$$y=\frac{WL_2x}{6EI(L_1+L_2)}\{x^2-L_1(L_1+2L_2)\},$$

and under the load

$$y_B=-\frac{2WL_1^2L_2^2}{6EI(L_1+L_2)}.$$

Hence the equation of the influence line for R_B is

$$R_B = \frac{y}{y_B} = -\frac{x}{2L_1{}^2L_2}\{x^2 - L_1(L_1 + 2L_2)\}. \quad . \quad . \quad . \quad (15.10)$$

When the load is on span L_2 similar methods lead to

$$R_B = \frac{y}{y_B} = -\frac{(L_2 - b)}{2L_1L_2{}^2}\{(L_2 - b)^2 - L_2(L_2 + 2L_1)\} \quad . \quad . \quad (15.11)$$

In particular, when $L_1 = L_2 = L$ these equations reduce to

$$R_B = \frac{x(3L^2 - x^2)}{2L^3} \quad . \quad . \quad . \quad . \quad . \quad (15.12)$$

and

$$R_B = \frac{(L - b)\{3L^2 - (L - b)^2\}}{2L^3} \quad . \quad . \quad . \quad (15.13)$$

The influence line is then as shown in Fig. 15.4.

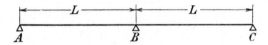

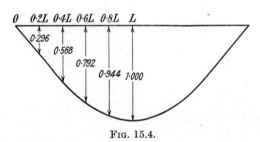

FIG. 15.4.

15.4. Influence line of shearing force for a continuous girder.—Let AEDC in Fig. 15.5 be the influence line of reaction at the support A of a continuous girder ABC, found as in the previous paragraph, and let X be any point on the girder between A and B.

If a load W is at G, between A and X, the shearing force at X is

$$F = -R_A + W$$
$$= W(1 - bc)$$

or, if W is made equal to unity,

$$F = 1 - bc.$$

If from A a line AK is drawn parallel to EC and cG is produced to meet it at e,

$$ec = AE = 1$$

and

$$eb = 1 - bc.$$

The intercept eb between the line AK and the curve ADC thus represents the shearing force at X for a unit load between A and X and AKM is the influence diagram for this section of the girder.

When the load is at any point H between X and B,

$$F = -R_A = -fg$$

and the influence diagram for this section of the girder is MND.

When the load has passed B and is at a point J between B and C, the shearing force at X is again

$$F=-R_A=+hj.$$

The influence diagram of shearing force for the span BC is therefore DjC and the complete diagram is as shown shaded in Fig. 15.5.

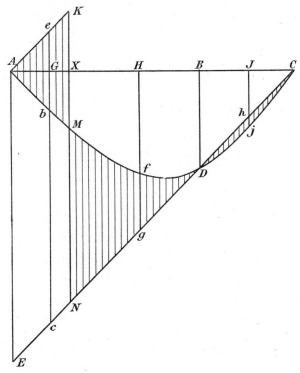

FIG. 15.5.

15.5. Influence line of bending moment for a continuous girder.—Let AEDC in Fig. 15.6 be the influence line of reaction at A for the beam already considered and X any point on the span AB at a distance x from A. If a load W is at the point G, between A and X, where the distance AG is a, the bending moment at X is

$$M_x=-R_Ax+W(x-a)$$

or

$$\frac{M_x}{x}=-R_A+W\left(\frac{x-a}{x}\right).$$

If W is unity

$$\frac{M_x}{x}=-bc+\frac{x-a}{x}.$$

If a perpendicular to AC from X cuts EC in H and HA is drawn

$$\frac{dc}{AE}=\frac{x-a}{x},$$

13

and since AE represents unity on the influence diagram,

$$dc = \frac{x-a}{x}.$$

Therefore

$$\frac{M_x}{x} = dc - bc = -bd.$$

When the load is at H, lying between X and B,

$$\frac{M_x}{x} = -R_A = -ef,$$

and when it is at J, on the span BC,

$$\frac{M_x}{x} = -R_A = +hj.$$

The influence diagram for the bending moment at X is then as shown shaded in Fig. 15.6.

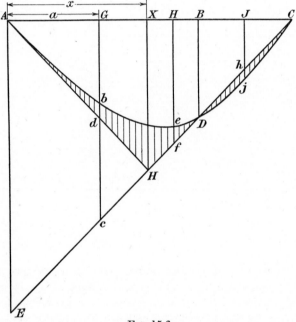

Fig. 15.6.

15.6. Influence lines of reactions for a continuous truss.—In paragraph
15.2 it was shown how the influence line of reaction for a single redundant support in a continuous truss might be obtained. The method will now be extended to two redundant reactions. The truss shown in Fig. 15.7 is simply supported at A and B and is continuous over supports at C and D. The influence lines of reactions at the points C and D are to be found. The load will be taken to travel along the top chord of the truss.

In the first place both the supports C and D are supposed to be removed and a unit load acting downwards is applied at C. A Williot-Mohr diagram is drawn as explained in paragraph 5.8 for the simply supported truss AB and from it the deflexion polygon for the top chord is obtained. A similar procedure is followed for a unit load acting downwards at D.   The polygons are also the influence lines for the deflexions at C and D respectively and from them we can measure

δ_C, the deflexion of point C under a unit load at any panel point M on the top chord

and δ_D, the deflexion of point D under a unit load at the same point M.

From the Williot-Mohr diagrams the following data are found :—

Δ_C, the vertical movement of the point C for a unit load at C,

Δ'_C, the vertical movement of the point C for a unit load at D,

Δ_D, the vertical movement of the point D for a unit load at D,

and Δ'_D, the vertical movement of the point D for a unit load at C.

Let R_C and R_D be the reactions at C and D when the supports are in position and a unit load acts at M, and suppose these forces to be applied upward to the truss deflected by the load at M.

Under the action of such forces alone the movement of C would be $R_C\Delta_C + R_D\Delta'_C$ and the movement of D would be $R_C\Delta'_D + R_D\Delta_D$.

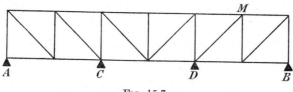

FIG. 15.7.

Since it is assumed that in the actual truss the points C and D do not move, these movements must be respectively equal to δ_C and δ_D i.e.

$$\delta_C = R_C\Delta_C + R_D\Delta'_C$$

and
$$\delta_D = R_C\Delta'_D + R_D\Delta_D.$$

The solution of these simultaneous equations gives the values of R_C and R_D.

The terms Δ_C, Δ'_C, Δ_D and Δ'_D are constant for a given truss and are found once and for all from the Williot-Mohr diagrams, while the terms δ_C and δ_D are measured directly from the influence diagrams.   The above equations can therefore be formed quickly for all panel points on the top chord and the values of R_C and R_D thus determined enable the influence lines of reaction at C and D to be drawn.   This method is considerably quicker than calculation by strain energy methods which requires lengthy computation for the load at each panel point.

The process can be extended to any number of redundant supports ; each redundancy needs the construction of a Williot-Mohr diagram and an influence line of deflexion, and if there are n such redundancies there will be n simultaneous equations to be solved for each load position.

15.7. Forces in redundant bars by influence diagrams.—The construction of influence lines enables the calculation of the forces in redundant bars of a truss to be made quickly for any position of the load.   Let Fig. 15.8 represent a truss supported at A and B having one redundant member PQ for which the force influence line is required when the bottom chord is loaded.   Suppose the bar PQ to be removed, and unit loads to act at P and Q as shown.   The forces in all the members of the resulting just-stiff frame can then be found and their changes of length calculated. A Williot-Mohr diagram and a deflexion polygon for the bottom chord is constructed as explained in paragraph 5.8. The ordinate δ_m to this deflexion polygon at any panel point M on the bottom chord is the vertical displacement of this point under unit loads at P and Q and by Clerk Maxwell's theorem it is therefore the amount by which the points P and Q separate when a unit load acts vertically at M. The polygon is therefore the influence line of separation of P and Q when the member PQ is removed.

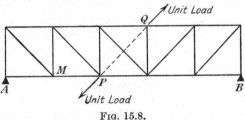

FIG. 15.8.

The free separation of P and Q can also be obtained from the Williot-Mohr diagram ; let this be Δ.

When the redundant member is in position and a unit load acts at M let R be the force in PQ. This force will cause the member to stretch by an amount $\dfrac{RL}{AE}$ where L is its length, A is its cross-sectional area and E is Young's modulus for the material. The force R will pull the points P and Q together by an amount $R\Delta$. The total separation of the two points in the absence of the member PQ is δ_m and so

$$R\Delta + \frac{RL}{AE} = \delta_m$$

or

$$R = \frac{\delta_m}{\Delta + \dfrac{L}{AE}}.$$

Hence, if the ordinates of the deflexion polygon for the bottom chord under unit loads at P and Q are divided by the term $\Delta + \dfrac{L}{AE}$ the polygon represents the influence line for the force in PQ.

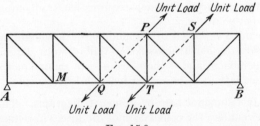

FIG. 15.9.

If the truss has two redundant members PQ and ST as shown in Fig. 15.9 the forces in them as a load crosses the truss may be found as follows.

PQ and ST are assumed to be removed and unit loads placed at P and Q. The stresses in the remaining bars are calculated, the alterations in their lengths determined, and a Williot-Mohr diagram is drawn from which the deflexion polygon for the loaded chord is obtained. This polygon is also the influence line representing the separation of points P and Q. Thus, if a load of unity is placed at any panel point M on the lower chord the ordinate to the influence line at M is the amount by which P and Q separate. Call this $_1\delta_m$. From the Williot-Mohr diagram we can also obtain Δ_1 the amount by which P and Q separate under unit loads at P and Q, and Δ'_1 the amount by which S and T separate under the action of the same loads.

Similar diagrams are drawn for unit loads acting at S and T and from them we obtain $_2\delta_m$ the separation of S and T for a unit load at M ; Δ_2 and Δ'_2 the separations of S and T and of P and Q respectively under unit loads at S and T.

The redundant bars PQ and ST are now supposed to be in position, the forces in them when a unit load is placed at M being R_1 and R_2 respectively.

Due to the force R_1 acting at P and Q,

P and Q approach by an amount $R_1\Delta_1$

and   S and T approach by an amount $R_1\Delta'_1$.

Due to the force R_2 acting at S and T,

P and Q approach by an amount $R_2\Delta'_2$

and   S and T approach by an amount $R_2\Delta_2$.

When R_1 and R_2 act together,

P and Q approach by an amount $R_1\Delta_1+R_2\Delta'_2$

while   S and T approach by an amount $R_1\Delta'_1+R_2\Delta_2$.

The lengths of the bars PQ and ST are increased by amounts $\dfrac{R_1L_1}{A_1E}$ and $\dfrac{R_2L_2}{A_2E}$ due to the loads in them and so

$$_1\delta_m=R_1\Delta_1+R_2\Delta'_2+\frac{R_1L_1}{A_1E}$$

and

$$_2\delta_m=R_1\Delta'_1+R_2\Delta_2+\frac{R_2L_2}{A_2E}.$$

From these simultaneous equations the values of R_1 and R_2 are found.

It will be noticed that $\Delta_1, \Delta'_1, \Delta_2$ and Δ'_2 are constant values for the frame whatever the position of the load on the bottom chord, while $_1\delta_m$ and $_2\delta_m$ are found from the respective deflexion polygons. By this method therefore the forces in the two redundant bars for any position of the load can be calculated by the solution of two simple simultaneous equations once the influence lines have been drawn. Here again, as in paragraph 15.6, strain energy methods require a long calculation for each load position and the advantage to be gained by the use of influence lines is considerable.

15.8. Influence line of thrust for a two-pinned arch.—Since a two-pinned arch is a statically indeterminate structure the calculation of the thrust involves the application of strain energy or similar methods of analysis. Examples of this calculation have already been given in Chapter 12 and a general expression for the thrust when a load acts at any point on a segmental rib is given in equation (12.29).

From this equation we can plot the H-line, as it is called for convenience, for any two-pinned segmental arch.

As an example, if the central angle 2ϕ is 120° and 2P is made equal to unity the following values are obtained ;

θ	60°	45°	30°	15°	0°
H	0	·197	·408	·57	·634

The influence line is shown in Fig. 15.10.

If, instead of being segmental, the arch is parabolic, the work is very much simplified by the assumption, explained in paragraph 12.10, that the second

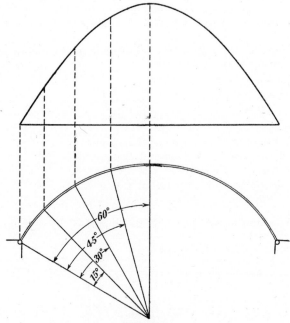

FIG. 15.10.

moment of area at any section is proportional to the secant of the angle of slope of the arch, $i.e.$ $I_x = I\dfrac{ds}{dx}$ where I is the second moment of area at the crown. If such a rib, having a span 2L and a central rise a, carries a load of unity at a distance l from the centre the horizontal thrust is, from equation (12.45),

$$H = \frac{5}{64aL^3}(5L^2 - l^2)(L^2 - l^2).$$

The ordinates to the H line for different values of $\dfrac{l}{2L}$ are given below ;

$l/2L$	0·5	0·4	0·3	0·2	0·1	0
H	0	$·0613\left(\dfrac{2L}{a}\right)$	$·1160\left(\dfrac{2L}{a}\right)$	$·1588\left(\dfrac{2L}{a}\right)$	$·1860\left(\dfrac{2L}{a}\right)$	$·1953\left(\dfrac{2L}{a}\right)$

From this table the H line can be plotted for any ratio $\dfrac{2L}{a}$.   If the arch is, in fact, of uniform section throughout there will be an error on account of the assumption as to the variation of the second moment of area, but unless $2L/a$ is small this will not be serious and it may usually be neglected.

The same method may be used for an arch of any shape but if it is of such form that the equations cannot be readily integrated the work involved in estimating H may be considerable since graphical integration will be necessary.

15.9. Influence line of bending moment for a two-pinned arch.—The bending moment at a point X on any two-pinned arch as shown in Fig. 15.11 is

$$M = H\bar{y} - V_A\bar{x} + [Wx']$$

where $\bar{x}$ and $\bar{y}$ are the co-ordinates of the point X taking A as the origin and x' is the distance of the load from X.   The last term only occurs when

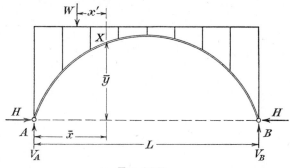

FIG. 15.11.

W is between A and X.   Now the equation to the influence line of bending moments at X on a beam of span AB is, if W is unity,

$$M' = -V_A\bar{x} + [Wx']$$

and the equation of the influence line of moment at X due to the thrust alone is

$$M'' = H\bar{y}.$$

The complete influence line for M is therefore the sum of the two separate influence lines for M' and M''.   The first of these is readily plotted as in paragraph 14.2, but the second is rather more troublesome since the ordinates of the H line have to be multiplied by a different value of $\bar{y}$ for each position of X.   If, however, we divide the equation for M throughout by $\bar{y}$ we have,

$$\frac{M}{\bar{y}} = H + \frac{M'}{\bar{y}}$$

and this is a more convenient form for plotting, since the H line is the same for all positions of X.   As an example we will consider a segmental arch rib having a central angle of 120°.   The H line is plotted from the data given in the last paragraph and is shown in Fig. 15.12.

The M' line is a triangle with its apex at $\bar{x}$ from A, the ordinate at that point being $\dfrac{\bar{x}(L-\bar{x})}{L}$ and so, if XD is made equal to $\dfrac{\bar{x}(L-\bar{x})}{L\bar{y}}$, the triangle ADB is the $\dfrac{M'}{\bar{y}}$ line and the shaded figure is the influence diagram of $\dfrac{M}{\bar{y}}$ for the point X. If a load W acts at a point which is a distance x from A the bending moment in the rib at X is $W\bar{y}\times$(ordinate FG). If the influence line is required for any other position on the rib it is only necessary to calculate the new value of the ordinate corresponding to XD and to complete the

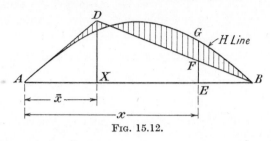

Fig. 15.12.

diagram, keeping the same curve for H. The advantages of plotting $M/\bar{y}$ instead of M are thus considerable.

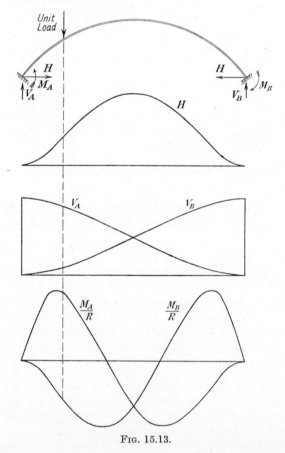

Fig. 15.13.

15.10. Influence lines for a fixed arch.—A general solution for the fixed arch carrying a vertical load at any point was given in paragraph 12.6 and the formulas quoted there can be used to plot the influence lines.   The load was taken as 2P so we must put $P=\frac{1}{2}$ to obtain the results in the correct form for the influence diagrams.

As an example we will consider an arch in which the rise is one-quarter of the span.   This gives a central angle $2\phi=106°\ 16'$ and upon substituting the trigonometrical functions for ϕ and putting $P=\frac{1}{2}$, equations (12.16) and (12.17) enable the necessary data for influence lines to be calculated.

The calculated values are given in Table 15.1 and the influence lines plotted from these values are shown in Fig. 15.13 on a base representing the span of the arch.

TABLE 15.1.

θ	H	V_A	V_B	$\dfrac{M_A}{R}$	$\dfrac{M_B}{R}$
0	·93	0·500	·500	− ·059	− ·059
5	·91	0·577	·423	− ·037	− ·074
15	·75	0·725	·275	+ ·019	− ·082
25	·52	0·849	·152	+ ·067	− ·069
35	·25	0·940	·061	+ ·091	− ·037
45	·05	0·989	·012	+ ·065	− ·009
53° 8′	0	1·000	0	0	0

15.11. Choice of redundant elements to simplify calculations.—A judicious choice of redundancies enables calculations in many instances to be considerably simplified and this is particularly so when the redundant elements can be taken to act at the same section of the structure.   The method to be described is due to Müller-Breslau.

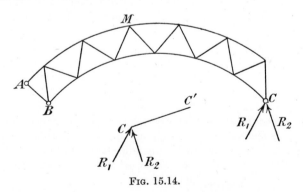

Fig. 15.14.

Suppose the structure shown in Fig. 15.14 is supported by pins at the points A, B and C.   If the pin C were removed the frame would be statically determinate and so, when supported as shown, there are two redundant elements.   These are usually taken to consist of a vertical and a horizontal reaction at C, but there is no reason why these particular directions should

13*

be chosen and we can in fact assume the two forces at C to act in any directions chosen arbitrarily.

Suppose then we take component reactive forces at C acting in the directions shown by R_1 and R_2, these being inclined at any angle to each other.

To draw the influence diagrams for these forces we proceed as explained in previous examples. A unit load is applied to C in the line of R_1, but in the opposite direction, and a Williot diagram is drawn. From this diagram the following data are measured :

$$\text{the vertical deflexion of a point M} \quad = \delta_1,$$
$$\text{the movement of C in the line of } R_1 = \Delta_1,$$
$$\text{the movement of C in the line of } R_2 = \Delta'_1.$$

A second diagram is drawn for a unit load acting in the line of R_2, but in the opposite direction, and corresponding data are obtained as follows :

$$\text{the vertical deflexion of M} \quad\quad = \delta_2,$$
$$\text{the movement of C in the line of } R_2 \quad = \Delta_2,$$
$$\text{the movement of C in the line of } R_1 \quad = \Delta'_2.$$

If a unit load acts vertically at M when the support C is removed the movements of C in the lines of R_1 and R_2 are δ_1 and δ_2 respectively. If the support is kept in position by reactive forces R_1 and R_2 the following equations must be satisfied :

$$R_1\Delta_1 + R_2\Delta'_2 = \delta_1$$
and
$$R_1\Delta'_1 + R_2\Delta_2 = \delta_2.$$

δ_1 and δ_2 can be obtained from the Williot diagrams for all panel points, the equations solved, and the R_1 and R_2 lines plotted.

This is a general result irrespective of the direction assumed for R_1 and R_2. Suppose, however, that from the Williot diagram for a unit load acting in the line of R_1 we find that point C moves to C'. If the line of action of R_2 is then made perpendicular to CC' there will be no movement of C in the line of R_2 under the action of the unit load in the line of R_1, i.e. $\Delta'_1 = 0$. But, by Clerk Maxwell's theorem $\Delta'_2 = \Delta'_1$ and the equations above reduce to the simple results

$$R_1 = \frac{\delta_1}{\Delta_1}$$

and
$$R_2 = \frac{\delta_2}{\Delta_2}.$$

A similar procedure can be followed for three redundant elements.

Fig. 15.15 represents a braced arch supported at the four points A, B, C and D by pins. The redundancies introduced by the pins at C and D can be represented by two forces acting in arbitrary directions as in the last example and by a couple applied to the section CD.

In the first place assume that a unit couple acts at the section CD, represented by two forces $\frac{1}{d}$ at a distance d apart as shown in the figure.

From the Williot diagram the displaced position of CD is found to be $C'D'$. Lines perpendicular to CC' and DD' are drawn from the centre points of these lines to intersect at O, the instantaneous centre of rotation of CD.

Imagine points C, D and O to be connected by a rigid plate and a force of unity to be applied at O in the direction R_1. This can be taken in any direction but will be assumed to be vertical for convenience. This force will produce no rotation of CD. From the Williot diagram for this force the direction of movement of O is determined and the second reactive force is made to act perpendicular to this movement as in the last example.

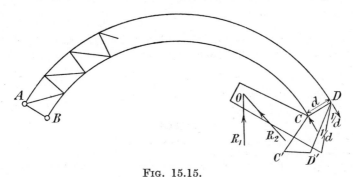

FIG. 15.15.

In general when the directions of the reactive forces are chosen arbitrarily, let a unit couple applied to CD produce

a vertical deflexion of any point M $=\delta_m$
a movement of O in the direction of $R_1=\Delta_m$
a movement of O in the direction of $R_2=\Delta'_m$
an angular rotation of CD $=\theta_m$.

Let a unit force in the line of R_1 produce

a vertical deflexion of M $=\delta_1$,
a movement of O in the direction of $R_1=\Delta_1$,
a movement of O in the direction of $R_2=\Delta'_1$,
an angular rotation of CD $=\theta_1$;

and let a unit force in the line of R_2 produce

a vertical deflexion of M $=\delta_2$,
a movement of O in the direction of $R_1=\Delta'_2$,
a movement of O in the direction of $R_2=\Delta_2$,
an angular rotation of CD $=\theta_2$.

When the supports at C and D are in position and a load of unity acts vertically at M let the reactive forces consist of a moment M_0 and forces R_1 and R_2. The following equations can then be formed :

$$M_0\Delta_m+R_1\Delta_1 +R_2\Delta'_2=\delta_1$$
$$M_0\Delta'_m+R_1\Delta'_1+R_2\Delta_2 =\delta_2$$
$$M_0\theta_m +R_1\theta_1 +R_2\theta_2 =\delta_m.$$

These must be solved simultaneously for each point on the influence line.

When the position of the point O and the directions for R_1 and R_2 are chosen as described above, however, we have

$$\theta_1 =\theta_2 =0$$
$$\Delta'_1=\Delta'_2=0$$
$$\Delta_m=\Delta'_m=0$$

and the equations reduce to the simple results

$$R_1 = \frac{\delta_1}{\Delta_1}$$

$$R_2 = \frac{\delta_2}{\Delta_2}$$

$$M_0 = \frac{\delta_m}{\theta_m}.$$

The whole of the data for plotting the R and M lines are available from the Williot diagrams and the calculations are of the simplest possible type.

REFERENCE

Lea, F. C. 1910. *Proc. Instn. Civ. Engrs.*, **185**, 277.

EXERCISES

(1) A beam of length L and uniform cross-section is encastré at both ends and rests at the centre of the span on a rigid support.

Show that the equation for the influence line of reaction at this support for each half of the beam is

$$R = 4\alpha^2(3 - 4\alpha)$$

where αL is the distance of the unit load from one end.

(2) A beam ABC of uniform cross-section is encastré at A and rests on a rigid support at B which is L from A. The end C is unsupported. If the distance of a unit rolling load from B is $x = \alpha L$ show that the influence line of reaction at B is given by the two equations

$$R = 1 - \frac{3\alpha}{2} + \frac{\alpha^3}{2} \text{ (when } x \text{ is between B and A)}$$

and

$$R = 1 + \frac{3\alpha}{2} \text{ (when } x \text{ is between B and C).}$$

(3) A beam of uniform flexural rigidity EI and length L is pinned at its ends and centre to three columns of the same material as the beam, each of height l.

The end columns each have a cross-sectional area A and the middle column 2A. If x is measured from the centre of the beam show that the influence line of reaction on the mid-support is given by

$$R = \frac{-6Lx^2 + 4x^3 + L^3 + \dfrac{24lI}{A}}{L^3 + \dfrac{48lI}{A}}$$

(4) A two-pinned segmental arch rib of 100 feet span has a rise of 20 feet. Plot the influence line for the horizontal thrust.

(5) If the arch in the last question is encastré at both ends plot the influence lines for the reactive forces and moments at the supports.

(6) An encastré parabolic arch rib has a span of 100 feet and a rise of 16 feet. Assuming that the second moment of area at any section is given by $I_0 \sec \alpha$ where I_0 is the value at the crown and α is the angle of slope of the rib at any point, plot the influence lines for the reactions at the supports.

(7) A Warren truss 12 feet deep consists of ten panels each 10 feet long. It rests on rigid supports at the ends and at the fourth panel point from one end. The cross-sectional areas of the members of the truss are such that if the intermediate support is removed and a load applied to that point the stress in all the loaded bars has the same numerical value.

Draw the influence line of reactions for the centre support for a load on the bottom chord.

CHAPTER 16

THE VOUSSOIR ARCH

16.1. Description and definitions.—In Chapter 12 we dealt with arches formed by continuous members, *i.e.* arched ribs or members connected to form braced structures. These are comparatively recent developments in the history of engineering but many centuries before it would have been feasible to build such structures the arch form was in common use. The early arches were made of a number of wedge-shaped blocks of masonry which were usually set in a jointing material of mortar or cement, although this is not essential to their stability. This type of structure is still commonly used for such diverse purposes as relieving the loads on a lintel over a window opening or bridging a gap to carry road or rail traffic.

Fig. 16.1 shows such an arch with the names of the various parts.

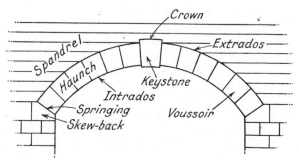

FIG. 16.1.

Many of these terms are of ancient origin.

The wedge-shaped blocks of which the arch is built are known as *voussoirs*. They are usually symmetrically disposed about a central voussoir known as the *key-stone* from a mistaken idea on the part of early builders that it had a special function to perform. As will be seen later, no single voussoir is of more importance structurally than any other and a key-stone is not essential, as shown by the occasional occurrence of arches with an even number of voussoirs. This, however, is unusual and while its rarity mainly arises from the belief in the importance of the key-stone, it is due to some extent to the prejudice of the mason against allowing a joint instead of a block of stone to occupy the central position. The key-stone in fact is an aesthetic and traditional feature rather than a structural requirement. The blocks in the abutments of the arch upon which the end voussoirs rest are known as *skew-backs* and the surface between a skew-back and an end voussoir is the *springing*. The highest point of the arch is the *crown* and the lower sections are the *haunches*. This is a general term and there is no hard and fast definition of how much of the structure is comprised in a haunch. The upper boundary line of the arch ring is known as the *extrados* and the inner

385

line as the *intrados*. The under surface of the structure is the *soffit*. When this type of arch is used for a bridge and a more or less level roadway is required, the *spandrels*, *i.e.* the spaces between the top of the arch and the roadway, are built up by *filling*. The weight of this filling has an important effect upon the load which the arch can carry as will appear in later discussion.

An arch bridge of steel or reinforced concrete usually consists of a number of ribs which are suitably bridged transversely to carry the road or railway. In a masonry bridge, on the other hand, the arch is the full width of the road. The under surface (or soffit) is often referred to as the *barrel* of the arch.

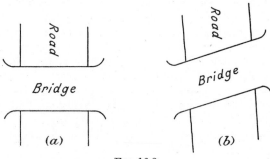

FIG. 16.2.

The simplest type of masonry arch occurs when the bridge crosses the gap to be spanned at right angles, as shown in Fig. 16.2 (*a*). Often, however, the crossing is not right-angled, as shown at (*b*) in the same figure. Such a structure is known as a *skew arch* and if it is built of solid blocks of masonry the setting-out and cutting of the voussoirs is more complicated and expensive than for (*a*).

Many arches are built of brickwork instead of masonry and the arch then consists of a sufficient number of rings to give the necessary depth, as shown in Fig. 16.3.

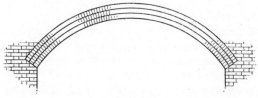

FIG. 16.3.

16.2. Historical.—The history of attempts to explain the behaviour of the voussoir arch has been reviewed elsewhere (Pippard and Chitty, 1951), and only a short summary will be given here.

As might be expected, the first arguments were based on the properties of the inclined plane and the wedge. Some writers approached the problem theoretically, assuming that the interacting surfaces of the voussoirs were polished and that the arch would fail by slipping. This line of argument assumed that the pressure acted normal to the face of each voussoir and led to the conclusion that the voussoirs must be of increasing depth towards the springings in order that the arch might be equilibrated.

In 1801, Atwood in England made experiments on two models of arches with polished metal voussoirs, in which he measured the pressure perpendicular to the face of certain voussoirs in order to prove formulas based on the wedge theory. Rennie's bridges at the beginning of the last century were designed more or less on the assumption of smooth faces on the voussoirs.

An alternative assumption was that the voussoirs were infinitely rough ; the arch must then fail by the rotation of some of the voussoirs about their edges, and this was actually shown to occur in model experiments made by the French engineer Couplet, in 1730. He, however, arrived at the erroneous conclusion that the joints of rupture for all arches were at the key-stone and at 30° to the horizontal.

A third line of attack, enunciated by Hooke but little developed during the eighteenth century, was derived from analogy with the loaded catenary.

Meanwhile, several important voussoir arches were being designed and erected in France under Perronet who initiated a number of experiments. In particular, in connexion with a bridge at Nemours, Chief Engineer Boistard made a number of model experiments in 1800 which led him to the conclusion that all bridges failed by opening of joints at the crown, at the haunches and at the abutments, and that in general the joints at the crown and abutments would open at the intrados and those at the haunches at the extrados. These experiments, together with others made by Rondelet about the same time, were of considerable importance, as they led to new theories of the behaviour of the arch.

In 1826 Navier, having propounded a straight line law for the pressure distribution across the face of voussoirs in contact, showed that if the resultant pressure at the crown and joints of rupture acted at one-third of the depth of the ring from the extrados and the intrados respectively, the joints would be just on the point of opening. This was re-introduced by Mery as a new idea in 1840 and is the beginning of the doctrine of the middle-third of which more will be said later.

Much of the Continental work seems to have remained unknown in England for a long time. Professor Robison of Edinburgh recorded the collapse of a bridge made in rather soft stone, the failure of which was ascribed to overloading at the crown : about a fortnight before final failure occurred, it was noticed that the stones on the soffit of the arch at 10 feet on either side of the centre and also at 20 feet on one side were cracking badly and it was considered by the masons that ultimate failure would take place at these points. Actually, it occurred by pivoting of segments of the arch about a point at the crown and at points about 15 feet or 16 feet on either side of the centre; the arch hovered for a short time and finally pivotted about points at the abutments. Professor Robison experimented on a model made of chalk and by over-loading the crown was able to reproduce this type of failure.

It is uncertain when the idea of the line of pressure or linear arch, which is the outcome of the third line of attack, was introduced on the Continent as a means of studying the voussoir arch, but in this country it was developed by Professor Moseley in 1835, who showed that this line must lie within the arch ring.

In 1846 Snell determined the joints of rupture and the amount of thickening of voussoirs required in the neighbourhood of the abutments of certain arches to keep the line of pressure inside the arch ring.   He also took account of the possible failure of the materials of the arch and the provision of sufficient bearing area to prevent it as a factor in modifying the position of the line of pressure.

In the same year Barlow pointed out that many lines of pressure could be drawn for an arch, all of which had equal validity.   He proposed as the correct one the line of pressure which passed through the centres of the crown and haunches.

In a sense this marks an advance in the formal approach to the problem ; interest was no longer centred on a state of limiting stability which no actual arch would reach, but on the correct choice of the line of pressure, assuming the arch to be of dimensions admitting of choice.   The prevailing view seems to have been that all lines of pressure which could be drawn within the arch ring were equally valid, and the matter of selection was simply one of convenience.

This is not so ; each linear arch corresponds to a definite condition at the abutments as will be shown later.

Woodbury in America, and Rankine in Great Britain, adopted the doctrine that the line of pressure must be within the middle-third, thus eliminating tensile stresses.   This is nowadays advocated by most writers, who still assume that if *any* linear arch for the given load can be drawn within the middle-third, the result will be satisfactory.

Rankine's design method is a compromise and, since it affords a key to many other design methods to be found in text books, it will be outlined. He assumed that the load system consists of vertical forces distributed in any symmetrical manner along the span.   A linear arch which will carry this system is selected in a more or less arbitrary manner.   Generally this linear arch is the same shape as that of the intrados of the completed arch.

The horizontal thrust at the crown is calculated from a formula, due to Navier, for an arch under normal pressure, *viz.*, the product of the intensity of pressure and the radius of curvature at the point considered.

The equilibrium of this linear arch can only be maintained by a system of horizontal pressures applied along its length ; between the crown and some point on the haunches these pressures must be directed outwards ; below that point they must be directed inwards.   Rankine called them conjugate pressures, and the point where the pressures change sign he termed the point of rupture.   If the pressures were omitted below this point the voussoirs of the actual arch would be forced outward and freed, while omission of the pressures above it would only tend to wedge them together.   The point of rupture corresponds to the position of maximum horizontal thrust, which is the sum of the Navier thrust at the crown and the conjugate pressure applied between the crown and that point.

Having determined the point of rupture and the maximum horizontal thrust, the arbitrary linear arch is abandoned and the real design is begun. That part of the arch below the point of rupture is included in the abutment and is given suitable horizontal backing ; the part above, which is the real arch, is designed to carry the vertical loads and a horizontal thrust equal to the maximum already determined.   With regard to this, Rankine stated (1862) : " The stability of an arch is secure if a linear arch balanced under the forces which act on the real arch can be drawn within the middle-third of the arch ring."   He emphasised the point thus : " It is true that arches have stood, and still stand, in which the centres of resistance of joints fall beyond the middle-third of the depth of the arch ring ; but the stability of such arches is either now precarious or must have been precarious while the mortar was fresh."

Since stability of a voussoir arch is not dependent upon fulfilment of the no-tension condition and since a condition of instability only occurs under much larger loads than those which just violate this condition, it must be assumed that Rankine used the word " stability " in a different sense from that now understood.

Meanwhile, speculation as to the " true " line of pressure continued on the Continent and various theories were advanced.

Hagen defined the most probable line as that for which the vertical projections of the minimum distances between the line of pressure and the boundaries of the arch ring were a minimum.   Another theory advanced in a slightly varying form by various writers, was that the true line gave minimum stresses at the critical sections.

Winkler suggested that the true line was that for which the sum of the squares of its distances from the centre line of the arch ring was a minimum. Since the bending moment on a small element of the ring is the thrust at the element multiplied by the distance from the centre line of the arch to the linear arch, and the strain energy in the element due to bending is proportional to the square of this bending moment, there is some consistency between Winkler's proposal and that of Castigliano, who analysed a masonry voussoir arch on the basis of his newly enunciated theorems of minimum strain energy.

Castigliano assumed that the abutments were rigid, and so long as the line of pressure of the arch ring was everywhere within the middle-third the ring would behave as a continuous elastic rib.   The thrust was first calculated for the complete arch by the method of minimum strain energy.   If the resulting line of pressure fell outside the middle-third at any section, the portions of the arch ring which were thereby put into tension were assumed to be removed and a second approximation was made using the modified arch ring.   This process was continued until no tension was found at any point and the stresses were then calculated by the usual methods.

One objection to the use of this method was the doubt as to whether a masonry arch exhibited a linear relationship between load and displacement ; this will be discussed later.

Although in the light of more recent work Castigliano's method appears to provide the soundest basis of design, it has not hitherto been generally accepted and reliance is still placed on a combination of older theories, which will be summarised in the next paragraph.

16.3. The accepted basis of design.—It is generally assumed that a voussoir arch may fail in any of four ways :

(1) By the development of excessive tensile stress in the jointing material.

(2) By the development of excessive compressive stress in the material.

(3) By the sliding of one voussoir over another.

(4) By spreading of the abutments.

The last of these can only be prevented by the provision of adequate stability in the abutments and foundations.   This is necessary for all arches and must be treated as a separate problem distinct from that of the design

of the arch itself.   The sliding of a voussoir depends upon the angle which
the resultant of the normal and transverse forces at any joint makes with
the normal to the joint.   If this angle is less than the angle of friction the
joint is safe against such failure ; if it is greater than the angle of friction,
the joint between voussoirs may need a mechanical key.

The calculation of the stresses at any section of the arch would be simple
if the correct linear arch could be drawn but, as already shown in the preceding paragraph, the selection of the correct one has given rise to considerable controversy in the past.   Only one point has been generally agreed
upon—that if tension is to be avoided the linear arch must fall within the
middle-third of the depth of the arch ring at every point.   If it is assumed
that the stress distribution is linear across any section this must be true, but
within this limitation any number of linear arches can be drawn.

Each of these possible linear arches is intimately associated with the
condition of fixity at the abutments (Pippard and Ashby, 1938) and this
needs emphasising.

Suppose that Fig. 16.4 represent a voussoir arch with fixed ends, which
carries any system of external loads.   Since it is assumed, as a basis of
design, that no tension shall be developed in the ring, the structure can be
treated as an arch-rib, as will be shown.

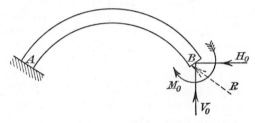

FIG. 16.4.

Such a rib has three redundant reactions at the support B, represented by
the couple M_0, together with the vertical force V_0, and the horizontal force
H_0 acting at the centre of the springing.

These three reactions can be replaced by a single force R acting at some
point in the springing line, and this is the point through which the linear arch
passes.   Since the structure is adequate if the end B is unsupported, the
actions M_0, H_0 and V_0 may be assigned any arbitrary values.   For each set
of values there will be a different position of the resultant action R ; that
is, the linear arch will start at a different point for each set.

These actions will, however, produce component displacements of the end
B which may be calculated by an application of the first theorem of
Castigliano.   Thus if U denotes the total strain-energy of the structure due
to the external system, then

$\dfrac{\partial U}{\partial M_0}$ =the angular rotation of section B in the direction of M_0,

$\dfrac{\partial U}{\partial H_0}$ =the horizontal movement of section B in the direction of H_0,

$\dfrac{\partial U}{\partial V_0}$ =the vertical movement of section B in the direction of V_0.

For one, and only one, set of values of M_0, H_0 and V_0 these movements will be zero ; that is, there will be no displacement of the support. For any other set the end B will be displaced and a different linear arch will be obtained. The arbitrary assumption of a particular linear arch thus tacitly assumes certain movements of the abutments, and it is therefore inconsistent to assume absolute fixity and at the same time to select a linear arch arbitrarily.

It has been customary, however, to make such an arbitrary choice and thus determine the thrust and bending moment at all sections of the arch. The stresses in the material calculated from these data are kept within the prescribed safe values.

16.4. The voussoir arch as an elastic structure.—The method of analysis used by Castigliano depends for its validity upon the assumption that a voussoir arch shows a linear relationship between load and displacement, and in 1890 the Austrian Society of Engineers carried out an exhaustive series of experiments to determine this point, among others. A number of arches were loaded to destruction and it was found that, until cracks started to develop, the measured displacements were approximately proportional to the applied loads. The development of cracks did not cause much alteration to the arch shape.

From these experiments it was rightly deduced that elastic theory was applicable to such structures. There appears to have been, however, an unwarranted deduction that the arches behaved as solid ribs and that the thrust could, therefore, be calculated by the method of minimum strain energy. This does not follow from the mere fact of a linear relationship between displacement and loading, since such a relationship would equally be observed if the structure were a three-pinned arch and, therefore, statically determinate.

In order to prove that the structure behaves as a solid rib it is necessary to show that the thrust of a voussoir arch is the same as that of a continuous rib of the same dimensions, and experiments carried out to elucidate the behaviour of the voussoir arch included an investigation of this point (Pippard, *et al.*, 1936). Model segmental arches were made with spans of 4 feet and rises of 1 foot, the voussoirs being carefully machined steel; one test arch had pinned ends while the other was supported on skewbacks. One end of the arch under test was fixed in position but the other was mounted on a carriage made as free from friction as possible and restrained by a 4 B.A. steel rod carrying a delicate optical extensometer. The loads in this rod could thus be measured, and the elastic stretch in the rod being taken up by a turnbuckle, the horizontal component of reaction at the free support was obtained direct. The arch was assumed to support a load of earth which filled the spandrels and formed a horizontal road surface, and this load was provided in the models by cans, appropriately weighted by shot, hung from the voussoirs. A point load of variable amount could in addition be applied to any voussoir.

In the first place, a solid rib of mild steel of the same dimensions as the voussoir arch was mounted as explained above. The dead loading remained constant, and the value of the thrust or horizontal component of reaction was measured for a range of loads applied to different points. From these a curve was drawn showing the thrust due to a unit load at any point in the

span of the arch.   The solid rib was then removed and the voussoir arch
with pinned ends erected in its place.   The experiment was repeated, and
it was found that until a limiting load, which varied with the point of
application, was reached the results were almost precisely as found for the
solid rib.   It was established, therefore, that within certain limiting loads
the voussoir arch behaved as a solid rib.   The limiting load is easily shown
to be that which produces a tensile stress in a joint adjacent to its point of
application and so reduces the bearing area of the voussoirs at that section.
Attention was then concentrated on the behaviour of the arch when a
gradually increasing load was applied to one voussoir, and the results
obtained can best be illustrated in diagrams.

Fig. 16.5 (a) shows a voussoir arch with its earth fill and in addition a
load applied to a particular voussoir.   As this point load is increased, the
horizontal thrust also increases.   For small values of W the thrust agrees
practically exactly with the values for a solid rib of the same size and with

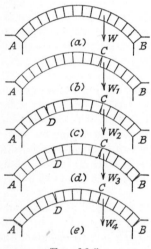

FIG. 16.5.

similar abutments.   At a particular value W_1
a change occurs in the rate of change of the
thrust with the applied load which is consistent
with the formation of a pin at C, indicating that
the arch has now effectively become two solid
sections AC and BC pinned together at C, as
shown at (b).   If the supports are allowed to
spread slightly, the " pin " can be clearly seen
to be formed by the hinging of the adjacent
voussoirs at C.   The new ratio of thrust to load
is maintained for a time, but at a load W_2
another change in the rate occurs which is due
to the formation of a second virtual pin at D,
as in Fig. 16.5 (c).   This pin is, however, on the
intrados of the arch, whereas the first one was
on the extrados.   The arch now consists of two
solid sections AD and BC connected by a third
solid section DC which is pinned to them, and is
essentially the structure of the cantilever bridge.

A still further increase in the load shows that at W_3 there is another change
in the rate of change of thrust with load due to the formation of a third " pin "
at the intrados at B.   The arch now consists of three solid sections of which
one, AD, is *encastré* at A, the other two being effectively solid pin-jointed links.
as in Fig. 16.5 (d).   During this process there is a progressive reduction in
the redundancy in the structure.   The original arch has three degrees of
redundancy, but with the formation of each successive pin, one degree of
redundancy is lost, so that (b) has two, (c) has one, and (d) has none, *i.e.*
(d) is statically determinate.   If loading is continued beyond W_3, a sudden
collapse of the arch occurs at a load W_4 due to the formation of a fourth pin
at A which turns the assembly into a mechanism.

These experiments clarified the mechanics of the voussoir arch and showed
that while Snell's theory of failure (1846) had a sound basis it was inadequate
and in certain respects faulty.

16.5. Behaviour of a masonry arch.—In the experiments outlined in the
last paragraph the arch was constructed without jointing material between

the voussoirs, and the usual assumption made in design, that no tensile stresses can be transmitted, was exactly satisfied.   It was shown that under these conditions, provided the correct linear arch fell everywhere within the middle-third of the arch ring, the structure behaved exactly like an arch-rib and could be analysed by methods applicable to such structures.

An increase in the point load finally produced a condition in which adjacent voussoirs were in contact only at the extreme edges, and a succession of virtual pin-joints were formed, which reduced the problem to comparatively simple statical terms.   Failure occurred when sufficient of these pins formed to transform the structure into a mechanism.   These experiments are described fully elsewhere (Pippard, 1936 or 1952).

If a jointing material is used in the construction of an arch the adhesion between this material and the voussoirs, and the nature of the material itself, may enable the joint to offer some resistance to tensile stress.   Also, the material may be such that it will fail in compression before the virtual pin can form at the extreme edge of the joint.

The general effects of the presence of jointing material of this type will, therefore, be to increase the range of loading for which the structure behaves as an arch-rib, since the linear arch can fall outside the middle-third without causing the opening of a joint, and also to reduce the load at which instability occurs, since the " pin " cannot reach the extreme edge of the joint.

If the material of which the voussoirs are made cannot withstand the compressive stresses developed, premature failure of the structure will occur.

Further experiments were carried out (Pippard and Ashby, 1938) on an arch having a clear span of 10 feet and a rise of 2 feet 6 inches to determine the applicability of the results of the previous work to actual structures.

Two sets of cast concrete voussoirs made of rapid hardening cement with limestone and granite chippings respectively were used.   The compressive strengths of the two concretes at 28 days were 1,740 lb. per square inch and 6,700 lb. per square inch.   The voussoirs were 10 inches deep, 6 inches thick and tapered from $6 \cdot 18$ inches to $5 \cdot 41$ inches in elevation.   The arch, with $\frac{1}{4}$ inch mortar joints, contained twenty-three voussoirs.   The load representing the arch filling was provided by lead shot carried in cans from the individual voussoirs.   Most of the tests were made with a light loading estimated on a depth of filling of 6 inches over the crown, the density being 70 lb. per cubic foot.   One test, however, was made with heavier loading estimated on a depth of filling of 12 inches over the crown, the density being 140 lb. per cubic foot.

Seven series of tests were made on arches built and loaded to the specifications shown in Table 16.1.

The non-hydraulic lime gave a mortar with practically no tensile strength, and it was used solely to form a bedding for the voussoirs.   It is also weak in compression.   The cement mortar was a mixture of rapid-hardening Portland cement and sand in the proportion 1 : 3 by weight.

In each test an increasing load was applied to one particular voussoir and observations were made of the initiation and development of cracks in the jointing material.

The test was continued until complete failure of the arch occurred, usually by the development of a fourth " pin-joint " causing the structure to become unstable, or occasionally by spalling of the voussoirs, or by slipping along a joint.   It was found that the load could be steadily increased to that at

TABLE 16.1.

Series	Voussoirs	Jointing material	Loading
1	Limestone	Non-hydraulic lime mortar	Light
2	,,	None	,,
3	,,	Rapid-hardening Portland cement mortar	,,
4	Granite	Non-hydraulic lime mortar	,,
5	,,	None	,,
6	,,	Rapid-hardening Portland cement mortar	,,
7	,,	,, ,,	Heavy

which a fourth pin developed, when a sudden collapse occurred. The centering of the arch, left in position a few inches clear of the soffit, prevented a complete break-up, and on removing the point load it was found that the structure returned to its original position unless slipping between voussoirs had occurred.

For full details of the test results reference should be made to the original paper, but they are shown in diagrammatic form in Figs. 16.6 and 16.7.

Fig. 16.6 gives the tests on both limestone and granite voussoir arches when jointed in lime mortar, and Fig. 16.7 those when cement mortar was used. Reference curves are plotted in each figure as follows. Curve A shows the concentrated load which must be applied to any voussoir to cause the linear arch to reach the middle-third point of any joint. Curves B and C show the loads which cause the linear arch to reach the middle-half and middle-three-quarter points respectively of any joint. Curve D gives the loads which cause the linear arch to touch the extrados of the arch ring at any joint. All of these curves are obtained on the assumptions that no cracking of a joint occurs, that is that the arch can be treated as a rib, and that the abutments are completely rigid. Curve E gives the maximum loads for which an *arbitrary* linear arch can be drawn wholly within the middle-third of the arch ring. As already shown, this involves the tacit assumption that the abutments are free to move as required, and although this method is widely used it is incorrect if the abutments are rigid, as they are intended to be. For the particular proportions of the experimental arch it is of interest to note that this curve coincides very closely with curve B, which shows the maximum loads keeping the linear arch within the middle-half, the abutments being rigid. The middle-half rule has been advocated by various authors and, at any rate in the test arch, its correct application would lead to the same results as the usual and incorrect application of the middle-third rule. Curve G gives the loads which would cause the arch to fail due to instability. The method of calculation is given in detail in paragraph 16.6.

Curve F is similar to curve G but is based on the assumption that the arch ring is 9 inches deep instead of its real value of 10 inches. This assumption was made as it was found in a number of the experiments with lime mortar that the tension crack only extended to within $1\frac{1}{2}$ inch of the edge of the ring at failure. If a linear distribution of stress is assumed, the centre of pressure is then $\frac{1}{2}$ inch from the edge.

It will be seen from Fig. 16.6 that only in one instance did the first crack appear at a load below that of curve B. The majority of arches in this series did not show any sign of cracking until the linear arch almost reached the extrados. The ultimate failures were grouped closely around curve F.

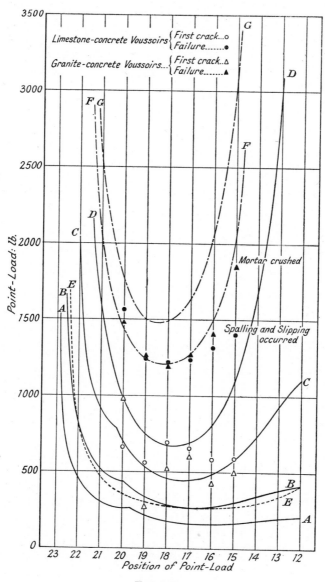

Fig. 16.6.

Those giving low values of ultimate load failed by crushing of the mortar or spalling of the voussoirs. It should be noticed that the results of the tests are not dependent to any marked extent upon the material of the voussoirs, indicating that the behaviour of the arch depends primarily on the jointing material.

Fig. 16.7 relating to tests with cement-mortar joints, shows that the linear arch always came well outside the arch ring before the first crack appeared, and in general ultimate failing loads were much higher than those based on the stability calculation for unjointed voussoirs. These results

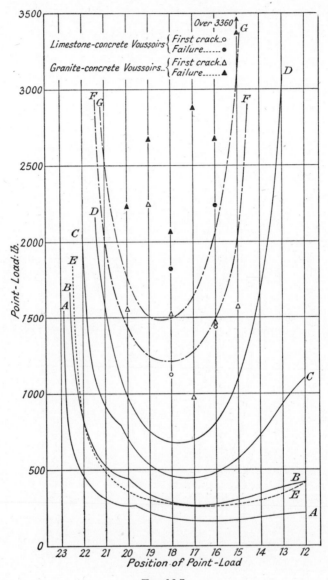

FIG. 16.7.

indicate that cement-mortar joints have an appreciable strength in resisting tension, which could well be taken into account in design.

The results are shown in Figs. 16.8 and 16.9 by a series of linear arches for lime- and cement-mortar jointed arches respectively. These are drawn for the loads at which the first crack appeared, and show the conservative nature of the middle-third rule. They were obtained by strain-energy analysis on the assumption that there was no movement of the abutments.

These tests were all carried out for light loading, since the point loads required to cause failure under heavy loading would have been inconveniently large. For comparison, however, one test was made with the heavy dead load. This arch showed no sign of failure until a point load of 3,545 lb. was applied, when it collapsed suddenly with a typical instability failure. The spalling was no worse than in previous tests. Under light loading the arch failed at 2,075 lb. applied to the same point. The ratio of the failing loads is 1.71, which is practically the ratio of the dead loading including the weight of the voussoirs.

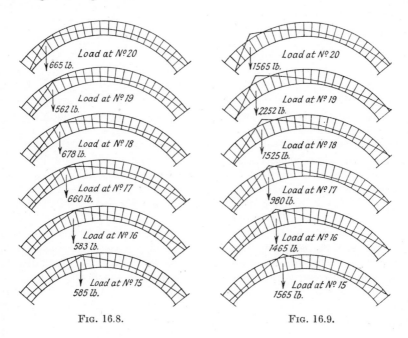

FIG. 16.8.   FIG. 16.9.

It is evident from these tests that, even when weak mortar is used, the middle-third criterion is pessimistic. This has been recognised by various authors, who have suggested that the middle-half core should be considered as the safe region for the linear arch. With good cement mortar, however, even this is conservative, and there is little doubt that no cracking of joints would occur if a wider margin still were adopted. It must be emphasised, in this connexion, that the development of tension at a single joint does not indicate that the structure is unsafe, since a very large margin of strength is available before instability occurs.

16.6. Calculation of the stability of a voussoir arch.—In an earlier paragraph it was shown that a voussoir arch increasingly loaded at a point may reach a state of instability due to the development of four virtual hinges which occur alternately at the intrados and extrados. The structure is thus turned into a four-bar mechanism and collapses. A method of calculating the magnitude of the load which must be applied at any point to cause this will now be described.

Fig. 16.10 shows an arch carrying any specified dead loading denoted by w_1, w_2 and w_3. The load W is just sufficient to put the structure into a state of unstable equilibrium. The unknown reactions are then V_A, V_B and H, as shown.

In the first place it will be assumed that the positions of the four virtual pins A, B, C and D are known. The section of the structure CDB is in

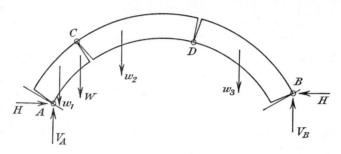

FIG. 16.10.

equilibrium under the forces acting upon it, which do not include the un-known W. Hence, by taking moments of these forces about C and D, two equations in H, V_B and the appropriate part of the dead-load system, are obtained. By eliminating V_B from these, the value of H is determined.

If moments of the forces on the structure are taken about A, an equation is obtained which contains W, V_B, H and the terms for the dead load. V_B is again eliminated by using the equation of moments about C, and since H has been found, W can be determined.

The positions of two of the pins are not precisely known, and some trial and error is necessary, but certain general rules reduce the uncertainty considerably. Thus, pin C always forms at the extrados of the joint adjacent to W, lying between W and the crown of the arch ; pin B always forms at the extrados of the springing farther away from W ; pin A is on the intrados, either at the other springing or on a joint near it, and the position of pin D can in most cases be judged very nearly.

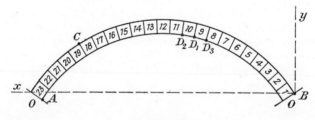

FIG. 16.11.

To find W it is therefore necessary to make a few trials for different pin-positions. H is calculated from a consideration of the equilibrium of the section CB as before, but for a few (perhaps two or three) different positions of D. That giving the lowest value of H will be the correct one, since it will give the lowest value of W whatever the position of A. After finding H, a few alternative positions for A are taken and the corresponding values of W calculated as already described. The lowest will be the correct one.

TABLE 16.2.

(1)	(2)	(3)	(4)	(5)	(6)	(7)	(8)	(9)
Reference points			x	y	Load w	Moment wx	Σw	Σwx
Int.	Mid.	Ext.						
23, 0			1·600	−0·027				
		23, 0	1·636	0			2,016	1,649
	23		1·593		108	172		
22, 23			1·550	0·035				
		22, 23	1·584	0·064			1,908	1,477
	22		1·540		106	163		
21, 22			1·496	0·091				
		21, 22	1·526	0·123			1,802	1,314
	21		1·481		107	159		
20, 21			1·437	0·144				
		20, 21	1·465	0·178			1,695	1,155
	20		1·419		100	142		
19, 20			1·369	0·191				
		19, 20	1·399	0·228			1,595	1,013
	19		1·353		94	127		
18, 19			1·307	0·233				
		18, 19	1·329	0·272			1,501	886
	18		1·283		86	110		
17, 18			1·237	0·270				
		17, 18	1·256	0·310			1,415	776
	17		1·210		83	100		
16, 17			1·165	0·301				
		16, 17	1·181	0·342			1,332	676
	16		1·135		77	88		
15, 16			1·090	0·326				
		15, 16	1·102	0·368			1,255	588
	15		1·057		74	78		
14, 15			1·013	0·345				
		14, 15	1·022	0·388			1,181	510
	14		0·978		71	69		
13, 14			0·936	0·357				
		13, 14	0·941	0·401			1,110	441
	13		0·898		68	61		
12, 13			0·857	0·364				
		12, 13	0·859	0·408			1,042	380
	12		0·818		68	56		
11, 12			0·778	0·364				
		11, 12	0·777	0·408			974	324
	11		0·737		68	50		
10, 11			0·700	0·357				
		10, 11	0·694	0·401			906	274
	10		0·657		71	47		
9, 10			0·622	0·345				
		9, 10	0·613	0·388			835	227
	9		0·578		74	43		
8, 9			0·545	0·326				
		8, 9	0·533	0·368			761	184
	8		0·501		77	39		
7, 8			0·471	0·301				
		7, 8	0·455	0·342			684	145

TABLE 16.2—*continued*.

(1)	(2)	(3)	(4)	(5)	(6)	(7)	(8)	(9)
Reference points			x	y	Load w	Moment wx	Σw	Σwx
Int.	Mid.	Ext.						
	7		0·425		83	35		
6, 7			0·398	0·270				
		6, 7	0·379	0·310			601	110
	6		0·353		86	30		
5, 6			0·328	0·233				
		5, 6	0·306	0·272			515	80
	5		0·283		94	27		
4, 5			0·267	0·191				
		4, 5	0·237	0·228			421	53
	4		0·217		100	22		
3, 4			0·199	0·144				
		3, 4	0·171	0·178			321	31
	3		0·154		107	16		
2, 3			0·140	0·091				
		2, 3	0·109	0·123			214	15
	2		0·096		106	10		
1, 2			0·085	0·035				
		1, 2	0·052	0·064			108	5
	1		0·043		108	5		
0, 1			0·036	−0·027				
		0, 1	0	0				

Since in most cases the critical values of W will be needed for all points on the arch the work should be done systematically, and the following method is recommended. The arch ring considered is shown in Fig. 16.11 and consists of 23 voussoirs 3·33 inches deep. The span is 10 feet and the rise 2 feet 6 inches.

Take B as origin with Ox as horizontal and Oy as vertical axes of reference. Starting from the left-hand abutment, the co-ordinates of the extrados and intrados of each joint are tabulated (in this particular case in terms of the mean radius) as shown in Table 16.2. The x co-ordinate of the centre of each voussoir is entered in column 4 of the Table, the dead load applied to it in column 6, and the moment of this dead load about the origin in column 7. The sum of all dead loads to the right of a joint and the sum of their moments are entered in columns 8 and 9.

As an example we will determine the load which must be applied to voussoir No. 19 to cause the arch to become unstable.

Taking moments about C for the part of the arch between C and B we obtain

$$x_C V_B = y_C H + x_C \overset{B}{\underset{C}{\Sigma}} w - \overset{B}{\underset{C}{\Sigma}} wx.$$

Point C is 18–19e, and on substituting numerical values from the table we have

$$1·329 V_B = 0·272 H + (1·329 \times 1501) - 886,$$

whence $\qquad\qquad\qquad V_B = 0·204 H + 835. \qquad . \qquad . \qquad . \qquad . \qquad . \qquad .$ (16.1)

For a first trial assume pin D to be at 9–10i. The moment equation for the part of the arch between D and B about this point is

$$0 \cdot 622 V_B = 0 \cdot 345 H + (0 \cdot 622 \times 835) - 227,$$

whence $V_B = 0 \cdot 554 H + 471.$ . . . . (16.2)

Eliminating V_B between (16.1) and (16.2),

$$H = 1{,}040 \text{ lb.}$$ . . . . (16.3)

For a second trial assume pin D at 10–11i ;

then $0 \cdot 700 V_B = 0 \cdot 357 H + (0 \cdot 700 \times 906) - 274,$

whence $V_B = 0 \cdot 511 H + 516.$ . . . . (16.4)

From (16.1) and (16.4)

$$H = 1{,}042 \text{ lb.}$$ . . . . (16.5)

Similarly, if pin D is at 8–9i

$$H = 1{,}045 \text{ lb.}$$ . . . . (16.6)

The position 9–10i is correct since it gives the lowest value for H. Selecting the left abutment (that is, 23–0i) as the pin A we obtain, by taking moments about A,

$$1 \cdot 600 V_B = -0 \cdot 027 H + (1 \cdot 600 \times 0 \cdot 2016) - 1{,}649 + 0 \cdot 247 W,$$

whence $V_B = -0 \cdot 017 H + 986 + 0 \cdot 155 W.$ . . . . . . (16.7)

Eliminating V_B between (16.1) and (16.7) and substituting for H from (16.3),

$$W = 512 \text{ lb.}$$

If pin A is at 23–22

$$W = 534 \text{ lb.}$$

The correct pins are, therefore, 0–1e ; 9–10i ; 18–19e ; and 23–0i, and the corresponding values for the load and horizontal thrust are W=512 lb. and H=1,040 lb. respectively.

It should be noticed that W is directly proportional to the dead load as shown experimentally and mentioned in the last paragraph, and so, from the standpoint of stability, a heavy filling is preferable to a light. The compressive stresses, however, are naturally increased in the same proportion and there is more danger of a failure from this cause.

16.7. Analysis and design methods for a voussoir arch.—As shown in paragraph 16.3, the existing methods of design for voussoir arches are based on a combination of principles some of which are applied in a way which is open to criticism. The work of Castigliano in this field appears to have received little attention although it was the first attempt to treat the subject rationally as an elastic problem. The experimental work done since the publication of his treatment, both in the laboratory and on actual structures, shows without doubt that the general line of approach which he advocated is sound and its adoption would lead to the more scientific design of these structures. There is, however, one aspect which so far has not been considered but is of importance. Hitherto in this chapter attention has been directed to the location of the linear arch within the actual ring without reference to the stresses developed in the material, and it is obvious that to specify limitations in position alone would be inadequate.

Suppose that at any joint the linear arch cuts the ring at a distance e from the centre line. The maximum and minimum stresses are then given by $\frac{P}{A}\left(1\pm\frac{6e}{d}\right)$ where P is the thrust on the joint, A is its cross-sectional area, and d is the depth of the joint. Hence the ratio of maximum to minimum stress occurring at the edges of the joint is $\dfrac{1+\dfrac{6e}{d}}{1-\dfrac{6e}{d}}$. When this ratio is negative a tensile stress occurs. If $e=\frac{d}{6}$, the minimum stress is zero and the middle-third rule is obtained. If $e=\frac{d}{4}$, the ratio is -5 and a tensile stress of one-fifth of the intensity of the compressive stress occurs. So, if a maximum compressive stress of 13 tons per square foot is permitted and reached at such a joint, the tensile stress at the other edge will be $2\cdot6$ tons per square foot or about 40 lb. per square inch. The compressive stress quoted is a reasonable one and the accompanying tensile stress is low for good cement mortar and probably quite safe for any kind of lime mortar likely to be used for this class of structure. In many instances, therefore, it would be undoubtedly safe to permit the linear arch to fall outside the middle-half as was shown in the experiments described in paragraph 23.6. It is, however, wise to adopt a conservative attitude in view of the uncertainties as to the effect of prolonged repetition of stress (Pippard and Chitty, 1941), the weathering of the materials and the possibilities of heavier traffic in the future than contemplated in design. Taking all these into consideration it appears reasonable to adopt the middle-half criterion.

The proposed arch ring should be treated as a solid rib with known or assumed conditions at the abutments and the true linear arch for these conditions should be found by a strain energy analysis. The linear arch should not fall outside the middle-half of the actual ring but should lie as closely as possible to the boundaries of this core. Trial-and-error methods may be necessary to determine the minimum depth of ring to meet this requirement. The compressive stresses should then be calculated to ensure that the allowable limit is not exceeded anywhere.

The resulting arch should be safe for all normal conditions and will have a large margin of strength against ultimate failure by instability. This may be calculated by the method described in the last paragraph.

The above treatment is suggested on the assumption that the arch can be divided into separate ribs as would be the case in steel or reinforced concrete structures. This is seldom true in masonry or brick arches which are generally of barrel construction. It then becomes necessary to make an assumption as to the effective width of the rib for design purposes and this depends on the type of load and on the type and depth of filling.

It is commonly assumed that a filling distributes a concentrated load through a cone of 90° apex angle so that a point load acting on a filling of 12 inches depth would be spread over a circular area of 12 inches radius at the bottom of the filling. Thus a point load on a barrel arch with this depth of filling could be assumed to be resisted by a rib 24 inches wide. This is, of course, only an assumption and is quoted simply to show one method of dealing with the problem ; special problems will require individual treatment and, unfortunately, very little data are available to assist the designer.

REFERENCES

Rankine, W. J. M.   1862.   " Manual of Civil Engineering."   Griffin.
Pippard, A. J. S., Tranter, E. and Chitty, L.   1936.   *J. Instn. Civ. Engrs.*, **4,** 281–306.
Pippard, A. J. S. and Ashby, R. J.   1938.   *J. Instn. Civ. Engrs.*, **10,** 383–404.
Pippard, A. J. S. and Chitty, L.   1941.   *J. Instn. Civ. Engrs.*, **17,** 79–86.
Pippard, A. J. S. and Chitty, L.   1951.   *Nat. Bldg. Studies*, **11,** H.M.S.O.
Pippard, A. J. S.   1952.   " Studies in Elastic Structures."   Arnold.

CHAPTER 17

THE BEAM CURVED IN PLAN

17.1. Torsional effects.—When a beam is subjected to a pure bending moment, transverse sections which were originally plane before strain occurred remain plane and even when shearing force is present the modification of the stress distribution is in most practical cases so small that the engineer's theory of bending based on the Bernoulli assumptions gives results of sufficient accuracy for most purposes. If a bar is subjected to a twisting moment, however, the assumption of planarity is totally incorrect except for solid circular sections and for hollow circular sections with concentric inner and outer boundaries. Any other section warps when twisted and the effect is to modify the stress distribution to such an extent that calculations based on the assumption of planarity give hopelessly misleading results. The torsional stiffness is also seriously affected by this warping; if originally plane sections remained plane after twist the torsional rigidity could be calculated simply as the product of the polar second moment of area of the section and the shear modulus of the material, *i.e.* $N(I_{xx}+I_{yy})$ where I_{xx} and I_{yy} are the second moments of area about the principal axes through the centroid and N is the shear modulus. This result is accurate for the circular sections mentioned before; for all others it is an over-estimate, in many cases to an enormous extent. In some structural sections of quite usual proportions, for example, the true value of the torsional stiffness as determined experimentally is only one or two per cent. of that calculated from the second moments of area. Various methods are available for estimating the torsional stiffness of non-circular sections (Case), but they are all long and tedious and in general only approximate; an experimental determination is more reliable and should be used where possible in preference to calculations. Table 17.1 gives a number of experimental values determined by Gibson and Ritchie (1914), expressed as the ratio of the flexural rigidity (EI) to the torsional rigidity (NJ). This ratio, γ, will appear in all the subsequent work of this chapter and it should be remembered that for the comparatively deep and narrow sections used in structural practice its

TABLE 17.1.

Section		$\gamma = EI/NJ$	
		Incorrect	Experimental
8 inches $\times$ 5 inches	Joist section		218·5
3 inches $\times$ 3 inches	,, ,,		93·1
$4\frac{3}{4}$ inches $\times$ $1\frac{3}{4}$ inches	,, ,,		287·0
3·16 inches $\times$ 1·66 inches	,, ,,	2·445	220·8
2 inches $\times$ 1 inch	,, ,,	2·485	98·9
$1\frac{1}{2}$ inches $\times$ $\frac{3}{4}$ inch	,, ,,	2·445	68·9
2 inches $\times$ 1 inch	Channel section	2·415	74·9

value will be large. In this table the stiffness of certain sections have been calculated on the incorrect basis of the polar moment, and the effect of cross-sectional warping is very evident from the disparity in results obtained.

At the end sections of a member subjected to torsion warping may be modified by the constraints and, further, if there is symmetry of design and loading the centre section will remain plane. The stresses at these particular sections will then differ from those based on the assumption of free warping ; at the centre there will be a plane section distribution and at the supports a distribution lying between those based on the assumption of free and completely restrained warping respectively. Since, however, the axial stresses which produce these modifications constitute a system having zero resultant it follows from the principle of Saint Venant that the stresses, except in the immediate vicinity of the end and centre sections, will be determined from the solution based on free warping. For the same reason, except in special cases, the torsional rigidity will be calculated on the same assumption.

When a straight member is subjected to transverse loading the resultant actions at any section are a bending moment and a shearing force. If, however, the member is curved in plan form, in which case it must be firmly held at the supports, there is a twisting moment in addition, and this twisting action considerably complicates the arithmetical work of stress calculation.

In Fig. 17.1 AB represents in plan a horizontal cantilever firmly built in at A and carrying a load W at the end B. The beam at A is supposed to

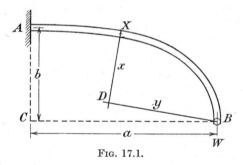

FIG. 17.1.

be normal to the wall to which it is fixed. If a line BC be drawn from B perpendicular to the wall the resultant actions at A will consist of :—

(a) A shearing force W tending to move the beam downwards at the wall section,
(b) a bending moment Wa tending to bend the beam convex upwards at the wall section,
(c) a torque Wb tending to twist the beam counterclockwise at the wall section.

The presence of the torque differentiates this problem from that of the straight beam.

At any other section such as X the resultant actions are similar. Through X a normal plane is drawn, its trace being XD. From B a perpendicular BD is drawn to XD. If the distances XD and DB are x and y, the bending moment and torque at X are Wy and Wx respectively.

17.2. The circular-arc cantilever.—As a preliminary to the analysis of the circular-arc bow girder, it is convenient to consider the behaviour of a

14

cantilever of circular plan form and to obtain expressions for the displacements of the free end in terms of general external actions.

Let AC in Fig. 17.2* represent such a cantilever of radius R firmly held at A and subtending an angle ϕ at the centre O. At an angular distance θ from OC a load W acts downwards and the free end of the girder, C, carries a bending moment M_0, a twisting moment T_0 and an upward vertical force F_0. M_0 will be taken as positive when it produces convexity of the beam upwards ; T_0 will be taken as positive when it produces clockwise rotation of the section C viewed from the free end and F_0 will be taken as positive when it tends to raise the free end. In all diagrams throughout this chapter downward loads acting on the girder will be represented by open circles and upward loads by solid circles. It is convenient in writing the long formulas which arise in the analysis to represent the angle $\phi-\chi$, where χ is any angle, by the symbol χ'. Thus the load point in Fig. 17.2 is defined either by θ or $\theta'=\phi-\theta$.

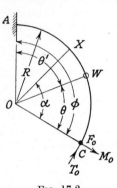

Fig. 17.2.

At any point X on the cantilever shown in the figure, at an angular distance α from OC, the resultant actions consist of a bending moment M, a twisting moment T and a shearing force F given by the expressions

$$M=M_0\cos\alpha+T_0\sin\alpha-F_0R\sin\alpha+[WR\sin(\alpha-\theta)],$$
$$T=-M_0\sin\alpha+T_0\cos\alpha+F_0R(1-\cos\alpha)-[WR\{1-\cos(\alpha-\theta)\}], \quad (17.1)$$
$$F=F_0-[W].$$

In these expressions the terms in W only occur when $\alpha>\theta$. The angular movement of the end C in the direction of M_0 is

$$\mu_0=\frac{\partial U}{\partial M_0}=\frac{1}{EI}\int M\frac{\partial M}{\partial M_0}ds+\frac{1}{NJ}\int T\frac{\partial T}{\partial M_0}ds,$$

where U is the strain energy in the cantilever due to bending and twisting. The effect of the energy due to shearing is very small and is neglected. The integrals in M_0, T_0 and F_0 extend over the whole length of the cantilever, that in W only over the range $\alpha=\theta$ to $\alpha=\phi$.

Similarly the clockwise twist of C, *i.e.* in the direction of T_0, and the upward vertical displacement of the end of the cantilever are, respectively,

$$\tau_0=\frac{\partial U}{\partial T_0}=\frac{1}{EI}\int M\frac{\partial M}{\partial T_0}ds+\frac{1}{NJ}\int T\frac{\partial T}{\partial T_0}ds$$

and

$$\Delta_0=\frac{\partial U}{\partial F_0}=\frac{1}{EI}\int M\frac{\partial M}{\partial F_0}ds+\frac{1}{NJ}\int T\frac{\partial T}{\partial F_0}ds,$$

or, from (17.1),

$$\mu_0=\frac{R}{EI}\int M\cos\alpha d\alpha-\frac{R}{NJ}\int T\sin\alpha d\alpha,$$

$$\tau_0=\frac{R}{EI}\int M\sin\alpha d\alpha+\frac{R}{NJ}\int T\cos\alpha d\alpha,$$

$$\Delta_0=-\frac{R^2}{EI}\int M\sin\alpha d\alpha+\frac{R^2}{NJ}\int T(1-\cos\alpha)d\alpha=-R\tau_0+\frac{R^2}{NJ}\int Td\alpha.$$

---

* In this and subsequent figures the axes of the couples are shown. Positive couples act clockwise when viewed along the direction of the arrow.

Expanding the terms in M and T as in (17.1) and integrating produces the following results, in which γ represents EI/NJ,

$$\frac{4EI\mu_0}{R}=M_0[(\gamma+1)2\phi-(\gamma-1)\sin 2\phi]-T_0(\gamma-1)(1-\cos 2\phi)$$
$$+F_0R[(\gamma-1)(1-\cos 2\phi)-4\gamma(1-\cos \phi)]$$
$$+2WR[\sin \phi \sin \theta'-\theta' \sin \theta+\gamma(2 \cos \theta-2 \cos \phi$$
$$-\sin \phi \sin \theta'-\theta' \sin \theta)]$$

$$\frac{4EI\tau_0}{R}=-M_0(\gamma-1)(1-\cos 2\phi)+T_0[(\gamma+1)2\phi+(\gamma-1)\sin 2\phi]$$
$$+F_0R[(\gamma-1)(2\phi-\sin 2\phi)-4\gamma(\phi-\sin \phi)]$$
$$+2WR[\theta' \cos \theta-\cos \phi \sin \theta'-\gamma(2 \sin \phi-2 \sin \theta$$
$$-\cos \phi \sin \theta'-\theta' \cos \theta)],$$

$$\Delta_0=-R\tau_0-\frac{R^2}{NJ}[M_0(1-\cos \phi)-T_0 \sin \phi-F_0R(\phi-\sin \phi)$$
$$+WR(\theta'-\sin \theta')].$$

(17.2)

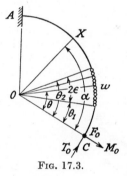

FIG. 17.3.

If the cantilever carries a continuous uniform load of intensity w over the segment between $\alpha=\theta_1$ and $\alpha=\theta_2$, instead of the concentrated load W, the terms in M_0, T_0 and F_0 in the above equations remain unaltered but those in W must be replaced by corresponding terms in w.

In Fig. 17.3, which shows the assumed loading, let β define any point between θ_1 and θ_2. The element of load at this point, $wRd\beta$, produces at X a bending moment $wR^2 \sin (\alpha-\beta)d\beta$, a twisting moment $-wR^2\{1-\cos (\alpha-\beta)\}d\beta$ and a shearing force $-wRd\beta$.

The resultant bending moment, twisting moment and shearing force at X due to the load will therefore be, if $\alpha>\theta_2$,

$$m=wR^2\int_{\theta_1}^{\theta_2}\sin (\alpha-\beta)d\beta=wR^2\{\cos (\alpha-\theta_2)-\cos (\alpha-\theta_1)\},$$

$$t=-wR^2\int_{\theta_1}^{\theta_2}\{1-\cos (\alpha-\beta)\}d\beta=-wR^2\{\theta_2-\theta_1+\sin (\alpha-\theta_2)$$
$$-\sin (\alpha-\theta_1)\},$$

$$f=-wR\int_{\theta_1}^{\theta_2}d\beta=-wR(\theta_2-\theta_1).$$

When α lies between θ_1 and θ_2 the limits of integration are α and θ_1, and then

$$m=wR^2\{1-\cos (\alpha-\theta_1)\},$$
$$t=-wR^2\{\alpha-\theta_1-\sin (\alpha-\theta_1)\},$$
$$f=-wR(\alpha-\theta_1).$$

When $\alpha<\theta_1$ there are no terms in w in equations (17.1). Substituting the above expressions in equations (17.1) and in the resulting equations for displacements, it is found that the terms in W are replaced by the following, in which 2ε represents the arc covered by the loading, $\theta_2-\theta_1$, and θ is the angular distance of the centre of the load, $\frac{1}{2}(\theta_1+\theta_2)$, from OC :

in the expression for $4EI\mu_0/R$,

$$4wR^2[(\gamma+1)\{\sin\varepsilon(2\cos\theta-\theta'\sin\theta)-\varepsilon\cos\varepsilon\cos\theta\}$$
$$+(\gamma-1)\sin\varepsilon\cos\phi\cos\theta'-2\gamma\varepsilon\cos\phi] :$$

in the expression for $4EI\tau_0/R$,

$$4wR^2[(\gamma+1)\{\sin\varepsilon(2\sin\theta+\theta'\cos\theta)-\varepsilon\cos\varepsilon\sin\theta\}$$
$$+(\gamma-1)\sin\varepsilon\sin\phi\cos\theta'-2\gamma\varepsilon\sin\phi] :$$

in the expression for Δ_0,

$$2wR^2(\varepsilon\theta'-\sin\varepsilon\sin\theta').$$

                                                                    (17.3)

In the limit when 2ε is made very small the expressions in (17.3) give the terms in the general displacement equations for a load $2wR\varepsilon$ concentrated at θ, and if this load is represented by W the expressions of (17.3) reduce to the W terms of (17.2).

17.3. The circular-arc bow girder with a concentrated load.—The results obtained in the previous paragraph for the circular-arc cantilever will now be applied to the analysis of the bow girder built in at both ends. Fig. 17.4 shows such a girder subtending an angle 2ϕ at the centre and carrying a single concentrated load 2W at an angular distance θ from the mid-point C.

This girder has three degrees of redundancy since it can be cut at any section and still carry any loads placed on it. If the three redundant elements are the bending moment, twisting moment and shearing force at

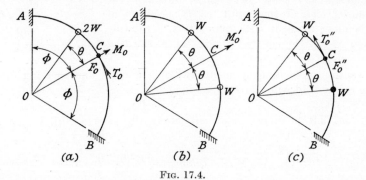

(a)   (b)   (c)

FIG. 17.4.

any section, an analysis may be made by a straightforward application of the principle of minimum strain energy, but this treatment leads to three simultaneous equations which are so involved that their solution in general terms is impracticable. The difficulty can, however, be avoided by using the method of superposition and dividing the loading into a symmetrical and a skew-symmetrical system as shown at (b) and (c) in Fig. 17.4. These are dealt with separately and the results summed algebraically to obtain the complete solution required. Instead of three simultaneous equations a direct solution is found for one of the redundant actions, and a pair of simultaneous equations for the determination of the other two which are then readily obtained explicitly.

In the symmetrical system (b), equal loads W act downward at the same distance θ from the centre line OC and the resultant actions at the centre reduce simply to a bending moment M_0' ; both the twisting moment T_0' and the shearing force F_0' are zero. In the skew-symmetrical system (c) a load W acts downward at θ from OC in the segment CA and a load W acts upward at θ from OC in the segment CB. The resultant actions at C are a twisting moment T_0'' and a shearing force F_0'' ; there is no bending moment. The total actions at C under the specified system (a) are then

$$M_0 = M_0' + M_0'' = M_0',$$
$$T_0 = T_0' + T_0'' = T_0'',$$
$$F_0 = F_0' + F_0'' = F_0''.$$

Considering the symmetrical system the conditions are

$$T_0' = F_0' = 0 \; ; \; M_0' = M_0$$

and, since there is no rotation of the centre section in the plane of action of M_0', $\mu_0' = 0$.

Substituting these conditions in the first equation of (17.2),

$$\frac{M_0}{2WR} = \frac{(\gamma+1)\theta' \sin \theta + (\gamma-1) \sin \phi \sin \theta' - 2\gamma(\cos \theta - \cos \phi)}{(\gamma+1)2\phi - (\gamma-1) \sin 2\phi}. \quad . \quad (17.4)$$

Under the skew-symmetrical system (c),

$$M_0'' = 0 \; ; \; F_0'' = F_0 \; ; \; T_0'' = T_0$$
$$\text{and } \Delta_0 = \tau_0 = 0.$$

Substituting these values in the second and third equations of (17.2) we obtain

$$T_0''[(\gamma+1)2\phi + (\gamma-1) \sin 2\phi] + F_0''R[(\gamma-1)(2\phi - \sin 2\phi) - 4\gamma(\phi - \sin \phi)]$$
$$+ 2WR[(\gamma+1)\theta' \cos \theta + (\gamma-1) \cos \phi \sin \theta' - 2\gamma(\sin \phi - \sin \theta)] = 0,$$
$$T_0'' \sin \phi + F_0''R(\phi - \sin \phi) - WR(\theta' - \sin \theta') = 0,$$

and the solution of these gives

$$\frac{F_0}{W} = 1 + \frac{2(\gamma+1)\{\theta' \cos \theta \sin \phi - \phi \sin \theta' - \theta\phi\} + 4\gamma \sin \theta \sin \phi - (\gamma-1) \theta \sin 2\phi}{(\gamma+1)2\phi^2 + (\gamma-1)\phi \sin 2\phi - 2\gamma(1 - \cos 2\phi)},$$
$$\quad . \quad . \quad . \quad . \quad (17.5)$$

$$\frac{T_0}{WR} = \left\{ \theta' - \sin \theta' - \frac{F_0}{W}(\phi - \sin \phi) \right\} \operatorname{cosec} \phi. \quad . \quad . \quad (17.6)$$

The resultant actions at the ends of the girder are found from (17.1) by putting $\alpha = \phi$ and using the appropriate values for the centre section actions. The support *reactions* must balance these end resultant actions.

For the symmetrical loading (b)

$$M_A' = M_B' = M_0' \cos \phi + WR \sin \theta',$$
$$T_A' = -T_B' = -M_0' \sin \phi - WR(1 - \cos \theta'),$$
$$F_A' = -F_B' = -W.$$

For the skew-symmetrical loading (c)

$$M_A'' = -M_B'' = T_0'' \sin \phi - F_0''R \sin \phi + WR \sin \theta',$$
$$T_A'' = T_B'' = T_0'' \cos \phi + F_0''R(1 - \cos \phi) - WR(1 - \cos \theta'),$$
$$F_A'' = F_B'' = F_0'' - W.$$

$$(17.7)$$

Superposing these, the total resultant actions are

$$\left.\begin{aligned}
&M_A = M_0 \cos\phi + T_0 \sin\phi - F_0 R \sin\phi + 2WR \sin\theta', \\
&T_A = -M_0 \sin\phi + T_0 \cos\phi + F_0 R(1-\cos\phi) - 2WR(1-\cos\theta'), \\
&F_A = F_0 - 2W, \\
&M_B = M_0 \cos\phi - T_0 \sin\phi + F_0 R \sin\phi, \\
&T_B = M_0 \sin\phi + T_0 \cos\phi + F_0 R(1-\cos\phi), \\
&F_B = F_0.
\end{aligned}\right\} \quad (17.8)$$

The resultant actions in the girder at the point of application of the load are found from (17.1) by putting $\alpha = 0$ in the two loading cases (b) and (c) and superposing the results. This leads to

$$\left.\begin{aligned}
&M_W = M_0 \cos\theta + T_0 \sin\theta - F_0 R \sin\theta, \\
&T_W = -M_0 \sin\theta + T_0 \cos\theta + F_0 R(1-\cos\theta), \\
&F_W = F_0 - 2W.
\end{aligned}\right\} \quad (17.9)$$

When the load is placed at mid-span these become

$$\left.\begin{aligned}
&M_W = M_0 = \frac{WR\{(\gamma-1)(1-\cos 2\phi) - 4\gamma(1-\cos\phi)\}}{(\gamma+1)2\phi - (\gamma-1)\sin 2\phi}, \\
&T_W = T_0 = 0, \\
&F_W = -F_0 = -W.
\end{aligned}\right\} \quad (17.10)$$

17.4. The semi-circular bow girder with a concentrated load.—In particular, for the semi-circular bow girder $2\phi = \pi$, and when this value is substituted in equations (17.4), (17.5), (17.6) and (17.8) the following general expressions are obtained for the resultant actions at mid-span and supports due to a load $2W$ at θ from the centre,

$$\left.\begin{aligned}
&\frac{M_0}{2WR} = \frac{1}{2\pi}\{(\pi-2\theta)\sin\theta - 2\cos\theta\}, \\
&\frac{F_0}{2W} = \frac{(\gamma+1)(\pi^2 - 2\theta\pi - 4\theta\cos\theta) - 8\gamma(1-\sin\theta)}{2\{(\gamma+1)\pi^2 - 8\gamma\}}, \\
&\frac{T_0}{2WR} = \frac{1}{4}(\pi-2\theta-2\cos\theta) - \frac{F_0}{2W}\left(\frac{\pi}{2}-1\right), \\
&M_A = 2WR\cos\theta + T_0 - F_0 R \ ; \quad M_B = -T_0 + F_0 R \ ; \\
&T_A = -2WR(1-\sin\theta) - M_0 + F_0 R \ ; \quad T_B = M_0 + F_0 R \ ; \\
&F_A = F_0 - 2W \ ; \quad F_B = F_0.
\end{aligned}\right\} \quad (17.11)$$

When the load $2W$ is at the centre of the girder, $\theta = 0$ and then

$$M_0 = M_W = -\frac{2WR}{\pi},$$

$$T_0 = T_W = 0,$$
$$F_0 = -F_W = W.$$

The resultant actions in the girder at the supports are, from (17.8),

$$M_A = M_B = WR,$$

$$T_A = -T_B = 2WR\left(\frac{1}{\pi}-\frac{1}{2}\right),$$

$$F_A = -F_B = -W.$$

At any other point in the girder the resultant actions are, from (17.1), using the particular values of M_0, T_0 and F_0 above,

$$M = -\frac{WR}{\pi}(2\cos\alpha - \pi\sin\alpha),$$

$$T = \frac{WR}{\pi}\{2\sin\alpha - \pi(1-\cos\alpha)\},$$

$$F = -W.$$

TABLE 17.2.—CENTRALLY LOADED SEMI-CIRCULAR GIRDER.

$\alpha°$	M/2WR	T/2WR	F/2W
0	−0·318	+ 0	−0·5
15	−0·178	+0·065	−0·5
30	−0·026	+0·092	−0·5
45	+0·128	+0·079	−0·5
60	+0·274	+0·026	−0·5
75	+0·401	−0·062	−0·5
90	+0·500	−0·181	−0·5

It should be noticed that for the centrally loaded semi-circular bow girder the resultant actions are independent of γ, *i.e.* of the shape of the cross-section. Table 17.2 gives calculated values of these actions and curves of bending and twisting moments are shown in Fig. 17.5.

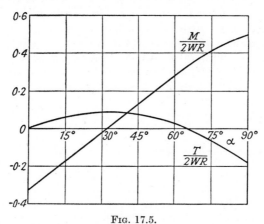

Fig. 17.5.

When the load is not central, the value of M_0 is still independent of γ but F_0 and T_0 are both affected by it and hence also the resultant actions at all points.

17.5. Approximate solutions for circular-arc girder with concentrated load. —Calculations of the values of M_0, T_0 and F_0 for a number of circular-arc girders with a concentrated load show that if γ is fairly large, *e.g.* above 50, its absolute value is not of serious importance. The terms $\gamma+1$ and $\gamma-1$ may be replaced with little error by γ, which then vanishes since it occurs in all terms in both the numerator and denominator. The experimental values given in Table 17.1 indicate that for many, if not most, common structural sections γ is likely to be large, and since its exact value is not easy to determine accurately, there is little justification for attempting to distinguish between the values of $\gamma \pm 1$ and γ. A useful and justifiable approximation is therefore possible for many practical purposes and the substitution of γ for $\gamma \pm 1$ in (17.4), (17.5) and (17.6) gives

$$\left. \begin{aligned} \frac{M_0}{2WR} &= \frac{\theta' \sin \theta + \sin \phi \sin \theta' - 2(\cos \theta - \cos \phi)}{2\phi - \sin 2\phi}, \\ \frac{F_0}{2W} &= \frac{1}{2} - \frac{\theta\{\sin \phi (\cos \theta + \cos \phi) + \phi\} - \sin \theta (2 \sin \phi + \phi \cos \phi)}{2\phi^2 + \phi \sin 2\phi - 2(1 - \cos 2\phi)}, \\ \frac{T_0}{2WR} &= \tfrac{1}{2}\{\theta' - \sin \theta' - \frac{F_0}{W}(\phi - \sin \phi)\}\operatorname{cosec} \phi. \end{aligned} \right\} \quad (17.12)$$

The general expressions of (17.8) and (17.9) are then valid for calculating the resultant actions at the ends of the girder and under the load, while equations (17.1) give the resultant actions at any point. In particular, if the load $2W$ is at the centre of the girder,

$$\frac{M_0}{2WR} = -\frac{(1 - \cos \phi)^2}{2\phi - \sin 2\phi}; \quad T_0 = 0; \quad \frac{F_0}{2W} = \frac{1}{2}.$$

17.6. The circular-arc bow girder with distributed load.—The circular-arc bow girder shown in Fig. 17.6 (a) carries a uniformly distributed load of intensity $2w$ over the segment between $\alpha = \theta_1$ and $\alpha = \theta_2$ and, as for the single concentrated load, this will be split into the symmetrical and skew-symmetrical systems shown in the same figure at (b) and (c) respectively. In (b) a load of intensity w acts downward over the arcs between θ_1 and θ_2 on each side of OC, and in (c) a load of intensity w acts downward over the same arc in the segment CA and upward over the corresponding arc in CB. Superposition of the resultant actions at any section due to these systems calculated separately will give the result required for the specified loading. As in paragraph 17.2, let $2\theta = \theta_1 + \theta_2$ and $2\varepsilon = \theta_2 - \theta_1$. For the symmetrical

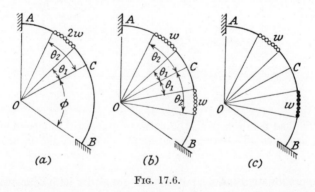

(a) (b) (c)

FIG. 17.6.

load system the conditions at mid-span are, as for the concentrated load dealt with in paragraph 17.3,

$$T_0' = F_0' = \mu_0' = 0$$

and the first equation of (17.2), when the term in W is replaced by that in w from (17.3), gives directly

$$M_0=-4wR^2\left[\frac{\sin \varepsilon\{(\gamma+1)(2\cos\theta-\theta'\sin\theta)+(\gamma-1)\cos\phi\cos\theta'\}}{(\gamma+1)2\phi-(\gamma-1)\sin 2\phi}-\varepsilon\{(\gamma+1)\cos\varepsilon\cos\theta+2\gamma\cos\phi\}\right] \quad (17.13)$$

For the skew-symmetrical system shown in Fig. 17.6 (c) the conditions at mid-span are

$$M_0''=\tau_0''=\Delta_0''=0 \; ;$$

the second and third equations of (17.2) and (17.3) then give

$$F_0=2wR\left[\varepsilon+\frac{2[(\gamma+1)\{\sin\theta\sin\phi(2\sin\varepsilon-\varepsilon\cos\varepsilon)+\sin\varepsilon(\theta'\cos\theta\sin\phi-\phi\sin\theta')-\varepsilon\theta\phi\}+(\gamma-1)\sin\phi(\sin\varepsilon\sin\theta-\varepsilon\theta\cos\phi)]}{(\gamma+1)2\phi^2+(\gamma-1)\phi\sin 2\phi-2\gamma(1-\cos 2\phi)}\right],$$

$$\qquad\qquad\qquad\qquad\qquad . \quad . \quad . \quad (17.14)$$

$$T_0=[2wR^2(\varepsilon\theta'-\sin\varepsilon\sin\theta')-F_0R(\phi-\sin\phi)]\operatorname{cosec}\phi \quad . \quad (17.15)$$

In the limit when 2ε is very small a point load $W=2wR\varepsilon$ acts at θ from OC, and the above three resultant actions at C reduce to the values given by equations (17.4), (17.5) and (17.6).

Uniformly distributed load over girder.—If the whole length of the girder is covered by a uniformly distributed load of intensity $2w$, the bending moment at mid-span is twice the value of M_0 given by (17.13) when $\theta=\varepsilon=\phi/2$, since that result is for an intensity $2w$ over half the span and therefore also for w over the whole span. Hence,

$$M_0=-2wR^2\left[\frac{4\{(\gamma+1)\sin\phi-\gamma\phi\cos\phi\}}{(\gamma+1)2\phi-(\gamma-1)\sin 2\phi}-1\right] \; ;$$

$$T_0=0 \; ; \quad F_0=0.$$

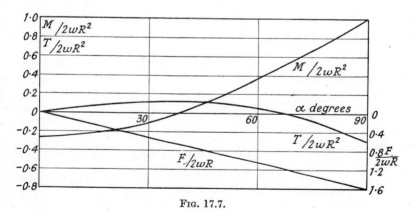

FIG. 17.7.

Then at any point α from the centre, from (17.1) and p. 417,

$$M=-2wR^2\left[\frac{4\cos\alpha\{(\gamma+1)\sin\phi-\gamma\phi\cos\phi\}}{(\gamma+1)2\phi-(\gamma-1)\sin 2\phi}-1\right],$$

$$T=2wR^2\left[\frac{4\sin\alpha\{(\gamma+1)\sin\phi-\gamma\phi\cos\phi\}}{(\gamma+1)2\phi-(\gamma-1)\sin 2\phi}-\alpha\right],$$

$$F=-2wR\alpha.$$

For the semi-circular bow girder $2\phi=\pi$, and when a uniform load $2w$ acts over the whole length the resultant actions at α from the centre are

$$M=-2wR^2\left(\frac{4\cos\alpha-\pi}{\pi}\right),$$

$$T=2wR^2\left(\frac{4\sin\alpha-\alpha\pi}{\pi}\right),$$

$$F=-2wR\alpha.$$

From these results the data of Table 17.3 were calculated and the bending moment, twisting moment and shearing force curves are shown in Fig. 17.7.

TABLE 17.3.—SEMI-CIRCULAR GIRDER WITH UNIFORM LOADING.

$\alpha°$	$M/2wR^2$	$T/2wR^2$	$F/2wR$
0	−0·273	0	0
10	−0·244	0·047	−0·174
20	−0·196	0·086	−0·349
30	−0·102	0·113	−0·524
40	+0·025	0·121	−0·698
50	0·181	0·102	−0·873
60	0·363	0·055	−1·047
70	0·565	−0·026	−1·222
80	0·779	−0·152	−1·396
90	1·000	−0·298	−1·571

As for the single concentrated load the results for the uniformly loaded arc-bow girder can be simplified if γ is reasonably large by putting $\gamma+1$ and $\gamma-1$ equal to γ and so eliminating these terms from the expressions for M, T and F.

17.7. General case of a curved cantilever.—So far the circular-arc girder only has been considered. If the plan form is any other shape the general method of approach is the same ; the resulting expressions cannot usually, however, be integrated by exact mathematical process but must be calculated approximately by graphical or arithmetical methods.

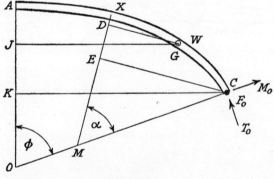

FIG. 17.8.

Consider the curved cantilever AC shown in Fig. 17.8 which is rigidly held at A and carries a bending moment M_0, a twisting moment T_0 and a shearing force F_0 at the free end C, and a downward load W at any point G. Let AO be the normal to the curve at A and CO the normal at C, the angle between these being ϕ. The resultant actions at A consist of a bending moment, a twisting moment and a shearing force given by

$$M_A = M_0 \cos \phi + T_0 \sin \phi - F_0(CK) + W(GJ),$$
$$T_A = -M_0 \sin \phi + T_0 \cos \phi + F_0(AK) - W(AJ),$$
$$F_A = F_0 - W,$$

where CK and GJ are the perpendicular distances from C and G to the normal AO.

At any other point X in the cantilever, where XM is the normal and GD and CE are the perpendiculars from G and C upon it, the resultant actions are

$$M = M_0 \cos \alpha + T_0 \sin \alpha - F_0(CE) + [W(GD)],$$
$$T = -M_0 \sin \alpha + T_0 \cos \alpha + F_0(XE) - [W(XD)],$$
$$F = F_0 - [W].$$

α is now the angle between the normals at X and C and the term in W only occurs when X lies between G and A. In order to plot the curves of M, T and F the values of α, CE, XE, GD and XD are required for points all round the cantilever and generally they can only be found by scaling from a drawing.

If, as in the case of the circular-arc girder, the movements of the free end under the loading specified are μ_0, τ_0 and Δ_0, we have

$$EI\mu_0 = \frac{\partial U}{\partial M_0} = \int M \frac{\partial M}{\partial M_0} ds + \gamma \int T \frac{\partial T}{\partial M_0} ds,$$

$$EI\tau_0 = \frac{\partial U}{\partial T_0} = \int M \frac{\partial M}{\partial T_0} ds + \gamma \int T \frac{\partial T}{\partial T_0} ds,$$

$$EI\Delta_0 = \frac{\partial U}{\partial F_0} = \int M \frac{\partial M}{\partial F_0} ds + \gamma \int T \frac{\partial M}{\partial F_0} ds,$$

and, on substituting the general expressions above, these become

$$\left.\begin{aligned}
EI\mu_0 =\ & \int \{M_0 \cos \alpha + T_0 \sin \alpha - F_0(CE) + [W(GD)]\} \cos \alpha\, ds \\
& + \gamma \int \{M_0 \sin \alpha - T_0 \cos \alpha - F_0(XE) + [W(XD)]\} \sin \alpha\, ds, \\
EI\tau_0 =\ & \int \{M_0 \cos \alpha + T_0 \sin \alpha - F_0(CE) + [W(GD)]\} \sin \alpha\, ds \\
& + \gamma \int \{-M_0 \sin \alpha + T_0 \cos \alpha + F_0(XE) - [W(XD)]\} \cos \alpha\, ds, \\
EI\Delta_0 =\ & -\int \{M_0 \cos \alpha + T_0 \sin \alpha - F_0(CE) + [W(GD)]\}(CE) ds \\
& + \gamma \int \{-M_0 \sin \alpha + T_0 \cos \alpha + F_0(XE) - [W(XD)]\}(XE) ds.
\end{aligned}\right\} \quad . \quad (17.16)$$

These integrals cannot be evaluated directly and the terms in them must be dealt with separately. The expression for $EI\mu_0$ can be expanded in the form

$$EI\mu_0 = M_0 \int_C^A \cos^2 \alpha\, ds + T_0 \int_C^A \sin \alpha \cos \alpha\, ds - F_0 \int_C^A (CE) \cos \alpha\, ds$$

$$+ W \int_G^A (GD) \cos \alpha\, ds + \gamma M_0 \int_C^A \sin^2 \alpha\, ds - \gamma T_0 \int_C^A \sin \alpha \cos \alpha\, ds$$

$$- \gamma F_0 \int_C^A (XE) \sin \alpha\, ds + \gamma W \int_G^A (XD) \sin \alpha\, ds$$

and the other expressions of (17.16) are similar. Each of the integrals must be evaluated and this is best done graphically. The curve CA is divided into a number of small equal lengths, δs, and at each division point the values of α, CE, GD, XE and XD are scaled. The products under the various integrals are calculated for each point, *e.g.* (CE) $\cos\alpha$, $\cos^2\alpha$, etc., and are plotted on base lines representing the appropriate parts of the perimeter of the curve. The areas between these curves and the base line corrected for the scales of the plots are the numerical values of the integrals required. A detailed example of the procedure will be given later to explain the method.

17.8. The non-circular bow girder.—The non-circular bow girder may be symmetrical or unsymmetrical about its centre line. If the former, the method of superposition as used for the circular-arc girder enables the resultant actions at the mid-point to be evaluated by the solution of one simple equation for M_0 and a pair of simultaneous equations in T_0 and F_0, but if the girder is unsymmetrical the redundant resultant actions at a particular point can only be found by the solution of three simultaneous equations.

In the first instance consider the symmetrical girder shown in Fig. 17.9 which carries a load 2W at any point G. This can be replaced by the

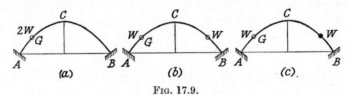

Fig. 17.9.

symmetrical arrangement of (*b*) superposed on the skew-symmetrical one of (*c*).

The conditions at C under these loads systems will be the same as for the circular-arc, *viz.*,

for (*b*) $\mu_0=0$; $T_0=0$; $F_0=0$;

and for (*c*) $\tau_0=0$; $\Delta_0=0$; $M_0=0$.

The first equation of (17.16) then gives a solution for M_0 in the form

$$\frac{M_0}{W}=-\frac{\int_G^A (GD)\cos\alpha ds+\gamma\int_G^A (XD)\sin\alpha ds}{\int_C^A \cos^2\alpha ds+\gamma\int_C^A \sin^2\alpha ds} \quad . \quad . \quad . \quad (17.17)$$

The other two equations of (17.16) give a pair of equations which enable T_0 and F_0 to be found, but nothing is gained by attempting a solution in general terms ; the various integrals must be evaluated and a numerical result found for any particular problem.

If the girder carries a distributed load of intensity 2w over any part of its span, it should be divided into a number of small elements, 2$w\delta s$, each of which is then treated as a separate concentrated load.

If the girder is not symmetrical in plan form about the centre, the analysis must be approached rather differently (Pippard and Barrow, 1926). Suppose that the cantilever shown in Fig. 17.8 represents a girder encastré both at

A and C and carrying a load W at G.*   The bending moment M_0, twisting moment T_0 and shearing force F_0 are no longer arbitrary actions applied to the free end of a cantilever but are the restraints imposed at C by the fixing.   Since the girder is assumed to be fully encastré C will be fixed both in position and also directionally about both axes so that μ_0, τ_0 and Δ_0 will all be zero.

The necessary equations are therefore given by (17.16) if the right-hand side in each equation is made equal to zero ; these must be solved simultaneously for M_0, T_0 and F_0.   To illustrate the analytical procedure the girder shown in Fig. 17.10 will be considered in detail.   This girder is actually symmetrical about its centre line and could be treated rather more simply by superposition, but the longer method is given to illustrate the general approach which is applicable to any plan form.

The girder is encastré at A and C and carries a single load W at the point G.   The plan form of the girder is set out accurately and the perimeter divided into a number of equal parts ; these should be as many as practicable

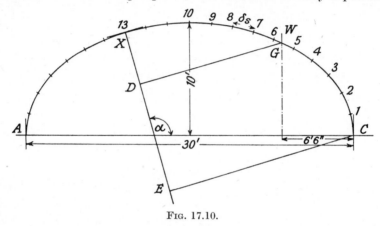

Fig. 17.10.

since the larger the number the more accurate will be the result.   At each of these division points normals to the curve, such as XE (at point 13), are drawn and from C perpendiculars such as CE are drawn to these normals.

The angle between the normals at X and C is α.   Perpendiculars, GD, are drawn from G to the normals at all division points between G and A.

When the equations of (17.16) are expanded it will be found that fifteen separate integrals have to be evaluated.   They are all functions of α and the lengths CE, XE, GD and XD ; these quantities must therefore be scaled from the drawing for every division point.   The fifteen integrals are listed in Table 17.4 together with their numerical values for the girder under consideration.   As examples of the process of evaluation we shall consider the two integrals $\int_C^A CE \sin \alpha ds$ and $\int_G^A GD \cos \alpha ds$.

The values of α, CE and GD measured for each division point are entered in Table 17.5.   From these the products CE $\sin \alpha$ and GD $\cos \alpha$ are calculated. Upon a base line representing the perimeter of the girder as shown in Fig. 17.11 the values thus calculated are plotted as ordinates at the appropriate

* Note that W is now the total load.   In cases where superposition was used 2W was taken for convenience.

TABLE 17.4.

Integral	Value	Integral	Value	Integral	Value
$\int_C^A \cos^2 \alpha\, ds$	$14 \cdot 19$	$\int_G^A GD \cos \alpha\, ds$	$-139 \cdot 3$	$\int_G^A XD \cos \alpha\, ds$	$-143 \cdot 9$
$\int_C^A \sin^2 \alpha\, ds$	$25 \cdot 63$	$\int_G^A XD \sin \alpha\, ds$	$118 \cdot 4$	$\int_C^A CE^2 ds$	$6122 \cdot 0$
$\int_C^A \sin \alpha \cos \alpha\, ds$	0	$\int_C^A CE \sin \alpha\, ds$	$374 \cdot 8$	$\int_C^A XE^2 ds$	$8951 \cdot 9$
$\int_C^A CE \cos \alpha\, ds$	$-67 \cdot 86$	$\int_C^A XE \cos \alpha\, ds$	$-215 \cdot 33$	$\int_G^A GD.CE ds$	$4540 \cdot 3$
$\int_C^A XE \sin \alpha\, ds$	$339 \cdot 12$	$\int_G^A GD \sin \alpha\, ds$	$243 \cdot 54$	$\int_G^A XD.XE ds$	$4726 \cdot 7$

points. Curves are drawn through the points thus obtained and the areas between them and the base measured by planimeter or other method. These

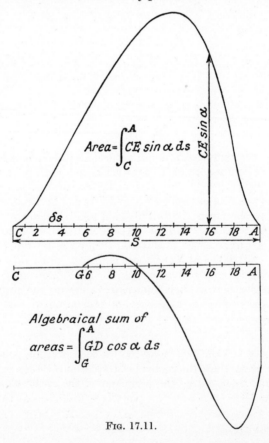

Fig. 17.11.

areas are corrected for the scales to which they are plotted and the required
values of the integrals are obtained.

TABLE 17.5.

Point	$\alpha°$	$\sin \alpha$	CE feet	CE $\sin \alpha$	$\cos \alpha$	GD feet	GD $\cos \alpha$
C	0	0	0	0			
1	15·5	0·2672	1·95	0·52			
2	30·0	0·5000	3·78	1·89			
3	43·8	0·6922	5·44	3·74			
4	53·0	0·7986	7·00	5·59			
5	60·7	0·8721	8·50	7·42			
6	67·5	0·9239	9·92	9·17	0·3827	0·82	0·31
7	73·8	0·9603	11·29	10·84	0·2790	2·79	0·77
8	79·6	0·9835	12·60	12·40	0·1805	4·75	0·86
9	84·8	0·9959	13·84	13·80	0·0907	6·63	0·60
10	90·0	1·0000	15·00	15·00	0	8·54	0
11	95·2	0·9959	16·05	16·00	−0·0907	10·38	−0·94
12	100·4	0·9835	16·92	16·65	−0·1805	12·07	−2·18
13	106·2	0·9603	17·55	16·87	−0·2790	13·61	−3·80
14	112·5	0·9239	17·85	16·50	−0·3827	14·98	−5·74
15	129·3	0·8721	17·66	15·40	−0·4894	16·06	−7·90
16	127·0	0·7986	16·95	13·53	−0·6018	16·76	−10·10
17	136·2	0·6922	15·13	10·48	−0·7217	16·70	−12·06
18	150·0	0·5000	11·31	5·65	−0·8700	15·39	−13·37
19	164·5	0·2672	6·27	1·68	−0·9636	12·41	−11·98
20	180·0	0	0	0	−1·0	8·23	−8·23

The values of the integrals are substituted in (17.16) and the resulting
expressions equated to zero. For the sake of illustration we take $\gamma = 10$ and
obtain the following equations :

$$270 \cdot 5M_0 - 3323F_0 + 1045W = 0,$$
$$167 \cdot 5T_0 - 2528F_0 + 1683W = 0,$$
$$-3323M_0 - 2528T_0 + 95641F_0 - 51807W = 0.$$

The simultaneous solution of these gives

$$M_0 = 6 \cdot 14 \ W,$$
$$T_0 = 2 \cdot 24 \ W,$$
$$F_0 = 0 \cdot 814W,$$

and the bending moment, twisting moment and shearing force at any point
in the girder can be obtained from the general equations for M, T and F,
on p. 415.

17.9. The transversely loaded circular ring.—The equations developed
earlier in this chapter provide means for an analysis of the circular ring
under any system of transverse loading. Let Fig. 17.12 represent a ring
carrying a system of loads, $W_1, W_2, W_3 \ldots W_q \ldots W_n$. These will all
be taken as downward in the analysis but clearly to satisfy the conditions
of equilibrium of the frame some of them must act upward. Any radius
OA is taken as a datum and the loads act at angular distances, $\theta_1, \theta_2 \ldots \theta_q$
$\ldots \theta_n$ measured from it. For equilibrium, the sum of the forces and their

moments about two axes must be zero. If we resolve about the axis OA and one at right angles to it, the equilibrium conditions are

$$\left.\begin{array}{l} \Sigma W_q \quad\quad =0, \\ \Sigma W_q \sin\theta_q =0, \\ \Sigma W_q \cos\theta_q =0. \end{array}\right\} \qquad . \quad . \quad . \quad . \quad (17.18)$$

The resultant actions in the ring at A are a bending moment M_0, a twisting moment T_0 and a shearing force F_0, and by the second theorem of Castigliano we have

$$\frac{\partial U}{\partial M_0}=\frac{\partial U}{\partial T_0}=\frac{\partial U}{\partial F_0}=0,$$

where U is the total strain energy of the ring. These conditions lead to the expressions of (17.2) but with each of the right-hand sides now equated to

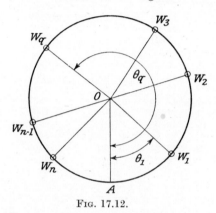

FIG. 17.12.

zero. Putting $\phi=2\pi$ and ΣW_q in place of the single term in W in those equations we obtain

$$0=(\gamma+1)2\pi M_0-R\Sigma[W_q\{(\gamma+1)(2\pi-\theta_q)\sin\theta_q+2\gamma(1-\cos\theta_q)\}],$$

$$0=T_0-F_0R+\frac{R}{2\pi}\Sigma[W_q\{(2\pi-\theta_q)\cos\theta_q+\sin\theta_q\}],$$

$$0=2\pi F_0-\Sigma[W_q(2\pi-\theta_q+\sin\theta_q)].$$

Making use of the conditions of equilibrium in (17.18) these reduce to

$$2\pi M_0+R\Sigma W_q\theta_q\sin\theta_q=0,$$

$$2\pi(T_0-F_0R)-R\Sigma W_q\theta_q\cos\theta_q=0,$$

$$2\pi F_0+\Sigma W_q\theta_q=0,$$

and the solution is

$$\left.\begin{array}{l} \dfrac{M_0}{R}=-\dfrac{1}{2\pi}\Sigma W_q\theta_q\sin\theta_q, \\[2mm] F_0=-\dfrac{1}{2\pi}\Sigma W_q\theta_q, \\[2mm] \dfrac{T_0}{R}=-\dfrac{1}{2\pi}\Sigma W_q\theta_q(1-\cos\theta_q). \end{array}\right\} \qquad . \quad . \quad . \quad (17.19)$$

In particular when the loading is symmetrical about the axis OA, $F_0=T_0=0$ and M_0 is as given in (17.19).

For a ring carrying loads and resting upon three supports, equations (17.18) are sufficient to determine the reactive forces provided by the supports, and equations (17.19) then give the resultant actions at any selected section. If there are more than three supports the reactions from all but three of them are redundant, and if the redundant reactive forces are represented by R_1, R_2, etc., acting upward, the additional conditions necessary for analysis are

$$\frac{\partial U}{\partial R_1} = \delta_1 \;; \quad \frac{\partial U}{\partial R_2} = \delta_2 \;; \quad \frac{\partial U}{\partial R_q} = \delta_q, \text{ etc.,}$$

where δ_1, δ_2, etc., are the amounts by which the supports rise.

Suppose, for example, that Fig. 17.13 represents a ring of radius R carrying loads of 2, 3 and 5 tons at 60°, 120° and 270° from an arbitrary datum OA. It rests on three supports, C, D and E which are 90°, 180° and 300° from the

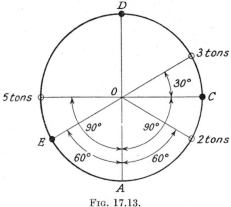

Fig. 17.13.

datum line respectively. Let the upward reactions at these points be R_C, R_D and R_E. Then, from equations (17.18),

$R_C + R_D + R_E - 10 = 0$,

$R_C \sin 90° + R_D \sin 180° + R_E \sin 300° - 2 \sin 60° - 3 \sin 120° - 5 \sin 270° = 0$,

$R_C \cos 90° + R_D \cos 180° + R_E \cos 300° - 2 \cos 60° - 3 \cos 120° - 5 \cos 270° = 0$,

which become, on substituting the values of the trigonometrical functions,

$$R_C + R_D + R_E - 10 = 0,$$
$$R_C - 0 \cdot 866 R_E + 0 \cdot 670 = 0,$$
$$-R_D + 0 \cdot 5 R_E + 0 \cdot 500 = 0.$$

The simultaneous solution of these is

$$R_C = 3 \cdot 05 \text{ tons} \;; \quad R_D = 2 \cdot 65 \text{ tons} \;; \quad R_E = 4 \cdot 3 \text{ tons.}$$

The resultant actions at A in the ring can now be found from (17.19), the calculations being set out as shown in Table 17.6. From the summations of columns (6), (5) and (8) respectively we have

$$\frac{M_0}{R} = +0 \cdot 255 \text{ tons} \;; \quad F_0 = 0 \cdot 588 \text{ tons} \;; \quad \frac{T_0}{R} = -0 \cdot 206 \text{ tons.}$$

The diagrams of bending moments, twisting moments and shearing forces can be plotted if required from the general expressions of (17.1).

Fig. 17.14 shows in diagrammatic form an example of a ring used in actual construction. This ring, supported on six equally spaced stanchions about 27 feet high supports a lime kiln of 16 feet overall diameter and about 53 feet high. It was designed by Imperial Chemical Industries (Alkali) Ltd., and is reproduced here by the courtesy of their chief engineer.

TABLE 17.6.

1	2	3	4	5	6	7	8
Load	θ	$\sin\theta$	$\cos\theta$	$W\theta$	$W\theta\sin\theta$	$W\theta\cos\theta$	(5)−(7)
2	$\dfrac{\pi}{3}$	0·866	0·5	2·094	1·813	1·047	1·047
−3·05	$\dfrac{\pi}{2}$	1·000	0	−4·791	−4·791	0	−4·791
3·0	$\dfrac{2\pi}{3}$	0·866	−0·5	+6·283	5·441	−3·141	9·424
−2·65	π	0	−1·0	−8·325	0	8·325	−16·650
5·0	$\dfrac{3\pi}{2}$	−1	0	+23·562	−23·562	0	23·520
−4·3	$\dfrac{5\pi}{3}$	−0·866	0·5	−22·515	19·498	−11·257	−11·257
			$\sum$	−3·692	−1·601		1·293

Since the loading is uniformly distributed to the ring the slope at the stanchions is zero and each section between stanchions may be treated as a

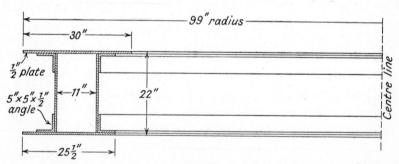

FIG. 17.14.

bow girder carrying one-sixth of the total weight of the ring, the kiln and the contained lime. The equations on p. 413 are then directly applicable.

The approximate value of I, the second moment of area, is 5,570 inch units. The torsional stiffness of the section is derived almost entirely from the hollow box portion which is 22 inches × 12 inches in overall dimensions and has a uniform wall thickness of $\frac{1}{2}$ inch. The value of J for such a section is $\dfrac{2ca_1^2a_2^2}{a_1+a_2}$ (Timoshenko, 1925) where a_1 and a_2 are the dimensions of the box measured between the centre lines of the flanges and webs, *i.e.* $21 \cdot 5$ inches and $11 \cdot 5$ inches in the present example, and c is the wall thickness. Hence, $J = 1,850$ inch units, and if N is assumed to be $\frac{2}{5}E$, the value of γ is $7 \cdot 5$.

Now $\phi = \pi/6$, and if $W = 2\pi R(2w)$ is the total load on the ring, the equations on p. 413 give

$$M_0 = -0 \cdot 00606WR,$$
$$M_A = 0 \cdot 0161WR,$$
$$T_B = -0 \cdot 000755WR.$$

R is 84 inches and if W is assumed to be 600 tons,

bending moment midway between stanchions $= 305$ inch-tons,
bending moment over stanchions $\quad = 811$ inch-tons,
twisting moment at stanchions $\quad = 38$ inch-tons.

The maximum bending stress over a support is by the usual method, $1 \cdot 6$ tons per square inch. The shearing stress due to torsion in a thin-walled section is constant and if q is this constant value the twisting moment of resistance in the present example is $2qca_1a_2$ (the Batho-Bredt result).

So $q = T/2ca_1a_2 = 0 \cdot 15$ tons per square inch.

REFERENCES
Gibson, A. H. and Ritchie, E. G. 1914. " The Circular-arc Bow-girder." Constable.
Case, J. " Strength of Materials." Arnold.
Timoshenko, S. and Lessells, J. M. 1925. "Applied Elasticity." Westinghouse Press.
Pippard, A. J. S. and Barrow, F. L. 1926. *Bldg. Res. Tech. Paps.*, **1**, H.M.S.O.

CHAPTER 18

THE DESIGN OF STEEL FRAMED BUILDINGS

18.1. Introduction.—So far in this book little evidence has been presented to show that structures do behave as simple theory indicates. In the past twenty-five years the development of reliable strain gauge techniques has made possible the study of the behaviour of actual structures under load and considerable data are now available (Conference, 1955). Only one form of structure however, the steel building frame consisting of lines of vertical stanchions joined by horizontal beams which support the floors and panel walls, has been studied comprehensively and this chapter will be devoted to a short account of that work which has been described more fully elsewhere (Baker, 1954).

As far back as 1909 regulations were drawn up governing the use of steel frames in London. These regulations, contained in the London County Council (General Powers) Act, 1909, not only served as the model on which the Codes of Practice governing the use of steel in buildings of almost all other countries in the world were based, but remained in force for twenty-three years. Long before the expiration of that period, the development in the manufacture of steel and the advance in the technique of steelwork made engineers feel that the regulations were unduly restrictive and that they did not allow full advantage to be taken of the excellent qualities which steel possesses as a material for building construction. It was in response to this feeling that the British Steel Industry and the Department of Scientific and Industrial Research collaborated in 1929 in setting up the Steel Structures Research Committee.

The first task undertaken by the Committee was a review of the regulations governing the design of steel framed buildings throughout the world. This showed that, although the method of design implied in every case was the same, there were some striking discrepancies in detail. It was felt desirable, therefore, in view of the considerable period which would elapse before the results of the full research programme were available, to draw up recommendations for a Code of Practice based on knowledge existing then, which would remove many restrictions. It must be emphasised that these recommendations, which were contained in the First Report of the Steel Structures Research Committee, published by H.M. Stationery Office in 1931, were not based on any new research but on the available knowledge and experience of practising engineers. The Code was accepted practically unchanged by the London County Council and was embodied in the original British Standard 449, issued in April 1932, by the British Standards Institution.

18.2. Orthodox design method.—The Clauses of the Code of Practice and of B.S.449 (1932), gave the magnitudes of the superimposed loads to be assumed in designing a building of a particular class, the permissible working stresses and other information. They did not set out the actual method to be used in proportioning the members of the frame, which consists in the main of lines of horizontal beams connected to vertical stanchions by brackets attached to the top and bottom flanges of the beams (Fig. 18.1), but what was implied there is now defined closely in the " simple design " of the current B.S.449 (1948).   In this method, which must be considered orthodox since it is still used almost exclusively for the design of multi-storey frames, the beams are assumed to be simply supported or connected to the stanchion by perfectly free hinges which apply no bending restraint. This assumption makes the choice of the necessary beam section easy, the vertical loads being known.   Since it is assumed that the ends of the beams are attached to the vertical stanchions by hinges the only force exerted on

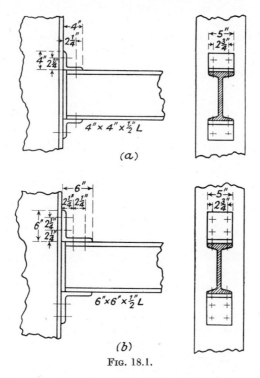

Fig. 18.1.

a stanchion by a beam is taken to be a vertical reaction.   When the beam is attached to the flange of a stanchion of I-section this acts at some distance from the centre-line ; conservative engineers take it to act 2 inches outside the face of the stanchion, representing approximately the position of the centre of the bottom bracket on which the beam rests, but B.S.449 (1948) allows the distance to be reduced to the thickness of the angle bracket, that is $\frac{1}{2}$ inch in the case of the connexions illustrated in Fig. 18.1.   The stanchion is designed to carry the eccentric reactions assumed to be applied in this way.

The permissible loads per unit area on stanchions, or " working stresses " as they are called in the Specification, were deduced from the Perry formula which is derived and discussed in paragraph 7.7.   These loads are based on the consideration of a hinge-ended compression member.   The stanchion lengths in a steel frame are not hinged at their ends but are continuous through many floors.   If a truly axial load is applied to this continuous member then, as it deflects under the load, restraining moments are induced at the ends of each storey length where the beam-to-stanchion connexions have sufficient rigidity to allow the beams, which frame in at each floor, to offer resistance to the change of slope of the stanchion. These restraining moments allow a member of given section to carry safely a greater axial load than would have been possible had it been hinge-ended. To take these restraints into account the orthodox method assumes that the member has an " effective length " less than its actual length and allows it to be designed as a hinge-ended strut having a length equal to this " effective length." Thus when designing a beam, and when calculating the moments it applies to the stanchions, the beam-to-stanchion connexions are assumed to have no rigidity but when designing a stanchion the real rigidity of the connexions is conveniently remembered. Faced with such contradictory assumptions, the Committee decided that no advance in design could be made until a study of the real behaviour of framed structures had been undertaken.

18.3. Preliminary investigations.—The first step in the investigation was the erection of an experimental frame, the stress distribution in which could be measured, to serve as a guide to the derivation of a sound method of stress analysis.

The frame consisted of six stanchions, the bases of which were bolted down to a concrete raft, and twenty-one beams, all 8-inch by 4-inch by

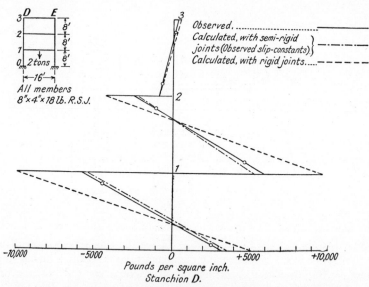

FIG. 18.2.—Maximum Fibre Stresses due to Bending in Plane of Frame.
Load : 2 tons at centre of D_1E_1.

18-lb. steel joists. Provision was made for the use of various types of bolted and riveted beam-to-stanchion connexions. Three of the stanchions were arranged with their webs parallel to the length of the frame and three with their webs perpendicular to the length of the frame, so that a large variety of one- and two-bay, three-storey frames could be built up.

The object of the tests on this frame was the determination of the stress distribution in the members due to the application of external loads. It was arranged that a central concentrated load could be applied to each beam in turn by means of a spring and turnbuckle and the stress distribution was found by measuring the strains at a number of sections of the members.

One of the first tests carried out was on the symmetrical single bay frame shown in Fig. 18.2. The beams were connected to the webs of the stanchions by type A connexions consisting of top and bottom flange-cleats made up of $3\frac{1}{2}$-inch by 3-inch by $\frac{5}{16}$-inch angle, 4 inches long and secured with $\frac{1}{2}$-inch diameter bolts. The distribution of observed stresses when a central concentrated load of 2 tons was applied to the beam at the first floor is shown in Fig. 18.2 and in Table 18.1. The Table gives the maximum stresses

TABLE 18.1.—COMPARISON OF BENDING STRESSES. SYMMETRICAL SINGLE BAY FRAME, FITTED WITH TYPE A CONNEXIONS. CONCENTRATED LOAD OF 2 TONS AT CENTRE OF BEAM D_1E_1.

Section	Observed, with type A connexions : lb. per square inch	Calculated, with semi-rigid joints (observed slip constants) : lb. per square inch	Calculated, with rigid joints : lb. per square inch
D_0D_1	$+3{,}100$	$+3{,}345$	$+\ 5{,}176$
D_1D_0	$-6{,}075$	$-5{,}775$	$-10{,}352$
D_1D_2	$+5{,}800$	$+5{,}354$	$+\ 9{,}916$
D_2D_1	$-2{,}450$	$-2{,}364$	$-\ 4{,}302$
D_2D_3	$-\ 850$	$-\ 890$	$-\ 831$
D_3D_2	$+\ 200$	$+\ 244$	$+\ 350$

($+$denoting tension, $-$compression, at the inside edge of the member) at the top and bottom of each stanchion length due to bending about the YY axis of the stanchion. The stresses in the stanchion for this condition of loading have been calculated on the assumption that the joints are perfectly rigid. They are shown in Fig. 18.2 and Table 18.1 (column 4). The fact is revealed that, although the bending stresses actually induced in the stanchion lengths are smaller than those which would have been found had the joints been perfectly rigid, the distributions of stress in the two cases are exactly similar in form, with the result that appreciable bending stresses are found in the top length 2–3 of the stanchion which is two storeys above the applied load. The magnitude of the observed bending stress is considerable. It must be remembered that the beam-to-stanchion connexions were not of a particularly rigid type and would in any case have been assumed in the orthodox design method to have been pin-ended so far as vertical loads on the beam were concerned. As the connexion was made to the web of the stanchion the eccentricity would have been taken by many designers as zero and by the conservative designer as not more than 2 inches. In actual fact the " equivalent eccentricity " of the connexion to stanchion D at the level of the first floor (that is to say, the distance from the axis of the stanchion at which the reaction arising from a similarly loaded simply supported beam would have had to act to produce the observed bending stresses in the stanchion) was $9 \cdot 3$ inches. The form of the bending stress or bending moment diagrams observed for these stanchion lengths is typical for a frame in which sway, relative horizontal deflexion of the beams in the plane of the frame, does not exist. The condition of bending in such stanchion lengths may be defined as " double curvature " bending.

A different condition is found when sway is present and this can be most easily seen from the results of tests on an asymmetrical frame, Fig. 18.3, in which the beams were joined by type A connexions to the flange of one

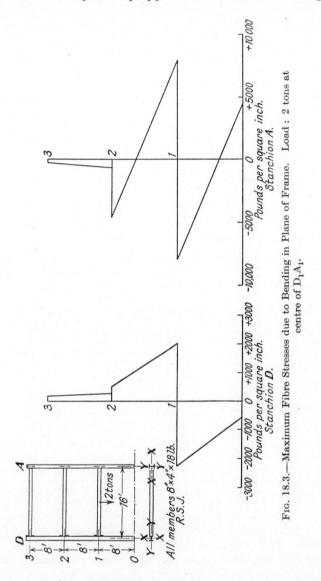

FIG. 18.3.—Maximum Fibre Stresses due to Bending in Plane of Frame. Load : 2 tons at centre of D_1A_1.

stanchion D and to the web of another stanchion A. The stresses observed in stanchions D and A due to the application of a central concentrated load of 2 tons to the beam at the first floor are shown in Fig. 18.3 and Table 18.2. It will be seen that the bending stress diagrams in the two stanchions are quite different, due to the sway which has arisen from the lack of symmetry in the structure. In the lengths 0–1 1–2 of stanchion A, double curvature

TABLE 18.2.—OBSERVED BENDING STRESSES. ASYMMETRICAL SINGLE BAY
FRAME FITTED WITH CONNEXIONS OF TYPE A.

Concentrated load of 2 tons at centre of Beam D_1A_1.

Section	Observed, with type A connexions: lb. per square inch
A_0A_1	$+4{,}560$
A_1A_0	$-8{,}120$
A_1A_2	$+8{,}100$
A_2A_1	$-4{,}520$
A_2A_3	$-\ \ \ 600$
A_3A_2	$-\ \ \ 200$
D_0D_1	$-\ \ \ 700$
D_1D_0	$-2{,}275$
D_1D_2	$+2{,}000$
D_2D_1	$+\ \ \ 525$
D_2D_3	$+\ \ \ 250$
D_3D_2	$+\ \ \ 150$

bending has resulted as before from the application of the load to the beam,
whereas in stanchion D the form of bending can be designated " single
curvature " bending.   The difference in these forms was found to be of the
first importance when the rational design of a stanchion length was under
consideration.

In addition to measurements of strains in these frames the characteristics
of the beam-to-stanchion connexions were found.   Relative rotation of the
ends of the members joined was measured by a simple arrangement of dial
indicators and a curve obtained showing the relation between the moment
transmitted by a connexion and the relative rotation of the members joined.
It was found that this relation (the characteristic curve for the connexion)
was by no means linear, and that, on the removal of load from a beam,
reverse bending moments remained at the ends of the beam.   These points
are discussed in paragraph 18.5 where it is also shown how the methods of
stress analysis given in paragraph 9.4 can be used when the characteristic
curves for the connexions are not straight lines.   An example of the stresses
calculated in this way is shown in Table 18.1 (column 3).

One other test carried out on the experimental frame must be mentioned.
A horizontal load of 349 lb. was applied to the top of the symmetrical single
bay frame (Fig. 18.2).   It was found that, while the distribution of stress
was of the same form, the maximum bending stress observed at the foot of
each stanchion was greater than would have been predicted on the assumption
of perfectly rigid joints.

A reliable method of design could only be produced if the behaviour of
the complex structure, consisting of the steel frame and the clothing of walls
and floors which makes up the finished building, was understood.   It was
decided, therefore, in view of the success of the work on the experimental
frame, to test actual buildings.   Since full details of these important tests are
available (Baker, 1954) only a review of the data collected on two buildings,
an hotel and an office block, will be given here.

18.4. Review of tests on buildings.—The buildings tested behaved in much the same way as the experimental frame. Appreciable restraining moments were developed at the ends of the beams and corresponding bending moments in the stanchion lengths. It was found that the method of stress analysis evolved could be made to give a reliable estimate of the stresses in a frame even when it was clothed.

The magnitudes of the restraining moments can be gauged from the fact that the equivalent eccentricity of a connexion lay between $30 \cdot 0$ and $44 \cdot 6$ inches for the bare frame of the hotel building and between $16 \cdot 0$ and $34 \cdot 3$ inches for the office building. These restraining moments, while reducing the maximum stresses in the beams by from 17 per cent. to 25 per cent. of those which would be found in similarly loaded simply supported beams, were at the same time responsible for large bending stresses in the stanchions, in some cases as much as 9 times those which would be estimated by the orthodox method.

Sway of the bare asymmetrical frames was detected but it was eliminated after the addition of floors and casing. The presence of sway makes it difficult to formulate simple expressions for the bending moments in the members of a frame adjacent to a loaded beam. In frames which are not to be clothed, therefore, great care must be exercised in drafting design rules, particularly for stanchions, since the distribution of bending stresses will depend very largely on the proportions of quite distant members. Evidence, both from these tests and by calculation, shows that it should be safe, in all but the most extreme cases, to neglect sway when the frame has floors of hollow tile or similar construction, brick walls and even light stanchion casings.

Among the many smaller matters illustrated by the tests was the considerable local stress which can be set up in a stanchion by unequal bearing on its base. The foot of one stanchion in the hotel building rested on a 5-inch thick steel slab. Strain readings taken 12 inches above the foot of the stanchion indicated that the stress at one corner of a flange was 17 times as great as that at any other corner. It was found that the holding-down bolts had not been screwed home as far as they might have been. A further test, made after these bolts had been tightened, showed that some redistribution of stress had taken place over the cross-section but that the stanchion was still unevenly bedded since at the one corner the stress was still more than three times that at any other. The load applied to this stanchion length by the placing of the floors must have been sufficient to produce local yielding in the foot of the stanchion, since when a test was carried out after the floors were in position the distribution of stress at the section 12 inches above the base was quite normal.

A knowledge of the other effects of the clothing added to the steel frame is essential. The placing of floors influences the stanchion stresses in three ways as follows :—

(a) The presence of beam casing or of hollow-tile floors increases the effective stiffness of the beam in the frame, and so, other influences being unaltered, tends to decrease the bending stresses in the stanchions.

(b) The concrete which is placed around the connexions when the floors are laid increases, to some extent, the rigidities of these connexions, with the result that the moments transmitted to the stanchions and the bending stresses induced in them tend to increase.

(c) The floors form slabs connecting all the bents of the framework, so that the effect of a load on one beam is felt not only in the stanchions into which the beam frames, as in the bare framework, but in adjacent stanchions also. Due to this slab effect, the stanchion stresses produced by the application of a concentrated load to a beam are likely to decrease.

It was not easy to study all these influences separately.

In the single bay portion of the hotel building the addition of floors decreased appreciably the bending stresses induced in the stanchions when a central concentrated load was applied to a beam framing into them. In ten of the twelve stanchion lengths tested the decrease in maximum bending stress varied from $37 \cdot 5$ to $21 \cdot 1$ per cent. Since in practice the applied load would be distributed over a considerable floor area it was essential to evaluate the slab effect. This was done by measuring the stresses in adjacent stanchions when a concentrated load was applied to a beam. From such measurements it was deduced that, in this particular structure, had a distributed load been applied to the whole floor area, the maximum stanchion bending stresses in the frame with floors laid would, with two exceptions, have varied between $10 \cdot 8$ per cent. less and $14 \cdot 7$ per cent. more than the corresponding stresses in the bare frame under the same load. In two stanchion lengths, however, increases of as much as 40 per cent. and $62 \cdot 5$ per cent. would have been found. Where the internal stanchion of the hotel was concerned the presence of floors decreased in every case the bending stresses induced when a concentrated load was applied to the beams framing into it.

A very different state of affairs was found in the office building, a considerable increase in stanchion bending stress occurring when the floors were in position. As measured by the equivalent eccentricity of a connexion, an increase of 53 per cent. was found in one stanchion of the single bay portion when a concentrated load was applied to a beam, that is to say without allowance for slab effect. When, as was fortunately possible in this building, a distributed load was applied to the floor so that the slab effect was automatically included, the increase in stress was as much as $66 \cdot 5$ per cent. over that which would have been estimated in the bare frame carrying the same load.

When the floor was laid in the two-bay portion of the office building, casing was at the same time poured around the internal stanchion. In spite of this and the fact that the floor was continuous past the internal stanchion, the increase of stanchion bending stress was no less than $61 \cdot 3$ per cent.

Although these effects are so different from those in the hotel building the reason is not difficult to find. In the hotel the bare beam-to-stanchion connexions were much less flexible than those of the office building. The addition of concrete would therefore increase the rigidity of the former far less than that of the latter and would make it much more likely for the decrease in stress, due to the added stiffness of the beams, to prevail.

Floors are not the only clothing likely to affect the stresses in the steel framework ; the fire-resisting casings added to the stanchions and the external walls will also play their part.

Apart from any effect due to the reduction in sway, the presence of casings and walls tends to stiffen the stanchions and so increases the moments developed in them. These increased moments may not, however, produce increased bending stresses in the steelwork since the total section of the stanchion is increased by the addition of casing. For the investigation of these effects additional tests were carried out after walls and stanchion casings had been built.

Although the stanchion casing of the hotel building was very light in form, two tests made on the fully clothed single bay portion showed that its presence decreased the maximum bending stress in each stanchion length below that observed when the floors alone were in place. The decrease in the five stanchion lengths concerned varied from 10 per cent. to 35·5 per cent. In one test, strain measurements were made on adjacent stanchions also, so that the slab effect could be evaluated. It was found that the stresses in the bare frame would have been approximately 31 per cent. more than the corresponding stresses in the completely clothed frame subjected to a distributed load. Only one test was carried out on the internal stanchion of the hotel building after the casing was in position. There, again, small but quite definite reductions in the stanchion stresses were found. From this it appears that the addition of clothing to this particular frame relieved the stresses in the steel framework appreciably.

Once more very different conditions were found in the office building. In one test on the single bay portion the presence of walls and casing, which were more substantial than those of the hotel building, brought about an increase in the total bending moment in the steel core of 19 per cent. of the value it would have had in the frame with floors alone in position. In one stanchion length the increase in the maximum bending stress was 47·2 per cent.

In the two-bay portion of the office building the increase in stress was more striking. In one length of the internal stanchion the maximum bending stress increased by 97 per cent. above the value it would have had in the frame without external walls and external stanchion casing. In other lengths of the same stanchion the corresponding increases were 41 and 27 per cent.

These tests have shown that the effect of clothing cannot be ignored. In a frame such as the hotel building, with a rigid type of bare steelwork connexion, the effect of the clothing may, in general, be to reduce the stresses somewhat below the values which would be estimated, by an accurate method of analysis, in the bare frame. In a frame, such as the office building, with more flexible connexions the stresses may be very appreciably increased. The bending stress found in a certain stanchion length of the fully clothed building was 2·89 times that which would have been set up in the bare frame. In other cases the increase in bending stress was as much as 60 per cent. It appears from this that, until more is known of the effect of cased connexions, the assumption must be made in the design of stanchions that, where a frame is encased in concrete, all connexions are perfectly rigid.

18.5. Behaviour of connexions.—The observations made on the experimental frame and on the office building showed that when a beam having end connexions of the simple bottom bracket and top cleat type of Fig. 18.1 is loaded, a curve similar to OAB, Fig. 18.4, represents the relation between

M, the moment transmitted through a connexion, and $\theta-\phi$, the relative rotation of the members joined by the connexion. It may be well to point out here that if the members had been joined by a frictionless pin the curve would have coincided with the axis OX, while if they had been rigidly connected it would have coincided with the axis OY.   When load is removed from the beam the relationship between moment and rotation is as shown by BCDE.   The moment has dropped to zero at D before the whole of the load has been removed from the beam and as the remainder of the load is removed a reversed moment comes into operation (D to E).   When the load has been completely removed (E) there remains an end moment OM tending

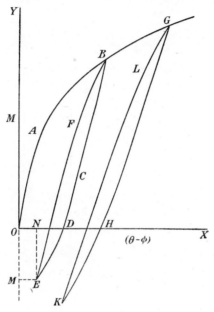

FIG. 18.4.

to cause sagging of the beam and a residual relative rotation, ON.   On reloading the curve traced out will be EFB, the point B being reached under the same load as before.   If still more load is now added the first loading curve OAB will be continued to G.

It will be seen from these curves that the connexion does not behave elastically.   This fact may have an important bearing on the frame as a whole and some knowledge of the cause of the deformations suffered by the connexion is essential to the designer.   A complete analysis of the behaviour of a connexion is difficult and no attempt will be made here to give more than a descriptive treatment.

When, due to the application of load to the beam, a small moment is transmitted through the connexion, the legs of the bottom bracket and top cleat forming the connexion will bend as if they were beams clamped firmly to the members at the rows of rivets nearest the roots of the angles.   If the vertical leg of the bottom bracket were perfectly fitted to the face of the stanchion it would be unable to bend.   It is always found in practice, however, that the fitting is not good and under small transmitted moments the bottom bracket bends as freely as the top cleat so that the end of the beam rotates about its centre of depth. In these circumstances the relation between rotation and transmitted moment is a straight line. As the transmitted moment increases, the pull in the rivets connecting the vertical leg of the cleat to the stanchion also increases. These rivets clamp the cleat efficiently until the pull in them exceeds their initial tension when they begin to extend elastically, increasing the flexibility of the connexion and giving the relation represented by AB in Fig. 18.4. This continues until, as the moment increases further, the distortion of the top cleat is such that yield occurs in it ; the flexibility then increases still more as shown by BG. This is the inelastic range during which the rate of change of moment decreases in a pronounced way.

Actually the behaviour is much more complex than this description indicates. Over no part of the range does there appear to be a true linear

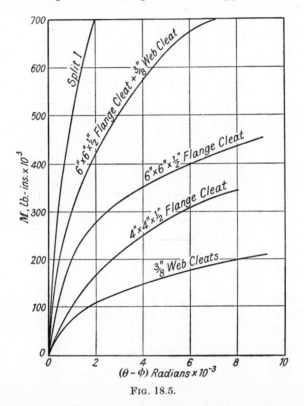

Fig. 18.5.

relation between moment and rotation ; some inelastic deformation occurs under the smallest moment. Other influences affecting the behaviour are the closing in of the vertical leg of the bottom bracket and the relative movement between the horizontal leg of the cleat and the beam. As the vertical leg of the bracket bends it comes sooner or later into contact with the face of the stanchion and is restrained. Thus after a certain, and generally small, transmitted moment has been reached, the centre of rotation of the end of the beam moves down from the axis of the beam until eventually, when the whole of the vertical leg of the bracket is in close contact with the stanchion, it is at the level of the bottom flange of the beam. This change in the position of the centre of rotation tends to increase the rigidity of the connexion. Relative movement between the horizontal leg of the cleat and the top flange of the beam may also occur. Sometimes, more particularly when bolts are used, this " slip " is sudden, the relative rotation increasing considerably for a very small increase in transmitted moment.

First loading curves for two bracket and top cleat (flange cleat) connexions are shown in Fig. 18.5, each curve being marked with the size of angle used for the cleats. In each case the connexions were 5 inches long, the beam 12 inches deep and the rivets $\frac{3}{4}$ inch diameter.

Another form of steelwork connexion consists of a pair of angles connecting the web of the beam to the stanchion. Such a web cleat connexion behaves in much the same way as the flange cleat type discussed above but is more flexible. A typical curve for a web cleat connexion made up of $6 \times 3\frac{1}{2} \times \frac{3}{8}$ inch angles 9 inches long joined to a 12-inch deep beam and to a stanchion by $\frac{3}{4}$-inch rivets is shown in Fig. 18.5.

Though the web cleat connexion alone is very flexible the addition of angles connecting the web of a beam to a stanchion already joined by flange

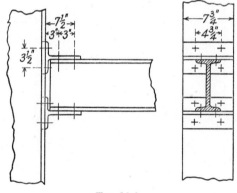

Fɪɢ. 18.6.

cleats increases the rigidity of the connexion considerably above that for the flange cleats alone. This is shown in Fig. 18.5 by the curve for a connexion made up of $6 \times 6 \times \frac{1}{2}$-inch flange cleats and $\frac{3}{8}$-inch web cleats to a 12-inch deep beam.

A type of connexion sometimes used when large moments have to be transmitted is the split I connexion (Fig. 18.6). Two large T's made by cutting one flange from a length of I section join the top and bottom flanges of the beam to the stanchion. It will be seen that this type of connexion is likely to be more rigid than that made up of flange or web cleats. Until the moment transmitted is considerable the only deformation which takes place is that due to stretch of the rivets through the flange of the split I and the small amount of flexure of this flange. A typical curve for such a connexion made with T's cut from a 15 in. $\times$ 6 in. $\times$ 45-lb. R.S.J. $7\frac{3}{4}$ inches long and fitted with $\frac{7}{8}$-inch rivets (Fig. 18.6) is shown in Fig. 18.5. It will be seen that the relation between moment and relative rotation is almost linear ; this continues until a moment of 9×10^5 lb.-in. is reached. Above this the rate of increase of moment decreases, due probably to slip between the web of the split I and the flange of the beam.

Steelwork connexions differ in one important respect from the rest of the structure of which they form part. They are, under normal loading conditions, overstrained ; that is to say the yield point of the material has been passed. This is not a source of danger when the material used is as ductile as structural steel, since tests have shown that the relative rotation needed to cause fracture is many times greater than that which can occur under normal circumstances in a steel frame.

The curves shown in Fig. 18.5 are for bare connexions. In many frames the connexions are encased in concrete. The tests on buildings showed that when the casing is of unreinforced concrete, such as that formed by the pouring of the floor slab, the rigidity of the connexion under working loads is increased to such an extent that in certain cases the connexion behaves

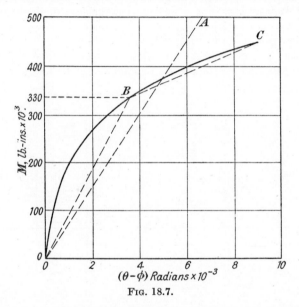

FIG. 18.7.

very nearly as a perfectly rigid joint. Laboratory tests on encased connexions showed that the flexibility is reduced to a very small value until a moment is transmitted which cracks the concrete. Under greater moments the curve is similar to that for the uncased connexion. It seems probable that the addition of a small percentage of reinforcement running just above the top flange of the beam and hooked around the stanchion would ensure the increased rigidity under all working conditions.

It will be seen from the curves of Fig. 18.5 that the relation between the moment transmitted by a connexion and the relative rotation between the members is not linear and this complicates the analysis of the stresses in the framework. It means that no exact analysis can be obtained by the method given in paragraph 9.4 where the assumption is made that such a linear relation exists. Fortunately the stresses can be calculated accurately enough for many practical purposes if the curves are replaced by a straight line. For example it is clear from Fig. 18.5 that a straight line passing through the origin can be chosen which will represent the curve for the split

I connexion without serious error. For the more flexible connexions a suitable substitute line can be plotted if an approximate preliminary estimate of the moment transmitted through the connexion can be made. If the connexion is made of $6 \times 6 \times \frac{1}{2}$-inch flange cleats the line OA, Fig. 18.7, will lead to a fairly accurate analysis of the stresses so long as the moment through the connexion lies within the range $3 \cdot 5 \times 10^5$ to 4×10^5 lb.-in.

Where a more accurate analysis is required the curve for the connexion can be replaced by its chords. Thus for the $6 \times 6 \times \frac{1}{2}$-inch flange cleats great accuracy will result from the use of the chords OB, BC.

In certain simple cases the stresses in beams fitted with flexible connexions can be found more exactly by a construction due to Professor C. Batho, to whom we owe much of our detailed knowledge of the behaviour of connexions (Batho and Rowan, 1934).

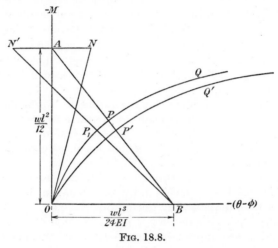

FIG. 18.8.

Suppose a beam of uniform cross-section and length l carries a uniformly distributed load of intensity w per unit length and is connected to rigid abutments by identical connexions having a flexibility defined by the curve OPQ in Fig. 18.8.

If ϕ is the change of slope and M is the moment at the end of the beam then from equation (9.3) the relation between the end moment and the end rotation is

$$M = \frac{2EI}{l}\phi - \frac{wl^2}{12}.$$

This is a straight line and can be drawn as AB in Fig. 18.8. The curve OPQ showing the relation between transmitted moment and angular rotation for the connexion is already plotted so that P, the intersection of AB and OPQ, gives the moment present at the end of the beam. The bending moment and the bending stress at any point in the beam can then be determined.

It is much more usual for a beam to be connected at its end to a stanchion which is flexible and will therefore change its slope when a moment is applied to it. Suppose the beam considered in the last example is connected at its ends to identical stanchions, the flexibility of which is known, so that on Fig. 18.8 it is possible to plot the line ON showing the change of slope of a

15

stanchion at the level where the beam is attached, due to any moment applied to it at that level.   If, as before, the curve OPQ defines the flexibility of the beam-to-stanchion connexion the change of slope suffered by the end of the beam when any moment M is transmitted from it through the connexion to the stanchion is given by the sum of the abscissæ of ON and OPQ corresponding to M.   The curve representing this sum is OP′Q′ and, as in the first example, the moment at the end of the beam when a uniformly distributed load of intensity w is applied is given by the intersection of OP′Q′ with the beam line AB.

The curve OP′Q′ need not be drawn if the following construction is used. Join B to N′ a point on NA produced such that N′A=AN.   Then P$_1$, the point where N′B cuts the curve OPQ gives the end moment on the beam.

This graphical method was extended by Batho to cover unsymmetrical arrangements of load and structure (Baker, 1954).

18.6. The problem of design.—The more important points demonstrated by the experimental investigations can be summarised as follows :—

(a) Standard types of riveted and bolted connexions are capable of transmitting large bending moments, and appreciable restraining moments are developed at the ends of a loaded beam in a steel framed building.

(b) Although there was some variation due to workmanship in the behaviour of connexions made to the same design, it was possible to produce a lower-limit curve for each type of connexion similar to those shown in Fig. 18.5, enabling a safe estimate of the restraining moment to be made.

(c) The moment transmitted through a connexion from a loaded beam develops bending moments in the stanchion which are many times greater than those usually taken into account.

(d) The bending moments developed in a stanchion due to load applied to a beam are appreciable, not only in the stanchion lengths to which the beam is attached but also in those more remote.

(e) The addition of floors, walls and stanchion casing to a frame does not bring about any fundamental change in the behaviour of the frame.

(f) Concrete casing can appreciably increase the rigidity of connexions in the working range.

(g) The presence of clothing decreases the maximum stresses in the steel beams of a frame but it may increase the bending stresses in the steel cores of the stanchions.

(h) The methods of stress analysis developed could be depended upon to give a true picture of the distribution of stress in the steelwork of a frame even when it was clothed.

The investigations thus showed that the stress calculations made by the orthodox method give a very faulty representation of the distribution of stress in a frame.   They emphasise shortcomings in stanchion design and the extravagance of the present method of beam design, in which restraining moments are neglected.   They also disprove the assumption that the worst conditions are provided for each member when every member carries its full load.

It is not easy to calculate the stresses in such a complicated structure as a building frame.   Simplified assumptions must be made but if they are so sweeping that the true behaviour of the frame is disguised, economy of material and evolution of the method of construction are impossible. The Steel Structures Research Committee endeavoured to produce a method of design which, while simple enough to be applied in ordinary practice, was based on an accurate estimate of conditions in the structure.

It is not difficult to see that the restraining moment developed at the end of a loaded beam joined to a stanchion by a certain connexion depends not only on the characteristics of the connexion but on the stiffness of the stanchion. If the stanchion can be assumed to be rigid, the restraining moment developed will have its maximum value ; as the stiffness decreases so does the restraining moment. The maximum stress in the beam is influenced by the magnitude of the restraining moment so that the suitability of a beam to carry a given load depends on the connexions at its ends and on the stanchions to which it is attached. In the same way the bending moment applied to the stanchion by a loaded beam is influenced by the proportions of the beam.

As a designer cannot afford to make a tentative design of the whole structure and then to modify each member as the effect of the remainder of the frame is appreciated, some means had to be found which would enable one member to be designed economically without reference to the actual properties of the rest of the structure. It was found that, while the stresses in each member are affected to some extent by the conditions of the rest of the frame, the maximum stress in a loaded beam fitted with a certain semi-rigid beam-to-stanchion connexion is not particularly sensitive to changes in the stiffness of the members into which it frames. A safe design without serious loss of economy would, therefore, result if a lower limit was assumed for the stiffnesses of these members when the restraining moment on the beam was estimated. It was found that the sum of the stiffnesses of the stanchion lengths into which a beam framed would not, except in special cases, be less than two-thirds of the stiffness of the beam. Assuming the stiffness of the stanchion lengths to be two-thirds that of the beam, it was possible to find, by the graphical method described on p. 437, the restraining moments at the ends of any loaded beam fitted with any type of standard connexion and therefore, taking account of the relief given by these moments, to design a beam which would be safe and more economical than those obtained by existing methods, whatever the actual sizes of the adjacent members in the structure. With the beams designed in this way the design of the stanchions could be approached with some confidence.

The difficulty in designing a stanchion length is to decide what conditions give rise to the greatest stress in the member. Fig. 18.9 gives diagrams showing the bending stresses in a symmetrically placed stanchion length, AB, deduced from the results of the tests on existing buildings, due to various arrangements of superimposed load on the beam. In the orthodox method of design it is usual to choose a stanchion section from a consideration of the conditions existing when all floors are loaded, Fig. 18.9 (a). This load will not, however, give rise to the greatest stress in the stanchion since, by removing load from the floors below on alternate sides of the stanchion, as shown in (b), considerable end bending moments are developed in AB. This removal does not reduce the magnitude of the end load on AB, but it does appreciably increase the maximum bending stress in the stanchion length.

The conditions shown in (*b*) do not necessarily develop the absolute maximum stanchion stress. If load is removed from part of the floor immediately above the stanchion length as shown in (*c*) the end bending

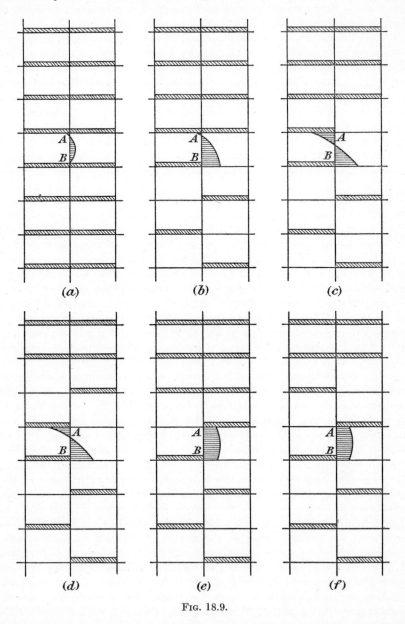

Fig. 18.9.

stresses are increased further and the decrease in axial end load arising from the removal of the load from the floor above may not compensate for this increase, leaving the maximum total stress greater than in (*b*). A further increase in end bending stress arises if other floors are unloaded as in (*d*), but in most structures the reduction in axial end load which follows outweighs this further increase. In these last three arrangements of load, shown in (b), (c) and (d), the bending moments applied by the beams to the ends of the stanchion length bend it in double curvature. Another condition has to be considered in which the stanchion length bends in single curvature. An arrangement of load which brings this about is shown in (e), together with the resulting form of the bending stress diagram. As before, the removal of further load, (f), increases the bending stress but decreases the axial stress.

It is impossible to say from inspection which of the arrangements of load shown in (b)–(f) will give the absolute maximum stress in the stanchion length, but it is certain that one or other of them will give a greater value than the arrangement of load hitherto used, Fig. 18.9 (a). It is clear that, for a complete treatment, the behaviour of a stanchion length under axial end load and end moments, producing both single and double curvature, must be studied. The arrangement of load which must be used in design depends on the relative values of the end moments for the various cases which in turn depend on the layout and dimensions of the frame concerned. This will be dealt with later.

The design of a stanchion length, therefore, resolves itself into two steps, (1) the determination of the end reactions applied to the member by that arrangement of load on the structure which produces the worst conditions in the member, and (2) the estimate of the maximum stress developed in the member by those reactions, which enables the suitability of the member to be judged.

18.7. Evolution of a method of design for beams.—Before the details of design for either beams or stanchions could be settled, a method of obtaining a definite margin of safety in the structure had to be considered. It will be seen from the discussion of the behaviour of the beam-to-stanchion connexions that if the load on a beam in a steel building frame is doubled, the maximum flexural stress in the loaded beam occurring at some section remote from the ends is more than doubled. The same conditions exist in the stanchions as is recognised in the orthodox method of design. To obtain an approximately uniform margin of safety it was decided, therefore, to adopt the basis of load factor commonly used in aeronautical engineering and to design each member so that if the design load was increased in a given ratio (the load factor) failure would be imminent. The simplest way of ensuring this would be to design the structure so that when it carried a load equal to the design load multiplied by the load factor, the yield stress of the material would be reached. This was considered to be too radical a departure from existing ideas, but the same result was obtained by other means. As a basis of strength the load factor was taken as 2 and the yield stress of the material as 18 tons per square inch.

In the orthodox method of design it is usual to assume a beam to be simply supported, to calculate the maximum bending moment produced in it by the application of the full dead and superimposed load, and to design the member to a given working stress. It was felt to be desirable to retain this general method but since a constant load factor had to be maintained it was impossible to use, in calculating the maximum moment, the real values of the restraining moments given by the lower limit curves. The following method, due to Mr. E. W. Butler of H.M. Office of Works, was used to obtain, from the lower-limit curves, other curves which would give the required load factor.

As explained in paragraph 18.5 a curve OP'Q' (Fig. 18.8) can be drawn giving the relation between the moment and rotation at the end of a symmetrically loaded beam from which, by the use of the beam-line AB, the restraining moment under the full design load can be found. If the load on the beam were doubled the restraining moment Q'N' (Fig. 18.10) would be given by the new beam-line A_1B_1 parallel to AB and such that $OA_1=2OA$. OQ' is drawn, cutting AB in R. Then, if the end restraining moment allowed for in the design of the beam is RN and if a nominal permissible flexural stress of 9 tons per square inch is worked to, the stress in the beam when the load is doubled will be 18 tons per square inch. A curve ORR' can be drawn by this construction to be used as the standard in design to replace the lower-limit curve.

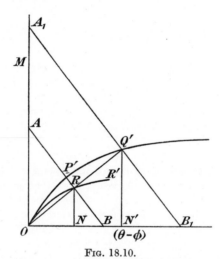

FIG. 18.10.

The lower-limit curves, and those of the type ORR', were deduced from the behaviour of connexions on beams of 12 inches depth. Since it was found that the moment required to produce a given deformation in the connexion was approximately proportional to the depth of the beam and that the angle of rotation for a given deformation was very nearly inversely proportional to the depth of the beam, it was possible to plot from each curve another showing the behaviour of the same connexion when attached to a beam of any depth. This was most easily done by plotting M/D against $D(\theta-\phi)$ where D denotes the depth of the beam ; this gives a curve showing the relation between the nominal pull P, equal to M/D, on the top cleat and the relative linear movement of the ends of the upper and lower faces of the beam. The restraining moment provided by a connexion attached to a beam of depth D can be found, using such a curve, by the beam-line method, the intercepts on the axes being OA, equal to M_F/D, and OB, equal to $\dfrac{M_F D l}{2EI}$,

where M_F denotes the fixed-end moment (that is, the moment present at the end of a similarly loaded beam with completely fixed ends), and equals $\frac{1}{12}wl^2$ when the load is uniformly distributed and of intensity w. As the restraining moment is being determined so that the beam can be designed, it is undesirable to have the second moment of area appearing in the expression for OB. Trial designs can be avoided at a slight sacrifice of economy by the use of a simplified method due to Professor Batho if a lower limit is taken for OB independent of the actual section of the beam.

If f_F is the maximum flexural stress in the beam section produced by the moment M_F, then $M_F = \dfrac{2f_F I}{D}$

and $$OB = \frac{M_F D l}{2EI} = \frac{f_F l}{E}.$$

When a single concentrated load acts on the span, f_F has its lowest value, equal to $f_s/2$, where f_s denotes the maximum stress which would be found in the beam if it were simply supported. This stress f_s cannot be less than 9 tons per square inch when the yield stress of the material and the load

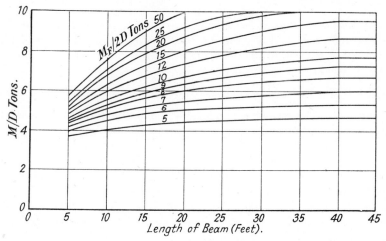

FIG. 18.11.—Standard Design Curves giving Restraining Moments at End of Beam for Class C Connexions.

factor are taken to be 18 tons per square inch and 2 respectively so that if, in drawing the beam-line, OB is made equal to $\dfrac{f_s l}{2E}$ and f_s has the value of 9 tons per square inch, a safe restraining moment is found, depending only on the length of the beam, the depth of the section and the load carried expressed in the form of M_F. By drawing beam-lines in this way it is a simple matter to prepare tables or to plot families of design curves for each type of connexion showing the relation between $M_F/2D$, l and P. Such design curves for a standard connexion of class C, formed of 6-inch by 4-inch by $\frac{3}{4}$-inch flange-cleats, are given in Fig. 18.11.

The argument given above was based on the consideration of a beam carrying a symmetrical load and with equal restraints at its ends. The results can, however, be applied when this symmetry does not exist. If the load is unsymmetrical but the restraints are equal, safety will be ensured if M_F is taken as the mean of the two fixed-end moments, so that the design curve of Fig. 18.11 gives the mean of the end moments, which is taken to be the restraining moment at each end of the beam. When the restraints are unequal and the load is unsymmetrical an error on the unsafe side may occur, but even in an extreme case it is so small as to be negligible.

The lower-limit and standard curves described above give the restraint provided by a bare beam-to-stanchion connexion. When the connexion is encased in concrete it is possible that the restraint will be considerably greater but owing to doubts about the load at which the casing would crack, it was decided to make no allowance for the added restraint.

The main clauses dealing with the design of beams in the Steel Structures Research Committee's Recommendations were as follows :—

Clause 2.—Where a beam of uniform web depth throughout its length is attached at one end to the flange of a stanchion, allowance may be made for the restraining moment present at that end of the beam in the following manner :—

The value of $\dfrac{M_F}{2D}$ shall be calculated, D being the depth of the beam and M_F the mean of the fixed-end moments and the appropriate table or curve (for example Fig. 18.11) used for the determination of the restraining moment M at the end of the beam.

Where in extreme cases, such as the upper storeys of certain frames, $\dfrac{K_B}{K_U+K_L}$ (K_B is the stiffness of the beam and K_U and K_L are the stiffnesses of the stanchion lengths above and below the beam) is found to exceed $1\cdot5$, no allowance shall be made for the restraining moment unless the procedure of *Clause* 3 (1) is followed. In calculating the stiffness of a member the gross second moment of area shall be used, no deduction being made for rivet holes. For a plated beam the stiffness shall be taken as the maximum gross second moment of area of the beam divided by its length.

Clause 3.—Where a beam is connected to the web of a member, either stanchion or beam, no allowance may be made for the restraining moment at that end except in the following cases :—

(1) Where a beam frames into one side of the web of a stanchion, there being no beam on the other side, and special provision is made to stiffen the web of the stanchion, allowance may be made for the restraining moment provided that the value of $\dfrac{K_B}{K_U+K_L}$ does not exceed $1\cdot5$. If $\dfrac{K_B}{K_U+K_L}$ exceeds $1\cdot5$ the value of $q=\dfrac{1}{1+\dfrac{2K_B}{3(K_U+K_L)}}$ shall be calculated, the restrain-ing moment M being determined as in *Clause* 2, $\dfrac{qM_F}{D}$ being substituted for $\dfrac{M_F}{2D}$ in the appropriate table or curve (for example Fig. 18.11).

(2) Where the connexion is balanced by a connexion of the same class to a beam on the opposite side of the member, the rivets or bolts in the vertical legs of the cleats serving both connexions, allowance may be made for the restraining moment as set out in *Clause* 2, the fixed-end moment being taken as that portion which is balanced by the fixed-end moment due to dead load only in the beam on the opposite side of the member.

18.8. Evolution of a method of design for stanchions.—Reference has already been made to the arrangements of live or superimposed load which are likely to produce the most rigorous conditions of stress in a stanchion length. The worst possible moment that can occur in any stanchion length is made up of two parts, one due to the dead load on all the beams and the other due to the most unfavourable combination of live loads, Fig. 18.9. The first step in the production of a method of design is, therefore, the collection of data which will enable these moments to be estimated. The magnitudes of the moments are affected by the proportions of the members making up the frame and by the characteristics of the connexions joining the members. The tests on existing buildings, while indicating that the methods of stress analysis derived earlier in the investigation were reliable, showed that the casing of a connexion could increase its rigidity very considerably. Since the end moments in a stanchion length increase as the rigidity of the connexions between the members increases, it was decided that, for the normal type of clothed steel frame, it would be necessary, in estimating stanchion moments, to assume that the joints in the frame were perfectly rigid. Making this assumption, which while giving the maximum possible moments had the additional advantage of removing one of the variables from the calculations, it was possible to draw up tables giving the desired information in a fairly compact form. Any exact determination of these worst moments can only be made, however, if the proportions of all the members in the frame are known. As the whole structure is not yet designed these proportions cannot be known, so that the data to be provided must be such that an upper limit value of the moment can be estimated from the meagre knowledge of the frame already possessed by the designer. All that has been determined at this stage is the sizes of the beams. It has been shown that the moments developed in the stanchions depend on the relation between beam and stanchion stiffness so that, if an economical upper-limit value for the moment is to be found, the designer must, as he does in the orthodox method of design, first choose a stanchion section and then, by the methods to be described later, find whether his choice is satisfactory. The sections of the beams at one floor level and of the stanchion lengths above and below that level being known, it was found possible to compile tables giving the maximum value of the bending moment which could be applied to the stanchion at that level, no matter what the arrangement of loaded beams or the proportions and layout of more distant members in the structure might be.

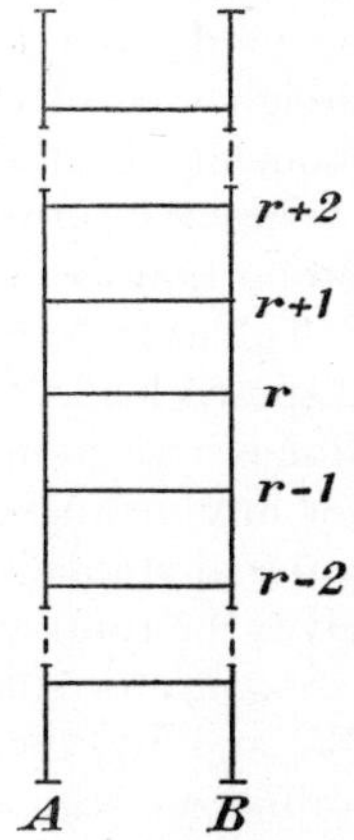

The calculations which had to be made before the tables of worst moments could be compiled were somewhat arduous and only a brief account of them can be given here.

The first step was to derive general expressions for the bending moments in all the members of a frame due to a load on any beam. For this the symmetrical single bay frame shown in Fig. 18.12 was considered. It was assumed that the stanchions were of uniform section, continuous through an infinite number of storeys and that all the beams were of the same section.

If uniformly distributed loads are applied to all the beams, the intensity

Fig. 18.12.

15*

on the rth being w_r, it is found, using the method and notation of paragraph 9.3, that the moment in stanchion A just below the rth beam is

$$M^A_{r(r-1)} = \frac{l^2}{12\sqrt{D^2-4}}\left[\; \ldots \; a(2a+1)w_{(r-2)} + (2a+1)w_{(r-1)}\right.$$

$$\left. + (2+a)w_r + a(2+a)w_{(r+1)} + \ldots \right] \quad \ldots \quad (18.1)$$

where $\qquad D = Q+4, \quad Q = \dfrac{K_r}{K_A} = \dfrac{\text{stiffness of beam}}{\text{stiffness of stanchion length}}$

and $\qquad a = \dfrac{-D+\sqrt{D^2-4}}{2}.$

This moment, though determined from the consideration of an infinite frame, is a close approximation to the moment in any intermediate stanchion length of a finite frame. Similar expressions can be obtained for the moments in bottom and topmost stanchion lengths.

The assumption that each member of a frame is most severely stressed when the structure is fully loaded is incorrect as Fig. 18.9 shows. The worst possible moment that can occur in any stanchion length is made up of two parts, one due to the dead load on all the beams and the other to the most unfavourable combination of live load. From equation (18.1) and from the similar expressions for bottom and topmost length moments it is a simple matter to determine the sum, ΣM, of the greatest bending moments due to live or dead load at the sections of a stanchion just above and just below a beam for any value of $\dfrac{K_B}{K_U+K_L}$ as set out in Tables 18.3 and 18.4 where M^D_F and M^L_F are the fixed-end moments of the beams due to dead and live load respectively.

In practice a stanchion will rarely be of the same section in all storeys as assumed in Fig. 18.12. Fortunately, ΣM depends almost entirely on the ratio $\dfrac{K_B}{K_U+K_L}$ at the beam level under consideration so that the tables may be used even though the stanchion changes section at that level. The designer is, of course, not interested in ΣM so much as in the individual moments in the stanchion lengths ; these can be found with sufficient accuracy by dividing ΣM between the upper and lower stanchion lengths in proportion to their stiffnesses.

Tables 18.3 and 18.4 refer only to a single bay frame carrying symmetrically disposed loads. It was found possible, however, to represent any multi-bay frame by a number of equivalent single bay frames and to make allowance for any arrangement of load on a beam. In this way the moments in an internal stanchion were obtained from the data already given. Table 18.5 gives the total moments due to the arrangements of live load causing double curvature or single curvature bending in an internal stanchion in terms of M^L_{F1} and M^L_{F2} the fixed-end moments due to live load on the beams, having stiffnesses K_{BL} and K_{BR}, to left and right of the stanchion. The table for the total dead load bending moments is, of course, the same as Table 18.3 but with $(K_{BR}+K_{BL})$ substituted for K_B and $(M^D_{F1}-M^D_{F2})$, the difference of the fixed-end moments due to dead load, for M^D_F.

The reactions at the ends of the stanchion length are now known and the next step is to find a convenient way of checking the suitability of the section chosen for the member. This entails finding the maximum total stress in the member or, more conveniently, demonstrating that the maximum stress does not exceed a certain permissible value. The method of checking adopted is based on the work set out in paragraph 7.19. There equation (7.47) shows the necessary values of the end bending stresses, f_A and f_B, arising from end moments M_A and M_B in the plane in which buckling would occur, acting on a practical strut subjected also to a given end load P, if the total maximum stress is not to exceed a certain permissible value p'.

TABLE 18.3.—$\Sigma M/M_F^D$ DUE TO DEAD LOAD.

$\dfrac{K_B}{K_U+K_L}$	Bottom length	Intermediate length	Topmost length
0	0·8616	1·0000	1·0000
0·5	0·6970	0·8648	0·8217
1·0	0·5886	0·7536	0·7041
2·0	0·4516	0·6012	0·5545
4·0	0·3098	0·4286	0·3958
8·0	0·1910	0·2728	0·2557

TABLE 18.4.—$\Sigma M/M_F^L$ DUE TO LIVE LOAD.

$\dfrac{K_B}{K_U+K_L}$	Bottom length	Intermediate length	Topmost length
0	1·1488	1·3590	1·0000
0·5	0·8712	1·0810	0·8338
1·0	0·7064	0·9044	0·7197
2·0	0·5162	0·6870	0·5699
4·0	0·3380	0·4676	0·4068
8·0	0·2010	0·2872	0·2614

As explained in that paragraph the expression is too complex for design purposes, but it is a simple matter to present the results in families of curves showing, for any ratio of f_B/f_A and therefore of M_B/M_A, the maximum value the end bending stress f_A can have without raising the total maximum stress above the permissible value. When M_B and M_A are known from Tables 18.3 and 18.5, together with P, the axial load, which is easily estimated, the suitability of the section can be tested.

This method of testing is complicated by the necessity of determining the ratio M_B/M_A and it is worth while to introduce a simplification by considering only the moment at the top end of the stanchion length which, in the type of frame under consideration, is always greater than that at the bottom end and by assigning to the moment at the bottom end a limiting value such that safety is ensured. It is not difficult to see that for single curvature bending the limit is given by assuming $M_B/M_A=1$. For double curvature bending the value to be assumed is not so obvious. Reference to Fig. 18.9 shows that when the loads are so arranged as to produce bending in double curvature a decrease in the magnitude of the moment at the lower end of the stanchion length may increase the maximum stress in the stanchion.

TABLE 18.5.—TOTAL BENDING MOMENT DUE TO LIVE LOAD.

$\dfrac{K_{BR}+K_{BL}}{K_U+K_L}$	Bottom length	Intermediate length		Topmost length	
	Double curvature	Double curvature	Single curvature	Double curvature	Single curvature
0·0	$1 \cdot 149 M_{F1}^L + 0 \cdot 287 M_{F2}^L$	$1 \cdot 359 M_{F1}^L + 0 \cdot 340 M_{F2}^L$	$1 \cdot 000 M_{F1}^L - 0 \cdot 000 M_{F2}^L$	$1 \cdot 000 M_{F1}^L + 0 \cdot 000 M_{F2}^L$	$1 \cdot 000 M_{F1}^L - 0 \cdot 000 M_{F2}^L$
0·2	$1 \cdot 017 M_{F1}^L + 0 \cdot 231 M_{F2}^L$	$1 \cdot 230 M_{F1}^L + 0 \cdot 280 M_{F2}^L$	$0 \cdot 887 M_{F1}^L - 0 \cdot 064 M_{F2}^L$	$0 \cdot 925 M_{F1}^L + 0 \cdot 007 M_{F2}^L$	$0 \cdot 891 M_{F1}^L - 0 \cdot 027 M_{F2}^L$
0·6	$0 \cdot 834 M_{F1}^L + 0 \cdot 159 M_{F2}^L$	$1 \cdot 043 M_{F1}^L + 0 \cdot 200 M_{F2}^L$	$0 \cdot 731 M_{F1}^L - 0 \cdot 110 M_{F2}^L$	$0 \cdot 807 M_{F1}^L + 0 \cdot 013 M_{F2}^L$	$0 \cdot 734 M_{F1}^L - 0 \cdot 061 M_{F2}^L$
1·0	$0 \cdot 706 M_{F1}^L + 0 \cdot 118 M_{F2}^L$	$0 \cdot 904 M_{F1}^L + 0 \cdot 151 M_{F2}^L$	$0 \cdot 626 M_{F1}^L - 0 \cdot 128 M_{F2}^L$	$0 \cdot 720 M_{F1}^L + 0 \cdot 016 M_{F2}^L$	$0 \cdot 626 M_{F1}^L - 0 \cdot 078 M_{F2}^L$
2·0	$0 \cdot 516 M_{F1}^L + 0 \cdot 065 M_{F2}^L$	$0 \cdot 687 M_{F1}^L + 0 \cdot 086 M_{F2}^L$	$0 \cdot 467 M_{F1}^L - 0 \cdot 134 M_{F2}^L$	$0 \cdot 570 M_{F1}^L + 0 \cdot 015 M_{F2}^L$	$0 \cdot 462 M_{F1}^L - 0 \cdot 092 M_{F2}^L$
4·0	$0 \cdot 338 M_{F1}^L + 0 \cdot 028 M_{F2}^L$	$0 \cdot 468 M_{F1}^L + 0 \cdot 039 M_{F2}^L$	$0 \cdot 314 M_{F1}^L - 0 \cdot 114 M_{F2}^L$	$0 \cdot 407 M_{F1}^L + 0 \cdot 011 M_{F2}^L$	$0 \cdot 308 M_{F1}^L - 0 \cdot 088 M_{F2}^L$
8·0	$0 \cdot 201 M_{F1}^L + 0 \cdot 010 M_{F2}^L$	$0 \cdot 287 M_{F1}^L + 0 \cdot 014 M_{F2}^L$	$0 \cdot 192 M_{F1}^L - 0 \cdot 081 M_{F2}^L$	$0 \cdot 261 M_{F1}^L + 0 \cdot 006 M_{F2}^L$	$0 \cdot 188 M_{F1}^L - 0 \cdot 068 M_{F2}^L$

For safety in this case the ratio f_B/f_A must be based on a consideration of the conditions which make the ratio of the corresponding end moments a minimum. This minimum ($-\cdot268$) is found in the topmost length of an external stanchion when the topmost beam only is loaded and when the ratio of beam to stanchion stiffness approaches zero. The relevant information given by the families of curves can now be embodied in two sets only, Figs. 18.13 and 18.14. The former refers to single curvature bending and is made up of curves for $f_B/f_A=1$, while the latter refers to double curvature bending and is made up of curves for $f_B/f_A=-\cdot268$. Both sets are based on a load factor of 2 and a yield stress in the material of 18 tons per square inch, that is to say the curves are plotted from the expressions

$$\frac{18-2p+f'}{2f_A+f'}=\frac{\sin\mu(l-x)}{\sin\mu l}+\frac{\sin\mu x}{\sin\mu l}\cdot\frac{2f_B+f'}{2f_A+f'} \qquad . \quad . \quad (18.2)$$

and
$$\tan\mu x=\operatorname{cosec}\mu l\left[\frac{2f_B+f'}{2f_A+f'}-\cos\mu l\right] \quad . \quad . \quad . \quad (18.3)$$

where
$$\mu=\sqrt{\frac{2P}{EI}}$$

and the notation is that of paragraph 7.19.

With these curves, which also make allowance for the effects of imperfections in the stanchions not included in the calculation of the end moments, and with the list of end moments given in Tables 18.3 and 18.5, a stanchion can be designed with comparative ease. The method will be most easily appreciated if an intermediate length is considered, the stanchion lengths above it having been already designed.

The first step is the choice of a provisional section for the stanchion length and the determination of the axial load per unit area (p) arising from the loads applied to the structure. The beams will have been designed by the method already described, so before a start is made with the stanchion design the stiffnesses of the beams framing into the upper end of the stanchion length, the fixed-end moments, M_{F1} and M_{F2}, and the reactions at the ends of these beams, will be known. The stiffness ratios $\dfrac{K_{BR}+K_{BL}}{K_U+K_L}$ about both axes of the stanchion can also be calculated. These enable the total bending moments on the stanchion due to dead load and to both critical arrangements of live load to be obtained from Tables 18.3 and 18.5, and it is essential that the ability of the section selected to sustain both these arrangements of load should be checked.

Single curvature loading will first be considered. Using the appropriate value of the stiffness ratio, the total bending moment about the XX axis of the stanchion at the top end due to live load is taken from Table 18.5 (column 4), and to this is added the dead load total bending moment from Table 18.3. The dead load will actually cause bending of the stanchion length in double curvature, but if serious complications are to be avoided some economy must be sacrificed and the dead load moment be assumed to produce bending in single curvature. The sum of these total moments is now divided between the stanchion length under consideration and that above in the ratio of their relevant stiffnesses, thus giving the end moment in single curvature about the XX axis at the top end of the stanchion length. The maximum fibre stress due to this end moment is calculated and similarly

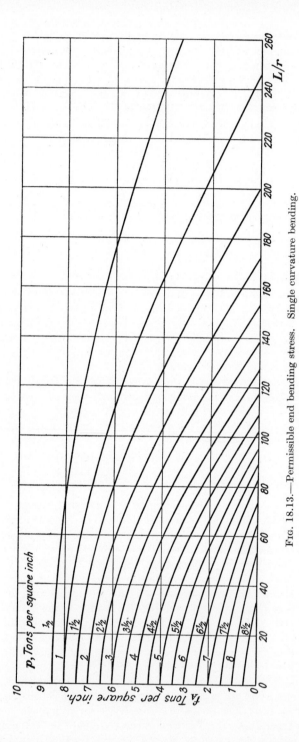

FIG. 18.13.—Permissible end bending stress. Single curvature bending.

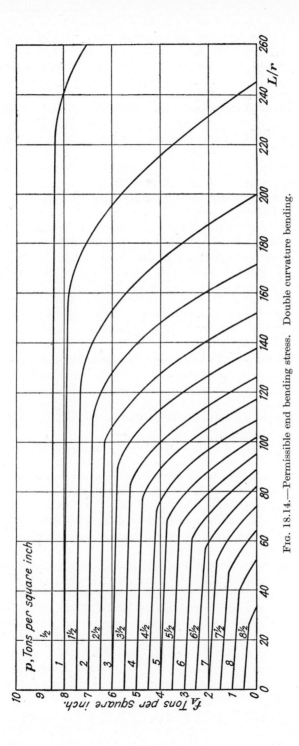

Fig. 18.14.—Permissible end bending stress. Double curvature bending.

the maximum fibre stress due to that arrangement of load producing bending in single curvature about the YY axis of the stanchion. The sum of these fibre stresses is the maximum single curvature end bending stress in the stanchion length. If this stress is less than the permissible end bending stress (f_A) given in Fig. 18.13 for the stanchion length, as defined by its slenderness ratio (L/r) and axial load per unit area (p), the section selected will be adequate to carry the forces imposed on it when the loads are such as to produce bending in single curvature.

The suitability of the section to resist double curvature bending is checked in a similar way. The sum of the total bending moments about the XX axis of the stanchion at its top end due to live loads (Table 18.5, column 3) and dead loads (Table 18.3) is, as before, divided between the stanchion lengths in proportion to their relevant stiffnesses, thus giving the bending moment and hence the bending stress in double curvature about the XX axis at the top end of the stanchion length. In the same way the bending stress, due to double curvature loading, about the YY axis of the stanchion, is determined. The sum of these stresses is the maximum double curvature end bending stress and the suitability of the section is checked from Fig. 18.14.

It might be thought that two other combinations of load, producing single curvature bending about one axis and double curvature about the other, should be considered. A comprehensive investigation, in which the true maximum stress in the stanchion under such loading has been found in a number of particular cases, makes it appear that those dealt with above will always be critical.

The fact that the end bending stresses about both principal axes are added in the above needs some explanation. Equations (18.2) and (18.3), refer only to bending in the plane in which buckling would occur but it can be proved that, if the end stresses arising from bending in a plane at right angles are assumed to arise from bending in the plane in which buckling would occur, safety is ensured.

A design method is of little value, however sound it may be, if it is too complex to be used conveniently in the design office. A number of practising engineers who gave the method described above a trial in their offices were of the opinion that while designers had no difficulty in applying it, the time taken in proportioning a stanchion was prohibitive. The reason was that the two critical loading conditions had to be considered separately for each stanchion length. To produce a method acceptable to the designer further simplification was essential.

It was desirable to arrange the data so that, while the principle of the original method would not be sacrificed, only one loading condition would, in effect, have to be considered. It was found possible, without serious loss of economy, to prepare a single set of curves giving the permissible end bending stress, which would ensure safety whether bending was in single or double curvature.

For a symmetrical frame in which $M_{F2}=M_{F1}$, the bending moment in single curvature is never greater than $1/1 \cdot 7$ times the moment in double curvature. If, therefore, the ordinates of Fig. 18.13 for any value of p are multiplied by $1 \cdot 7$, the composite lower-limit curve, formed from this and the corresponding double curvature curve of Fig. 18.14 by taking that portion of each which gives the lower value of the permissible end bending stress (f_A), will, if used in conjunction with the double curvature moments,

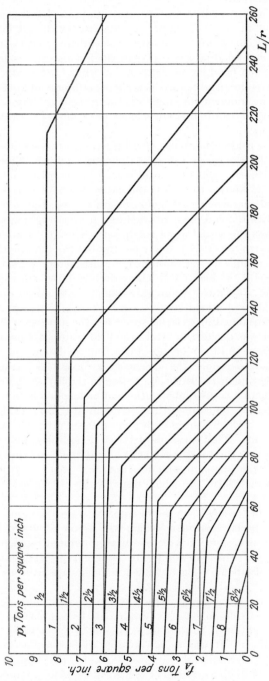

Fig. 18.15.—Permissible end bending stress (composite curve).

ensure safety in all cases whether the critical loading is such as to produce bending in double or single curvature. Such composite lower-limit curves are shown in Fig. 18.15.

These composite strut curves are so drawn that safety is ensured provided that the moment in single curvature is not greater than $1/1 \cdot 7$ times the moment in double curvature. It must be remembered that the curve giving the permissible end bending stress (f_A) in single curvature is based on the assumption that the bending moments at the ends of the stanchion length are equal. This is important since as a result, although in an asymmetrical frame the bending moment for single curvature loading may be more than $1/1 \cdot 7$ times that due to double curvature, the composite strut curves are always satisfactory.

Some further consideration must now be given to the moments of Tables 18.3 and 18.5. It is not easy to assess the axial load in a stanchion length resulting from the arrangement of load on the beams which produces these moments, but it is known to be less than that when all beams are loaded. The conditions arising when a stanchion length is subjected to this full axial load, together with the end moments deduced from the tables, are therefore more rigorous than the actual worst conditions. The combination of circumstances giving rise to the latter is likely to arise but rarely in practice, so that if rather worse conditions are assumed, a satisfactory stanchion section could be produced if the load factor chosen was reduced, for example, from 2 to $1 \cdot 25$. The stanchion, while safe under these impossibly rigorous conditions, would have a load factor greater than $1 \cdot 25$ under more normal loads. It was considered inadvisable to set out the method of design in this way ; instead, it was decided to retain the load factor of 2 used in plotting the curves in Figs. 18.13, 18.14 and 18.15, but to follow the lead set by earlier codes, and to reduce the specified live axial load assumed in all storeys below the topmost. If this reduction in the live axial load is justifiable, similar reduction is justifiable in the end moments due to the live load. This was arranged by omitting all the terms in M_{F2} from Table 18.5, thus giving a reduction which varies with the stiffness ratio but which never exceeds 20 per cent. This omission of the M_{F2} term is merely a device to secure a reduction in the total moment, while at the same time simplifying the calculation of that moment, and does not mean that the critical arrangements of load, which form the whole basis of this work, have in any way been altered.

The moments in topmost lengths of internal stanchions and in external stanchions need special treatment, which will not be discussed here, but it was not difficult to produce a table of suitably reduced moments which, if used in conjunction with the composite strut curve, brings about a considerable saving of labour. The amended moments are given in Tables 18.6 and 18.7.

In addition to the foregoing, provision had to be made for designing frames of all types. The Tables given above could only be compiled in their simple form on the assumption that all stanchion lengths in the same storey were of the same stiffness. It was found possible to specify correction factors for use when this condition did not exist, by which the tabulated moments could be multiplied to give safe values of the moments in any unsymmetrical frame (*Clause* 18 below). A further correction factor was needed when the intensity of load on the beam framing into the lower end of a stanchion length

TABLE 18.6.—TOTAL BENDING MOMENT DUE TO DEAD LOAD.

$\dfrac{K_{BR}+K_{BL}}{K_U+K_L}$.	Bottom length; $\left(\dfrac{\text{total moment}}{M_F^D}\right)$.	Intermediate length; $\left(\dfrac{\text{total moment}}{M_F^D}\right)$.	Topmost length; $\left(\dfrac{\text{total moment}}{M_F^D}\right)$.
0	0·862	1·000	1·000
0·1	0·820	0·975	0·957
0·2	0·783	0·950	0·918
0·3	0·752	0·920	0·882
0·4	0·725	0·893	0·852
0·5	0·697	0·865	0·822
0·6	0·671	0·842	0·794
0·7	0·648	0·820	0·769
0·8	0·627	0·798	0·745
0·9	0·606	0·776	0·722
1·0	0·589	0·754	0·704
1·25	0·545	0·709	0·659
1·5	0·511	0·669	0·619
1·75	0·482	0·632	0·583
2·0	0·452	0·601	0·555
2·5	0·405	0·546	0·503
3·0	0·367	0·500	0·461
3·5	0·336	0·462	0·426
4·0	0·310	0·429	0·396
5·0	0·268	0·375	0·349
6·0	0·236	0·333	0·310
7·0	0·211	0·300	0·279
8·0	0·191	0·273	0·256
10·0	—	—	0·227
12·0	—	—	0·197
14·0	—	—	0·174
16·0	—	—	0·156

was greater than that on the beam framing into the upper end (*Clause* 17 below).

The more important clauses in the Committee's recommendations setting out the method of stanchion design are :—

(11) For each stanchion length a steel section shall be chosen and its adequacy shall be tested by the method set out in Clauses 12–18.

(12) The total load (P) carried by each stanchion length shall be determined on the assumption that all beams are freely hinged at their ends.

(13) For the purpose of calculating the total load the live load for the roof and topmost storey shall be calculated in full, but for the lower storeys a reduction of the live loads may be allowed in accordance with the following Table :—

Next storey below topmost storey .	10 per cent. reduction of live load.
,, ,, ,, · · · ·	20 ,, ,, ,, ,, ,, ,,
,, ,, ,, · · · ·	30 ,, ,, ,, ,, ,, ,,
,, ,, ,, · · · ·	40 ,, ,, ,, ,, ,, ,,
All succeeding storeys · · · ·	50 ,, ,, ,, ,, ,, ,,

No such reduction shall be allowed on any floor scheduled for an applied loading of 100 lb. or more per square foot.

TABLE 18.7.—TOTAL BENDING MOMENT DUE TO LIVE LOAD.

$\dfrac{K_{BR}+K_{BL}}{K_U+K_L}$.	Bottom length ; $\left(\dfrac{\text{total moment}}{M_F^L}\right)$.	Intermediate length ; $\left(\dfrac{\text{total moment}}{M_F^L}\right)$.	Topmost length ; (total moment/M_F^L).	
			Internal stanchion	External stanchion
0	1·149	1·359	1·360	1·000
0·1	1·080	1·290	1·261	0·961
0·2	1·017	1·230	1·175	0·925
0·3	0·961	1·175	1·098	0·892
0·4	0·912	1·125	1·031	0·861
0·5	0·871	1·082	0·968	0·834
0·6	0·834	1·043	0·915	0·807
0·7	0·796	1·004	0·869	0·781
0·8	0·763	0·968	0·823	0·759
0·9	0·732	0·934	0·782	0·738
1·0	0·706	0·904	0·746	0·720
1·25	0·648	0·837	0·669	0·673
1·5	0·596	0·780	0·602	0·635
1·75	0·554	0·729	0·548	0·601
2·0	0·516	0·687	0·503	0·570
2·5	0·456	0·615	0·431	0·517
3·0	0·408	0·556	0·390	0·474
3·5	0·370	0·508	0·358	0·436
4·0	0·338	0·468	0·334	0·407
5·0	0·289	0·404	0·293	0·357
6·0	0·252	0·356	0·261	0·318
7·0	0·224	0·318	0·235	0·287
8·0	0·210	0·287	0·214	0·261
10·0	—	—	0·181	0·222
12·0	—	—	0·157	0·193
14·0	—	—	0·139	0·171
16·0	—	—	0·124	0·153

(14) The axial load in tons per square inch of gross cross-sectional area of steel (p) shall be determined.

(16) Where the fixed-end moments of the beams framing into the upper and lower ends of a stanchion length are the same in each bay and where each of these beams is attached at its remote end to a stanchion having a relevant stiffness at least as great as that of the stanchion under consideration, the procedure shall be as follows :—

(1) M_{FX}^D, the moment about the XX axis of the stanchion due to dead load on the beams attached to the upper end of the stanchion length, shall be calculated. M_{FX}^D shall be the algebraic sum of the resolved components, about the XX axis of the stanchion, of the fixed-end moments at the ends, attached to the stanchion, of these beams and of the moments about the XX axis of the stanchion due to the reactions at their ends. The total moment on the stanchion about its XX axis at the upper end of the stanchion length due to the dead load shall then be determined from Table 18.6 for the appropriate value of the stiffness ratio $\dfrac{K_{BR}+K_{BL}}{K_U+K_L}$, where K_L and K_U are the relevant stiffnesses, that is in this case about the XX axis, of the stanchion length under consideration and of the one above, and K_{BR} and K_{BL} are the relevant stiffnesses

of the beams, that is in this case the stiffnesses of the beams framing into the upper end of the stanchion length at right angles to the XX axis of the stanchion.

(2) In the same way the maximum moment M_{FX}^L about the XX axis of the stanchion due to the most unfavourable arrangement of live load on the beams attached to the upper end of the stanchion length shall be calculated. The total moment on the stanchion about its XX axis at the upper end of the stanchion length due to live load shall then be determined from Table 18.7.

(3) The end bending moment in the stanchion length about its XX axis shall be taken as the sum of the dead and live load total moments determined in *Clause* 16 (1)–(2) multiplied by the ratio of the relevant stiffness of the stanchion length under consideration to the sum of the relevant stiffnesses of that stanchion length and of the one above. The maximum bending stress in the steel section at the upper end of the stanchion length due to this end bending moment shall be calculated.

(4) The same procedure as that set out in *Clause* 16 (1)–(3) shall be adopted for the determination of the maximum end bending stress due to the moments about the YY axis.

(5) Where a beam makes a skew connexion to a stanchion the fixed-end moment at the end of the beam shall, for the determination of M_F^D and M_F^L, be resolved into its components about the XX and YY axes of the stanchion, and the relevant stiffnesses of the beam shall be the stiffness of the beam multiplied by the sines of the angles between the axis of the beam and the XX and YY axes of the stanchion respectively.

(6) The total end bending stress shall be taken as the sum of the maximum end bending stresses calculated under *Clause* 16 (1)–(5). The magnitude of this total end bending stress shall not exceed the value given for the stanchion length, as defined by its slenderness ratio (L/r_y), by the curve of Fig. 18.15 appropriate to the axial load per unit area (p).

(17) Where the fixed-end moment of a beam framing into the lower end of a stanchion length is greater than the fixed-end moment of the corresponding beam framing into the upper end, the fixed-end moment of the upper beam shall be increased in the ratio $\dfrac{2+V}{3}$, where V is the ratio of the fixed-end moment of the lower beam to that of the upper. This increased moment shall be used in the determination of the total end bending stress at the upper end of the stanchion length. The total end bending stress at the lower end of the stanchion length shall also be determined using the actual values of the fixed-end moments of the beams framing into the lower end of the stanchion length. The greater of these two end bending stresses shall then be taken as the total end bending stress to be used in determining the adequacy of the section as in *Clause* 16 (6).

(18) (1) Where a beam frames at its remote end into the web of another beam, the fixed-end moment at the end of the beam attached to the stanchion shall be increased by the appropriate correction factor as given in Table 18.8.

TABLE 18.8.—CORRECTION FACTOR (CONNEXION TO
BEAM AT REMOTE END).

$\dfrac{K_{BR}+K_{BL}}{K_U+K_L}$	Factor
0·1	1·47
0·5	1·36
1·0	1·29
2·0	1·20
4·0	1·13
8·0	1·07
16·0	1·04

(2) Where a beam frames at its remote end into a stanchion of less stiffness than the stanchion under consideration, the fixed-end moment shall be increased by the appropriate correction factor (Table 18.9). Where the stiffness of the stanchion at the remote end is not less than one-half that of the stanchion under consideration no correction factor need be used. Where the beam frames into the flange of the stanchion under consideration and is attached at its remote end to the web of another stanchion, the section of which is not known, the ratio (S) shall be taken as $\frac{1}{16}$.

No mention has so far been made of the steps to be taken when dealing with horizontal or wind loads.

It was recommended by the Steel Structures Research Committee that the method of design described above should apply " to the steel framework of building structures formed with horizontal girders and vertical columns and provides only for the stresses caused by vertical forces. Any structure for

TABLE 18.9.—CORRECTION FACTOR (CONNEXION TO STANCHION AT REMOTE END).

$\dfrac{K_{BR}+K_{BL}}{K_U+K_L}$	Stiffness ratio S			
	$\frac{1}{16}$	$\frac{1}{8}$	$\frac{1}{4}$	$\frac{1}{2}$
0·1	1·27	1·18	1·10	1·04
0·5	1·30	1·25	1·18	1·09
1·0	1·25	1·22	1·17	1·09
2·0	1·18	1·16	1·14	1·08
4·0	1·11	1·10	1·09	1·05
8·0	1·07	1·06	1·05	1·03
16·0	1·04	1·03	1·03	1·02

$$S = \frac{\text{Sum of stiffnesses of upper and lower stanchion lengths at remote end of beam.}}{\text{Sum of stiffnesses of upper and lower stanchion lengths at end under consideration.}}$$

which the method of design is used must be so constructed as to resist horizontal forces due to wind or other causes, without significant horizontal sway, by means of its floor slabs in association with vertical walls or braced vertical frames."

This decision was based on the evidence provided by a lengthy investigation of the effect of wind loads on frames having semi-rigid connexions.   It was found that the bending moments in the stanchions due to wind loads increased rapidly in magnitude as the connexions departed from the condition of complete rigidity.   It was considered desirable to relieve such frames of the stresses arising from wind shear and therefore, where floors and walls do not supply adequate bracing, special wind bents are demanded.

REFERENCES

Steel Structures Research Committee, First Report, 1931.   H.M.S.O.

Batho, C. and Rowan, H. C.   1934.   Steel Structures Research Committee, Second Report, H.M.S.O.

Baker, J. F.   1954.   " The Steel Skeleton," *Vol. I, Elastic Behaviour and Design.* Camb. Univ. Press.

Conference on the correlation between calculated and observed stresses and displacements in structures.   Prel. Vol. 1955.   Instn. Civ. Engrs.

CHAPTER 19

THE THEORY OF MASONRY DAMS

19.1. Function and types of dams.—In the conservation of water, either for domestic or power purposes, it is often necessary to form an artificial lake by building a barrier across a valley. This barrier or dam can be made in various ways. One type is an earthen embankment with a central core wall of impermeable clay or concrete carried in a trench down to a sound rock foundation. The design of such dams is largely a matter of experience, although the increase in knowledge of soil mechanics in recent years has led to a much better appreciation of the principles underlying their behaviour and resulted in the establishment of a scientific basis of design. A different type of structure is the dam built of masonry or concrete ; this may be a gravity dam which relies upon the weight and disposition of the material to resist the water pressure ; an arch dam consisting of a single arch spanning the valley and abutting on its sides, or a dam consisting of a number of arches with artificial buttresses of masonry to take the thrusts of intermediate spans. Since the design of earth banks can be more suitably treated in works on soil mechanics than in those dealing with general theory of structures and the theory of the arch dam is very complicated and demands lengthy design computations, attention will be mainly directed in the present book to the theory of masonry dams of the gravity type. Fig. 19.1 shows the profile of such a dam; the water pressure acts on the face AB which is known as the back of the dam. The downstream face, CD, is the front of the dam. The points at which a horizontal section such as EF cuts the front and back of the profile are, respectively, the toe and heel of that section. The height of the top of the dam above the spillway level, a, is known as the freeboard.

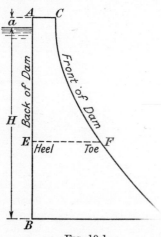

Fig. 19.1.

19.2. Development of design principles.—The earliest enunciations of the principles underlying the design of gravity dams were made by French civil engineers of the nineteenth century. In 1853 Sazilly suggested that only two types of failure needed consideration ; the first was the possibility that the section of the dam above any plane such as EF in Fig. 19.1 might slide relative to the section below it, and the second that the compressive stress developed when the reservoir was full of water might be greater than the material could stand without crushing. The first of these conditions was not considered to be of primary interest, since there was no record of any failure of this type, and so control of compressive stress became effectively the only canon of design. A third danger was, however, envisaged, namely that the dam might overturn about the toe of any section under the pressure of the impounded water.

These simple criteria were considered sufficient until, in 1870, Professor W. M. Rankine was consulted about the design of the Periyar dam in India and took the opportunity to make a study of the general problem. In a report of historical importance (Rankine, 1872), he introduced two new ideas into the theory.   The first of these related to the allowable compressive stress : it had been customary, and is still the practice, to calculate only the vertical component of such stresses and the French engineers, Graeff and Delocre, had assumed that the same permissible value could be assigned to both the heel and toe.   Rankine, however, pointed out that the principal stress was larger than that calculated by usual methods, and, since the batters of the back and front of the dam were different, it was unreasonable to adopt the same value for the allowable vertical components at both points. The front of the dam has a much flatter slope than the back, which is usually nearly vertical, and so the vertical component at the toe must be less than that at the heel if the masonry is to be equally stressed for the two conditions of the reservoir full and empty.

Far more important, however, than this correction of current ideas about compressive stresses was the dictum that since mortar was weak in tension, no tensile stresses ought to be allowed anywhere in the dam.   The acceptance of this view leads to the formulation of the middle-third rule with which Rankine is usually credited.   In fact, Navier had enunciated it in 1826 and Mery in 1840 applied it to arch design, but Rankine appears to have been first to adopt the no-tension condition as a criterion in the design of dams. The particular profile which he proposed as a result of his investigation will be dealt with later in this chapter.

In 1895 the failure of the Bouzey dam near Epinal in France, directed attention to the dangers of providing inadequate strength in such structures. Unwin, after investigation, recorded his opinion that Bouzey was the first and only case on record of a high dam failing by overturning (Unwin, 1896). The failure assumed particular importance in this country in view of interest in the new Vyrnwy dam for the Manchester and Liverpool water supply, and considerable controversy developed upon the criterion of safety which ought to be adopted.

In 1904, Atcherley and Karl Pearson propounded a completely new and startling theory.   They suggested that tensile stress might be developed on vertical planes as well as on horizontal and that if such a possibility were taken into account, as it ought to be, the profile would be considerably modified.   The discussion aroused by this theory has been summarised elsewhere (Pippard, 1950), and by the time it had ended in 1908 with the rejection of the new ideas, the theory of gravity dams seemed to have been placed on a reasonably sound scientific basis, and it was generally accepted that the principal factors in safeguarding such structures were to ensure that the compressive stress did not at any point exceed the safe value, either when the reservoir was full or empty, and, secondly, that at no point in the structure was tensile stress allowed.   Since the second criterion meant that the resultant force fell within the middle third of the base, the danger of the dam overturning was automatically eliminated.

An American engineer based a complete design method on these principles

(Wegmann, 1888) and this appeared to be the last word on the subject. Later, however, another factor assumed importance which will be discussed in the next paragraph.

19.3. Uplift in masonry dams.—Since masonry and concrete are porous, water will percolate through a dam from the back to the front, and this percolation is increased by small cracks or fissures in the material. This occurs at all levels, but is probably most pronounced at the base section where the dam meets the foundation rock. At the heel of any section the pore water pressure corresponds to the head of water above the section, and at the toe it is equivalent to the head of tail water there, or if above tail water level, it is zero : there is a drop from one to the other through the dam. The pressure in the pores exerts uplift on the structure and must be taken into account in design. This question was discussed in a course of lectures given at the University of London (Hellstrom, 1936), and we cannot do better than quote the lecturer. He says in reference to concrete dams :—

"A controversial question in connexion with the design of gravity dams is the uplift pressures. It is no exaggeration to say that many failures of such dams are due to the fact that no account was taken of uplift pressure. In my opinion, it is a crime not to pay due attention to uplift pressure, even if the foundation of the dam is first-class hard rock without visible fissures, and even if grouting has been carried out.

" The measures generally taken to reduce the uplift pressure are as follows : providing the dam with a cut-off trench filled with concrete near the upstream face of the dam, placing drains along the downstream side of this trench and along the foundation where fissures exist and providing drainage in the dam itself, either in the form of vertical drain pipes near the upstream face at a comparatively short distance from each other or arranging for large drainage galleries through the whole body of the dam.

" Measurements of uplift pressure at existing dams have shown conclusively that, so far as foundation level is concerned, uplift forces do exist, even in cases where the foundation rock has been grouted and drainage has been provided.

" The uplift force with which the designer of dams is principally concerned is a product of pressure and area. It is often argued that the latter factor is of greater importance than the former, but the determination of the area over which uplift pressure is exerted is far more difficult than the measurement of the pressure itself. So far no satisfactory information has been obtained regarding the proportion of the total horizontal base area on which the measured uplift pressures act. All that is known is that they cannot act on more than the full area, but nothing is known of the effective area at the base of the dam where concrete comes into contact with rock."

After a discussion of suggested methods for allowing for uplift, Hellstrom continues :—

" Other American engineers calculate with 100 per cent. uplift intensity at the upstream face, reducing it to 50 per cent. at the drainage gallery, if any, near the upstream face, and taking it as varying by a straight line to zero or tail water pressure at the downstream face, assuming the uplift pressure as acting on the full area at all points (Houk, 1932).

" Terzaghi has made certain interesting experiments to determine the uplift pressure (1934). These experiments and investigations have shown that the effective area on which uplift may act in concrete is practically 100 per cent.

" Horizontal construction joints in a dam are always vulnerable points. Moreover, there is never any guarantee that some more or less horizontal layers in a concrete between such joints may not occasionally be of inferior quality and more or less porous. Water may get into such layers directly, or through vertical cracks which are often found in dams near the foundation. As it has been found that also horizontal cracks may occur, and that, as will be referred to later, deterioration of the concrete particularly near the upstream face is possible, there seems to be no reason why, if all these circumstances are taken into account, safe assumptions should not be made for the design of all dams and especially for such important dams where large quantities of water, if suddenly released, would cause appreciable damage. In Sweden for the last three decades or so, gravity dams have been designed to withstand uplift pressure varying in a straight line from 100 per cent. water pressure at the upstream face to 100 per cent. tail water pressure at the downstream face, acting upon 100 per cent. of the base area. The additional quantity of concrete required to make the dam able to withstand such uplift pressure calculated over the whole area is not considerable, and the extra margin of safety from failure that may thereby be attained is to be recommended."

More recently, a report has been published by a Sub-Committee of the American Society of Civil Engineers (1952) who reviewed the data available for masonry dams and made certain suggestions. Unfortunately, the evidence was not sufficient for the Committee to prepare a specific code for dealing with the effects of uplift, and to this extent their report is inconclusive. A majority came to the opinion that when designing a new dam it was advisable to assume that the uplift pressure affected the whole area of the dam at any level and that in small structures, at least, it would be advisable to assume that this pressure varied linearly from the full hydrostatic head at the heel to the actual pressure at the toe. If, in a large structure, foundation conditions were such, in the opinion of the engineer, as to justify the same assumption, the Committee considered that these conditions should be improved by grouting, drainage and other measures. Some members, however, expressed the view that these proposals, which are the same as those suggested by Hellstrom, were too drastic. There is thus no consensus of opinion in this matter but it would appear prudent, in the absence of adequate drainage in a dam, to adopt the conservative view indicated. It should be observed in this connexion that in the opinion of the American Committee no credit for drainage systems should be allowed unless there is adequate assurance that the drains will be properly inspected and maintained.

The American report deals only with masonry dams and concrete structures are specifically excluded. The Committee in fact recommended that a new Committee should be set up to deal with the problem of uplift in such dams. The remarks quoted from the lectures by Hellstrom, on the other hand, relate to concrete dams so that in the absence of further data it would appear that the same assumptions can be applied to both masonry and concrete.

19.4. Assumptions as to stress distribution in masonry.—If a masonry dam and its foundation be assumed to consist of a homogeneous mass of elastic material the stresses at any point in it can be calculated, provided that the conditions of loading on all the faces are known exactly. The calculation is laborious and difficult and in general is unnecessary.

It may be assumed with reasonable accuracy for all sections of a dam except in the immediate neighbourhood of the abutments that there are little or no shearing forces on transverse vertical sections, or, in other words, any section of the dam between two such sections may be assumed to be in equilibrium under its own weight, the water pressure on the back and the reactive forces from the foundation.

The forces due to the water pressure are known accurately, and since the face of the dam is exposed to the air there can be no normal or tangential stresses at any point on this boundary. There remain the reactive forces from the foundation and, from the nature of the problem, it is quite impossible for these to be known accurately.

If the dam is assumed to be rigid it can sink bodily or rotate under the action of the forces on it but no movements it may undergo can distort the base boundary ; if this was initially a straight line it will remain straight. If the foundation is perfectly elastic it follows, since the reaction at any point is proportional to the displacement, that the vertical reactive stresses upon the base of the dam follow a linear law. If the dam is not rigid, or the foundation not perfectly elastic, this distribution will be modified, but since it is impossible to know the elastic condition of the foundation an exact distribution cannot be determined. It is therefore customary to assume a linear variation of normal stress across any horizontal section of the profile. It should be realised that this is no more than assumption and that the whole of the existing theory of masonry dams is built upon it.

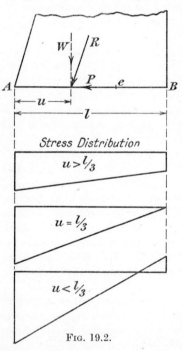

FIG. 19.2.

Evidence obtained by more exact methods will be referred to later and the justification for this assumption discussed.

In Fig. 19.2 let AB be any horizontal section of a dam and let the resultant of the weight and water pressure for unit length of the dam be R, the line of action of R cutting AB at u from A. Let the length of AB be l.

R can be resolved into its two components W, acting normal to AB and P, acting along BA. P is a shearing force and its effect will be considered later. W is a load applied normally to a rectangular section of width unity and depth l ; the eccentricity is $\frac{l}{2} - u$. The direct compressive stress on this base section is $\frac{W}{l}$ and the maximum stress due to the bending moment $W\left(\frac{l}{2} - u\right)$

is
$$\pm \frac{6W}{l^2}\left(\frac{l}{2} - u\right) = \pm \frac{3W}{l}\left(1 - \frac{2u}{l}\right).$$

Hence the maximum compressive stress, at A, is $\dfrac{2W}{l}\left(2-\dfrac{3u}{l}\right)$ and the minimum compressive stress, at B, is $\dfrac{2W}{l}\left(\dfrac{3u}{l}-1\right)$. If $u=l/3$ the minimum compressive stress is zero and the maximum compressive stress is $\dfrac{2W}{l}$ If $\dfrac{2l}{3}>u>\dfrac{3}{l}$ the stress everywhere is compressive and if $u<l/3$ tensile stress is developed at the point B. The three cases are shown in Fig. 19.2.

Hence, if tensile stress is to be eliminated, the line of action of the resultant force must cut the base section within the middle third of its length.

A simple illustration of the application of the middle-third rule is to be found in the determination of the necessary base width B of a trapezoidal dam of height H and top width b. The back is vertical and water is supposed to reach to the top of the dam. By taking moments about the vertical back, the centre of gravity of the profile from that datum is

$$\bar{x}=\frac{B^2+Bb+b^2}{3(B+b)}.$$

The weight of one foot length of the dam is

$$W=\frac{(B+b)Hw_m}{2},$$

where w_m is the density of the masonry, and the over-turning moment due to the water pressure on one foot length of the dam is

$$M=\frac{wH^3}{6},$$

where w is the density of the water.

When the reservoir is full the line of resistance must cut the base section at $2B/3$ from the heel if there is to be zero stress at the heel. The distance between the lines of resistance for the reservoir empty and full is therefore

$$v=\frac{2B}{3}-\bar{x}=\frac{B^2+Bb-b^2}{3(B+b)}.$$

Equating the overturning moment of the water pressure to the restoring moment due to the weight of the dam, $i.e.$ $M=Wv$, we find

$$H^2=\rho(B^2+Bb-b^2),$$

where ρ is the specific gravity of the masonry.

Or, if α be written for b/B,

$$B=\frac{H}{\sqrt{\rho}}\frac{1}{\sqrt{1+\alpha-\alpha^2}}$$

The value of the denominator is the same for $\alpha=\alpha_1$, and for $\alpha=1-\alpha_1$ so there are two trapezoidal profiles of given height H and the same base width B which comply with the no-tension condition. One of them has a top width b and the other a top width $B-b$. The minimum value of the base width occurs when $\alpha=\frac{1}{2}$ and is $2H/\sqrt{5\rho}$. If $\alpha=0$ or 1 the base width is $H/\sqrt{\rho}$, $i.e.$ the extreme complementary trapezoidal sections are triangular and rectangular with the same base widths.

The middle-third rule follows directly from the assumption of a linear stress distribution : it is not true for any other. It was pointed out in a paper referred to previously (Atcherley and Pearson, 1904), that if this assumption is adopted it follows with almost equal validity that the distribution of shear stress across the horizontal section arising from the pressure is parabolic. This will be dealt with in paragraph 19.8.

19.5. Analysis of an existing profile.—Before discussing various profiles which have been suggested it is advisable to examine a method for analysing a section already proposed since it is quite usual procedure to draw a profile, analyse it to determine whether the essential points have been adequately

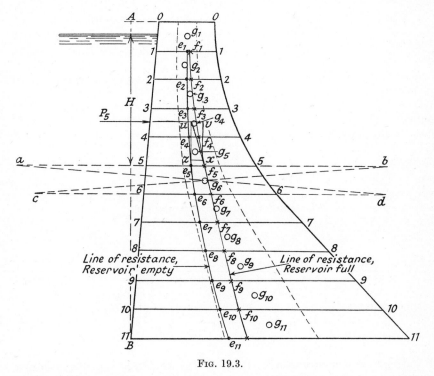

Fig. 19.3.

covered and modify it by a process of trial and error until a satisfactory design is achieved.

If the profile in Fig. 19.3 is to be analysed, the procedure is as follows. Divide the profile into a number of sections by horizontal lines 11, 22, ... etc., sufficiently closely spaced for the front and back of the dam to be considered as formed by straight lines between successive sections.

Find the centre of area of each of the trapeziums thus formed : this may be done graphically as shown for 5566 by making $5a = 5b = 66$ and $6c = 6d = 55$ and joining ad and bc. The intersection of these lines at g_6 is the centre of area.

Consider now a length of one foot along the dam and calculate the weights of the portions of the dam between successive sections : these weights act through g_1, g_2, etc., and will be denoted by w_1, w_2, etc. If a vertical from g_1 meets 11 at e_1, e_1 is the point where w_1, the resultant of the weights above 11, acts when the reservoir is empty and its position determines the distribution of stress across 11 for this condition. The resultant of w_1 and w_2 acting through g_1 and g_2 respectively, must now be found and this is done most accurately by taking moments of these weights about a line such as AB. It may be found graphically by a link polygon but direct calculation is preferable. This resultant cuts 22 at e_2 and the process is continued for each section in turn to find $e_3, e_4 \ldots e_{11}$. The line through $e_1, e_2 \ldots e_{11}$ is known as the line of resistance for the reservoir empty and must cut any section within the middle third of its width if tension at the toe is to be avoided when the reservoir above that section is empty.

A corresponding line of resistance for the reservoir full must also be found and section 55 will be taken to illustrate the method. The resultant weight $w_1+w_2+w_3+w_4+w_5=W_5$ say, above this section, acts through the centre of area of 0055 which has already been found. The pressure on the back of the dam above section 55 is $P_5=\dfrac{w\mathrm{H}^2}{2}$ where w is the density of the water, and this acts at $H/3$ above 55. It is usual to assume this to be always horizontal and to make no allowance for the fact that there is a downward component due to the batter of the back ; this assumption is on the side of safety. The line of action of the pressure P_5 is produced to cut that of W_5 at u ; uv and uz are made proportional to P_5 and W_5 respectively and the resultant given by ux cuts the section 55 at f_5 which is a point on the line of resistance for the reservoir full. This is done for all sections and the complete line $f_1, f_2 \ldots f_{11}$ is obtained.

For the elimination of tension at the heel when the reservoir is full this line must cut every section within the middle third.

The maximum compressive stress at any section can be obtained once these lines of resistance are found : let the appropriate line of resistance for the reservoir empty cut any section, say 55, at c from the mid-point of the section. Then if l_5 is the width of that section the direct compressive stress on it is W_5/l_5 lb. per square foot, since we consider one foot of the dam.

The bending stress is
$$\frac{\mathrm{M}y}{\mathrm{I}}=\frac{6c\mathrm{W}_5}{l_5^2},$$

and the total maximum compressive stress is
$$\frac{\mathrm{W}_5}{l_5}\left(1+\frac{6c}{l_5}\right).$$

19.6. The Rankine profile.—Reference has already been made in paragraph 19.2 to the report made by Professor W. M. Rankine upon the choice of a profile for the Periyar dam in India, and his work in this connexion will now be considered in more detail. The profile is often referred to as if it were of general application but in fact it was designed for a particular height and upon certain specific assumptions. In the Report, after a preliminary discussion on methods of construction, allowable stresses, etc., Rankine summarises the conditions to be satisfied in his design as follows :—

(1) The vertical intensity of compressive stress at the back of the dam is not to exceed that due to a column of masonry 160 feet high.

(2) The vertical intensity of compressive stress at the front is not to exceed that due to a column of masonry 125 feet high at the point where it is a

maximum and is to diminish below that point. This was to allow for the steadily increasing batter.

(3) The lines of resistance when the reservoir is full and empty respectively must lie within or near to the middle third of the thickness of the dam.

The limits set to the compressive stresses were determined by reference to the dam across the River Furens.

Rankine points out that these conditions do not specify exactly any particular profile but are limits which must be satisfied in the chosen design. He thus makes it clear that a number of different profiles can be found to comply with the specification and explains that in his selection of a particular form which will fulfil the conditions he was guided by the consideration that one which lent itself to easy calculation of areas and centres of gravity was preferable to a more complex one if equally satisfactory in other respects. He therefore chose logarithmic curves to define the front, back and centre lines of the profile and the result is shown in Fig. 19.4. The thickness at a depth of 120 feet was made 84 feet of which one-fourteenth, or 6 feet, lies upstream of OX, the common asymptote of all three curves, and thirteen-fourteenths, or 78 feet, lie downstream of OX.

The thickness of the dam at any depth x below the top is given by

$$t = t_1 e^{\frac{x - x_1}{a}} \quad . \quad . \quad . \quad . \quad . \quad . \quad (19.1)$$

where t_1 is the specified thickness (84 feet) at the depth x_1 (120 feet), a is the constant sub-tangent, common to all three curves, and is 80 feet.

The formula can be expressed in common logarithms in the form

$$\log t = \log t_1 + 0 \cdot 4343 \left(\frac{x - x_1}{a} \right) \quad . \quad . \quad . \quad . \quad (19.2)$$

The total width of the dam at any depth can then be calculated, and at every section one-fourteenth of this width lies upstream and the remainder downstream of the vertical asymptote OX.

Putting $x = 0$ in the equation, the top width of the dam t_0 is found to be $18 \cdot 74$ feet and the fact that the formula gave a width suitable for a roadway was one of the factors which influenced Rankine in his choice.

The area of any section of the dam from the top down to a depth x is

$$\int_0^x t\,dx = a(t - t_0).$$

Rankine shows from the properties of the logarithmic curves chosen that the vertical line through the centre of gravity of a section above a given level is midway between the middle of the thickness at that level and the middle of the top thickness.

The moment of the water pressure, assuming the back of the dam to be vertical, acting on a section x below the top is $wx^3/6$ and so the distance between the lines of pressure for the reservoir full and empty at any depth x is this moment due to the water pressure divided by the weight of the dam above the section, i.e.,

$$\frac{wx^3}{6w_m \int t\,dx} = \frac{x^3}{6\rho a(t - t_0)}$$

where ρ is the specific gravity of the masonry. This was assumed by Rankine to be 2 and as a result the distance between the two lines of resistance was $x^3/12a(t - t_0)$, and both can be plotted very easily. The mean intensity of pressure on the masonry at any section is, from the equation

for the area, $w_m a\left(1-\dfrac{t_0}{t}\right)$ and on the usual assumption of linear stress distri-

bution across the section the maximum intensity of compressive stress is

$$p=w_m a\left(1-\frac{t_0}{t}\right)\left(1+\frac{6r}{t}\right),$$

where r is the distance of the line of resistance from the middle of the section.

Rankine concluded his report by giving rules for profiles of other depths and these will be summarised. The profile shown in the figure can be used economically for depths of 180 feet to 110 feet. Between this latter depth and 80 or 90 feet the waste of material is unimportant but for depths

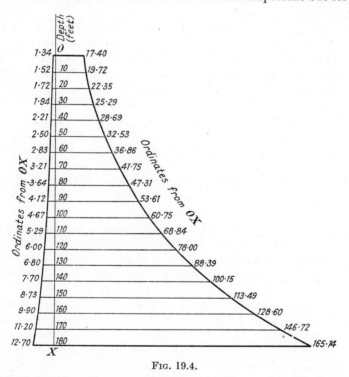

FIG. 19.4.

much less than 90 feet there is excessive strength. As an example, if the profile be used for a dam only 50 feet high, 40 per cent. more material than necessary will be required. For a dam less than 120 feet in height he suggested the following method. Construct a profile for 120 feet " with all the thicknesses and ordinates diminished in the same proportion with the depth. The intensity of the vertical pressure at each point will be diminished in the same proportion also, but this does not imply waste of material, the whole strength of the material being required in order that there will be no appreciable tension in any part of the wall."

As a final check on the design to discover to what extent the conditions prescribed by himself had been satisfied, Rankine made calculations of the stresses at different levels. He found that the compressive values were equivalent to heights of masonry of 154 and 124 feet at the back and front

16

of the dam respectively, instead of the prescribed values of 160 and 125 feet, and that there were some small deviations outside the middle third indicating a small amount of tension but not sufficient to be of practical importance.

The necessary dimensions for plotting this profile are given on Fig. 19.4.

19.7. The Wegmann profile.—A direct method for determining the profile of a gravity dam is, as already stated in paragraph 19.2, due to E. Wegmann and was used by him in the design of actual structures. It is claimed that this method gives the minimum weight of material to withstand any specified head of water. The equations are in some instances rather cumbersome, but their solution is quite simple. Every dam, according to its height, is divided into five or fewer stages, the controlling condition in each stage being a different one.

Stage I.—This is a top section, rectangular in profile. The top width of the dam, fixed by practical considerations such as the roadway to be built across it, will govern the height of this section. The limit of this stage will be reached when the line of resultant action for the reservoir full cuts the base section at the middle-third point since, if the rectangular profile be continued beyond this, tensile stress will be developed at the heel.

Stage II.—In this stage the front of the dam is battered sufficiently to ensure that the line of resultant action for the reservoir full always cuts a horizontal section at the front middle-third point. The limit of this stage is reached when the line of resultant action for the reservoir empty cuts the base at the back middle-third point. If the back of the dam is made vertical below this section, tensile stress will be developed at the toe when the reservoir is empty.

Stage III.—The front of the dam is battered to comply with the condition in Stage II and the back to a sufficient extent to eliminate tensile stress at any section when the reservoir is empty above that section. The limit of this stage is reached when the compressive stress at the toe of the dam for the reservoir full reaches a prescribed value.

Stage IV.—In this stage the batter on the front of the dam is increased sufficiently to keep the compressive stress at the toe at the prescribed value, while the batter on the back is made sufficient to eliminate tension at the toe as in Stage III. The limit of this stage is reached when the compressive stress at the heel for the reservoir empty reaches its prescribed value. This value is generally higher than that for the toe for the reasons given earlier in this chapter.

Stage V.—The batters for both front and back of the dam are governed in this final stage by the necessity of keeping the compressive stresses in the masonry to the prescribed values when the reservoir is empty and full.

The general method of design is to fix the required top width of the dam and the necessary freeboard. An equation can then be obtained for determining the height of Stage I. A horizontal section at some arbitrary depth below the bottom section of Stage I is next considered and another formula determines the width of the dam at this point. The process is repeated step by step, until a criterion for the position of the line of resultant action for the reservoir empty shows that the limit of Stage II has been reached.

Corresponding formulas and appropriate criteria for the other stages are similarly used until the required depth below top waterlevel has been reached.

The details of the method will be best understood by a study of the worked example given later.

Fig. 19.5 represents a section of the profile of a dam in any stage.

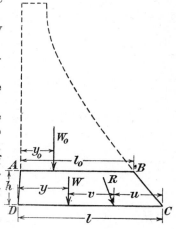

Let l_0 be the width of the dam already determined,

   l,   the width of the section to be calculated,

   h,   the arbitrary distance between these sections,

   u,   the distance from the toe to the line of resultant action for the reservoir full on the lower section,

   v,   the distance between the lines of resultant action for the reservoir full and empty measured along the lower section,

   y,   the distance from the heel to the line of resultant action for the reservoir empty on the lower section,

FIG. 19.5.

   y_0,   the corresponding distance for the upper section,

   A_0,   the area of the profile above AB,

   A,   the area of the profile above DC,

   W_0, the weight of masonry above AB per unit length of dam,

   W,   the weight of masonry above DC per unit length of dam,

   ρ,   the specific gravity of the material of the dam,

   w,   the density of water

and H, the head of water above DC.

Then
$$l = u + v + y, \qquad \cdots \qquad (19.3)$$

$$A = A_0 + \left(\frac{l + l_0}{2}\right) h \qquad \cdots \qquad (19.4)$$

and
$$W = \rho w \left\{ A_0 + \left(\frac{l + l_0}{2}\right) h \right\} \qquad \cdots \qquad (19.5)$$

By equating the overturning moment of the water pressure about the point where the line of resultant action for the reservoir full cuts the lower section to the restoring moment of W about the same point, we have

$$\frac{w H^3}{6} = W v,$$

or
$$v = \frac{H^3}{6\rho \left\{ A_0 + \left(\frac{l + l_0}{2}\right) h \right\}} \qquad \cdots \qquad (19.6)$$

We can now deduce the equations for the different stages.

Stage I.—Let the top width of dam $= L$
         and the freeboard $= a$.

In this stage, which is rectangular,

$$l=l_0=\mathrm{L},$$
$$y=l/2$$

and u must not be less than $l/3$.

At a depth of water H let u reach the limiting value of $l/3$. Then substituting these values of u and y and that for v from equation (19.6) in equation (19.3) we have

$$l=\frac{l}{3}+\frac{\mathrm{H}^3}{6\rho\left\{\mathrm{A_0}+\left(\dfrac{l+l_0}{2}\right)h\right\}}+\frac{l}{2}.$$

Also since $h=\mathrm{H}+a$, $\mathrm{A_0}=0$ and $l=l_0=\mathrm{L}$
we obtain

$$\mathrm{H}^3=\rho\mathrm{L}^2(\mathrm{H}+a) \quad . \quad . \quad . \quad . \quad (19.7)$$

which determines H.

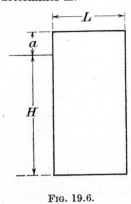

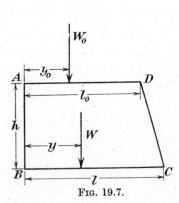

FIG. 19.6.   FIG. 19.7.

In the special case when $a=0$ this reduces to

$$\mathrm{H}=\mathrm{L}\sqrt{\rho}. \quad . \quad . \quad . \quad . \quad (19.8)$$

Stage II.—The back is vertical and the front battered to keep the line of resultant pressure on the middle-third point when the reservoir is full.

So $u=l/3$
and $y>l/3$ with a limiting value $y=l/3$.

To determine an expression for y we take moments of the area of profile as shown in Fig. 19.7 about the vertical face and obtain

$$\mathrm{A}y=\mathrm{A_0}y_0+\text{moment of trapezium ABCD.}$$

But moment of ABCD $=\dfrac{hl_0^2}{2}+\dfrac{(l-l_0)h}{2}\left\{l_0+\dfrac{l-l_0}{3}\right\}$

$$=\frac{h}{6}(l_0^2+ll_0+l^2).$$

$\therefore$ $\mathrm{A}y=\mathrm{A_0}y_0+\dfrac{h}{6}(l_0^2+ll_0+l^2),$

or $y=\dfrac{\mathrm{A_0}y_0+\dfrac{h}{6}(l_0^2+ll_0+l^2)}{\mathrm{A_0}+\left(\dfrac{l+l_0}{2}\right)h} \quad . \quad . \quad . \quad . \quad (19.9)$

which must be not less than $l/3$.

From equation (19.3)

$$l=\frac{l}{3}+\frac{H^3}{6\rho\left\{A_0+\left(\frac{l+l_0}{2}\right)h\right\}}+\frac{A_0y_0+\frac{h}{6}(l_0{}^2+ll_0+l^2)}{A_0+\left(\frac{l+l_0}{2}\right)h}$$

which reduces to

$$l^2+l\left(\frac{4A_0}{h}+l_0\right)=\frac{1}{h}\left(\frac{H^3}{\rho}+6A_0y_0\right)+l_0{}^2 \quad . \quad . \quad . \quad (19.10)$$

This quadratic determines l for any arbitrary value of h. This is substituted in equation (19.9) and if y is greater than $l/3$ the value of h chosen is such as to lie within Stage II.

This value of l is then taken as l_0 for determining the length of the next section by repeating the calculation. The process is continued until a depth is reached for which the calculated value of l on substitution in equation (19.9) gives $y=l/3$. The limit of Stage II has then been reached.

Stage III.—In which the no-tension condition is observed both for the reservoir full and empty. At each section in this stage therefore the limiting values are

$$y=l/3$$

and

$$u=l/3.$$

$\therefore$

$$l=\frac{l}{3}+\frac{H^3}{6\rho\left\{A_0+\left(\frac{l+l_0}{2}\right)h\right\}}+\frac{l}{3}$$

which gives

$$l^2+l\left(\frac{2A_0}{h}+l_0\right)=\frac{H^3}{\rho h} \quad . \quad . \quad . \quad . \quad (19.11)$$

When the reservoir is full, since there is no stress at the heel, the maximum compressive stress at the toe is

$$p'=\frac{2W}{l}=\frac{2\rho w\left\{A_0+\left(\frac{l+l_0}{2}\right)h\right\}}{l} \quad . \quad . \quad . \quad (19.12)$$

and this must not exceed the prescribed stress for the toe of p.

As before, an arbitrary value of h is chosen and l calculated from (19.11). This is substituted in the expression for p' and provided $p'<p$ the calculated width is allowable. A new value of h is taken and the design carried a section lower. This process is repeated until $p'=p$, which indicates that the limit of Stage III has been reached.

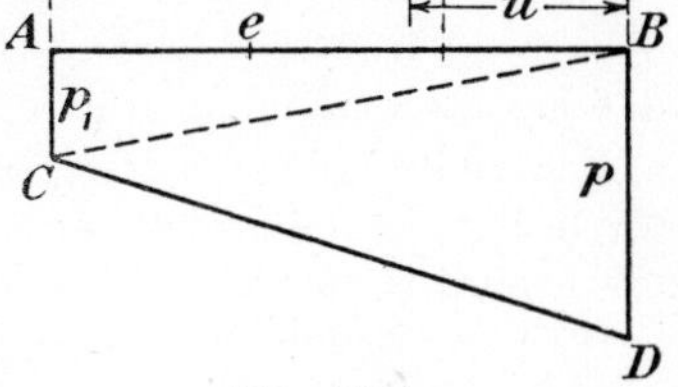

Stage IV.—In this stage the maximum compressive stress at the toe is limited to p. The line of resultant pressure for the reservoir full will fall within the middle third as shown in Fig. 19.8 giving a stress distribution

FIG. 19.8.

across the section under consideration as shown, p_1 being the compressive stress at the heel and p that at the toe.

Let e be the middle-third point nearer the heel. Since the moment of the load which produces the given stress distribution about any point is equal to the moment of the diagram we have, by taking moments about e,

$$W(\tfrac{2}{3}l-u)=\frac{pl^2}{6}$$

since the moment of the triangle ACB about e is zero.

So

$$p=\frac{2W}{l}\left(2-\frac{3u}{l}\right)$$

and

$$u=\frac{2l}{3}-\frac{pl^2}{6A\rho w}.$$

Also

$$y=l/3$$

$\therefore$

$$l=\frac{2l}{3}-\frac{pl^2}{6A\rho w}+\frac{H^3}{6\rho\left\{A_0+\left(\dfrac{l+l_0}{2}\right)h\right\}}+\frac{l}{3}$$

which gives

$$l^2=\frac{wH^3}{p}. \qquad . \quad . \quad . \quad . \quad . \quad (19.13)$$

The compressive stress at the heel when the reservoir is empty is, since $y=l/3$,

$$q'=\frac{2W}{l}, \qquad . \quad . \quad . \quad . \quad . \quad (19.14)$$

and the limit of Stage IV is reached when l is of such a value that $q'=q$, the prescribed stress for the heel.

Stage V.—The compressive stresses at the heel and toe for the reservoir empty and full are kept to the values q and p respectively.

As in Stage IV,

$$u=\frac{2l}{3}-\frac{pl^2}{6A\rho w}$$

and by analogy

$$y=\frac{2l}{3}-\frac{ql^2}{6A\rho w}$$

$\therefore$

$$l=\frac{2l}{3}-\frac{pl^2}{6A\rho w}+\frac{H^3}{6\rho\left\{A_0+\left(\dfrac{l+l_0}{3}\right)h\right\}}+\frac{2l}{3}-\frac{ql^2}{6A\rho w}$$

or

$$l^2\left(\frac{p+q}{\rho wh}-1\right)-l\left(\frac{2A_0}{h}+l_0\right)=\frac{H^3}{\rho h} \quad . \quad . \quad . \quad (19.15)$$

from which l is found.

Distribution of batter between front and back of dam.—In Stages III, IV and V both the front and back of the dam are battered and so, although the value of l has been found at any depth its position relative to l_0 is not yet known.

Fig. 19.9 represents a section of the dam in any of these Stages, O being the heel and t the projection of the lower section beyond the vertical through the heel of the upper section.

If the trapezium is divided into the triangles OAB, CDE and the rectangle ACDB and moments are taken for the whole profile about O,

then

$$Ay=A_0(y_0+t)+\frac{ht^2}{3}+l_0h\left(t+\frac{l_0}{2}\right)+h\left(\frac{l-l_0-t}{2}\right)\left(\frac{l+2l_0+2t}{3}\right).$$

In Stages III and IV, $y=l/3$ and on substituting this value and that of A we obtain

$$t=\frac{2A_0(l-3y_0)-hl_0{}^2}{6A_0+h(2l_0+l)} \qquad \qquad \text{(19.16)}$$

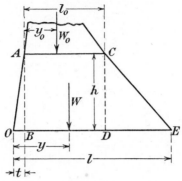

FIG. 19.9.

and since all the terms in the right-hand expression are known, t can be calculated.

In Stage V,
$$y=\frac{2l}{3}-\frac{ql^2}{6A\rho w}$$

$\therefore$
$$Ay=\frac{2l}{3}\left\{A_0+\left(\frac{l+l_0}{2}\right)h\right\}-\frac{ql^2}{6\rho w}$$

which gives, on equating to the expression for Ay above, the result

$$t=\frac{A_0(4l-6y_0)+l^2\left(h-\dfrac{q}{\rho w}\right)+l_0h(l-l_0)}{6A_0+h(2l_0+l)} \qquad \text{(19.17)}$$

As an example of the use of Wegmann's method a profile has been designed in detail from the following data :—

> Total head $=218\cdot65$ feet.
> Freeboard $=\ \ 6\ \ $ feet.
> Top width $=\ \ 20\ \ $ feet.
> Specific gravity of masonry $=2\cdot25$.
> Density of water $\qquad=62\cdot4$ lb. per cubic foot.
> Allowable compressive stress at toe $\ \ =\ 8$ tons per square foot.
> Allowable compressive stress at heel $\ =10$ tons per square foot.

The work is arranged as shown in Table 19.1. In the first place the value of h is calculated for the rectangular portion of Stage I by the use of equation (19.7). The values of u, v and y for this value of h, namely, $38\cdot65$ feet, are entered in the appropriate columns. We are now able to design Stage II and h is chosen as 10 feet. The values of u, v, y, l and A for $h=38\cdot65$ are the values of u_0, v_0, y_0, l_0 and A_0 for the level we are now considering and are entered in the appropriate columns. The values of l and y are determined from equations (19.10) and (19.9) respectively. v is found from equation (19.6). A new section, still keeping $h=10$ feet so that $H=52\cdot65$ feet, is dealt with in the same way and the process is continued until the calculated

TABLE 19.1.

Stage	t ft.	q' tons per sq. ft.	p' tons per sq. ft.	A sq. ft.	l ft.	u ft.	v ft.	y ft.	A_0 sq. ft.	l_0 ft.	u_0 ft.	v_0 ft.	y_0 ft.	$H+a$ ft.	H ft.	h ft.
Stage I	—	—	—	773	20·0	6·7	3·3	10·0	0	20·0	0	0	0	38·65	32·65	38·65
Stage II	—	—	—	993	24·0	8·0	5·8	10·2	773	20·0	6·7	3·3	10·0	48·65	42·65	10
	—	—	—	1,259	29·2	9·7	8·8	10·7	993	24·0	8·0	5·8	10·2	58·65	52·65	10
	—	—	—	1,580	35·0	11·7	11·5	11·8	1,259	29·2	9·7	8·8	10·7	68·65	62·65	10
	—	—	—	1,615	35·7	11·9	11·9	11·9	1,580	35·0	11·7	11·5	11·8	69·65	63·65	1
Stage III	1·3	—	5·7	2,014	44·1	14·7	14·7	14·7	1,615	35·7	11·9	11·9	11·9	79·65	73·65	10
	1·0	—	6·0	2,495	52·2	17·4	17·4	17·4	2,014	44·1	14·7	14·7	14·7	89·65	83·65	10
	0·7	—	6·4	3,054	59·7	19·9	19·9	19·9	2,495	52·2	17·4	17·4	17·4	99·65	93·65	10
	0·4	—	6·9	3,688	67·2	22·4	22·4	22·4	3,054	59·7	19·9	19·9	19·9	109·65	103·65	10
	0·3	—	7·4	4,395	74·1	24·7	24·7	24·7	3,688	67·2	22·4	22·4	22·4	119·65	113·65	10
	0·2	—	8·0	5,172	81·3	27·1	27·1	27·1	4,395	74·1	24·7	24·7	24·7	129·65	123·65	10
Stage IV	1·1	8·3	8·0	6,034	91·2	31·5	29·3	30·4	5,172	81·3	27·1	27·1	27·1	139·65	133·65	10
	1·1	8·6	8·0	6,998	101·7	36·4	31·4	33·9	6,034	91·2	31·5	29·3	30·4	149·65	143·65	10
	1·1	9·0	8·0	8,068	112·4	41·6	33·3	37·5	6,998	101·7	36·4	31·4	33·9	159·65	153·65	10
	1·0	9·0	8·0	9,248	123·6	47·3	35·1	41·2	8,068	112·4	41·6	33·3	37·5	169·65	163·65	10
	1·0	9·8	8·0	10,541	135·0	53·2	36·8	45·0	9,248	123·6	47·3	35·1	41·2	179·65	173·65	10
	0·5	10·0	8·0	11,231	141·0	56·4	37·6	47·0	10,541	135·0	53·2	36·8	45·0	184·65	178·65	5
Stage V	3·2	10·0	8·0	12,713	155·4	63·2	39·1	53·1	11,231	141·0	56·4	37·6	47·0	194·65	188·65	10
	3·6	10·0	8·0	14,345	171·0	70·7	40·5	59·8	12,713	155·4	63·2	39·1	53·1	204·65	198·65	10
	4·2	10·0	8·0	16,138	187·6	78·7	41·8	67·1	14,345	171·0	70·7	40·5	59·8	214·65	208·65	10
	4·7	10·0	8·0	18,101	205·0	87·3	42·7	75·0	16,138	187·6	78·7	41·8	67·1	224·65	218·65	10

value of y becomes nearly $\frac{1}{3}$ of the calculated value of l.   It will be seen
that this occurs when H=62·65 feet.   The next section is taken 1 foot
below this level and y is then exactly $l/3$, indicating that the limit of Stage II
is reached with a head of water of 63·65 feet.   We now enter Stage III and
h is again taken as 10 feet.   The value of l is calculated from equation
(19.11). u, v and y are all equal to $\frac{1}{3}$ of this value and are entered in the
appropriate columns.   The maximum compressive stress at the toe is
calculated from equation (19.12) and entered under p'.   The process is
continued in sections for which h=10 feet until, when H=123·65 feet,
p'=8 tons per square foot, which is the allowable limit for the toe stress.
Stage IV is now entered with a further increase in depth of 10 feet; l, u and
q' are calculated from the appropriate equations for this stage and the limit
is reached at H=178·65 feet at which depth q'=10 tons per square foot, the

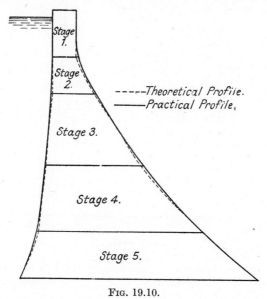

FIG. 19.10.

allowable compressive stress at the heel.   In Stage V the values of l are
calculated from equation (19.15) and u, y and v from the equations for Stage
V.   The only remaining calculations to be made are those to determine the
amount of batter, the appropriate equations being (19.16) in Stages III and
IV and (19.17) in Stage V.   The theoretical profile obtained in this way is
plotted in Fig. 19.10 which also shows a faired profile which could actually
be used.

The modifications of the Wegmann equations due to the inclusion of
uplift terms have been investigated by E. H. Brown (1956).   The general
result is to reduce the effective specific gravity of the masonry to $\rho-1$ and
so continue Stage III to a considerably greater depth.

19.8. Distribution of shearing stress in a masonry dam.—In a paper
previously cited (Atcherley and Pearson, 1904), it was shown that the
assumption of linear distribution of normal stresses on a horizontal section
of a dam leads to a parabolic distribution of shear stress across that section
except for the special case of a triangular profile, when the distribution is

16*

linear.   Unwin subsequently gave a treatment (1905) which produced the same results and his method, somewhat modified, will be followed here.

Fig. 19.11 represents one foot length of a dam ABC.   Let ADEB be the normal stress distribution on the section AB, assumed linear.   The weight of one cubic foot of masonry will be taken as the unit of force.   The stress at any point in masonry units per square foot can then be represented as a *column* of masonry and if this is drawn to the same scale as the profile, the area ADEB will be equal to the area ABC.

If PT is any vertical section, the shearing force along PT is the difference between the weight and upward thrust on either side of PT, *i.e.*

PTCB−PREB.

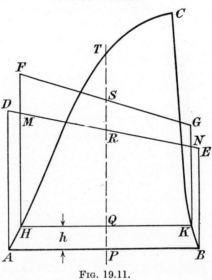

Fig. 19.11.

Let HK be another horizontal section at a height *h* above AB and HFGK the stress distribution curve for this section.   The shearing force on QT is then

QTCK−QSGK.

Therefore the shearing force on the length PQ is

(PTCB−PREB)−(QTCK−QSGK)

i.e.   (PTCB−QTCK)−(PREB−QSGK)

or   PQKB−(PQKB+KNEB−RSGN)

i.e.   RSGN−KNEB.

Hence the average shear stress on PQ is

$$\frac{\text{RSGN}-\text{KNEB}}{h}.$$

If *h* is small this is the vertical shear stress at P and therefore the complementary horizontal shear stress at the same point.

If the back of the dam is vertical over the length *h* as in Fig. 19.12 the area KNEB is zero and the shear stress is $\frac{\text{RSGN}}{h}$.   In modern dams the back is either vertical or only slightly battered and so the area KNEB can usually be neglected.

Take the point N in Fig. 19.12 as origin. Then the equations of the lines ND and GF are

$$y = m_1 x$$

and
$$y = m_2 x + c, \quad \text{where } c = NG.$$

Let TP be x from N,

then
$$RS = (m_2 x + c) - m_1 x,$$

the area
$$RSGN = \frac{(m_2 - m_1)x^2}{2} + cx$$

and the shear stress
$$s = \frac{(m_2 - m_1)x^2}{2h} + \frac{cx}{h}.$$

This is a parabola except when $m_2 = m_1$; it is then a straight line.

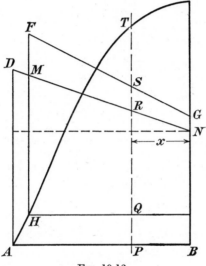

FIG. 19.12.

Let f_h = normal stress at the heel on section AB,

f_h' = normal stress at the heel on section δh above it

and f_t = normal stress at the toe on section AB.

Then
$$m_1 = \frac{f_t - f_h}{AB}$$

and
$$c = f_h' + \delta h - f_h = -(f_h - f_h') + \delta h.$$

Since δh is very small

$$m_1 - m_2 = \frac{dm}{dh}\delta h$$

and
$$f_h - f_h' = \frac{df}{dh}\delta h.$$

The area of RSGN obtained above can therefore be expressed in the form

$$-\frac{x^2}{2}\frac{dm}{dh}\delta h + x\left(1 - \frac{df_h}{dh}\right)\delta h$$

and the shear stress

$$s = -\frac{x^2}{2}\frac{dm}{dh} + x\left(1 - \frac{df_h}{dh}\right).$$

In a triangular profile with vertical back of height h and base width nh

$$W=\frac{nh^2}{2} \text{ masonry units}$$

and

$$P=\frac{h^2}{2\rho} \text{ masonry units.}$$

The eccentricity of loading from the mid-point of the base is $\frac{h}{6}\left(\frac{2}{\rho n}-n\right)$.

Then

$$f_t=\frac{h}{\rho n^2}$$

$$f_h=h\left(1-\frac{1}{\rho n^2}\right)$$

$$m=\frac{2}{\rho n^3}-\frac{1}{n}$$

and

$$\frac{dm}{dh}=0.$$

Also

$$\frac{df_h}{dh}=1-\frac{1}{\rho n^2}$$

and

$$s=\frac{x}{\rho n^2}$$

which is a triangle with its maximum ordinate $\frac{h}{\rho n}$ at the toe where $x=nh$.

If the profile is rectangular with base width b and height h,

$$W=bh \text{ masonry units,}$$

$$P=\frac{h^2}{2\rho} \text{ masonry units}$$

and the eccentricity of loading on the base is given by

$$\frac{3e}{h}=\frac{P}{W}=\frac{h}{2\rho b}$$

i.e.

$$e=\frac{h^2}{6\rho b}.$$

Then

$$f_t=h\left(1+\frac{h^2}{\rho b^2}\right)$$

and

$$f_h=h\left(1-\frac{h^2}{\rho b^2}\right),$$

so that

$$m=\frac{2h^3}{\rho b^3}$$

and

$$\frac{dm}{dh}=\frac{6h^2}{\rho b^3}.$$

Also

$$\frac{df_h}{dh}=1-\frac{3h^2}{\rho b^2},$$

so that

$$s=\frac{3h^2}{\rho b^2}\left(x-\frac{x^2}{b}\right).$$

This is a parabola with $s=0$ at $x=0$ and at $x=b$ and a maximum ordinate $\frac{3h^2}{4\rho b}$ at $x=b/2$.

In any other profiles the curves of shearing stress can be obtained graphically. It should be noticed that there can be no shearing stress at any point
where the boundary of the profile is vertical. This is shown in the triangular
section where the back is vertical and in the rectangular where both front
and back are vertical. It frequently happens that the bottom part of a dam,
which is under the ground, is rectangular in profile and horizontal sections
will have shearing curves with zero values at both the toe and the heel.

19.9. Stresses on vertical sections of masonry dams.—Reference was made
in paragraph 19.1 to a theory put forward by Atcherley and Karl Pearson,
who suggested that the method of guarding against tensile stress by a consideration of horizontal sections only was completely inadequate since in most

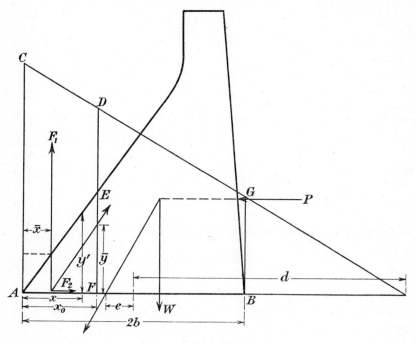

Fig. 19.13.

existing dams an examination of stress distribution along vertical sections
showed serious tensile stresses over a large part of the profile. Fig. 19.13 is
the profile of a masonry dam of base width $2b$. The weight is W and the
water pressure P. The line of resultant action for the reservoir full cuts the
base at a distance e from the mid-point.

The distribution of normal stresses on the base is assumed as usual to be
linear and to be represented by the diagram ACGB. The stresses are in
masonry units so that this diagram is the same area as the profile.

CG is produced to cut the line of AB and the distance from the intersection to the mid-point of the base is denoted by d.

If the normal stress at the mid-point of the base is f,

the stress at B is

$$f\left(1 - \frac{3e}{b}\right)$$

and

$$\frac{d}{d-b}=\frac{f}{f\left(1-\dfrac{3e}{b}\right)}$$

from which

$$d=\frac{b^2}{3e}.$$

The stress at a distance x from the toe is then

$$\frac{W}{2b}\left(\frac{d+b-x}{d}\right).$$

The assumption, which is very nearly true, that the front of the dam is linear for some distance from the base enables the height at the distance x to be expressed as

$$y'=mx.$$

The intercept between the front of the dam and the stress distribution curve is then, for this linear range,

$$y=\frac{W(d+b)}{2bd}-x\left(m+\frac{W}{2bd}\right)$$

and this represents the resultant upward intensity of stress on the base at x from the toe. The upward force on a length x_0 of the base is then $\int_0^{x_0} ydx$ so that

$$F_1=\frac{W(d+b)x_0}{2bd}-\frac{x_0^2}{2}\left(m+\frac{W}{2bd}\right).$$

Its vertical line of action is given by $\bar{x}=\dfrac{1}{F_1}\displaystyle\int_0^{x_0} yxdx$, or

$$\bar{x}=x_0\frac{\frac{1}{2}W(d+b)-\frac{1}{3}x_0(2bdm+W)}{W(d+b)-\frac{1}{2}x_0(2bdm+W)}.$$

The distribution of shear stress on the base is assumed to be parabolic in accordance with the principles discussed in paragraph (19.8) and to be represented by the equation

$$s=\frac{3P}{4b}\left(\frac{2bx-x^2}{b^2}\right).$$

Since this gives a zero value at the toe it would apply more accurately to a profile having a rectangular base section as indicated by the dotted line on the diagram. This is quite usual so that the assumed shear stress distribution is probably reasonably close to the actual. The total shearing force over a length of base x_0 is $\int_0^{x_0} sdx$, or

$$F_2=\frac{3P}{4b}\left(\frac{bx_0^2-\frac{1}{3}x_0^3}{b^2}\right).$$

The forces F_1, F_2 and the resultant forces on the face EF are in equilibrium, hence :—

$$\text{Total shearing force on EF}=F_1$$
$$\text{and total thrust on} \quad \text{EF}=F_2.$$

If the line of action of the resultant of these two forces cuts EF at $\bar{y}$ from the base

$$\frac{\bar{y}}{x_0 - \bar{x}} = \frac{F_1}{F_2}$$

which gives, upon substituting the values of $\bar{x}$, F_1 and F_2,

$$\bar{y} = \frac{b^2}{3Pd} \frac{W(d+b) - \frac{1}{3}x_0(2bdm + W)}{b - \frac{1}{3}x_0}.$$

This is the equation of the line of resistance for vertical sections for that portion of the dam over which the front face is approximately the straight line $y' = mx$. It is a hyperbola, the asymptotes of which are

$$x = 3b$$

and

$$y = \frac{2bdm + W}{P}e.$$

The average shear stress on the vertical section is $\dfrac{F_1}{mx_0}$ since mx_0 is the height of the section EF. If the reasonable assumption is made that the maximum shear on the section is 50 per cent. greater than the mean,

$$s_{max} = \frac{3}{2} \frac{W(d+b) - \frac{1}{2}x_0(2bdm + W)}{2bdm}$$

which is a linear expression having its maximum value of $\dfrac{3}{4} \dfrac{W(d+b)}{bdm}$ masonry units at the toe of the dam. This emphasises the importance of thickening the toe as indicated by the dotted line in Fig. 19.13.

The maximum tensile stress on the section EF occurs at F and is

$$t = \frac{F_2}{mx_0}\left(\frac{6c}{mx_0} - 1\right)$$

where $c = \bar{y} - \dfrac{mx_0}{2}$ is the eccentricity of loading on this section.

If the value of t is negative it indicates that the stress at F is compressive. Substituting for c, F_2 and $\bar{y}$ the expression becomes

$$t = \frac{3}{2bdm^2}\{W(d+b) - \frac{1}{3}x_0(2bdm + W)\} - \frac{3P}{b^3m}x_0(b - \frac{1}{3}x_0),$$

which is a parabola with a vertical axis.

The value of t when $x_0 = 0$, i.e. at the toe, is

$$t_0 = \frac{3W(d+b)}{2bdm^2}.$$

The maximum value occurs when $\dfrac{dt}{dx_0} = 0$, i.e. when

$$-\frac{1}{2bdm^2}(2bdm + W) = \frac{3P}{b^3m}\left(b - \frac{2x_0}{3}\right)$$

or when

$$x_0 = \frac{b^2}{2P}\left(\frac{2bdm + W}{2dm}\right) + \frac{3b}{2}$$

and is

$$t_{max} = t_0\left\{1 - \frac{1}{12\varepsilon}\left(3\varepsilon + \frac{b}{x_0}\right)^2\right\}$$

where

$$\varepsilon = \frac{3P}{bmt_0}.$$

The values of t_0 and t_{max} having been calculated the parabola can be plotted.

After the front of the dam departs from the linear a graphical method must be used to determine further points on the curves if these are found to be necessary. The procedure is as follows :—a vertical section is taken and the area bounded by this section, the normal stress curve and the front of the dam is obtained by a planimeter or otherwise. This gives the value of F_1, its line of action being through the centre of gravity of the area which is determined graphically. F_2 can be calculated directly from the formula. These two forces are compounded graphically and the value of $\bar{y}$ thus found. The stresses are then calculated in the usual way.

The authors of the paper which has been outlined above also considered the effect of assuming a linear distribution of shear stress across the horizontal section and found substantially the same qualitative results, viz., that considerable tensile stresses existed in vertical sections for more than half the width of the dam measured from the toe. Their conclusions were tested by means of models. In one of these the profile was divided into horizontal laminae and in the other into vertical laminae. Under load applied to the back to represent fluid pressure the behaviour of these models was in accordance with their expectation from the theoretical considerations. Their general conclusions, given in the words of the paper itself, are as follows :—

" (1) The current theory of the stability of dams is both theoretically and experimentally erroneous, because :—

" (a) Theory shows that the vertical and not the horizontal sections are the critical sections.

" (b) Experiment shows that a dam first gives by tension of the vertical sections near the tail.

" (2) An accepted form of profile is shown to be stable as far as the horizontal sections are concerned, but unstable by applying the same conditions of stability to the vertical sections.

" (3) The distribution of shear over the base must be more nearly parabolic than uniform, but as no reversal of our statements follows when we pass from the former to the latter extreme hypothesis, it is not unreasonable to assume the former distribution will describe fairly closely the facts until we have greater knowledge.

" (4) In future we hold that in the first place masonry dams must be investigated for the stability of their vertical sections. If this be done we feel pretty certain that most existing dams will be found to fail, if we accept the criteria of stability usually adopted for their horizontal sections. This failure can be met in two ways :—

" (a) By a modification of the customary profile. We think it probable that a profile like that of Vyrnwy dam would give better results than more usual forms.

" (b) By a frank acceptance that masonry, if carefully built, may be trusted to stand a definite amount of tensile stress. It is perfectly idle to assert that it is absolutely necessary that the line of resistance shall lie in the middle third for a horizontal treatment, when it lies well outside the middle third for at least half the dam for a vertical treatment."

With the publication of these conclusions there began a controversy in which many distinguished engineers took part. It was concerned with the issues as to whether tension occurred on vertical sections, and how shearing stresses were distributed on horizontal planes. Several experimental researches were inspired by a desire to solve these problems, the most notable being that of J. S. Wilson and W. Gore (1908), whose experiments were directed to finding a solution of the " mathematician's dam " by the help of indiarubber models. They claimed that very good approximate solutions had been found to a problem which was too complex for mathematical analysis. Their most important result, confirmed by other workers, was that although slight tension might occur on a plane near the heel of the base section at the junction with the foundation, there was no tension elsewhere in a dam of normal profile.

It was not until many years later that the development of relaxation methods made possible a mathematical analysis of the stresses, but when this was done (Zienkiewicz, 1947) the conclusions reached by Wilson and Gore were found to be well justified.

Zienkiewicz analysed a profile designed by the Wegmann method and found that the maximum compressive stresses when the reservoir was full did not generally exceed those calculated on the usual engineering assumptions, and that for the same condition some tension developed in the portion below ground level at the upstream side of the dam. In the upper portion of the dam engineering assumptions and elastic theory produced results which agreed well and when the reservoir was empty the agreement was very close. This result has since been confirmed independently in connexion with calculations made on an arch dam (Allen, Chitty, Pippard and Severn, 1956).

Fig. 19.14 shows a comparison of the experimental results obtained by Wilson and Gore and those calculated by Zienkiewicz. The two profiles have been drawn to different scales, and the stress curves have been re-plotted in terms of masonry units for easy comparison of the important feature, which is the close agreement in the *shape* of the curves, both for vertical and shearing stresses.

19.10. The arch dam.—The theoretical treatment of the arch dam presents great difficulties, and although many attempts have been made to obtain solutions of sufficient accuracy for design purposes which can be applied reasonably quickly, none of them has gained general acceptance. An outline of these methods has been given by Jaeger (1950), and a more detailed treatment by Bourgin (1953), but before referring specifically to any of them the problem must be considered generally. Suppose then that an arch dam of circular plan form and constant height is located in a rigid valley without any shear connexion between it and the base or abutments. Under the action of gravity forces and water pressure all elementary vertical strips of the structure are in the same state of stress, and a complete solution of the problem is found if the values of these stresses can be determined at every point in a vertical section. The water pressure on the back and the gravity forces will, in any such strip, produce vertical direct stresses, shearing stresses on horizontal planes and circumferential direct stresses. If the base is assumed to be connected with the rigid rock, the problem will be complicated by the imposition of this extra shear constraint and whereas the first assumptions reduce the structure to what is in effect a segment of a tube of varying thickness, the new condition requires that the same tube shall suffer no distortion of its base section. An elementary vertical strip is now in the condition generally assumed in the analysis of a gravity dam

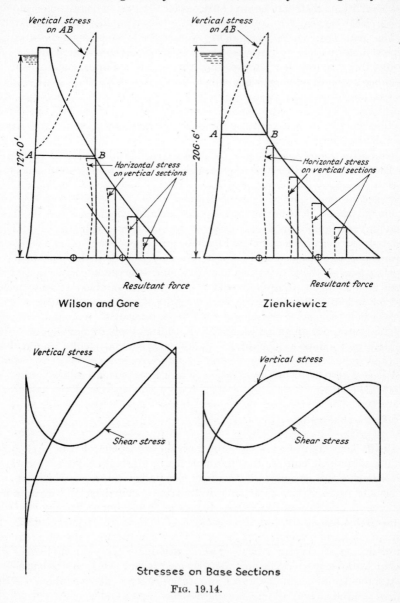

Stresses on Base Sections

FIG. 19.14.

with, however, the addition of hoop stresses. Upon the first set of assumptions the end sections of the dam can slide radially, and upon the second set they can deflect about the fixed bases. If however, the ends are built into the abutment to provide resistance to shear, all strains at these sections will be prevented and elementary vertical strips will no longer all behave similarly. The centre strip of the dam will, from considerations of symmetry remain free from resultant shearing forces on its vertical faces.   There will be a transition from the state of stress at the centre section to that at the abutments and a complete solution of the problem now demands the determination of all the stresses at any point in the structure and not only in a typical vertical strip.

The real problem is even more complicated than this ; few valleys approximate closely to the shape assumed which gives a dam of constant height, but are irregular and unsymmetrical.   If a dam in such a valley is assumed to be divided into a number of elementary vertical strips each of which is analysed on the assumption that the vertical faces are free from shear, the resulting strains will be incompatible, *i.e.* the vertical face of one section will not be exactly the same shape when strained as the contiguous face of the next section.   In the actual structure these differences are adjusted by the development of shearing stresses between adjacent strips.

Another very important factor which makes an exact solution impossible is that the valley rock will not be rigid but will have elastic properties which are hard to assess and which will almost certainly vary considerably from point to point.   Even if they were determinate, however, and were un-varying, the strains in an irregular mass of elastic abutment due to the reactive forces from the dam could not be accurately found ; yet upon these strains will largely depend the magnitude of the stresses, both in the structure and in the rock of the abutments and foundation.   These considerations show that approximate methods of design are all that can be expected but these are of varying degrees of complexity, and all that can be done here is to mention a few of those which have been used.

The simplest assumption of all is that an arch dam can be divided into a number of completely separate horizontal rings free to move at the abutments.   Since the arches are circular in plan form and the water pressure is radial at every point, the stress is purely tangential and is calculated from the thin ring formula

$$f = \frac{whR}{t}$$

where h is the head of water at the section under consideration, R is the radius of the ring and t is the thickness of the ring.   The Bear Valley dam in California was designed and built on this assumption in 1884.

An extension of this method is to assume that the water load is taken entirely on separate horizontal arch rings as before but to assume also that these arches are encastré at the abutments.   This is the method used by the Italian engineers and has resulted in the spectacular structures in the Eastern Alps (Semenza, 1952).   The equations for the encastré arch under radial load are derived as for any other arch ring (Chapter 12), but it is important to take rib-shortening into account since this is the only effect which produces bending moments under such load conditions.

These methods do not take any account of the load carried by vertical strips of the dam acting as cantilevers, and while this neglect may be reasonably justified for dams in narrow gorges, it leads to serious miscalculation for those in wider valleys.

The U.S. Bureau of Reclamation have developed a systematic method of analysis applicable to any valley, known as the trial load method (U.S. Bureau of Reclamation, 1950).   This visualises the dam as consisting of two inter-penetrating structural systems ; one of these is a series of vertical cantilevers and the other a series of arches. The load from the water pressure is divided by repeated trial between the two systems in such proportions that the displacements of both are the same at a number of selected points. The method is based on the following general assumptions :—

1. The foundation and abutments are uniformly elastic in all directions.

2. The concrete in the dam is homogeneous and uniformly elastic in all directions.

3. The dam may be considered as fixed to the abutments and the foundations.

4. The vertical construction joints in the dam are grouted before the water load is applied so that the structure acts as a monolith and arch action begins as soon as the reservoir starts to fill.

5. Material of the dam, base and abutments is stressed well below the limit of elasticity.

6. All vertical loads are carried by the cantilever elements and each cantilever acts independently of its neighbours.

More recently a solution of the elastic equations for a particular arch dam at Dokan on the Lesser Zab River in Iraq has been obtained by relaxation analysis (Allen, Chitty, Pippard and Severn, 1956) which has given all the stress components throughout the structure.

It is usual to supplement calculations for important dams of this type by tests on models. These are often made of plaster of paris or similar material and are loaded mechanically to represent both gravity and water loads. Such tests have shown that the margin of strength in an arch dam designed by the usual methods is considerable. In the work on the Dokan dam referred to above, a rubber model loaded by water pressure was used to provide an indication of the behaviour of the structure, to furnish data for analysis and to check the results obtained by the calculations. The results of the experiments on this model were also used to obtain independent estimates of the more important stresses in the structure (Chitty and Pippard, 1956).

Reference has been made only to loads due to gravity and to water pressure but stresses of serious magnitudes can be caused by seasonable variations of temperature ; these cannot be determined with great accuracy but they must be allowed for as far as possible. Further, in districts subject to seismic activity a severe earthquake shock may also produce serious stresses and these also need consideration in design.

REFERENCES

Rankine, W. M. 1872. *Engineer, Lond.*, **33**, 1–2.
Rankine, W. M. 1881. *Misc. Sc. Papers*, 550–561. Griffin & Co.
Wegmann, E. 1888. " The Design & Construction of Dams." Wiley.
Unwin, W. C. 1896. *Cassier's Mag.*, **11**.
Atcherley, L. W. and Pearson, K. 1904. *Drapers Co. Res. Memoirs.* Dulau & Co.
Unwin, W. C. 1905. *Engineering, Lond.*, **79**, 825.
Pearson, K. 1905. *Engineering, Lond.*, **80**, 35.
Wilson, J. S. and Gore, W. 1908. *Proc. Instn. Civ. Engrs.*, **172**, 107.
Houk, I. E. 1932. *Civ. Eng. (N.Y.)*, **2**, 578–579.
Terzaghi, K. 1934. *Ing. und Arch.-Vereines*, **86**, 1–9.
Terzaghi, K. 1934. *Die Bautechnik*, **29**.

Terzaghi, K. 1934. *Die Bautechnik*, **45**.

Hellstrom, B. 1936. *Engineer, Lond.*, **161**, 276.

Zienkiewicz, O. C. 1947. *J. Inst. Civ. Engrs.*, **27**, 244–271.

Pippard, A. J. S. 1950. *J. Inst. Civ. Engrs.*, **33**, 264–284.

U.S. Bureau of Reclamation. 1950. *Treatise on Dams.* Chap., **10**. U.S.A.

Jaeger, C. 1950. *Civ. Engng., Lond.* (Apr.–Sept.).

Jaeger, C. 1951. *Engl. Elect.*, **12**, (4), 3–28.

Sub-committee on Uplift in Masonry Dams. 1952. *Trans. Amer. Soc. Civ. Engrs.*, **117**, 1218–1252.

Semenza, C. 1952. *Proc. Instn. Civ. Engrs.*, **1**.1, 508–537.

Bourgin, A. 1953. " The Design of Dams." Pitman.

Brown, E. H. 1956. *Proc. Instn. Civ. Engrs.*, **5**. III, 196–212

Allen, D., Chitty, L., Pippard, A. J. S. and Severn, R. T. 1956. *Proc. Instn. Civ. Engrs.*, **5**.1, 198–258.

Chitty, L. and Pippard, A. J. S. 1956. *Proc. Instn. Civ. Engrs.*, **5**.1, 259–275.

CHAPTER 20

EARTH PRESSURE AND THE DESIGN OF EARTH RETAINING STRUCTURES

20.1. The general problem of earth pressure.—The problem of estimating the pressure to be resisted by earth retaining structures has exercised the minds of engineers since the publication of Coulomb's well known wedge theory in 1776. The factors controlling earth pressure are, however, of a complex character, and include the relative rigidities of the soil and of the structure supporting it and the action of water pressure within the soil. It is only within the past 20 years that developments in the field of Soil Mechanics have enabled the relative importance of these various factors to be properly understood (see various references at the end of the chapter, p. 513), while the distribution of the force acting on a wall still cannot be theoretically predicted with accuracy owing to the difficulty of representing the stress-strain characteristics of the soil by simple parameters. Semi-empirical methods play an important part, therefore, in actual design procedures.

In order to understand the factors controlling earth pressure it is necessary to consider first the state of stress in an undisturbed soil mass, and then to examine the extent to which this may be modified by lateral deformation.

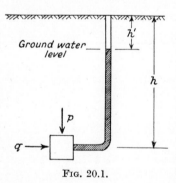

Ground water level

FIG. 20.1.

20.2. Earth pressure at rest.—The vertical stress p at a depth h in a homogeneous soil mass of unlimited lateral extent and bounded by a horizontal surface is ρh where ρ is the density of the soil (Fig. 20.1). If ground water is present below a depth h', the base of a column of soil of depth h will be acted upon by an uplift pressure u, which, in the absence of seepage, is equal to $\rho_w(h-h')$, where ρ_w is the density of water. The stress carried by the granular structure of the soil is reduced by this amount; the effective stress, p', which controls the mechanical behaviour of the soil structure, is then equal to the total stress p less the uplift pressure u,

i.e.
$$p'=p-u \ . \qquad \qquad (20.1)$$

or
$$p'=\rho h-\rho_w(h-h') . \qquad \qquad (20.2)$$

Soil above ground water level, with the exception of clay and silt, is usually not fully saturated and has a lower density than the saturated soil below ground water level. The appropriate value of ρ must be used accordingly.

The horizontal stress q may similarly be divided into the hydrostatic component $\rho_w(h-h')$ and the effective horizontal stress q', where

$$q'=q-\rho_w(h-h'). \qquad \qquad (20.3)$$

490

It is then possible to relate the horizontal and vertical effective stresses by the expression

$$q' = K_0 p' \qquad \cdots \qquad (20.4)$$

where K_0 is known as the coefficient of earth pressure at rest.

If the stratum of soil has been formed by natural sedimentation, or by a process of artificial deposition in which no lateral yield is permitted, K_0 is found to be a constant depending only on the type of soil and the method of deposition. For loose sands the value of K_0 is about $0\cdot45$, and for dense sands about $0\cdot35$. A wider range of values is encountered in clays, depending on the size and mineralogy of the particles, and may vary between $0\cdot4$ and $0\cdot7$. If the stratum has been *overconsolidated*, by being subjected to a surcharge which has subsequently been removed, the values of K_0 will be higher, as the deformation characteristics of soil are not fully reversible, and values exceeding $1\cdot0$ may be encountered. In a perfectly elastic medium $K_0 = \nu/(1-\nu)$ where ν is Poisson's ratio (Richardson, 1909).

The total horizontal pressure is thus given by the expression

$$q = u + K_0 p'$$

or

$$q = \rho_w(h - h') + K_0\{\rho h - \rho_w(h - h')\} \qquad \cdots \qquad (20.5)$$

20.3. Lateral deformation ; active and passive pressures.—If lateral yield of the soil is now permitted, the lateral pressure will decrease as the shear strength of the soil is progressively mobilised, until a condition of plastic

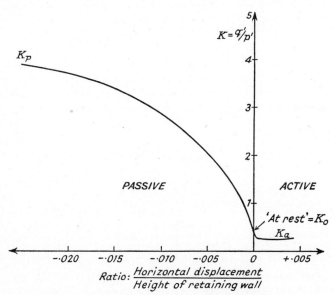

FIG. 20.2.   Displacements required to cause transition to active and passive states in sand (diagrammatic).

equilibrium is reached when further yield leads to no further drop in pressure. This is the state of stress visualised by Rankine (1857) in his theory of earth pressure, and the pressure corresponding to it is referred to as the *active* pressure, as it represents the pressure still to be balanced when the shear strength of the soil is fully mobilised.

If on the other hand, the soil is subjected to lateral compression, the earth pressure will rise above the *at rest* value until the shear strength has been fully mobilised in the reverse direction. The corresponding earth pressure is referred to as the *passive* pressure, and represents the maximum resistance to lateral displacement which can be maintained by the soil.

Rankine himself used the terms active and passive in a different sense ; the definitions above represent current practice in civil engineering.

The relative magnitudes of the displacements required to cause the transition from the *at rest* state to the active and passive states in a sand stratum are shown diagrammatically in Fig. 20.2, and illustrate the influence of two factors. First, in a frictional material, the change in lateral pressure in passing from the *at rest* state to the passive state is many times greater than the reduction in stress in passing from the *at rest* state to the active state. Secondly, the soil does not obey Hooke's law, and the modulus of deformation on reducing a stress (as in the transition to the active state) is much larger than that on applying an increase in stress for the first time (as in the passive case).

20.4. Earth pressure coefficients for active and passive Rankine states.—

In a semi-infinite soil mass bounded by a horizontal surface free from shear

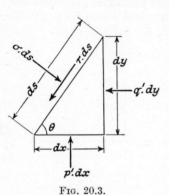

FIG. 20.3.

stress, the vertical normal stress p' will, by symmetry, be a principal stress. The active pressure, being by definition the minimum normal pressure in a horizontal direction, is therefore also a principal stress. The two principal stresses may be resolved into a shear stress τ and a normal pressure σ' acting on a plane inclined at an angle θ to the horizontal, as in Fig. 20.3.

Resolving in the direction of the shear stress, the value of τ is found to be

$$\tau = (p' - q') \sin \theta \cos \theta. \quad . \quad . \quad (20.6)$$

Resolving in the direction of the normal stress, the value of σ' is found to be

$$\sigma' = p' \cos^2 \theta + q' \sin^2 \theta. \quad . \quad . \quad . \quad . \quad (20.7)$$

Rankine assumed that limiting equilibrium would be reached when the ratio τ/σ' reached a maximum value given by the expression

$$\tau = \sigma' \tan \phi \quad . \quad . \quad . \quad . \quad . \quad . \quad (20.8)$$

where, in modern terminology, ϕ is the angle of internal friction. This expression is found experimentally to be true for dry or submerged clean sand or gravel. For cohesive soils a more general failure criterion is required, as discussed in paragraph 20.12.

From equations (20.6) and (20.7) the ratio τ/σ' is

$$\frac{\tau}{\sigma'} = \frac{p' - q'}{p' \cot \theta + q' \tan \theta} \quad . \quad . \quad . \quad . \quad (20.9)$$

Differentiating this expression with respect to θ and equating to zero to obtain the condition for the maximum value of τ/σ' we find

$$\frac{p'}{q'} = \tan^2 \theta. \quad . \quad . \quad . \quad . \quad . \quad (20.10)$$

Substituting this in equation (20.9) we have

$$\left(\frac{\tau}{\sigma'}\right)_{max}=\frac{p'-q'}{2\sqrt{p'q'}}. \quad \ldots \ldots \ldots \quad (20.11)$$

In the active state

$$\left(\frac{\tau}{\sigma'}\right)_{max}=\tan\phi$$

i.e.

$$\tan\phi=\frac{p'-q'}{2\sqrt{p'q'}}.$$

Now

$$\operatorname{cosec}^2\phi=1+\cot^2\phi$$

$$=\left(\frac{p'+q'}{p'-q'}\right)^2$$

or

$$\sin\phi=\frac{p'-q'}{p'+q'}$$

i.e.

$$\frac{q'}{p'}=\frac{1-\sin\phi}{1+\sin\phi}.$$

This leads to the expression for the minimum or active lateral pressure

$$q'_a=p'\left(\frac{1-\sin\phi}{1+\sin\phi}\right). \quad \ldots \quad \ldots \ldots \quad (20.12)$$

Similarly, the maximum, or passive, lateral pressure is given by the expression

$$q'_p=p'\left(\frac{1+\sin\phi}{1-\sin\phi}\right). \quad \ldots \quad \ldots \ldots \quad (20.13)$$

These expressions are usually written

$$\left.\begin{array}{c}q'_a=K_ap'\\q'_p=K_pp'\end{array}\right\} \quad \ldots \ldots \ldots \quad (20.14)$$

where K_a and K_p are termed the coefficient of active earth pressure and the coefficient of passive earth pressure respectively. Typical values are given in Table 20.1.

TABLE 20.1.

VALUES OF K_a AND K_p FOR THE RANKINE STATE WITH A HORIZONTAL GROUND SURFACE.

ϕ	25°	30°	35°	40°	45°
K_a	0·41	0·33	0·27	0·22	0·17
K_p	2·46	3·00	3·69	4·60	5·83

By a simple trigonometrical transformation it follows that

$$\left.\begin{array}{l}\dfrac{1+\sin\phi}{1-\sin\phi}=\tan^2(45°+\phi/2)\\[2mm]\dfrac{1-\sin\phi}{1+\sin\phi}=\tan^2(45°-\phi/2)\end{array}\right\} \quad \ldots \ldots \quad (20.15)$$

These values may be substituted for p'/q' in equation (20.10) to give the inclinations of the planes on which limiting equilibrium is reached in the active and passive states respectively and lead to the values, illustrated in Fig. 20.4 :

$$(a) \text{ active state,} \quad \theta = 45° + \phi/2$$
$$(b) \text{ passive state,} \quad \theta = 45° - \phi/2.$$

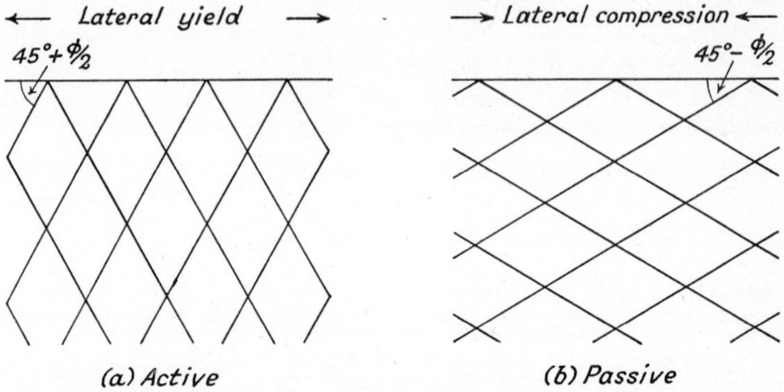

FIG. 20.4.   Rupture planes in active and passive Rankine states.

Rupture planes at these angles may be observed in triaxial test specimens of sand when these are made to fail by lateral yield or lateral compression respectively.

20.5. Influence of ground water.—It should be noted that although the expressions for K_a and K_p are identical in form with those obtained by Rankine, the stresses are here expressed as effective stresses. The total lateral pressure intensities, as in paragraph 20.2, will be

$$q_a = q'_a + u = K_a \{ \rho h - \rho_w (h - h') \} + \rho_w (h - h') \quad . \quad . \quad (20.16)$$
$$q_p = q'_p + u = K_p \{ \rho h - \rho_w (h - h') \} + \rho_w (h - h') \quad . \quad . \quad (20.17)$$

The importance of the water pressure term can best be illustrated by a numerical example.   For a typical loose sand the dry density may be taken as 95 lb. per cubic foot, and the saturated density as 122 lb. per cubic foot. The value of K_0 will be $0 \cdot 45$, and for $\phi = 30°$ K_a and K_p will be $0 \cdot 33$ and $3 \cdot 0$ respectively.   Saturation has little influence on the value of ϕ in cohesionless soils.   The total lateral pressure at a depth h and the percentage due to water pressure, calculated from these data, are given in Table 20.2 for completely dry sand and for sand with the ground water level at the surface.

TABLE 20.2.

INFLUENCE OF LEVEL OF WATER TABLE ON HORIZONTAL PRESSURE IN GROUND
(pressures in lb. per sq. foot).

State of Sand	At Rest		Active		Passive	
	Total Pressure	% due to Water	Total Pressure	% due to Water	Total Pressure	% due to Water
Dry	$43h$	0	$32h$	0	$290h$	0
G.W.L. at Surface ...	$89h$	70	$82h$	76	$241h$	26

The results given in Table 20.2 illustrate the following points :

(1) The position of the water table exerts a most important influence on the magnitude of the total lateral pressure, and in the *at rest* and *active* states may lead to values at least twice as great as those for the dry material.

(2) When the water table is near the ground surface, the major component of the lateral thrust is due to water pressure, and hence it is as important to know the water levels accurately as to know the soil properties.

(3) A rise in the water table reduces the passive resistance. (This is particularly marked for higher values of K_p.)

It also follows from equations (20.16) and (20.17) that increase in total lateral pressure with depth is linear both above and below the water table, the rates of increase being $K\rho$ and $\{K(\rho-\rho_w)+\rho_w\}$ respectively. This leads

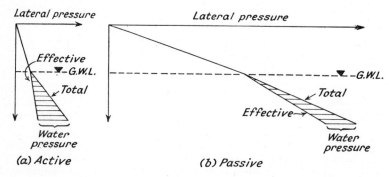

Fig. 20.5.   Pressure-depth diagrams for active and passive Rankine states.

to the pressure-depth diagrams illustrated in Fig. 20.5, and enables the position of the resultant lateral thrust to be determined directly.

20.6. Calculation of earth pressure on actual structures.—Conditions encountered in practice depart in several important respects from the assumptions on which the idealised active and passive Rankine states are based. This is a direct consequence of the fact that all changes in the state of stress in the ground are accompanied by finite deformations, as illustrated in Fig. 20.2. For a rigorous solution it is therefore necessary to achieve compatibility of both stresses and deformations within the soil mass and at its boundary with the structure. This is, however, not practicable as an engineering method, since the stress-strain characteristics of the soil are, in general, non-linear, and vary with the magnitude and direction of the stress increments. In practice simplified methods are used ; these have been checked by large scale model tests carried out by Terzaghi (1934), Tschebotarioff (1949) and Rowe (1952), and also by field measurements.

Two principal factors lead to a modification of the Rankine state of stress : first, shear stresses due to friction at the boundary between the soil and the structure resulting from relative movement, and secondly, the mode of deformation of the structure which may result in the limiting state of stress not being achieved throughout the soil adjacent to it.

20.7. The wedge theory : active pressure.—For the state of stress in the ground behind the vertical back AB of a retaining wall as in Fig. 20.6 (a) to correspond with the Rankine active state, the vertical shear stresses on AB must be zero, and the vertical pressure on the horizontal plane BX must be the same as that beneath the ground behind the wall at this level. Under these conditions a series of rupture planes such as BC, B_1C_1 would occur, inclined at $45° + \phi/2$ to the horizontal.

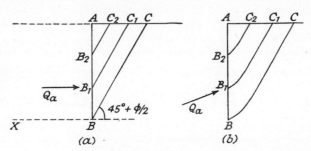

FIG. 20.6. (a) Rupture surfaces behind wall in Rankine active state.
(b) Modification of rupture surfaces by wall friction.

In practice lateral yield results in a tendency for the soil to settle relative to the wall, and friction at this boundary leads to vertical shear stresses in the soil. These decrease in magnitude with distance from the wall, and result in curved rupture surfaces, as in Fig. 20.6 (b).

The effect on the stability of the wall is twofold. The earth pressure is reduced by about 20 per cent. in a typical case and the resultant force on the wall is directed downward, which reduces the overturning moment significantly. Although the actual rupture surface is curved, the magnitude of the earth pressure can be calculated with sufficient accuracy by the wedge theory, first described by Coulomb in 1776.

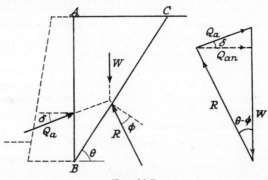

FIG. 20.7.

The application of this principle to the simple instance of a horizontal ground surface behind a vertical boundary without water pressure is illustrated in Fig. 20.7.

If δ is the angle of friction mobilised between the back of the wall and the soil, and ϕ the angle of internal friction of the soil, the resultant force Q_a between the soil and the wall will be inclined at an angle δ to the resultant normal force Q_{an}, and the resultant force R on the assumed rupture plane will be inclined at an angle ϕ to the normal. The relationship between Q_a,

R and the weight W of the soil above the rupture plane is given by the force polygon in Fig. 20.7, from which it follows that

$$Q_{an} = \frac{W}{\tan \delta + \cot (\theta - \phi)}.$$

For a wall of height H

$$W = \tfrac{1}{2}\rho H^2 \cot \theta.$$

Hence

$$Q_{an} = \frac{\rho H^2 \cot \theta}{2\{\tan \delta + \cot(\theta - \phi)\}}. \qquad \qquad (20.18)$$

The value of θ producing the maximum value of Q_{an} represents the surface on which rupture will occur. By making $\dfrac{dQ_{an}}{d\theta} = 0$ this maximum value is found to be

$$Q_{an} = \tfrac{1}{2}\rho H^2 K_a \qquad \qquad (20.19)$$

where

$$K_a = \left\{ \frac{\cos \phi \sqrt{\cos \delta}}{\sqrt{\cos \delta} + \sqrt{\sin (\delta + \phi) \sin \phi}} \right\}^2 \qquad (20.20)$$

It should be noted that when $\delta = 0$

$$K_a = \frac{\cos^2 \phi}{(1 + \sin \phi)^2} = \frac{1 - \sin \phi}{1 + \sin \phi},$$

which is the value of K_a given by the Rankine theory as in equation (20.12).

Values of K_a, the coefficient of active earth pressure, for typical values of ϕ and δ are given in Table 20.3.

TABLE 20.3.

VALUES OF K_a FOR COHESIONLESS SOIL : VERTICAL WALL SUPPORTING GROUND WITH HORIZONTAL SURFACE.

δ	ϕ					
	20°	25°	30°	35°	40°	45°
0°	0·49	0·41	0·33	0·27	0·22	0·17
10°	0·44	0·37	0·31	0·25	0·20	0·16
20°	0·41	0·34	0·28	0·23	0·19	0·15
30°	—	—	0·26	0·21	0·17	0·14

20.8. The use of active earth pressure coefficients in design.—The values of K_a modified by wall friction may be used when ground water is present in an expression analogous to that obtained for the Rankine state, equation (20.16) i.e.,

$$q_{an} = K_a\{\rho h - \rho_w(h - h')\} + \rho_w(h - h'). \qquad (20.21)$$

If the ground behind the wall is subjected to an extensive uniform surcharge of intensity w per unit area, the vertical effective stress will be increased by this amount and the lateral pressure on the wall will be increased by $K_a w$ at all levels. The most general form for q_{an} is thus

$$q_{an} = K_a\{w + \rho h - \rho_w(h - h')\} + \rho_w(h - h') \qquad (20.22)$$

The vertical component of stress on the wall is equal to the effective horizontal pressure multiplied by tan δ, i.e.

$$\tau = K_a\{w + \rho h - \rho_w(h - h')\}\tan \delta \quad . \quad . \quad . \quad (20.23)$$

For important structures both δ and ϕ should be measured for the actual materials involved. For less important work approximate values may be taken from the Code of Practice for Earth Retaining Structures (1951), from which the values of ϕ in Table 20.4 are quoted.

TABLE 20.4.

TYPICAL VALUES OF ϕ FOR COHESIONLESS MATERIALS : DRY OR SUBMERGED.

Material	ϕ deg.
Loose sand	30 to 35
Compact sand	35 ,, 40
Sandy gravel	35 ,, 45
Rock filling	35 ,, 45
Ashes or broken brick	35 ,, 45
Shale filling	30 ,, 35

The value of δ depends on three factors :—

(a) The nature of the surface of the structure. The value of δ is always less than ϕ, and in the absence of test data the Code recommends 20° for concrete or brick, 15° for uncoated steel piling and 30° for steel piling coated with tar or bitumen.

(b) The ability of the structure to support the vertical component. This is usually in doubt only in cases such as a strutted excavation where the sheet piling does not penetrate below the excavation sufficiently far to carry the vertical load, or in sinking a caisson, where the friction is directed in the opposite direction.

(c) The presence of continual vibration. In such instances δ should be taken as zero.

20.9. The calculation of passive pressure.—The influence of wall friction on the passive earth pressure coefficient K_p may also be examined by the use of the wedge theory, but the departure of the actual rupture surface from the plane assumed in the wedge analysis then leads to a more serious error in the calculated value of the coefficient. The error, which is on the unsafe side, increases as the ratio δ/ϕ is increased, and for a horizontal surface more elaborate methods of calculation must be used if this ratio is greater than one-third.

The types of analysis used to obtain more accurate values of K_p include the examination of curved failure surfaces by iterative methods (Packshaw, 1946), and the numerical solution of the equations of plastic equilibrium for the appropriate boundary conditions (Caquot and Kerisel, 1948). The values in Table 20.5 have been obtained by interpolation from the tables published by Caquot and Kerisel.

The relative movement required to mobilise full wall friction in the passive state is difficult to assess. As the value of δ has a marked influence on the magnitude of K_p, a conservative estimate of δ is usually made unless it is clear that the wall will tend to move downwards relative to the ground.

A value of one-half that used in the active case is recommended in the Code of Practice. It is also obvious that the vertical component of wall friction on an anchor block, for example, cannot exceed the weight of the block.

TABLE 20.5.

VALUES OF K_p FOR COHESIONLESS MATERIALS : VERTICAL WALL PRESSING AGAINST GROUND WITH HORIZONTAL SURFACE.

δ	ϕ					
	20°	25°	30°	35°	40°	45°
0°	2·0	2·5	3·0	3·7	4·6	5·8
10°	2·6	3·2	4·1	5·3	7·0	9·6
20°	—	3·5	5·2	7·0	9·7	14·2
30°	—	—	—	8·4	12·6	19·4

20.10. Wedge analysis for irregular boundaries.—Consideration has so far been given only to a vertical wall with a horizontal ground surface and a horizontal ground water table. The wedge analysis described in paragraph 20.7 can, however, be generalised to apply to a battered wall and an inclined ground surface.

The values of K_a and K_p derived from this solution, and also from more accurate solutions involving curved rupture surfaces, are tabulated in the published earth pressure tables.

These solutions are, however, only applicable to practical problems under the following alternative special conditions,

(a) the soil is completely free from water pressure
(b) the soil is completely submerged, when the earth pressure can be calculated in terms of the submerged density of the soil, and added to the water pressure
(c) the water pressure at any depth is constant throughout the slope.

The instances in which practical conditions approximate to these conditions are so rare that the very elaborate analysis of the complete wedge theory is of little more than academic interest today and is not reproduced here. Solutions can, however, readily be obtained directly from the wedge analysis for any specified conditions using a semi-graphical procedure. Two examples will be considered.

Fig. 20.8 illustrates a battered wall supporting ground whose surface cannot be represented by a single inclined line. The ground water table is horizontal. An arbitrary rupture plane BC is selected and the total weight of soil W above this plane is calculated. The reactions at the boundaries AB and BC are divided into hydrostatic pressure and effective stress components. If MN represents the water level within the wedge, the resultant force due to hydrostatic pressure normal to AB is $\frac{1}{2}MB^2 \sin \alpha$ per unit length of wall, and the corresponding resultant, R_w, normal to BC is $\frac{1}{2}NB^2 \sin \theta$. The resultant Q_a' of the effective stresses acting on AB is inclined to the normal at an angle δ ; the corresponding resultant acting on BC is inclined to the normal at an angle ϕ. The force polygon can thus be drawn, as shown in Fig. 20.8.

Rupture is most likely to occur on the plane which gives the maximum value of Q_a'. It follows that this value corresponds to the maximum value of the total thrust Q_a, which is the resultant of Q_a' and Q_w, since the term Q_w remains constant. This maximum may be found after three or four trials by plotting the values of Q_a against the position of the point C as in Fig. 20.8.

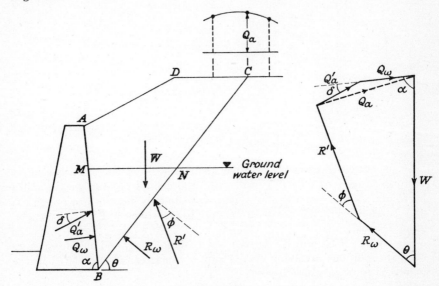

FIG. 20.8.

In many instances ground water conditions cannot be represented by a horizontal water table, corresponding to static ground water. Indeed, the presence of a retaining wall, particularly if it is provided with effective drains and weep holes, will modify the water-table in the ground behind it, and lead to steady seepage. The water-table will vary seasonally and the design of the wall should be based on the worst conditions. The loss in pressure head resulting from seepage flow means that the pressure at any point does not correspond directly with its depth below the water table, but should be determined from the flow pattern obtained by one of the procedures described in standard text books on Soil Mechanics or Hydraulics.

A typical flow pattern is illustrated in Fig. 20.9 by an orthogonal system of flow lines and equipotential lines (lines of equal pressure head). The water in a standpipe at a point would rise to the level at which the equipotential through that point met the free surface or zero pressure line. The resultant water pressure on BN can thus be obtained by graphical summation. In the simple illustration of Fig. 20.9 the water pressure on the back of the wall will be zero if the drain is efficient, and the force polygon will be as shown.

20.11. Influence of deformation on pressure distribution.—It will be clear from Fig. 20.2 that the load due to earth pressure, unlike the more usual external load systems, is itself a function of the deformation of the structure and cannot be assigned a unique value without some qualification as to the movement involved. The values of active and passive pressure calculated

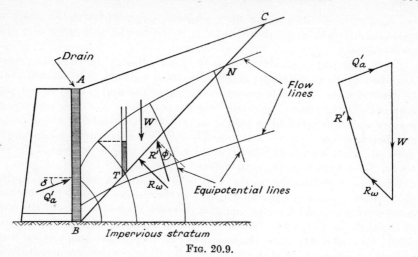

FIG. 20.9.

by either the Rankine or wedge methods correspond to states of plastic equilibrium.

This point is illustrated diagrammatically in Fig. 20.10. Curve 1 represents the load-displacement curve of the soil mass supported by a wall, and curves 2 and 3 the corresponding load-displacement curves of two walls of different rigidities. The load due to earth pressure decreases from the value

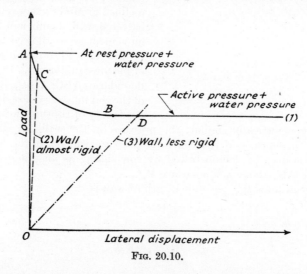

FIG. 20.10.

corresponding to the total at-rest pressure, equation (20.5), at zero lateral deformation (point A), to the value corresponding to the total active pressure, equation (20.22), at point B, and for larger displacements remains almost constant.

For a relatively rigid wall, such as a basement strutted by floor beams and a heavy raft, the load-displacement curve will be very steep and is represented by curve 2. The intersection C of this curve with curve 1 gives the load carried by the wall, and will lie close to A, the at-rest pressure. For a

17

less rigid wall, represented by the load-displacement curve 3, the point of intersection D will lie to the right of B, and the wall will carry only the active pressure.

For a wall tilting about its base or moving bodily forward, the tests described by Terzaghi (1934) and Rowe (1952) indicate that point B may be reached when the displacement of the top of the wall is $0 \cdot 05$ to $0 \cdot 1$ per cent. of its height, depending on the density of the soil. For design purposes, gravity walls are assumed to belong to this class and stability calculations are therefore based on the active pressure. This also applies to anchored sheet pile walls, for which Rowe (1952) has shown the elastic yield of the tie bars to be sufficient for the active state to be reached.

When the soil adjacent to the wall is in the at-rest state, the pressure distribution is given by equation (20.5). In the absence of water pressure the resultant force would therefore act at a distance above the base of the wall of one-third of its height. When the soil adjacent to the wall has passed wholly into the active state, the magnitude of the pressure on a vertical wall is given by equation (20.22) for level ground with water pressure and uniform surcharge. In the absence of water pressure and surcharge the height of the centre of pressure should again be one-third that of the wall ; this has been confirmed by large scale model tests.

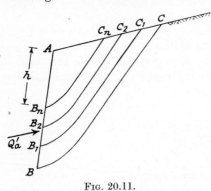

FIG. 20.11.

The same result would be expected for the more general conditions of an inclined ground surface retained by a battered wall, if sufficient freedom of movement were allowed for the soil behind the wall to pass into the state of plastic equilibrium. Provided the boundaries ABC, AB_1C_1, AB_2C_2, etc., of the soil masses enclosed by each of the family of rupture surfaces in Fig. 20.11 are geometrically similar, the pressure on the wall AB will increase linearly with depth, and the centre of pressure will be at the lower third point. This may be demonstrated by considering as an independent wall any section AB_n above a slip surface B_nC_n.

The normal force Q'_{an} per unit length of wall is

$$Q'_{an} = \tfrac{1}{2}\rho K_a h^2 \qquad \ldots \quad \ldots \quad \ldots \quad (20.24)$$

where $AB_n = h$.

Hence
$$q'_{an} = \frac{dQ'_{an}}{dh} = \rho K_a h. \qquad \ldots \quad \ldots \quad \ldots \quad (20.25)$$

This reasoning applies whatever the shape of the slip surfaces, provided they are geometrically similar.

Since the active pressure represents the lower limit of the pressure on the wall, it immediately follows (Southwell, 1932) that incomplete mobilisation of friction on the intermediate surfaces B_1C_1, etc., would involve higher pressures on the upper sections of the wall and a consequent rise in the level of the centre of pressure. This is confirmed by experiments in which the freedom of the upper part of the wall to deflect and thus allow the development of plastic equilibrium is restricted.

It would be out of place to discuss this aspect of the problem in detail, but since it is the condition commonly encountered in deep excavations, attention is drawn to two points. Such excavations are generally lined with relatively flexible timber or steel sheeting, and the upper strut is placed when the excavation is shallow and relatively little lateral yield has occurred. Before excavation has proceeded sufficiently for the next strut to be placed, the lower part of each exposed face is free to yield inwards, until it is ultimately restrained by the next strut. The resulting deformation for an excavation progressively deepened in this way leads to an incomplete development of the plastic state adjacent to the excavation. The pressure distribution is found to be approximately parabolic, Fig. 20.12, with the centre of pressure from 0·45 to 0·55 of the height of the sheeting above its base, while the resultant lateral thrust is about 10 per cent. higher than the active pressure given by the wedge theory.

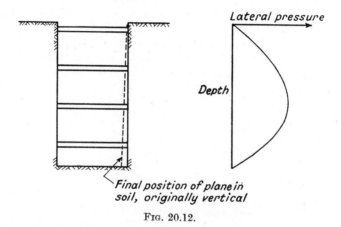

Fig. 20.12.

The distribution of passive pressure in frictional soils is controlled by the same factors. Much larger lateral displacements are, however, required before the soil passes wholly into the passive state, as indicated in Fig. 20.2. Tests indicate that in loose sand movements of up to 5 per cent. of the height of the wall may be necessary before the passive pressure is fully mobilised. For smaller movements, the centre of pressure will not necessarily be at the lower third point of the depth, but may deviate considerably on either side, depending on the relative movements of the top and bottom of the wall. Typical experimental results are given by Rowe (1952).

20.12. Active pressure in cohesive soils.—In his consideration of the limiting states of equilibrium of a soil mass, Rankine assumed that only the frictional strength of the soil could be relied on, and that the maximum shear stress reached on a surface of rupture was therefore directly proportional to the normal pressure. The corresponding failure criterion as given in equation (20.8) is $\tau = \sigma' \tan \phi$.

Though this assumption greatly simplifies the mathematical treatment, cohesion does in fact play an important part in many earth pressure problems and it is then necessary to use the more general criterion of failure

$$\tau = c + \sigma' \tan \phi. \qquad \ldots \qquad (20.26)$$

For a given soil stratum the term due to cohesion, c, is assumed to be a constant which is independent of the orientation of the rupture surface. Its value depends on the type of soil and on the geological history of the stratum, and is determined by standard test procedures.

The modification of Rankine's equations to take account of cohesion was made by Bell (1915) who, like Rankine, did not consider the influence of water pressure in the soil.

The full solution may readily be obtained by extending the analysis given in paragraph 20.4. The shear stress τ and normal effective stress σ' are given, as before, by equations (20.6) and (20.7),

$$\tau = (p' - q') \sin \theta \cos \theta,$$
$$\sigma' = p' \cos^2 \theta + q' \sin^2 \theta,$$

where p' and q' are respectively the effective vertical and horizontal stresses.

The active state is produced by lateral yield, which causes the horizontal stress to decrease until the shear strength is fully mobilised on the most critical plane. The stresses on this rupture plane must then satisfy the failure criterion and at the same time lead to the highest value of q'.

Substituting for τ and σ' in equation (20.26), and rearranging the terms, an expression for q' is obtained in terms of p', the constants c and ϕ and the angle θ,

$$(p' - q') \sin \theta \cos \theta = c + (p' \cos^2 \theta + q' \sin^2 \theta) \tan \phi$$

whence

$$q' = p' - \frac{p' \tan \phi + c}{\sin \theta \cos \theta + \sin^2 \theta \tan \phi}. \qquad \qquad (20.27)$$

For the maximum value of q', $\dfrac{dq'}{d\theta} = 0$

i.e.,
$$0 = \cos^2 \theta - \sin^2 \theta + 2 \sin \theta \cos \theta \tan \phi$$
$$= \cos 2\theta + \sin 2\theta \tan \phi.$$

Hence $\qquad \cot 2\theta = -\tan \phi = \cot (90° + \phi)$

and $\qquad \theta = 45° + \phi/2. \qquad \qquad \qquad (20.28)$

For a given value of ϕ, it follows therefore that the inclination of the rupture planes is independent of the magnitude of the cohesion. The value of q' is obtained by substituting the corresponding value of θ in equation (20.27) which leads to

$$q'_a = p' \left(\frac{1 - \sin \phi}{1 + \sin \phi} \right) - 2c \sqrt{\frac{1 - \sin \phi}{1 + \sin \phi}}. \qquad \qquad (20.29)$$

The first term is identical with the Rankine value, to which q'_a simplifies when c is zero.

By using equation (20.15), the expression can be written

$$q'_a = p' \tan^2 \left(45° - \frac{\phi}{2} \right) - 2c \tan \left(45° - \frac{\phi}{2} \right) \qquad \qquad (20.30)$$

or $\qquad q'_a = K_A \cdot p' - K_{AC} \cdot c, \qquad \qquad \qquad (20.31)$

where K_A and K_{AC} are coefficients dependent on ϕ.

Typical values of K_A and K_{AC} are given in Table 20.6.

It will be seen from equation (20.31) that at the ground surface, where p' is zero, the active condition corresponds to a state of tension in the ground,

TABLE 20.6.

VALUES OF K_A AND K_{AC} FOR COHESIVE SOIL IN THE ACTIVE RANKINE STATE, GROUND SURFACE HORIZONTAL.

ϕ	0°	5°	10°	15°	20°	25°	30°
K_A	1·00	0·85	0·70	0·59	0·48	0·41	0·33
K_{AC}	2·00	1·83	1·68	1·54	1·40	1·27	1·15

the horizontal pressure being equal to $-K_{AC}.c$. The tension zone extends to the depth where $q'_a=0$, i.e., where $K_A.p'=K_{AC}.c$.

Then
$$p'=\frac{K_{AC}.c}{K_A} \qquad \qquad (20.32)$$

In the absence of water pressure, the vertical pressure p' is equal to ρz, where z is the depth of the tension zone and hence, from equation (20.32) :

$$z=\frac{K_{AC}}{K_A}\frac{c}{\rho}. \qquad \qquad (20.33)$$

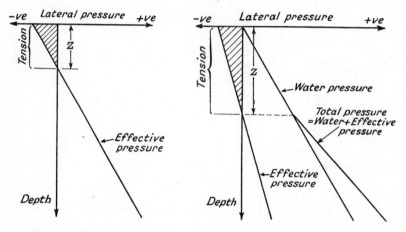

(a) Above Ground Water Level   (b) Ground Water Level at Surface

FIG. 20.13. Rankine active state for soil having both cohesion and friction.

Substituting the values of K_A and K_{AC} as in equation (20.30),

$$z=\frac{2c}{\rho}\cot\left(45°-\frac{\phi}{2}\right). \qquad \qquad (20.34)$$

For ground where water pressure acts, the value of p' is given by equation (20.2). In the limiting case when the water level is at the surface, $h'=0$ and

$$p'=z(\rho-\rho_w).$$

The depth of the zone in which tension would exist in the soil is then

$$z=\frac{2c}{(\rho-\rho_w)}\cot\left(45°-\frac{\phi}{2}\right) \qquad \qquad (20.35)$$

Negative effective stresses cannot be relied upon in permanent engineering work, particularly at the boundary with a wall, and in the diagrams of lateral pressure against depth in Fig. 20.13 the shaded areas relating to these negative stresses are neglected when calculating the total lateral thrust. The expression for the total lateral pressure including the water pressure and the surcharge w thus becomes

$$q_{an}=\rho_w(h-h')+[K_A(w+\rho h-\rho_w\overline{h-h'})-K_{AC}.c]. \qquad (20.36)$$

The term in square brackets is only included when it has a positive value.

20.13. The wedge theory for cohesive soils.—The modification of the state of stress adjacent to a wall due to shear forces at the boundary can be considered in terms of the wedge theory. The simple case of a vertical wall and horizontal ground surface is illustrated in Fig. 20.14. Vertical cracks are assumed to form in the zone in which tension is present and the mass of soil whose equilibrium is to be considered is represented by the boundary ABCD. The depth z of the zone of tension is assumed to be given by

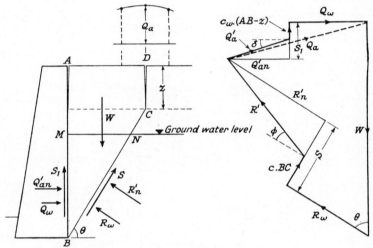

FIG. 20.14.

equation (20.34) although adjacent to the wall, where vertical shear occurs, this is only an approximation.

The forces normal to the rupture plane are the resultants R_w due to hydrostatic pressure and R'_n due to the effective stresses. The shearing force S, tangential to the rupture plane is, from equation (20.26),

$$S=c.BC+R'_n\tan\phi. \qquad (20.37)$$

The corresponding forces on AB are the resultants Q_w due to hydrostatic pressure, and Q'_{an} due to the effective stresses. The cohesion and friction along this boundary will in general be less than within the intact soil and are represented by c_w, the coefficient of wall adhesion, and δ, the angle of wall friction. c_w is assumed to act only below the limit of the tension zone, and the vertical force on the boundary is then

$$S_1=c_w(AB-z)+Q'_{an}\tan\delta. \qquad (20.38)$$

For a given rupture plane the values of the weight W, of the water pressure terms R_w and Q_w, and of the cohesion terms cBC and $c_w(AB-z)$, can all be calculated. The values of R' and Q'_a are obtained from the force polygon as shown in Fig. 20.14, which also gives the magnitude and direction of the resultant Q_a due to both water pressure and effective stress. The most critical plane is determined by three or four trials as in the previous analysis.

No general analytical solution of this problem is possible even when the water pressure is zero. The results of a large number of numerical solutions by Packshaw (1946) have shown, however, that the influence of wall friction and adhesion can be represented by a modification of the coefficients K_A and K_{AC} in equation (20.31), without serious loss of accuracy. Approximate values for these coefficients are given in Table 20.7, which is based on values in the Code of Practice.

TABLE 20.7.

VALUES OF COEFFICIENTS K_A AND K_{AC} FOR COHESIVE SOILS ON VERTICAL WALL. GROUND SURFACE HORIZONTAL.

Co-efficient	Values of δ	Values of c_w/c	Values of ϕ					
			0°	5°	10°	15°	20°	25°
K_A	0	All	1·00	0·85	0·70	0·59	0·48	0·41
	ϕ	values	1·00	0·78	0·64	0·50	0·40	0·32
K_{AC}	0	0	2·00	1·83	1·68	1·54	1·40	1·27
	0	1·0	2·83	2·60	2·38	2·16	1·96	1·76
	ϕ	0·5	2·45	2·10	1·82	1·55	1·32	1·15
	ϕ	1·0	2·83	2·47	2·13	1·85	1·59	1·41

20.14. Passive pressure in cohesive soils.—By an analysis similar to that given in paragraph 20.12, it can be shown that the maximum resistance to lateral thrust is

$$q'_p = p' \tan^2\left(45° + \frac{\phi}{2}\right) + 2c \tan\left(45° + \frac{\phi}{2}\right) \quad . \quad . \quad . \quad (20.39)$$

which may be written

$$q'_p = K_P . p' + K_{PC} . c. \quad . \quad . \quad . \quad . \quad (20.40)$$

Values for the coefficients K_P and K_{PC} taken from the Code of Practice are given in Table 20.8. They are approximate values based on the wedge theory for various values of wall friction and adhesion.

TABLE 20.8

VALUES OF COEFFICIENTS K_P AND K_{PC} FOR COHESIVE SOILS ; VERTICAL WALL PRESSING AGAINST GROUND WITH HORIZONTAL SURFACE.

Co-efficient	Values of δ	Values of c_w/c	Values of ϕ					
			0°	5°	10°	15°	20°	25°
K_P	0	All	1·0	1·2	1·4	1·7	2·1	2·5
	ϕ	values	1·0	1·3	1·6	2·2	2·9	3·9
K_{PC}	0	0	2·0	2·2	2·4	2·6	2·8	3·1
	0	0·5	2·4	2·6	2·9	3·2	3·5	3·8
	0	1·0	2·6	2·9	3·2	3·6	4·0	4·4
	ϕ	0·5	2·4	2·8	3·3	3·8	4·5	5·5
	ϕ	1·0	2·6	2·9	3·4	3·9	4·7	5·7

It will be seen that q_p' is positive for all values of p', and so no tension cracks develop in the passive state.

20.15. Soil treated as a purely cohesive material.—Hitherto it has been assumed that the hydrostatic pressure in the ground is either known from the level of the ground water table or can be determined from the flow pattern resulting from seepage. Cohesive soils are, however, generally of low permeability, and the tendency towards volume change in the soil, resulting from stress release when the wall is first constructed, leads to a temporary modification of the hydrostatic pressure.

In temporary excavations in clay this initial stage is of primary interest. Under these conditions the explicit determination of the hydrostatic pressure is unnecessary and use can be made of the fact that a saturated clay, when sheared under conditions of zero drainage, behaves as a purely cohesive material *with respect to changes in total stress*. An analysis based on this principle is termed a " $\phi = 0$ " analysis. Justification for it has been given by Skempton (1948) and will not be discussed in detail here. It is

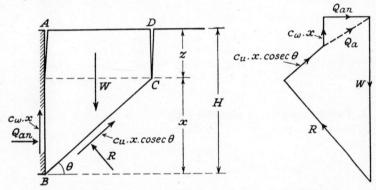

FIG. 20.15. The " $\phi = 0$ " analysis, using the wedge theory.

sufficient to accept the conclusion that the strength terms may be replaced by the *apparent cohesion* c_u, measured in a test in which no flow of water from the sample is permitted, and that the analysis may then be made in terms of total stresses.

In this special instance analytical solutions of the example given in the previous paragraph are possible both by the wedge theory and by methods using a surface of rupture which satisfies more closely the conditions of stress compatibility. The wedge analysis is illustrated in Fig. 20.15.

If z is the limit of depth of tension cracks and H is the height of the wall, it is convenient to put $x = H - z$. The weight W of the mass of soil ABCD per unit length is then

$$W = \rho(xz \cot \theta + \tfrac{1}{2} x^2 \cot \theta). \quad . \quad . \quad . \quad (20.41)$$

From the force polygon it can be seen that

$$W \sin \theta - Q_{an} \cos \theta - c_u x \operatorname{cosec} \theta - c_w x \sin \theta = 0 \quad . \quad . \quad (20.42)$$

whence $\quad Q_{an} = \rho(\tfrac{1}{2}x^2 + xz) - c_u x \sec \theta \operatorname{cosec} \theta - c_w x \tan \theta. \quad . \quad . \quad (20.43)$

The inclination of the most critical surface occurs when $\dfrac{dQ_{an}}{d\theta} = 0$, *i.e.*, when

$$\cot^2 \theta = 1 + \frac{c_w}{c_u}. \quad . \quad . \quad . \quad . \quad . \quad (20.44)$$

Substituting this value in equation (20.43) and putting $x = H - z$ gives

$$Q_{an} = \tfrac{1}{2}\rho(H^2 - z^2) - 2c_u\sqrt{1 + \frac{c_w}{c_u}} \cdot (H - z). \quad . \quad . \quad . \quad (20.45)$$

If the plastic zone is fully developed adjacent to the wall, the lateral pressure q_{an} at a depth h is

$$q_{an} = \frac{dQ_{an}}{dh} = \rho h - 2c_u\sqrt{1 + \frac{c_w}{c_u}}. \quad . \quad . \quad . \quad (20.46)$$

In the limit when wall adhesion is equal to the shear strength of the intact soil $c_w = c_u$ and then

$$q_{an} = \rho h - 2\sqrt{2} \cdot c_u. \quad . \quad . \quad . \quad . \quad . \quad (20.47)$$

It will be noticed that the use of the wedge theory leads to an anomaly in the magnitude of the lateral pressure immediately below the tension zone whose depth z for the $\phi = 0$ case is, from equation (20.34), equal to $\dfrac{2c}{\rho}$. This can only be avoided by more rigorous analysis, which is generally not justified since the magnitude of the resultant thrust is not much affected by the approximations involved in the wedge method.

20.16. Distribution of lateral pressure in cohesive soils.—If the displacement of the wall is sufficient for the full development of the plastic zone adjacent to it the distribution of active pressure is given by equation (20.36), and of passive pressure by equation (20.40). It follows that in the active state the centre of pressure will lie a little below the lower third point, as in Fig. 20.13, and that in the passive state it will lie above the lower third point. The exact positions will depend on the relative values of K_A and K_{AC}, or K_P and K_{PC}, and on the ground water level.

Partial restraint by strutting will raise the level of the centre of pressure on the active side, but in a deep strutted excavation it is unlikely to rise above mid-height. In considering the initial pressure on the timbering of a deep excavation in clay to which the $\phi = 0$ analysis is applicable, the possible amount of redistribution of pressure is determined within narrower limits by the initial strength of the clay. Very soft clay will behave almost as a dense fluid and little redistribution of stress is possible, the centre of pressure therefore being close to the lower third point. In clay which initially is relatively strong, sufficient redistribution may occur to bring the centre of pressure up to the mid-height as in Fig. 20.12. A more detailed discussion is given by Terzaghi (1943), and an analysis of field data by Skempton (1953).

20.17. Some structural problems involving earth pressure.—Three important classes of structure have been referred to in the preceding paragraphs—strutted excavations, anchored sheet pile walls and gravity walls—and it is of interest, in concluding this discussion of earth pressure, to indicate how their design is related to the earth pressure calculations.

Strutted excavations.—The construction of deep basements for high buildings, and of trenches for services or for the cut-off beneath a dam, commonly involve open excavations of up to 50 feet in depth, and, in exceptional cases, of 200 feet. The safe and economical design of the sheeting and strutting is then a major problem.

17*

As indicated in paragraphs 20.11 and 20.16, the total lateral thrust Q_{an} at any stage can be calculated with reasonable accuracy, but its distribution will depend on the actual lateral yield permitted during excavation. To allow for the unpredictable variations in yield which occur in practice, an envelope of the probable variations in distribution is used in design, as indicated in Fig. 20.16. The area of this envelope represents a total thrust 44 per cent. greater than the actual active thrust Q_{an}. In general the sheeting cannot carry vertical shear forces and therefore wall friction and adhesion are assumed to be zero.

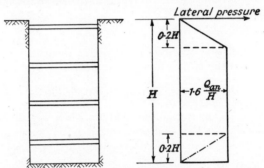

FIG. 20.16.   Lateral pressure envelope used in design of struts. (For dense sands reduction indicated by dotted line — · — · — is used.)

The safety of a deep excavation in soft clay depends not only on the design of the strutting, but on the adequacy of the shear strength of the soil to maintain the unbalanced vertical pressure at the bottom of the excavation. An analysis of this problem and supporting field evidence is given by Bjerrum and Eide (1956).

Anchored sheet pile walls.—Many permanent quay walls are now constructed of anchored sheet piling as shown in Fig. 20.17. Their design involves the calculation of the active pressure behind the wall and the passive pressure at its toe. These pressures, and in particular their distribution, determine the bending moment in the piles and the tie bar pull. If the tie bar is carried to an anchor block or wall, the permissible anchor pull will be determined by the passive pressure on the anchor.

Experimental work by Rowe (1952) has shown that the pressure on the back of the wall will approximate to the active pressure without redistribution. The position of the centre of pressure on the front of the wall, where the soil is in the passive state, will, however, rise with increasing flexibility of the wall owing to the relatively larger displacements at the surface C due to " bowing " as indicated in Fig. 20.17 (c) and (d). This rise of the centre of pressure shortens the effective span, and may reduce the maximum bending moment to less than 50 per cent. of that carried by a rigid wall; the anchor pull is also modified. Details of the design procedure and the empirical reduction factors are given by Rowe (1952) and Terzaghi (1953).

The initial calculation for a rigid wall is illustrated by a simple example in Fig. 20.17 (b). Curve 1 represents the effective active pressure on the wall, and curve 2 represents this active pressure plus the water pressure on the back of the wall, less the water pressure on the front. Curve 3 represents the effective passive pressure, and curve 4 the passive values divided by a suitable load factor (2 or 3 for sands). Q_{an} and Q_{pn} are the resultant active and passive forces given by curves 2 and 4 respectively.

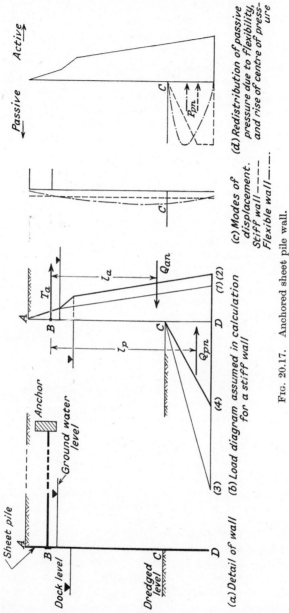

FIG. 20.17.   Anchored sheet pile wall.

The necessary penetration CD of the pile is obtained from the equation for moment equilibrium about the point B,

$$Q_{an}l_a = Q_{pn}l_p \qquad . \quad . \quad . \quad . \quad . \quad . \quad (20.48)$$

and the anchor pull, T_a per unit length, is obtained by equating horizontal forces,

$$T_a = Q_{an} - Q_{pn}. \qquad . \quad . \quad . \quad . \quad . \quad . \quad (20.49)$$

The corresponding load diagram leads to the bending moment distribution. Calculated penetrations are usually increased by an additional 20 per cent. to allow for subsequent errors in dredging, erosion, etc. It is also necessary in practice to ensure that the anchor is far enough from the wall to be effective, and that the removal of material by dredging in front of the wall does not lead, in clays, to deep-seated shear failure.

Gravity walls.—Massive walls of concrete, masonry or brickwork, are frequently used for dock walls and other permanent earth retaining structures, particularly where local materials can be utilised and where the foundation strata are suitable.

Theoretically, a gravity wall may fail in any of the ways described in Chapter 19 in the analysis of gravity dams retaining water. Practical

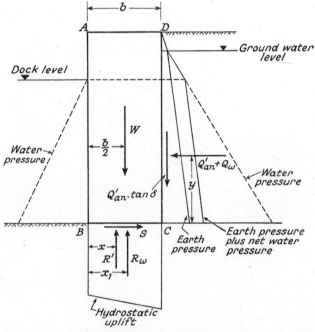

Fig. 20.18.   Load diagram for a rectangular section dock wall retaining frictional soil.

considerations, however, direct the designer's attention primarily to conditions at the base of the wall. Gravity walls seldom exceed 50 feet in height, and failure due to excessive compressive stress in the masonry is therefore improbable: as the walls are not primarily water retaining structures, limited tensile stresses are permissible. Failure can therefore only occur by the wall sliding bodily forward on its foundations, overturning bodily about the toe, or by failure of the foundation strata due to combined compressive and shear stresses beneath the base of the wall.

The stability against overturning can be analysed, as illustrated in the example in Fig. 20.18, by taking moments about the toe (point B) to determine the position of the vertical reaction on the base of the wall, R'. In this example Q'_{an} is the effective lateral thrust and Q_w the force representing the difference in water pressure between the back and front of the wall.

The resultant of Q'_{an} and Q_w acts at a height y. The vertical force due to wall friction is $Q'_{an} \tan \delta$. The weight W can be calculated and the magnitude and position of the force R_w on the base due to hydrostatic uplift can be determined as for a dam, assuming linear distribution across the base. The remaining forces are the effective vertical reaction R′ and the shear force S. Then resolving vertically,

$$R' = W + Q'_{an} \tan \delta - R_w, \quad \ldots \ldots \quad (20.50)$$

and taking moments about point B,

$$R'x = \frac{Wb}{2} + Q'_{an}b \tan \delta - R_w x_1 - (Q'_{an} + Q_w)y. \quad \ldots \quad (20.51)$$

These equations give the values of R′ and x. It is usually taken as a design rule that the reaction should lie within the middle third, $i.e.$ that $x > b/3$.

Equating horizontal forces, the shear force is

$$S = Q'_{an} + Q_w \quad \ldots \ldots \ldots \quad (20.52)$$

If sliding is resisted only by base friction it is necessary that

$$S < R' \tan \delta_b \quad \ldots \ldots \ldots \quad (20.53)$$

where δ_b is the angle of friction between the base and the foundation material.

Since the middle-third requirement can be satisfied without difficulty by varying the width b, provided the soil properties and water heads are known, few overturning failures have been recorded, most failures being due to overstressing either of the foundation strata or of the junction with the base of the wall. Reference should be made to the Code of Practice and to text books on Soil Mechanics for a more detailed discussion of these modes of failure, and to specialist papers ($e.g.$ Meyerhof, 1953) for an analysis of safe bearing capacity under combined vertical pressure and horizontal shear stress.

20.18. Factor of safety.—The difficulty of adhering to a unified concept of factor of safety when analysing a structural problem involving earth pressure will be obvious. It may be accepted, however, that as a general rule active earth pressure is treated as a structural load. The best estimate is made of its magnitude under the most severe water level conditions, and the structure is designed to carry this load with a conventional factor of safety or load factor.

The passive pressure, on the other hand, represents the ability of the soil to carry an applied load, and a load factor of 2 or 3 is generally allowed in calculating the passive resistance.

When the hydrostatic pressures are large and the cohesion and friction values small, it should be remembered that the passive pressure cannot be less than that corresponding to a fluid equal in density to the soil. It is therefore more realistic to apply the load factor only to the difference between this value and the calculated passive pressure.

REFERENCES

Coulomb, C. A. 1776. *Mémoires Académie Royale des Sciences.* Paris, **7**.
Rankine, W. J. M. 1857. *Phil. Trans.*, **147**, 9–27.
Richardson, L. F. 1909. *Phil. Trans.*, **210**, 307–357.
Bell, A. L. 1915. *Min. Proc. Instn. Civ. Engrs.*, **199**, 233–272.

Southwell, R. V. 1932. *Min. Proc. Instn. Civ. Engrs.*, **234**, 216–218.

Terzaghi, K. 1934. *Engng. News Rec.*, **112**, 136–140.

Terzaghi, K. 1936. *J. Boston Soc. Civ. Engrs.*, **23**, 71–78.

Terzaghi, K. 1943. " Theoretical Soil Mechanics." New York. John Wiley.

Packshaw, S. 1946. *J. Instn. Civ. Engrs.*, **25**, 233–256.

Skempton, A. W. 1948. *Proc. Second Int. Conf. Soil Mech.*, **1**, 72–78.

Caquot, A. and Kerisel, J. 1948. *Tables for the calculation of passive pressure, active pressure and bearing capacity of foundations.* Paris. Gauthier-Villars.

Tschebotarioff, G. P. 1949. *Final Report Large Scale Earth Pressure Tests with Model Flexible Bulkheads.* Princeton Univ., N.J.

Civil Engineering Code of Practice. 1951. *Earth Retaining Structures.* London. Inst. of Struct. Engrs.

Rowe, P. W. 1952. *Proc. Instn. Civ. Engrs.*, **1** (1), 27–70.

Skempton, A. W. 1953. *Proc. Third Int. Conf. Soil Mech.*, **2**, 353–361.

Meyerhof, G. G. 1953. *Proc. Third Int. Conf. Soil Mech.*, **1**, 440–445.

Bjerrum, L. and Eide, O. 1956. *Géotechnique*, **6**, 32–47.

EXERCISES

(1) A temporary excavation 25 feet in depth is to be made in clay, having an apparent cohesion c_u of 400 lb. per square foot. The density is 100 lb. per cubic foot.

Four rows of struts are to be used (as in Fig. 20.16), the first at 3 feet below ground level, and the remaining three at intervals of 6 feet. Calculate the total lateral thrust per foot run, and estimate the load for which the struts in each row must be designed, assuming that the sheeting is hinged at the lines of the 2nd and 3rd rows of struts. The lateral spacing of the struts is 8 feet.

(6·5 tons per foot run ; 12·2 tons ;
19·2 tons ; 15·3 tons ; 27·5 tons.)

(2) An anchored sheet pile quay wall is to be constructed at a site where both the foundation strata and the filling behind the wall are of sand. The dredged level is to be 30 feet below the level of the quay, giving a depth of water of 25 feet. Ground water level may rise 3 feet above dock water level.

Calculate the necessary penetration to ensure stability and the anchor pull per foot run, if the tie bars are horizontal and at a depth of 4 feet. Determine how these values should be modified to allow for a uniform surcharge on the quay of 5 cwt. per square foot.

The angle of internal friction of the sand is 35°. The angle of wall friction may be taken as 20° for both active and passive pressure, and a load factor of $2\frac{1}{2}$ should be applied to the passive resistance. The density of the sand above the water table is 105 lb. per cubic foot, and where saturated, 125 lb. per cubic foot.

In calculating water pressures assume complete cut off at the bottom of the piles.

(12·5 feet ; 3·3 tons per foot run ;
14·2 feet ; 4·7 tons per foot run.)

(3) The water level in front of a mass concrete lock wall of rectangular cross section is normally kept 4 feet below the coping, and ground water level in the sand fill behind stays at this level.

If the water level drops 8 feet during the operation of the lock, find the base width necessary to ensure stability against overturning. The height of the wall is 24 feet.

The density of the sand above the water table is 100 lb. per cubic foot, and, where saturated, 120 lb. per cubic foot. The angle of internal friction ϕ is 30° and the angle of wall friction δ is 20°. Density of concrete is 150 lb. per cubic foot.

(15·4 feet.)

CHAPTER 21

EXPERIMENTAL STRUCTURAL ANALYSIS

21.1. Introduction.—Many problems of structural design are amenable to mathematical treatment without other aid, but some are not so tractable and require the help of experiments for their solution. These may be adequate by themselves or they may be better used as an auxiliary aid to mathematical analysis. The early engineers relied largely upon tests to furnish information as to the strength and behaviour of particular structural units just as they do today, but it is comparatively recently that the use of experiments has been extended to actual design problems as a substitute for calculation. The development of the experimental approach, however, has been rapid and there is now a very extensive literature dealing with all aspects of this branch of structural analysis (*e.g.* Hetényi, 1950).

The uses of experiment in this connexion are varied, and before describing particular techniques they will be briefly considered under the following heads :—

(*a*) Exploratory experiments made before mathematical analysis.

(*b*) Confirmatory experiments made after analysis.

(*c*) Experiments made in conjunction with analysis to provide essential data or to obtain empirical formulas.

(*d*) Analytical experiments to replace computation in specific problems.

(*e*) Experiments of an *ad hoc* nature.

Exploratory experiments.—These are undertaken to study the behaviour of structures or components under test conditions with a view to subsequent mathematical analysis. They are not meant to provide exact data but simply to clarify the problem, and in designing them the aim should be to simplify and idealise the conditions as much as possible. An example of this is the research into the behaviour of the voussoir arch referred to in paragraph 16.4 in which simple preliminary experiments on a small model showed clearly the mechanics of the structure and influenced the whole of the subsequent work.

Confirmatory experiments.—The mathematical treatment of practical problems is usually only made possible by more or less drastic simplifications, and it is generally desirable and often essential that the legitimacy of the simplifying assumptions should be verified. In some instances the assumptions have been so well established in the past that they may be accepted without reserve, but in others, experimental tests are imperative before the results of the analysis can be used with confidence. The importance of confirmatory experiments varies considerably with the problem, but prudence would dictate such checks in any case of doubt.

Data-providing experiments.—These serve two purposes ; first, data may be needed for the correlation of analytical results with practical conditions. For example, the Perry strut formula was obtained by mathematical

515

reasoning some time before it was possible to use it for design purposes since the constant η of paragraph 7·7, introduced to allow for the departure of the strut from perfection of shape, material and loading, needed evaluation.

This constant cannot be specified numerically for any particular strut, but a comprehensive study of experimental results from many sources enabled its assessment statistically (Robertson, 1928), and the formula, which until then had been only of academic value, became the standard for strut design in Great Britain.

Secondly, experiments under this head may be made in conjunction with a sketchy mathematical theory, or even without any logical background, to obtain empirical formulas. Many of the strut tests mentioned above had such an object and much early work on concrete must be included in this category.

Analytical experiments.—A valid and well-established mathematical procedure may be available for the solution of a particular problem, but it may entail long and laborious computation. Simple experimental methods can then often be used with considerable saving of time ; the experiments may replace numerical calculations completely or serve as a check and so save a second set of calculations.

Ad hoc experiments.—Perhaps the commonest of all, these are made to determine the actual strength or behaviour of a particular unit, and range from a test to destruction on a small component to the proof loading of a completed structure.

We can now turn attention to some of the methods used in the experimental analysis of structures.

21.2. Direct measurement of stress.—The most obvious method of experimentation is to build a scale model of a structure to be studied and load it in a similar manner to the prototype. This provides direct information as to stress distribution which can very simply be translated into terms of the full scale structure, and is often useful as an aid to design. A somewhat elaborate investigation of this sort made in relation to airship design (Pippard and Baker, 1925) serves as a good example of the possibilities of this approach, although the type of structure to which it was particularly related is now only a matter of history.

The high degree of redundancy possessed by a rigid airship structure makes the application of the more usual mathematical methods of analysis described in Chapter 6 a practical impossibility and it was necessary to produce, for design purposes, approximate formulas of a generalised type to enable the internal forces in the various members to be determined from a knowledge of the resultant actions at any section of the hull. Before these formulas could be used with confidence their accuracy had to be checked and, as this could not be done against results obtained by more accurate mathematical analysis, recourse had to be made to experimental methods.

The experimental structure and some details of its construction are shown in Fig. 21.1. The framework was 3 bays in length, each bay being 30 inches long and of hexagonal cross-section, the side of the hexagon being 25 inches. With the object of the experimental work in view the structure was built to conform as nearly as possible to the assumptions made in deriving the formulas to be tested. Fig. 21.1 shows the design of joint adopted so that the members would be subjected to as little end bending restraint as possible, the assumption having been made in the analytical work that the structure was pin-jointed. The joints were $1\frac{1}{4}$-inch diameter Hoffmann steel balls, partially softened to receive $\frac{7}{32}$-inch diameter steel dowels, the other ends of which were screwed into plugs in the ends of the members, leaving $\frac{1}{16}$-inch between the faces of the joint and the plug. While these dowels had the necessary strength their small flexural rigidity ensured that the amount of restraint offered by them would be small. To test the efficacy of the arrangement a strut 24 inches long and ·75 inch diameter fitted with the dowel ends was tested in compression and failed at a load of 7,645 lb., the calculated Euler critical load being 7905 lb.

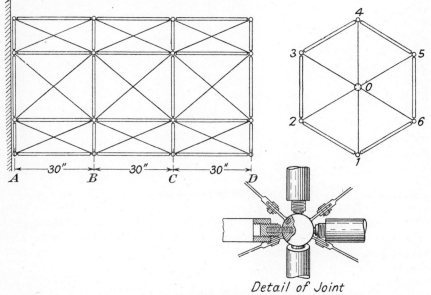

Detail of Joint

Fig. 21.1.

The transverse and longitudinal members of the structure were made of steel tube, $\frac{7}{8}$-inch outside diameter and 22 gauge thick, while all cross bracing members were 4 B.A. swaged rods, ability to resist compression being obtained by initially tensioning them.

The strains in the members were measured by means of a simple type of extensometer. Along each member of the structure was placed a gauge of thin aluminium, corrugated for the sake of stiffness. It was attached to the member at one end by a hardened steel knife-edge and small set screw ; at the other end was a small circle of glass marked on the underside with a fine cross hair at right angles to the axis of the member, the glass being held in contact with the member by rubber bands. A fine line was scratched on the member to coincide as nearly as possible with the line on the glass. The distance between the scratches on the member and on the glass was measured by a specially designed micrometer-microscope and the alteration in this distance under different conditions of loading gave the elongation or contraction of the gauge length. The gauges were 15 inches long between the point of attachment to the member and the line on the glass. Calibration curves obtained by direct loading tests were used to reduce the micrometer-head readings to loads in the member. Dead loads were applied to the

TABLE 21.1.

Member	Measured load lb.	Calculated load lb.
A_1B_1	335·5	343·0
A_2B_2	200·0	206·0
A_3B_3	−196·1	−206·0
A_4B_4	−352·0	−343·0
A_1B_2	73·0	70·7
A_2B_1	− 26·5	− 27·2
A_2B_3	105·0	106·0
A_3B_2	−110·0	−106·0
A_3B_4	25·5	27·2
A_4B_3	− 74·0	− 70·8
B_1C_1	188·4	206·0
B_2C_2	123·5	123·6
B_3C_3	−115·5	−123·6
B_4C_4	−211·0	−206·0
B_1C_2	68·0	62·0
B_2C_1	− 35·0	− 36·0
B_2C_3	103·2	106·0
B_3C_2	−110·0	−106·0
B_3C_4	36·2	36·0
B_4C_3	− 63·0	− 62·0

structure and the strains, and from them the stresses, were found in all the members. Table 21.1 shows a typical set of experimental results obtained when a radial load of 400 lb. was applied at joint D of the end bulkhead. It will be seen from a comparison between the measured loads and those obtained by calculation that the experimental method gave satisfactory results.

21.3. Experimental slope deflexion method of analysis.—Another simple method of analysis in which loads are applied to model structures makes use of the slope-deflexion relations derived in Chapter 9 and is of particular value in the determination of the internal reactions of structures such as building frames which are made up in the main of straight members of uniform cross-section. This method does not call for the use of elaborate and expensive apparatus or any very refined technique and might well be employed in a design office. The model structure can be made quickly and cheaply since it is only necessary to ensure that the centre lines of its members represent to some convenient scale the centre lines of the members of the structure to be analysed and that the second moments of area of its members are proportional to those of corresponding members of the structure. Hence, if the whole of the model is made of material of the same thickness, the depths of the members must be proportional to the cube roots of the second moments of area of the members of the structure. Additional refinement may be introduced by making the model of material of different thicknesses, so that both the second moments of area and the depths are proportional to those of the actual sections. Any load may be applied which does not overstrain the model and will be governed by the dimensions of the members and the type of microscope used.

W. M. Wilson and G. A. Maney (1915) described tests which they carried out on a xylonite model to check the deflexions and the changes in slope as calculated by the slope-deflexion method for wind loads on a building frame. The agreement between theory and experiment led to the analysis of the stresses in such frames by the direct measurement of the slopes and deflexions of models under load (Baker, 1932).

The necessary equations are derived in paragraph 9.3, the convention as to signs, as shown in Fig. 9.9, being as follows :—

(1) The rotation of a joint is positive when clockwise.
(2) The deflexion of one end of a member relative to the other is positive when the line joining the ends rotates clockwise.
(3) The end moments applied by the joints to the members are positive when they tend to cause a clockwise rotation.

The bending moments at the ends A and B of a member AB of uniform cross-section throughout its length are given by

$$M_{AB} = \frac{2EI_{AB}}{l_{AB}}\left[2\phi_A + \phi_B - 3\frac{\delta_{AB}}{l_{AB}}\right] - \frac{A_{AB}}{l_{AB}}$$

and
$$M_{BA} = \frac{2EI_{AB}}{l_{AB}}\left[\phi_A + 2\phi_B - 3\frac{\delta_{AB}}{l_{AB}}\right] + \frac{A_{AB}}{l_{AB}}$$

where E denotes the modulus of elasticity of the material,

I_{AB} denotes the second moment of area of the member AB,

ϕ_A and ϕ_B denote the changes of slope at A and B,

δ_{AB} is the deflexion of one end of the member relative to the other, due to the applied loads,

A_{AB} is the area of the free bending moment diagram for AB

and l_{AB} is the length of the span AB.

If, therefore, the changes of slope and deflexions in a loaded model can be measured, the bending moments can be evaluated from the above equations, and the bending moments in a similar frame under a similar load system can be deduced.

Following the lead given by Wilson and Maney, tests were made on xylonite models, but they were not satisfactory as it was impossible to obtain readings with any accuracy owing to the creep of the xylonite. So a model two-storey, two-bay frame was cut out of sheet brass $\frac{1}{32}$-inch thick. The foot of each stanchion was held in a steel clamp representing the foundation slab and a double row of $\frac{1}{8}$-inch diameter steel balls under each beam and stanchion supported the model in a horizontal position, but left it free to move under load. Load was applied to each beam through a turnbuckle and spring balance. Small clamps carrying aluminium pointers 6 inches long could be fixed at any point on the model. When load was applied the horizontal deflexions of the frame and of the free ends of the pointers were measured by means of micrometer-microscopes.

The brass models behaved satisfactorily and there was no appreciable creep. The only serious trouble likely to arise with models of this type is the buckling of members out of the plane of the frame, but this can be prevented by placing small weights on top of the frame to keep it in contact with the balls.

This slope deflexion method has some advantages over other methods when used to determine stresses in building frames. It has been useful in

elucidating the behaviour of frames with semi-rigid connexions, but its
sphere of usefulness is limited and when curved members or those of varying
cross-section are encountered, one of the methods described in a later
paragraph will prove more suitable.

Another example of this method of analysis, Fig. 21.2, shows a model of
an elevator rib for a large aeroplane arranged for test.   A load of 1 lb. was

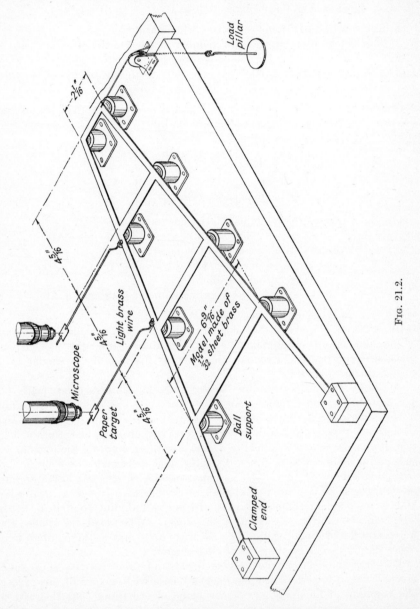

FIG. 21.2.

suspended from the end of the rib and the moments at each end of all the
chord bays were measured as described.   The results are tabulated below
together with the values calculated by a complete theoretical analysis.

TABLE 21.2.

Chord section		1	2	3	4
Left-hand section	Experiment	0·750	0·467	0·325	0·209
	Calculated	0·790	0·488	0·341	0·240
Right-hand section	Experiment	0·546	0·372	0·276	0·287
	Calculated	0·549	0·384	0·290	0·280

21.4. Mechanical methods of plotting influence lines.—The use of influence lines in the study of structures has been discussed in Chapters 14 and 15. Such diagrams can often be obtained by mechanical methods (Beggs, 1927). The fundamental basis of such methods is Clerk Maxwell's reciprocal theorem as given in paragraph 4.10.

Fig. 21.3 shows an elastic structure which has three redundant reactions. If the support B is removed the initial conditions may be restored by the application of a vertical force V_0, a horizontal force H_0 and a moment M_0. These redundant reactions must be determined before the resultant actions at any section can be found.

Suppose the load W to be removed and *a purely vertical* displacement of known amount Δ_B imposed at B. This will necessitate the application of unknown actions V′, H′ and M′ at B in the directions of V_0, H_0 and M_0.

Under this distortion let the point of application of W move in the direction of W by an amount Δ_W. Then we have two distinct force and displacement

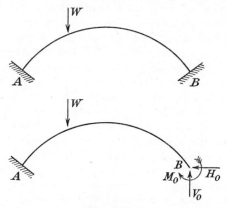

FIG. 21.3.

systems, one relating to the loaded structure in its original condition and the other to the displaced structure with no load acting at W.

Tabulating these we have

System 1 (*Original conditions*)

Force	V_0	H_0	M_0	W
Displacement	0	0	0	δ

System 2 (*Displaced structure*)

Force	V′	H′	M′	0
Displacement	Δ_B	0	0	Δ_W

Then by the reciprocal theorem,

$$V_0\Delta_B + H_0(0) + M_0(0) + W\Delta_W = V'(0) + H'(0) + M'(0) + 0(\delta)$$

or
$$V_0\Delta_B + W\Delta_W = 0.$$

If W is unity

$$V_0 = -\frac{\Delta_W}{\Delta_B}. \qquad \qquad \qquad (21.1)$$

The negative sign in equation (21.1) indicates that the displacement Δ_W is in the opposite direction to W.

If instead of applying a vertical displacement Δ_B at B, a *purely horizontal* displacement Δ'_B is imposed, the same argument leads to

$$H_0 = -\frac{\Delta_W'}{\Delta'_B} \qquad \qquad \qquad (21.2)$$

where Δ_W' is now the displacement of W in its line of action due to Δ'_B.

Similarly, if a *pure rotation* θ is imposed at B we find

$$M_0 = -\frac{\Delta_W''}{\theta} \qquad \qquad \qquad (21.3)$$

where Δ_W'' is the displacement of W in its line of action and due to the imposition of θ.

Equations (21.1), (21.2) and (21.3) are correct as long as the structure obeys a linear law between deformations and the forces causing them and is the basis of the method originally devised for the experimental determination of redundant reactions or forces in a structure (Beggs, 1927).

A model representing the structure to be analysed is made of any suitable material such as sheet xylonite and is mounted on a drawing board in a way representative of the prototype. The section at which redundant actions are to be determined is cut and re-connected through the medium of an instrument known as a deformeter. This instrument consists of two bars which can be moved relatively to one another by the insertion of accurately ground plugs. The ends of the cut member are clamped to these bars which are then displaced as required by small, known, amounts. The movements of other points on the model caused by these displacements are measured accurately by a micrometer-microscope and equations (21.1), (21.2) and (21.3) then enable the values of the redundant actions to be found. A deformeter, differing in some particulars from the original design by Beggs, is shown in Fig. 21.4. The bars, held together by springs, are separated by two plugs of equal diameter " a " resting in grooves with an angle 2θ, when the model is in its initial un-displaced state as shown in Fig. 21.4 (a).

If these plugs are replaced by others of slightly larger diameter $a+\Delta$, a displacement $\Delta \sec \theta$, normal to the line joining the centres of the plugs is applied between the cut faces of the model (Fig. 21.4 (b)) and if by plugs of diameter $a-\Delta$, an equal displacement in the opposite direction is applied. When a small plug is inserted in one notch and a large plug in the other, a pure rotation is applied (Fig. 21.4 (c)) of amount $\Delta \sec \theta/l$ where $2l$ is the distance between plug centres.

A relative shear displacement of the faces is obtained if two equal rectangular plugs are first placed in the notches so that the movable arm of the deformeter is moved in one direction relative to the fixed arm, and are then reversed to move it in the opposite direction (Fig. 21.4 (d)).

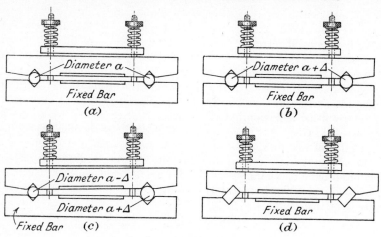

FIG. 21.4.

The relative displacements of the bars should always be measured by the microscope and not calculated.

To determine the reactions at a support such as B in Fig. 21.3, the fixed bar of the deformeter is secured to the drawing board on which the model is mounted, in such a position that the end B of the model can be clamped in the movable bar without straining the model when the normal plugs are in position.

A micrometer-microscope is focussed on a point in the structure where an applied load is assumed to act and the micrometer is oriented so that the movable cross hair is at right angles to the direction of the assumed load. If the normal thrust component of the reaction at B is required the standard plugs are removed from the deformeter and a pair of larger diameter plugs are inserted to produce a small normal displacement of the support. The movement of the point under the microscope is measured and the vertical thrust component at B is then found from equation (21.1).

The deformeter may also be used to give the internal actions at any section in a redundant structure. The model is cut at the section where the thrust, shear and moment components of the internal action are required, the deformeter bars being clamped to the model, one on each side of the cut. The deformeter must now be mounted so that it can move freely with the model when plugs of various sizes are introduced between the bars.

The procedure is then the same as for the determination of the support reactions given above.

The Beggs' deformeter enables influence lines for any structure to be obtained no matter what the variation in section of a member or the shape of its axis. There are, however, certain precautions which must be observed if accuracy is to be obtained. The deformations are small and temperature changes can affect the results seriously (Lobban, 1934). Appreciable errors can also arise as a result of slight inaccuracy in orienting the microscope.

Another method involving comparatively large displacements is useful for finding the horizontal reactions for such structures as two-hinged arch ribs, portals, etc. (Pippard and Sparkes, 1936). A model of the structure to be analysed is cut out of xylonite, as for Beggs' method, and pinned at the hinge points, say A and B, to a drawing board on which a piece of smooth paper is fastened. Initial positions of a number of points on one edge of the model are marked on the paper. The support B is then unpinned, given a small horizontal displacement and the new positions of the points on the model marked on the paper. On removing the model the vertical distances between the two positions of the rib can be measured and these, divided by the displacement given to B, give the values of the ordinates of the influence line for the horizontal thrust in the arch. The displacement given is such that the resulting deflexion is large enough to be measured by an ordinary finely divided scale. For an arch rib of uniform cross-section, depth $\frac{1}{4}$ inch, with a ratio of rise to span of one to four and a span of 12 inches it was possible, without overstraining the xylonite, to give a hinge displacement which produced a maximum vertical deflexion of about $\frac{1}{4}$ inch. The method can be used conveniently in a drawing office where micrometer-microscopes are not available.

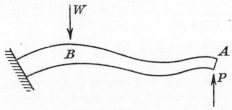

FIG. 21.5.

These methods require the construction of a scale model of the structure to be analysed and the influence of the scales needs consideration.

Let Fig. 21.5 represent an elastic structure in which the bending strain energy is such a large proportion of the whole that the contributions due to direct and shearing stresses may be neglected. If Δ_P and Δ_W are the displacements of the points A and B respectively under the action of loads P and W we have

$$\frac{\Delta_P}{\Delta_W} = \frac{\dfrac{\partial U}{\partial P}}{\dfrac{\partial U}{\partial W}} = \frac{\displaystyle\int \frac{M}{EI}\frac{\partial M}{\partial P}\,ds}{\displaystyle\int \frac{M}{EI}\frac{\partial M}{\partial W}\,ds}.$$

If a model of the structure is made so that the geometrical configuration is m times full size and the flexural rigidity of the model at any point is n times that of the prototype at the corresponding point, we have

$$\frac{\Delta'_P}{\Delta'_W} = \frac{\dfrac{m^3}{n}\displaystyle\int \frac{M}{EI}\frac{\partial M}{\partial P}\,ds}{\dfrac{m^3}{n}\displaystyle\int \frac{M}{EI}\frac{\partial M}{\partial W}\,ds} = \frac{\Delta_P}{\Delta_W}.$$

where Δ'_P and Δ'_W are the displacement of points on the model corresponding to A and B on the prototype.

So, in making a model for experimental analysis, the scales adopted for the geometrical configuration and for the flexural rigidities are independent and can be chosen as convenient. This is often a matter of importance as will be indicated later.

The result is independent of the absolute values of P and W, providing their ratio is constant.

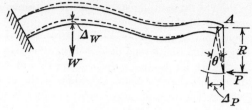

FIG. 21.6.

Suppose now that a couple M_0 is applied to A and that A is restrained against all movements except that of rotation.   If, in the model, the flexural rigidities only are changed, the ratio $\dfrac{\Delta_W}{\theta}$ will be the same both in the model and in the prototype.   To investigate the effect of a scale change m in the geometry of the model, it is convenient to replace the couple M_0 by a force P acting at the end of a rigid arm at a radius R (Fig. 21.6).   Then, in the actual structure, from equation (21.1),

$$\frac{R\Delta_W}{\Delta_P}=-\frac{RP}{W}$$

and, since $R\theta=\Delta_P$,

$$\frac{\Delta_W}{\theta}=-\frac{M_0}{W}.$$

If W is made equal to unity

$$M_0=-\frac{\Delta_W}{\theta}.$$

In the model

$$\frac{mR\Delta'_W}{\Delta'_P}=-\frac{mRP}{W}$$

or

$$\frac{\Delta'_W}{\theta'}=-m\frac{M_0}{W}.$$

Hence

$$M_0=-\frac{\Delta'_W}{m\theta'}.$$

Thus the model results must be corrected for scale before they are applied to the full-sized structure.

In structures such as braced frameworks the strain energy due to bending is often very small in comparison with that due to axial forces and in such cases the extensional rigidities (AE) of members in the model are made proportional to those of the prototype.   If the structure is one in which both bending moments and axial forces contribute appreciably to the strain energy the model must be such that both the flexural and extensional rigidities of the various parts bear the same relationship to the prototype.   This might necessitate a true scale model of the actual structure and thus prohibit experimental analysis since the chief value of such a method often lies in its cheapness and the quickness with which it can be done.   For a complicated structure which is virtually incalculable, however, the expense of making a correct model may be amply justified.

In certain instances, as pointed out by M. N. Gogate, however, a suitable choice of scales enables a model to be made which will take account of the effects due to both direct and bending stresses without the need to reproduce the cross sectional shapes of the members to scale.

Suppose that a member of any cross section subjected to axial load and bending is to be represented in a model by a rectangular strip cut from sheet of thickness t. As before let m and n be the linear and flexural rigidity scales and, in addition, let the extensional rigidity of the model be p times that of the prototype. The results above can then be extended to include direct stress, and if R is the axial load

$$\frac{\Delta'_P}{\Delta'_W} = \frac{\dfrac{m^3}{n} \displaystyle\int \frac{M}{EI} \frac{\partial M}{\partial P}\, ds + \dfrac{m}{p} \displaystyle\int \frac{R}{AE} \frac{\partial R}{\partial P}\, ds}{\dfrac{m^3}{n} \displaystyle\int \frac{M}{EI} \frac{\partial M}{\partial W}\, ds + \dfrac{m}{p} \displaystyle\int \frac{R}{AE} \frac{\partial R}{\partial W}\, ds},$$

which can only be equal to the corresponding value of $\dfrac{\Delta_P}{\Delta_W}$

if
$$m^2 = \frac{n}{p} = \frac{d^2}{12k^2}$$

where k is the radius of gyration of the cross section of the prototype and d is the depth of the corresponding model member. Hence a necessary condition to ensure that correct allowance is made for both direct and bending stresses is

$$d = 2\sqrt{3}\, mk.$$

This result is independent of p which can be any convenient value, bearing in mind that the thicknesses of all model members must be so chosen that p is constant throughout the structure. This complicates the manufacture of the model, since it necessitates either reduction of a standard thickness of sheet by filing or, alternatively, making the bars separately of the correct thickness and joining them by acetone.

To illustrate the results which may be achieved by these experimental methods a few examples will be described. These results were obtained by the large displacement method but a deformeter and measuring-microscopes could have been used. In all of them the unit of displacement was $\frac{1}{48}$-inch, and measurements were made directly by a scale.

1. *Influence line for reaction in a continuous beam.*—The first example is that of a continuous beam, which is the simplest possible illustration. A small strip of xylonite of uniform cross-section as shown in Fig. 21.7, was pinned at the three supporting points C, A and B to a sheet of paper on a drawing-board, and a sharp pencil used to mark the position of the upper edge of the beam. The pin at C was removed, the point displaced by a small amount, and the pin replaced. The new position of the beam was then marked and the beam removed from the paper. The vertical distance between the two curves at any point when divided by the vertical displacement imposed at C gave a point on the influence line for the reaction at C, and a sufficient number of such points were calculated and the required influence line was plotted. The experimental points are shown in Fig. 21.7 together with the calculated influence line, and the agreement is seen to be good.

2. *The influence line of thrust for a two-pinned segmental arch.*—An arch of uniform cross-section was represented by a model having a span of 12

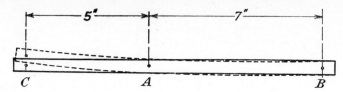

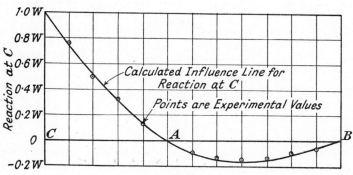

Fig. 21.7.

inches and a rise of 3 inches.   Fine scratches were made on one side of the model normal to the surface and were used as guides for pricking positions on the paper.   The initial positions of the scratches were marked, and the pin at one end of the model was then given a small displacement in the line joining the supports.   The new positions of all points around the model were then marked.   On removing the model from the paper the vertical distances between the marks at each point were measured and divided by the displacement given to the pin.   These values, given in Table 21.3, are points on the experimental influence line of thrust and the table also gives the theoretical values for comparison.

TABLE 21.3.

ANGLE SUBTENDED BY ARCH AT CENTRE$= \phi$.   HORIZONTAL DISPLACEMENT OF $B = 12 \cdot 5$ UNITS.

Angular distance from A	0	$\dfrac{\phi}{8}$	$\dfrac{\phi}{4}$	$\dfrac{3\phi}{8}$	$\dfrac{\phi}{2}$	$\dfrac{5\phi}{8}$	$\dfrac{3\phi}{4}$	$\dfrac{7\phi}{8}$	ϕ
Vertical displacement . .	0	3·0	5·8	7·9	8·8	7·8	5·7	2·9	0
H Experimental	0	0·24	0·47	0·63	0·71	0·62	0·46	0·23	0
H Calculated .	0	0·261	0·508	0·688	0·746	0·688	0·508	0·261	0

3. *Two-pinned arch with a variable cross-section.*—The same procedure as above was used to determine the influence line of thrust for a two-pinned arch in which the cross-section varied.   The depth of the model was made proportional at every section to the cube root of the true second moment of area at that section.   Fig. 21.8 shows the dimensions of the prototype and also the experimental and calculated influence lines.

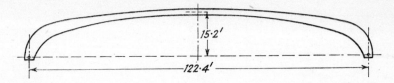

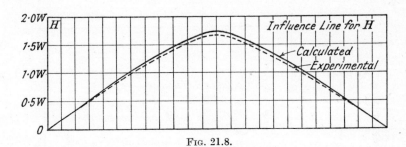

Fig. 21.8.

4. *Influence line of thrust for a spandrel-braced arch.*—The arch shown in Fig. 21.9 is the Lengue bridge designed by Sir Ralph Freeman for which he published (1906) the calculated influence line of thrust. The structure is braced and it was assumed that the forces in all bars were axial. The areas of the bars in the model were therefore made proportional to the areas in the actual bridge and this example differs from the others given, in which resistance to applied loads was obtained by bending actions. The experimental influence line is compared in Fig. 21.9 with that given by Freeman.

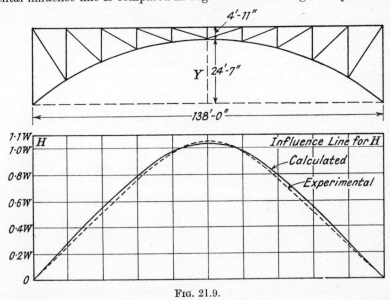

Fig. 21.9.

21.5. Experimental analysis of stresses in rings.—The methods of the preceding paragraph may be used to analyse the stresses in rings of any shape, and are particularly useful for such structures as the frames of aeroplane fuselages. The examples to be given (Pippard and Sparkes, 1938) were solved by imposing displacements sufficiently large to be measurable by an ordinary scale but the same general procedure would be followed if a Beggs' deformeter were used.

If the ring shown in Fig. 21.10 is cut at any section A, the original conditions of equilibrium can be restored by the application to this section of unknown forces H_0 and V_0, and an unknown couple M_0. These may either be calculated or determined experimentally in the following way. A model of the ring is made of xylonite, the second moments of area at all sections being proportional to the second moments of area of the prototype at corresponding sections. The model is cut at the section where the redundant reactions are required. To determine H_0 a known deformation Δ_H is imposed between the faces at A in the direction of H_0 in such a way that there is neither vertical nor angular displacement of the section. The

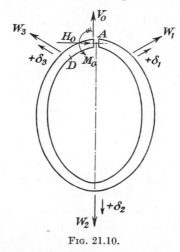

FIG. 21.10.

displacements δ_{1H}, δ_{2H} and δ_{3H} of W_1, W_2 and W_3 respectively in their own lines of action are measured and then

$$H_0 = \frac{W_1\delta_{1H} + W_2\delta_{2H} + W_3\delta_{3H}}{\Delta_H}.$$

Similarly, to determine V_0, a displacement Δ_V is imposed between the cut faces in the direction of V_0 and, if δ_{1V}, δ_{2V} and δ_{3V} are again the displacements of W_1, W_2 and W_3 in their own lines of action

$$V_0 = \frac{W_1\delta_{1V} + W_2\delta_{2V} + W_3\delta_{3V}}{\Delta_V}.$$

The reaction M_0 is found by imposing a known angular displacement θ between the cut faces at A and, as before, measuring the appropriate displacements δ_{1M}, δ_{2M} and δ_{3M}. Then

$$M_0 = \frac{W_1\delta_{1M} + W_2\delta_{2M} + W_3\delta_{3M}}{m\theta}$$

where m is the linear scale of the model.

The experimental procedure adopted, which proved satisfactory, was as follows : the xylonite model was made with an arm $\frac{3}{4}$ inch wide and $4\frac{1}{4}$ inches long, normal to the model at A, as shown in Fig. 21.11. Two holes, $\frac{1}{8}$ inch diameter, were drilled, one on the axis of the ring at A, and the other on the centre line of the arm about 3 inches from the first hole. The arm was stiffened by screwing to it two narrow strips of 16 gauge brass after the surfaces in contact had been treated with a strong adhesive. A saw cut was then made along the line AB (Fig. 21.11) and the two cut faces were filed parallel.

One arm of the model was screwed to a drawing board* and $\frac{1}{8}$ inch diameter steel balls were inserted between the semi-circular notches at B and C (Fig. 21.12). A scratch on the outside of the movable arm and

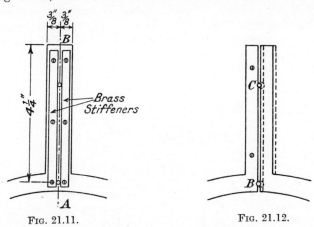

FIG. 21.11.   FIG. 21.12.

normal to the board was used to guide a pin point to a piece of paper under the model, thus marking the first position of the arm. The balls were then replaced by two equal but larger balls. The new position of the scratch on the movable arm was marked and the distance between the two pin pricks was the displacement imposed in the direction of H_0.

An angular displacement was obtained by inserting $\frac{1}{8}$ inch diameter balls at B and C (Fig. 21.13) and marking the position of the scratch. The ball at C was then removed and a larger one inserted thus causing the movable arm to rotate about B. The new position was marked and the rotation was then the distance between the two pricks divided by the distance between B and C.

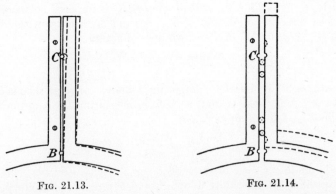

FIG. 21.13.   FIG. 21.14.

* It is advisable to place a thin piece of paper between the arm and the board to act as packing and prevent friction between the model and the board when the former is displaced.

A displacement in the direction V_0 was obtained by inserting the $\frac{1}{8}$ inch diameter balls between the cut faces as shown in Fig. 21.14. The position of the scratch on the movable arm was marked as before. Using the balls as rollers, the movable arm was displaced in the direction of V_0 and the new position of the scratch marked. The distance between the pricks was the displacement.

The procedure will be illustrated by a circular ring of constant section under the system of loading shown in Fig. 21.15. The ring was 12 inches mean diameter, $0 \cdot 5$ inches wide and $0 \cdot 18$ inches thick. Scratches were made on the inner edge of the model and normal to the face at the load points A, B and C, and one arm was screwed to a drawing board. Using

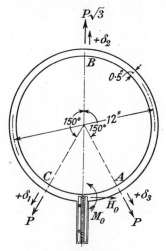

FIG. 21.15.

the scratches to guide a needle point to paper placed under the model, the positions of A, B and C were marked before and after the appropriate displacement of the movable arm had been made. Very fine lines were drawn through the pricks at right angles to the direction in which the displacement was required, and the distances between the lines measured with a finely divided scale. The results obtained are given in Tables 21.4 and 21.5. Δ is the displacement of the scratch on the movable arm and d is the distance, 4 inches, of the scratch from the centre of rotation. The angular rotation between the cut faces of the ring is then $\dfrac{\Delta}{d}$.

TABLE 21.4.

Test No.	Δ	δ_1	δ_2	δ_3	$-M_0 = \dfrac{d}{\Delta}(\delta_1 + \delta_3 + \delta_2 \sqrt{3})P$
1	$13 \cdot 5$	$1 \cdot 3$	$6 \cdot 3$	$-8 \cdot 6$	$1 \cdot 06P$
2	$13 \cdot 8$	$1 \cdot 2$	$6 \cdot 4$	$-8 \cdot 8$	$1 \cdot 02P$
3	$13 \cdot 0$	$1 \cdot 1$	$5 \cdot 9$	$-8 \cdot 0$	$1 \cdot 02P$

Average value of M_0 = $1 \cdot 03P$.
Calculated value of $M_0 = 1 \cdot 067P$. Difference $= 3\frac{1}{2}$ per cent.

TABLE 21.5.

Test No.	Δ	δ_1	δ_2	δ_3	$-H_0 = \dfrac{(\delta_1 + \delta_3 + \delta_2 \sqrt{3})P}{\Delta}$
1	5·7	−0·4	0	2·7	0·404P
2	5·8	−0·2	0	2·6	0·414P
3	5·7	−0·4	0	2·7	0·404P

Average value of H_0 = 0·407P.
Calculated value of H_0= 0·417P.   Difference= 2·4 per cent.

Another ring ·08 inch thick, 10 inch mean diameter and 0·5 inch wide was mounted in the same way, and the influence line of bending moments at any section due to radial loads was determined. The comparison between the experimental and calculated values is shown in Fig. 21.16.

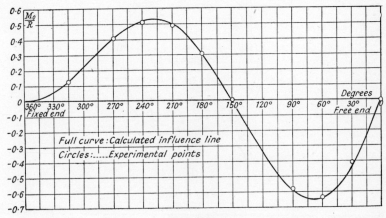

FIG. 21.16.

To illustrate the advantage of a suitable choice of scales, the link shown in Fig. 21.17 was investigated.

To apply measurable deformations to a true scale model of the link, considerable force would have to be used and would cause yielding or buckling. Only very small deformations could safely be applied and a Beggs' deformeter would be necessary.

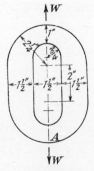

FIG. 21.17.

The method already described can, however, be used if the scales of the model are altered to produce a more flexible ring, and by making the linear scale twice full size (*i.e.* $m=2$), and the width of the model at all sections $\frac{3}{8}$ths of the width of the actual link, a sufficiently flexible model was obtained as shown in Fig. 21.18. Angular deformations were applied and measurements made as before to obtain M_0 at the section A for loads of magnitude

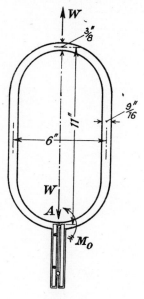

FIG. 21.18.

W acting along the major axis of the link.   The results are given in Table 21.6.

TABLE 21.6.

Test No.	Δ	δ_{W}	$-M_0 = \dfrac{d}{m\Delta}(\delta_{\mathrm{W}})W$
1	12·1	2·7	0·446W
2	13·2	3·0	0·454W
3	11·0	2·4	0·436W

Average value of M_0 $= -0\cdot445W$.
Calculated value of $M_0= -0\cdot460W$. Difference$= 3$ per cent.

In connexion with an investigation of the stresses in the Dome of Discovery (Makowski and Pippard, 1952), built for the Festival of Britain, 1951, experiments were made with the object of checking the accuracy of formulas for loaded rings which had been deduced on the assumption that a number of separate supports could be replaced by a suitable continuous elastic support. The ring girder of the dome was carried on 24 bipods ; the apex of each was free to move radially but was restrained against tangential movements other than those due to elastic deformation of the legs of the bipod. The formulas to be tested were those applicable both to loading in the plane of the ring and to loads normal to it (Pippard, 1952).

The experimental rings for the former tests were cut from xylonite $\frac{3}{16}$-inch thick and were 18 inches in diameter and $\frac{3}{8}$-inch by $\frac{3}{16}$-inch cross-section. They were mounted as shown in Fig. 21.19.

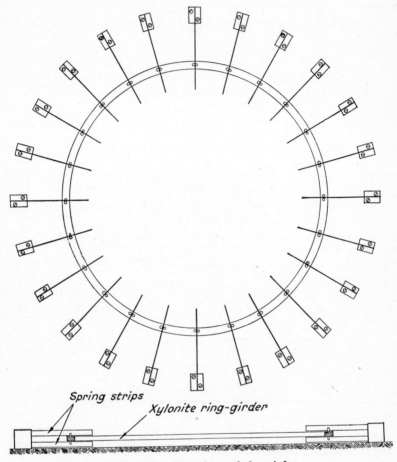

Spring strips

Xylonite ring-girder

Fig. 21.19. Experimental ring-girder.

The small spring strips supporting the ring allowed free radial movement but resisted tangential movement as required by the conditions of the analysis. Radial and tangential point loads of 1 lb. were applied separately in the plane of the ring and displacements of a number of points were measured. A comparison of the figures obtained with those calculated from the formulas is given in Fig. 21.20 for the radial and in Fig. 21.21 for the tangential loads.

To verify a formula for loads normal to the plane a mild-steel ring was suspended from twenty-four similar and equally spaced helical springs. Equal loads were hung from the ring at each supporting point to give the springs initial tensions. An additional point load of 1 lb. was then suspended from support 13 and the ring displacements were measured. The agreement

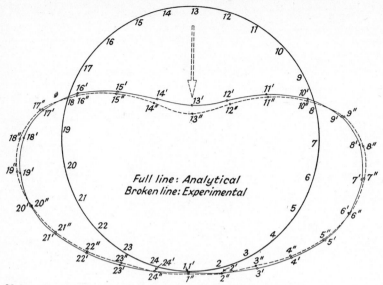

FIG. 21.20.   Comparison of experimental and analytical displacements of a ring-girder resulting from a radial load.

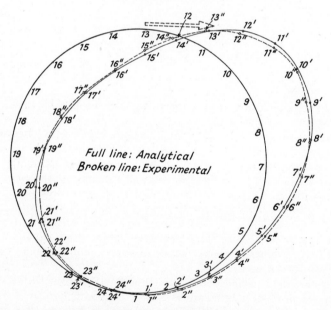

FIG. 21.21.   Comparison of experimental and analytical displacements of a ring-girder resulting from a tangential load.

between these and the calculated values is practically exact as shown in Fig. 21.22.   Alternate springs were then removed so that the ring was supported at twelve equidistant points and the experiment repeated.   The result is also shown in the same Figure, the agreement between calculated and experimental values again being almost exact.   Repetitions of this procedure left six and finally only three supporting points, and the differences between the measured displacements and those calculated on the assumption of continuous supports are seen from Fig. 21.22 to be remarkably small.

These experiments left little room for doubt as to the accuracy of the analysis and since all the calculated displacements gave such good agreement with measured values it may reasonably be assumed that the calculated bending moments would be equally reliable.

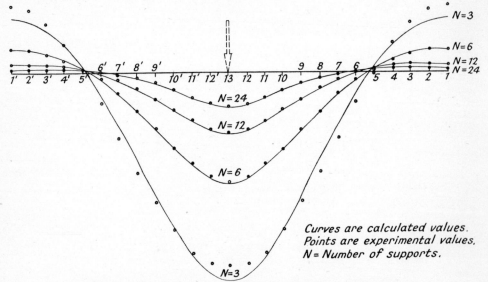

Curves are calculated values.
Points are experimental values.
N = Number of supports.

FIG. 21.22.   Deflexions of a ring-girder resulting from a lateral load.

21.6. Experimental analysis of space frames.—From what has been said in the last two paragraphs it will be clear that the stress analysis of plane structures by experimental methods is comparatively straightforward and can be done with the minimum of special equipment. The treatment of space frames by the direct method has been described in paragraph 21.2 but the indirect approach, using Clerk Maxwell's reciprocal theorem, can also be used with advantage in certain types of structures. An excellent example of such a structure is the braced dome and this will be used to illustrate the technique. It should not be assumed that only this kind of frame can be so dealt with ; the principles involved are equally applicable to other space frames although details of experimentation may have to be adjusted to special needs.

A braced dome is usually built of members lying on the surface of a solid of revolution or of straight members connecting points lying on that surface. The Dome of Discovery, built for the Festival of Britain 1951 and shown in Fig. 21.23, was the biggest and most recent of such structures. The bracing members considered individually were arched ribs and, if they had acted independently, stress analysis would have presented no special problems ; they were, however, connected together at all points of inter-section, and in consequence the structure exhibited a very high degree of redundancy. Analysis by classical methods leads to such a large number of simultaneous equations that their solution is impracticable. Relaxation treatment is possible, although the computation is considerable and requires

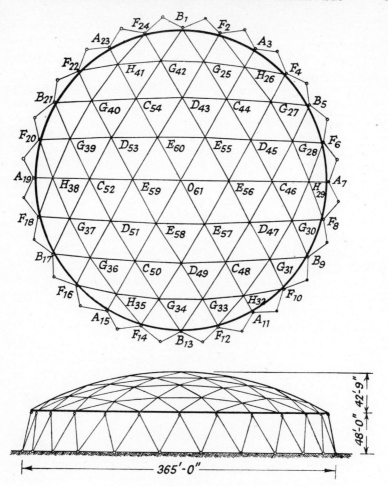

FIG. 21.23. The Dome of Discovery.

workers skilled in the particular technique and this method was in fact applied to the Dome of Discovery (Lazarides, 1952).   Approximate methods of analysis can be devised, but the danger of under-estimating the stresses can only be avoided at the risk of over-estimating them and so losing the economical advantage which is one of the main features of the design.   In view of these difficulties an experimental stress determination was attempted (Makowski and Pippard, 1952).

On the assumptions that the ribs and the supporting struts would take axial loads only and that the heavy steel ring-girder would be subjected to bending moments only, a geometrically and elastically similar model was built.   The ribs and the ring-girder were made from mild-steel rods and the supporting bipods from thin brass tubes.

The supporting struts were pin-connected to the ring-girder and to the support bases by means of small flexible pins, enabling small adjustments to be made to the lengths of struts and heights of joints.   The support plates were so constructed as to fix the feet of the bipods in position, but at the same time to ensure their freedom of rotation, without the possibility of play between the ball-joint and base plate.

The span of the model was 10 feet 6 inches.

The stresses in the bars of the intersecting lattice will be direct tensions or compressions under any system of loads applied to the joints ; the stresses in the ring-girder on the other hand, will be almost entirely due to bending. Hence, the strain energy from bending of the bars and from direct stresses in the ring may be neglected.

For any load system on the prototype structure, let P be the force in any bar of the lattice and M the bending moment at any point in the ring-girder. The component deflexion of a node p in the direction of W, the load acting there, is then

$$\delta = \sum \frac{PL}{AE}\frac{\partial P}{\partial W} + \int \frac{M}{EI}\frac{\partial M}{\partial W}ds$$

where AE is the extensional rigidity of the bar carrying P, and EI is the flexural rigidity of the ring-girder at the point considered. The summation extends to all members of the lattice and the integration to the whole of the ring-girder. Suppose now that a model of the prototype is made, such that the extensional rigidity of a lattice bar is $k_1 AE$ and the flexural rigidity of the ring-girder is $k_2 EI$, whilst the linear scale of the model is k_3 times, and the load scale k_4 times that of the prototype, so that the load at p is $k_4 W$.

Then the deflexion of p on the model is

$$\delta' = \frac{k_3 k_4}{k_1}\sum \frac{PL}{AE}\frac{\partial P}{\partial W} + \frac{k_3{}^3 k_4}{k_2}\int \frac{M}{EI}\frac{\partial M}{\partial W}ds.$$

For the displacements of the prototype and those of the model to be proportional

$$\frac{k_3 k_4}{k_1} = \frac{k_3{}^3 k_4}{k_2}$$

or

$$\frac{k_3{}^2 k_1}{k_2} = 1.$$

Then

$$\frac{\delta'}{\delta} = \frac{k_3 k_4}{k_1}$$

and the model and prototype will be elastically similar.

It will be observed that the assumption that the energy in the lattice arises from direct stress only and that in the ring-girder from bending stress only, removes all restrictions as to the actual cross-sectional shapes of the members ; provided that the values of AE and EI satisfy the scale requirements of the above equation their actual cross-sections do not matter and simple models can be used.

If the support at any point, which we will call A, is released and an arbitrary displacement Δ is imposed in the X direction so that it has no component displacements in the directions of the mutually perpendicular axes Y and Z then, if any node, say a, is thereby displaced δ in some specified direction, it follows from Clerk Maxwell's theorem that a load W applied in that direction at a will produce a reaction $-\dfrac{W\delta}{\Delta}$ in the X direction at A.

If, therefore, displacements are successively applied in three mutually perpendicular directions to a released support point, the resulting displacements of the nodes can be measured and influence coefficients of reactions can be calculated.

When displacements were imposed on the model, some of the compression members tended to buckle, with a consequent reduction in their effective flexural rigidities. This was prevented by attaching splints made of lengths of $\frac{1}{8}$-inch-diameter rod to those members by soft wire ; since the splints were unconnected to the joints, they carried no axial load but stabilised the struts against buckling.

To determine the force in a bar of the loaded structure experimentally, the distance between the nodes connected by that bar must be altered by a known amount Δ'. This was done by inserting very small turnbuckles in those bars which were to be analysed.

The displacements of the various joints of the structure caused by the change of length of a bar were measured and the forces in the bar were then

$$-\left(\frac{\delta_x}{\Delta'}\right)_q, \ -\left(\frac{\delta_y}{\Delta'}\right)_q \text{ and } -\left(\frac{\delta_z}{\Delta'}\right)_q \text{ for unit loads applied at joint } q \text{ in the}$$

directions X, Y and Z respectively. Displacements of the joints were measured by cathetometers.

The dome was analysed for a unit vertical load acting at the apex, O_{61}.

Table 21.7 gives the experimental loads in members of the dome under this load and for comparison a complete relaxation analysis was made. The results of this analysis are given in the same table and the general agreement between experiment and calculation is excellent. In some cases apparently large discrepancies appear, but it is probable that they arise from certain irregularities in the erection of the model. The dome is very flat and in consequence sensitive to small errors in this respect.

Two methods of experimental analysis of space structures have been described in this paragraph

  (a) displacement of supports and calculation of reaction coefficients ;
  (b) direct determination of the forces in particular members by alteration of lengths in individual bars.

The first method is specially useful for simple structures on a limited number of supports. In these, a knowledge of the component reactions eliminates the redundancy and usually enables the stresses in all members to be computed very simply.

In space structures having a large number of supports, the stresses in the supporting struts caused by unit loads acting at various joints of the structure are very small and even a small error in the determination of a strut load can introduce quite a large error in the forces in members at a distance from the strut.

In structures with very stiff ring-girders or a complicated and highly redundant lattice, it is of only limited help to know the forces in the supporting struts ; the direct determination of loads in the members, on the other hand, gives results simply and quickly. This method can be used for any structure with straight members and is especially valuable for highly redundant structures. The load in a member determined by this method does not influence the accuracy of the result for loads in neighbouring bars, since every member is treated independently.

TABLE 21.7.

Bars	Experimental	Mean	Analytical
$\left\{\begin{array}{l} O-E_{58} \\ O-E_{60} \\ O-E_{56} \end{array}\right.$	$\left.\begin{array}{c} -2\cdot130 \\ -2\cdot156 \\ -2\cdot290 \end{array}\right\}$	$-2\cdot192$	$-2\cdot184$
$\left\{\begin{array}{l} E_{58}-E_{59} \\ E_{56}-E_{57} \\ E_{60}-E_{55} \end{array}\right.$	$\left.\begin{array}{c} +1\cdot545 \\ +1\cdot515 \\ +1\cdot520 \end{array}\right\}$	$+1\cdot527$	$+1\cdot514$
$\left\{\begin{array}{l} E_{60}-D_{53} \\ E_{56}-D_{45} \\ E_{58}-D_{49} \end{array}\right.$	$\left.\begin{array}{c} -0\cdot143 \\ -0\cdot204 \\ -0\cdot065 \end{array}\right\}$	$-0\cdot137$	$-0\cdot139$
$\left\{\begin{array}{l} E_{57}-C_{48} \\ E_{55}-C_{44} \\ E_{59}-C_{52} \end{array}\right.$	$\left.\begin{array}{c} -0\cdot633 \\ -0\cdot526 \\ -0\cdot555 \end{array}\right\}$	$-0\cdot571$	$-0\cdot543$
$\left\{\begin{array}{l} C_{50}-D_{51} \\ C_{54}-D_{43} \\ C_{46}-D_{47} \end{array}\right.$	$\left.\begin{array}{c} +0\cdot307 \\ +0\cdot310 \\ +0\cdot366 \end{array}\right\}$	$+0\cdot327$	$+0\cdot308$
$\left\{\begin{array}{l} C_{50}-H_{35} \\ C_{46}-H_{29} \\ C_{54}-H_{41} \end{array}\right.$	$\left.\begin{array}{c} -0\cdot164 \\ -0\cdot180 \\ -0\cdot175 \end{array}\right\}$	$-0\cdot173$	$-0\cdot250$
$\left\{\begin{array}{l} C_{48}-G_{33} \\ C_{44}-G_{27} \\ C_{52}-G_{39} \end{array}\right.$	$\left.\begin{array}{c} 0 \\ -0\cdot034 \\ +0\cdot026 \end{array}\right\}$	$-0\cdot003$	~0
$\left\{\begin{array}{l} D_{47}-G_{31} \\ D_{51}-G_{37} \\ D_{43}-G_{25} \end{array}\right.$	$\left.\begin{array}{c} -0\cdot139 \\ -0\cdot158 \\ -0\cdot175 \end{array}\right\}$	$-0\cdot157$	$-0\cdot137$
$\left\{\begin{array}{l} G_{34}-G_{33} \\ G_{40}-G_{39} \\ G_{27}-G_{28} \end{array}\right.$	$\left.\begin{array}{c} +0\cdot170 \\ +0\cdot190 \\ +0\cdot189 \end{array}\right\}$	$+0\cdot183$	$+0\cdot172$
$\left\{\begin{array}{l} H_{32}-G_{31} \\ H_{38}-G_{37} \\ H_{26}-G_{25} \end{array}\right.$	$\left.\begin{array}{c} +0\cdot133 \\ +0\cdot108 \\ +0\cdot070 \end{array}\right\}$	$+0\cdot104$	$+0\cdot135$
$\left\{\begin{array}{l} H_{32}-A_{11} \\ H_{38}-A_{19} \\ H_{26}-A_{3} \end{array}\right.$	$\left.\begin{array}{c} -0\cdot121 \\ -0\cdot088 \\ -0\cdot087 \end{array}\right\}$	$-0\cdot099$	$-0\cdot156$
$\left\{\begin{array}{l} H_{29}-F_{8} \\ H_{35}-F_{16} \\ H_{41}-F_{24} \end{array}\right.$	$\left.\begin{array}{c} 0 \\ +0\cdot018 \\ +0\cdot039 \end{array}\right\}$	$+0\cdot019$	$+0\cdot012$
$\left\{\begin{array}{l} G_{28}-F_{6} \\ G_{34}-F_{14} \\ G_{40}-F_{22} \end{array}\right.$	$\left.\begin{array}{c} -0\cdot103 \\ -0\cdot101 \\ -0\cdot096 \end{array}\right\}$	$-0\cdot100$	$-0\cdot094$
$\left\{\begin{array}{l} G_{31}-B_{9} \\ G_{37}-B_{11} \\ G_{25}-B_{1} \end{array}\right.$	$\left.\begin{array}{c} -0\cdot060 \\ -0\cdot039 \\ -0\cdot078 \end{array}\right\}$	$-0\cdot059$	$-0\cdot031$

For both methods large displacements are recommended, since catheto-meters, micrometer screws, or even ordinary dial gauges are accurate enough for measuring joint displacements, which in the experiments described were of the order of $\frac{1}{2}$ inch.

REFERENCES

Snell, G. 1846. *Proc. Instn. Civ. Engrs.*, **5,** 439–478.

Freeman, R. 1906. *Proc. Instn. Civ. Engrs.*, **167,** 343–367.

Wilson, W. M. and Maney, G. A. 1915. *Eng. Exp. Bull.*, **80,** Univ. of Illinois ; Urbana.

Pippard, A. J. S. and Baker, J. F. 1925. *Phil. Mag.*, **50,** 97–112.

Beggs, G. E. 1927. *J. Franklin Inst.*, **203, 375**-386.

Baker, J. F. 1932. *Inst. Civ. Engrs., S.E.P.*, **131.**

Lobban, C. H. 1934. *J. Inst. Eng. & Ship Bldrs. Scotland,* **77,** 169–226.

Pippard, A. J. S. and Sparkes, S. R. 1936. *J. Instn. Civ. Engrs.*, **4,** 79–92.

Pippard, A. J. S., Tranter, E. and Chitty, L. 1936. *J. Instn. Civ. Engrs.*, **4,** 281–306.

Pippard, A. J. S. and Sparkes, S. R. 1938. *R. & M.*, **1851.** H.M.S.O.

Pippard, A. J. S. and Ashby, R. J. 1939. *J. Instn. Civ. Engrs.*, **10,** 383–404.

Pippard, A. J. S. and Chitty, L. 1941. *J. Instn. Civ. Engrs.*, **17,** 79–86.

Hetényi, M. 1950. " Handbook of Experimental Stress Analysis." Chapman & Hall.

Pippard, A. J. S. and Chitty, L. 1951. "A Study of the Voussoir Arch." H.M.S.O.

Makowski, Z. S. and Pippard, A. J. S. 1952. *Proc. Instn. Civ. Engrs.*, **1,** III. 421–441.

Pippard, A. J. S. 1952. " Studies in Elastic Structures." Arnold.

CHAPTER 22

PLASTIC THEORY

22.1. Introduction.—This book has so far been concerned with the behaviour of structures within the elastic range. While the engineer now has at his command methods which make the analysis of the elastic stresses in almost any structure possible, he is not in such a favourable position when it comes to the problem of elastic design, the proportioning of a structure so that the stresses in it will not exceed permissible limits. Some of the complexity of this problem has been seen in Chapter 18. The experience obtained in deriving the rational design method described there, for the comparatively straightforward case of the steel multi-storey building frame, showed that elastic behaviour is too complicated to form the basis of a simple and acceptable but still rational design method for all forms of redundant structure. Attention had to be directed, therefore, to another approach and in 1936 work was started in England on an examination of the plastic behaviour of steel structures. This has, in the course of twenty years, led to the development of a new branch of the theory of structures which provides the engineer with a powerful rational design method. The subject has grown to such proportions that it can only be touched on lightly here but it has been described fully elsewhere (Baker, Horne and Heyman, 1956).

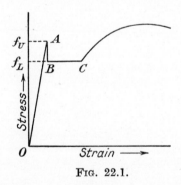

FIG. 22.1.

22.2. The single span beam.—Robertson and Cook (1913) were the first to give a satisfactory explanation of the way in which a mild steel beam fails in flexure. If the material of the beam is normalised mild steel it will have a stress-strain relation in tension as shown in Fig. 22.1. The point A represents the upper yield of the material, the upper yield stress being f_U. As straining of the test piece continues, an immediate drop in stress to f_L at B, the lower yield point, will occur. From B the material extends without any increase in load to C, BC being the region of complete plasticity. After C the plastic flow ceases and load has to be added before any further extension is produced.

542

It will be assumed that the stress-strain relation in compression is identical with that in tension ; that plane sections before bending remain plane after bending, and that longitudinal fibres are free to expand and contract laterally as in the simple elastic theory of bending.

When a member is subjected to pure bending about a principal axis, the distribution of stress across the section will be of the form shown in Fig. 22.2 (a) so long as the applied bending moment is small. This form will persist as the bending moment increases, until the stress at the extreme fibres eventually reaches the value f_U, the upper yield stress of the material. As the bending moment is increased further a drop in stress to f_L, the lower yield value, must occur in these extreme fibres in accordance with the stress

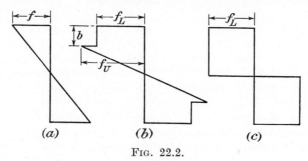

(a) (b) (c)

FIG. 22.2.

strain relation of Fig. 22.1. The stress in more and more fibres will reach the upper yield value and will drop back to the lower as shown in Fig. 22.2 (b). Eventually, under a certain bending moment, the whole of the section will have yielded, giving the stress distribution shown in Fig. 22.2 (c). A further simplifying assumption has been made in this argument, that the extreme fibres and all others after reaching the lower yield stress remain in a state of complete plasticity, *i.e.* within the range BC, Fig. 22.1, until the whole section has yielded.

An expression for the moment of resistance can be derived as in paragraph 3.4. For a rectangular section of depth d and width w the moment of resistance will be

$$\mathrm{M}=\frac{w}{6}\{6b(d-b)f_\mathrm{L}+(d-2b)^2 f_\mathrm{U}\} \quad . \quad . \quad . \quad . \quad (22.1)$$

when the fibres to a depth b, Fig. 22.2 (b), have reached the plastic state.

The " carrying capacity," that is the moment which produces complete plasticity throughout the whole section of this member, Fig. 22.2 (c), is

$$\mathrm{M_P}=\frac{wd^2}{4}f_\mathrm{L} . \quad . \quad . \quad . \quad . \quad . \quad . \quad (22.2)$$

If a steel beam is simply supported over a span l and is subjected to an increasing uniformly distributed load, the relation between load and central deflexion will be linear until a point A is reached, Fig. 22.3, when the extreme fibres at the centre are about to yield, the total load then being $\dfrac{8\mathrm{M_Y}}{l}$. Although this is considered the point of " failure " in orthodox structural design the beam is not near collapse. More load can be added, though the rate of change of deflexion will increase until at B, under a load $\dfrac{8\mathrm{M_P}}{l}$, the centre

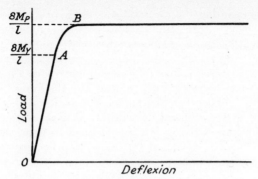

Fig. 22.3.   Load deflexion curve for simply supported
beam.

section becomes completely plastic and the beam suffers large deflexions.
It is important to remember that the beam does not collapse catastrophically
at this load as would a beam of brittle material on failure.   If the load were
reduced slightly the growth of deflexion would stop and the beam would
support the load quite happily.   The ratio of the load causing large deflexions
to that causing first yield is M_P/M_Y.   For a steel, such as that in most rolled
steel joists, having no upper yield, this ratio depends only on the shape of
the cross-section and so is called the " shape factor."   For a rectangular
section it has the value $1 \cdot 5$ and for most standard I-sections, bent about the
major axis, $1 \cdot 15$ approximately.

The importance of this plastic behaviour can be seen most simply from a
consideration of an encastré beam of uniform section subjected to a uniformly
distributed load, Fig. 22.4 (a).   In the elastic range the bending moment at
the ends will be twice that at the centre, so that yielding will begin at the
ends of the beam.   When this condition is reached, the load on the beam
will be

$$W_Y = \frac{12M_Y}{l} \quad . \quad . \quad . \quad . \quad . \quad (22.3)$$

and the bending moment diagram will be that shown in Fig. 22.4 (b).   As
the load is increased, plastic zones will be developed at the ends of the beam
and this condition will continue until complete plasticity has been reached
at these sections.   As the load is further increased, the full plastic moment
M_P at the ends will remain constant, plastic " hinges " having formed there,
and further yield will occur at the centre, plastic zones being formed as in
Fig. 22.4 (c).   The final stage is reached when the centre section also becomes
completely plastic and the beam is no longer capable of resisting additional
load since it is virtually a mechanism with hinges at ends and centre.   The
bending moment diagram and the extent of the zones at collapse are shown
in Fig. 22.4 (d).   Since the moments at ends and centre have the value M_P
it follows that the total load at collapse is

$$W_P = \frac{16M_P}{l} \quad . \quad . \quad . \quad . \quad . \quad (22.4)$$

or from equations (22.3) and (22.4)

$$\frac{W_P}{W_Y} = \frac{4}{3} \times \frac{M_P}{M_Y} = \frac{4}{3} \times \text{shape factor.}$$

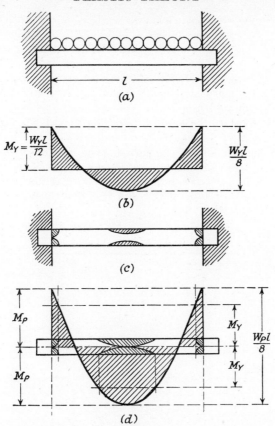

Fig. 22.4. Behaviour of an encastré beam.

Thus an encastré beam designed by the orthodox elastic method can support one-third more load before collapse than the simply supported beam designed to carry the same working load. This is unnecessary and extravagant. If the simply supported beam is strong enough for its purpose, that is to say if its load factor is adequate, then there is, in general, no reason why the same load factor should not be used in the design of the encastré beam. This results in a considerable economy of material. This economy, which is available in all redundant structures, coupled with that arising from the simple direct design technique made possible in the drawing office, is the main advantage of the plastic method, but being rational it has other advantages. It shows, for instance, that for encastré beams and similar structures there need be no anxiety about the effect of the sinking of supports or of the incompleteness of the fixing at the ends. Relative sinking of supports has no effect on the carrying capacity of a structure and the joints need not be completely rigid, a condition impossible to secure in practice, so long as they are capable of developing the full plastic moments of the members joined.

22.3. Continuous beams.—It can be seen from Fig. 22.4 (d) that it would not be a difficult matter to design an encastré beam of uniform section to collapse under any given load system. A continuous beam can be analysed or designed in much the same way since it will collapse, or come to the end of its useful life, when plastic hinges have formed over the supports and at some intermediate section of a span, thus transforming that span, at least, into a mechanism.

Fig. 22.5 (*a*) shows a beam of uniform section throughout, its plastic moment being M_P, hinged at the ends A and D and resting on supports at B and C. It is subjected to a central concentrated load W. The carrying capacity of the beam can be found by drawing first, Fig. 22.5 (*b*), the free moment diagram B'E'C', that is the bending moment diagram for the loaded span imagined simply supported. On this is superimposed the moment diagram A'B"C"D', due to the restraining moments at the ends of the spans, so giving the net bending moment diagram shown hatched. Plastic hinges will clearly form at B, C and E so that the restraining moment

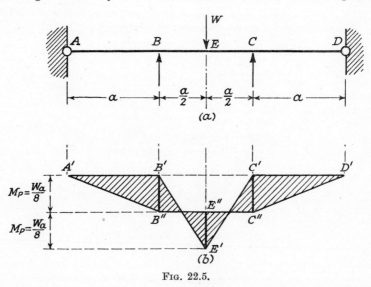

FIG. 22.5.

diagram must be so drawn that $B'B''=E'E''=C'C''=\dfrac{Wa}{8}=M_P$. Thus the central span alone collapses when the load applied to the beam is $\dfrac{8M_P}{a}$. The work would be only slightly more complicated if the spans were not all of the same section. If, for instance, AB and CD were of smaller section than BC, collapse would occur when plastic hinges formed at E, at B in the span AB and at C in the span CD. The carrying capacity would be found as in Fig. 22.5 (*b*) but with B'B" and C'C" representing the plastic moments of the outside spans to the same scale that E'E" represented that of the central span. In fact, if graphical " cut and try " methods are used there is no difficulty in finding the carrying capacity of any beam of uniform section between supports however complicated the load system and however numerous the spans. The reason for this is that the carrying capacity of a span depends not on the stiffnesses of all the spans in the beam, which complicate elastic analysis, but only on the plastic moments of resistance of the span itself and those on either side. This also makes design straightforward so that, what is a troublesome problem approached elastically, a continuous beam strengthened with flange plates over parts of its length, can be proportioned with ease.

22.4. The portal frame.—The approach to portal frame design is similar to that adopted for continuous beams but it is somewhat complicated by the fact that for each form of frame and load system there are several possible modes of collapse. Take the simplest case, the rectangular portal with fixed feet subjected to concentrated vertical and horizontal loads, Fig. 22.6 (*a*). This may collapse, the frame becoming a mechanism, by the formation of plastic hinges at A, C, D and E, Fig. 22.6 (*b*), or by the four necessary hinges forming at A, B, D and E, Fig. 22.6 (*c*). There is a third mode of partial collapse, Fig. 22.6 (*d*), whereby the portal reaches the end of its useful life by the formation of three hinges in the beam BCD. Graphical methods, similar to those used for continuous beam problems, are available for the study of each of the modes so that the true carrying capacity of a particular frame under given loads can be found after a little trouble, but

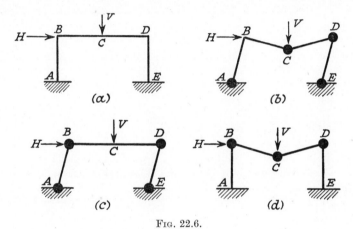

Fig. 22.6.

powerful analytical methods have now been developed which make the analysis and direct design of the most complicated frames a straightforward matter.

The plastic method of design for rectangular portals was much used in the 1939–45 War for air raid shelters and other protective devices. It is now complete for single storey building frames and two hundred or more examples of structures thus designed were in existence at the end of 1955. They were produced with great economy of effort in the design office and with a saving of 25 to 30 per cent. in steel compared with similar structures designed elastically.

22.5. The continuous stanchion.—It is impossible to ignore problems of instability when applying the plastic method, since it would be foolish to estimate the strength of a structure on plastic hinge formation if, before the structure had become a mechanism in this way, collapse had occurred due to instability. The most intractable of these problems is that of the continuous stanchion to which much consideration was given in Chapter 18. It will be remembered that the design method described there was based on the assumption that the member failed when the stress at any section, due to the axial load and beam moments, first reached the yield stress of the material. This was the only justifiable assumption to make at that time, though it was thought to be very much on the safe side.   It has been borne out by a later experimental investigation of the strength of continuous stanchions which has shown that the axial load at collapse is far less sensitive to the effect of bending from the beams than was the permissible axial load of Figs. 18.13 and 18.14.   For an I-section stanchion of slenderness ratio 45, for instance, bent in single curvature, the axial load at collapse only fell by about 8 per cent. when the beam loads were increased from zero to the value which produced yield in the stanchion before any axial load was applied.   That is to say the real collapse load was only reduced by 8 per cent. while the permissible axial load was reduced to zero.   When bending was in double curvature the effect of beam load was even less marked.   It must be emphasised, however, that in these tests the beams were designed to be elastic throughout, so that, while great economies could clearly be achieved by designing the stanchions for plastic collapse, it would be at the expense of the beams.   The complication of designing a multi-storey structure in which beams and stanchions become plastic at the same time is too great to contemplate at the moment.   There is, however, an alternative approach which is much more practicable, that is to design the beams of the structure by the plastic method but to proportion the stanchions by a method modelled closely on that of Chapter 18, so that they are still elastic when the beams collapse.

22.6. Reinforced concrete structures.—The load deflexion curve for a simply supported concrete beam lightly reinforced, so that failure takes place by yield of the mild steel reinforcement, is of the same form as that for the mild steel beam discussed in paragraph 22.2 and illustrated in Fig. 22.3. The mechanics of failure of reinforced concrete members are, however, much more complex than those of rolled steel joists.   Though they are not yet fully understood it is known that even in a beam carrying a central point load, yield of the reinforcement takes place over a considerable length of the beam.

When a concrete beam is over-reinforced so that failure of the beam takes place by crushing of the concrete, the load deflexion curve does not exhibit such a typical " ductile " form.   Instead of maintaining the maximum or " collapse " load for a very large deflexion (which can be as much as one-fifth of the span of a concrete beam with 1 per cent. tensile reinforcement and much more for rolled steel joists) the load falls after a small, though real, deflexion to as low as one-quarter of the maximum.   This lower load is, however, maintained for a large deflexion, the beam thus acquiring a belated "ductile" quality.   It is clear, therefore, that continuous reinforced concrete structures, like those of mild steel, can be designed capable of supporting a considerable increase of load after the condition which is usually considered as failure has occurred.

An interesting series of tests carried out at the Building Research Station (Glanville and Thomas, 1939) showed that redistribution of bending moments does take place in reinforced concrete as in steel portals, but that special care has to be taken to ensure that the shear reinforcement and the anchorage of the reinforcement are sufficient for the actual shear and bond conditions developed in the plastic range.   The subject has been given further attention in recent years (A. L. L. Baker, 1953).

REFERENCES

Robertson, A. and Cook, G. 1913. *Proc. Roy. Soc. A.*, **88**.

Glanville, W. H. and Thomas, F. G. 1939. "Moment Redistribution in Reinforced Concrete." *Bldng. Res. Tech. Pap.*, **22**. London, H.M.S.O.

Baker, A. L. L. 1953. *Proc. Instn. Civ. Engrs.*, **2**, III, 269–310.

Baker, J. F., Horne, M. R. and Heyman, J. 1956. "The Steel Skeleton," *Vol. II. Plastic Behaviour and Design.* Cambridge University Press.

APPENDIX

BERRY FUNCTIONS

TABLE I

$$f(\alpha) = 6(2\alpha \operatorname{cosec} 2\alpha - 1) / (2\alpha)^2, \quad \phi(\alpha) = 3(1 - 2\alpha \cot 2\alpha) / (2\alpha)^2,$$
$$\psi(\alpha) = 3(\tan \alpha - \alpha) / \alpha^3. \quad (\alpha \text{ in radians})$$

$\alpha°$	$f(\alpha)$	$\phi(\alpha)$	$\psi(\alpha)$	$\alpha°$	$f(\alpha)$	$\phi(\alpha)$	$\psi(\alpha)$
0	1·0000	1·0000	1·0000	38	1·2517	1·1412	1·2140
1	1·0001	1·0001	1·0001	39	1·2683	1·1503	1·2281
2	1·0006	1·0003	1·0005				
3	1·0013	1·0007	1·0011	40	1·2858	1·1600	1·2429
4	1·0023	1·0013	1·0019	41	1·3042	1·1701	1·2584
5	1·0036	1·0020	1·0030	42	1·3236	1·1807	1·2747
6	1·0051	1·0029	1·0044	43	1·3440	1·1918	1·2918
7	1·0070	1·0040	1·0060	44	1·3654	1·2035	1·3099
8	1·0092	1·0052	1·0078	45	1·3880	1·2158	1·3289
9	1·0116	1·0066	1·0099	46	1·4118	1·2288	1·3489
				47	1·4370	1·2425	1·3700
10	1·0144	1·0082	1·0123	48	1·4635	1·2568	1·3922
11	1·0175	1·0100	1·0150	49	1·4915	1·2720	1·4157
12	1·0209	1·0120	1·0179				
13	1·0246	1·0140	1·0210	50	1·5211	1·2879	1·4405
14	1·0286	1·0163	1·0245	51	1·5524	1·3048	1·4666
15	1·0329	1·0188	1·0282	52	1·5856	1·3226	1·4944
16	1·0376	1·0214	1·0322	53	1·6208	1·3415	1·5237
17	1·0427	1·0243	1·0365	54	1·6582	1·3615	1·5549
18	1·0481	1·0273	1·0411	55	1·6979	1·3827	1·5880
19	1·0538	1·0306	1·0460	56	1·7403	1·4052	1·6232
				57	1·7853	1·4291	1·6607
20	1·0599	1·0341	1·0512	58	1·8335	1·4546	1·7007
21	1·0664	1·0377	1·0568	59	1·8850	1·4818	1·7434
22	1·0734	1·0416	1·0628				
23	1·0807	1·0458	1·0690	60	1·9401	1·5109	1·7891
24	1·0884	1·0502	1·0756	61	1·9994	1·5421	1·8381
25	1·0966	1·0548	1·0825	62	2·0631	1·5755	1·8908
26	1·1052	1·0596	1·0898	63	2·1318	1·6115	1·9476
27	1·1143	1·0647	1·0976	64	2·2060	1·6503	2·0089
28	1·1239	1·0701	1·1058	65	2·2865	1·6922	2·0753
29	1·1340	1·0758	1·1144	66	2·3741	1·7377	2·1474
				67	2·4695	1·7872	2·2260
30	1·1446	1·0817	1·1234	68	2·5739	1·8412	2·3119
31	1·1558	1·0879	1·1329	69	2·6886	1·9005	2·4061
32	1·1675	1·0945	1·1428				
33	1·1799	1·1013	1·1533	70·0	2·8152	1·9657	2·5100
34	1·1928	1·1086	1·1643	70·1	2·8286	1·9725	2·5210
35	1·2065	1·1161	1·1759	70·2	2·8421	1·9795	2·5321
36	1·2208	1·1241	1·1880	70·3	2·8557	1·9865	2·5433
37	1·2359	1·1324	1·2007	70·4	2·8695	1·9936	2·5546

TABLE I (*continued*)

$\alpha°$	$f(\alpha)$	$\phi(\alpha)$	$\psi(\alpha)$	$\alpha°$	$f(\alpha)$	$\phi(\alpha)$	$\psi(\alpha)$
70·5	2·8835	2·0008	2·5660	75·5	3·8321	2·4855	3·3421
70·6	2·8976	2·0080	2·5776	75·6	3·8579	2·4987	3·3631
70·7	2·9118	2·0153	2·5893	75·7	3·8841	2·5120	3·3845
70·8	2·9262	2·0227	2·6011	75·8	3·9107	2·5255	3·4062
70·9	2·9407	2·0302	2·6130	75·9	3·9376	2·5392	3·4282
71·0	2·9554	2·0378	2·6250	76·0	3·9650	2·5531	3·4505
71·1	2·9703	2·0454	2·6372	76·1	3·9927	2·5672	3·4731
71·2	2·9853	2·0531	2·6495	76·2	4·0208	2·5814	3·4961
71·3	3·0005	2·0609	2·6620	76·3	4·0494	2·5959	3·5194
71·4	3·0159	2·0688	2·6746	76·4	4·0784	2·6107	3·5431
71·5	3·0314	2·0767	2·6873	76·5	4·1078	2·6256	3·5671
71·6	3·0471	2·0848	2·7001	76·6	4·1376	2·6408	3·5914
71·7	3·0630	2·0929	2·7131	76·7	4·1680	2·6561	3·6162
71·8	3·0790	2·1011	2·7263	76·8	4·1987	2·6718	3·6412
71·9	3·0953	2·1095	2·7396	76·9	4·2300	2·6876	3·6667
72·0	3·1117	2·1179	2·7530	77·0	4·2617	2·7037	3·6926
72·1	3·1283	2·1264	2·7666	77·1	4·2940	2·7201	3·7189
72·2	3·1451	2·1350	2·7804	77·2	4·3267	2·7367	3·7456
72·3	3·1621	2·1437	2·7943	77·3	4·3600	2·7535	3·7727
72·4	3·1792	2·1524	2·8084	77·4	4·3938	2·7707	3·8003
72·5	3·1966	2·1614	2·8226	77·5	4·4281	2·7881	3·8283
72·6	3·2142	2·1704	2·8370	77·6	4·4631	2·8058	3·8568
72·7	3·2320	2·1795	2·8516	77·7	4·4986	2·8237	3·8857
72·8	3·2500	2·1887	2·8663	77·8	4·5346	2·8420	3·9151
72·9	3·2683	2·1980	2·8812	77·9	4·5713	2·8606	3·9450
73·0	3·2867	2·2074	2·8963	78·0	4·6086	2·8795	3·9754
73·1	3·3054	2·2170	2·9116	78·1	4·6465	2·8987	4·0063
73·2	3·3243	2·2266	2·9270	78·2	4·6851	2·9182	4·0377
73·3	3·3434	2·2364	2·9427	78·3	4·7243	2·9380	4·0697
73·4	3·3627	2·2463	2·9585	78·4	4·7643	2·9582	4·1022
73·5	3·3823	2·2563	2·9746	78·5	4·8049	2·9788	4·1353
73·6	3·4022	2·2664	2·9908	78·6	4·8462	2·9997	4·1690
73·7	3·4223	2·2767	3·0072	78·7	4·8883	3·0210	4·2032
73·8	3·4426	2·2871	3·0238	78·8	4·9311	3·0426	4·2381
73·9	3·4632	2·2976	3·0407	78·9	4·9748	3·0647	4·2737
74·0	3·4841	2·3082	3·0577	79·0	5·0192	3·0871	4·3098
74·1	3·5052	2·3190	3·0750	79·1	5·0644	3·1100	4·3467
74·2	3·5266	2·3299	3·0925	79·2	5·1105	3·1333	4·3842
74·3	3·5483	2·3410	3·1102	79·3	5·1575	3·1570	4·4224
74·4	3·5702	2·3522	3·1282	79·4	5·2053	3·1812	4·4613
74·5	3·5925	2·3635	3·1464	79·5	5·2541	3·2058	4·5010
74·6	3·6150	2·3750	3·1648	79·6	5·3038	3·2309	4·5415
74·7	3·6379	2·3866	3·1834	79·7	5·3545	3·2565	4·5828
74·8	3·6610	2·3984	3·2023	79·8	5·4062	3·2826	4·6248
74·9	3·6845	2·4104	3·2215	79·9	5·4589	3·3092	4·6677
75·0	3·7083	2·4225	3·2409	80·0	5·5127	3·3363	4·7115
75·1	3·7323	2·4348	3·2606	80·1	5·5675	3·3640	4·7561
75·2	3·7568	2·4472	3·2806	80·2	5·6235	3·3922	4·8017
75·3	3·7815	2·4598	3·3008	80·3	5·6807	3·4211	4·8482
75·4	3·8066	2·4726	3·3213	80·4	5·7390	3·4505	4·8957

TABLE I (*continued*)

$\alpha°$	$f(\alpha)$	$\phi(\alpha)$	$\psi(\alpha)$	$\alpha°$	$f(\alpha)$	$\phi(\alpha)$	$\psi(\alpha)$
80·5	5·7986	3·4805	4·9442	84·3	9·6229	5·4026	8·0508
80·6	5·8595	3·5112	4·9937	84·4	9·7939	5·4884	8·1896
80·7	5·9217	3·5426	5·0442	84·5	9·9711	5·5773	8·3335
80·8	5·9853	3·5746	5·0959	84·6	10·1549	5·6694	8·4827
80·9	6·0502	3·6073	5·1488	84·7	10·3457	5·7651	8·6375
				84·8	10·5438	5·8644	8·7982
81·0	6·1166	3·6408	5·2028	84·9	10·7497	5·9677	8·9653
81·1	6·1845	3·6750	5·2580				
81·2	6·2540	3·7100	5·3145	85·0	10·9638	6·0750	9·1391
81·3	6·3251	3·7458	5·3722	85·1	11·1867	6·1867	9·3200
81·4	6·3978	3·7824	5·4314	85·2	11·4189	6·3031	9·5084
81·5	6·4722	3·8199	5·4919	85·3	11·6610	6·4245	9·7049
81·6	6·5485	3·8582	5·5538	85·4	11·9137	6·5511	9·9098
81·7	6·6265	3·8975	5·6173	85·5	12·1776	6·6833	10·1239
81·8	6·7065	3·9378	5·6823	85·6	12·4535	6·8215	10·3478
81·9	6·7885	3·9790	5·7489	85·7	12·7423	6·9662	10·5821
				85·8	13·0448	7·1178	10·8275
82·0	6·8725	4·0213	5·8172	85·9	13·3621	7·2767	11·0849
82·1	6·9587	4·0646	5·8873				
82·2	7·0471	4·1091	5·9591	86·0	13·6954	7·4436	11·3552
82·3	7·1378	4·1547	6·0328	86·1	14·0457	7·6190	11·6394
82·4	7·2309	4·2015	6·1084	86·2	14·4144	7·8037	11·9384
82·5	7·3265	4·2496	6·1861	86·3	14·8032	7·9984	12·2537
82·6	7·4246	4·2989	6·2658	86·4	15·2135	8·2038	12·5865
82·7	7·5255	4·3496	6·3478	86·5	15·6473	8·4210	12·9384
82·8	7·6292	4·4017	6·4320	86·6	16·1067	8·6510	13·3109
82·9	7·7359	4·4553	6·5186	86·7	16·5939	8·8949	13·7060
				86·8	17·1116	9·1541	14·1259
83·0	7·8456	4·5104	6·6077	86·9	17·6627	9·4299	14·5727
83·1	7·9584	4·5671	6·6994				
83·2	8·0746	4·6255	6·7938	87·0	18·2506	9·7241	15·0495
83·3	8·1943	4·6856	6·8910	87·1	18·8791	10·0387	15·5592
83·4	8·3176	4·7475	6·9911	87·2	19·5525	10·3757	16·1052
83·5	8·4447	4·8114	7·0944	87·3	20·2758	10·7375	16·6917
83·6	8·5759	4·8772	7·2008	87·4	21·0548	11·1273	17·3233
83·7	8·7112	4·9451	7·3107	87·5	21·8961	11·5483	18·0054
83·8	8·8508	5·0152	7·4241	87·6	22·8076	12·0043	18·7444
83·9	8·9951	5·0876	7·5412	87·7	23·7983	12·5000	19·5478
				87·8	24·8792	13·0408	20·4240
84·0	9·1442	5·1624	7·6622	87·9	26·0631	13·6330	21·3839
84·1	9·2983	5·2398	7·7874				
84·2	9·4578	5·3198	7·9168	88·0	27·3653	14·2844	22·4396

Between 88° and 90° the functions can be calculated by the approximate formulas—

$$f(\alpha)=\frac{54\cdot71}{90-\alpha}, \quad \phi(\alpha)=\frac{27\cdot36}{90-\alpha}+0\cdot61, \quad \psi(\alpha)=\frac{44\cdot35}{90-\alpha}+0\cdot26,$$

α being in degrees.

TABLE II

$$F(\alpha)= 6(1-2\alpha \operatorname{cosech} 2\alpha) / (2\alpha)^2, \quad \Phi(\alpha)= 3(2\alpha \coth 2\alpha -1) / (2\alpha)^2,$$
$$\Psi'(\alpha)= 3(\alpha -\tanh \alpha) / \alpha^3.$$

α Radians	$F(\alpha)$	$\Phi(\alpha)$	$\Psi'(\alpha)$	α Radians	$F(\alpha)$	$\Phi(\alpha)$	$\Psi'(\alpha)$
·00	1·0000	1·0000	1·0000	·50	·8945	·9391	·9092
·01	0·9999	1·0000	0·9999	·51	·8906	·9369	·9059
·02	·9998	0·9999	·9998	·52	·8868	·9346	·9026
·03	·9996	·9998	·9996	·53	·8828	·9323	·8992
·04	·9992	·9996	·9994	·54	·8789	·9300	·8957
·05	·9988	·9993	·9990	·55	·8748	·9276	·8922
·06	·9983	·9990	·9986	·56	·8708	·9253	·8887
·07	·9977	·9987	·9981	·57	·8667	·9229	·8851
·08	·9970	·9983	·9975	·58	·8626	·9204	·8815
·09	·9962	·9979	·9968	·59	·8584	·9180	·8779
·10	·9953	·9973	·9960	·60	·8542	·9155	·8743
·11	·9944	·9968	·9952	·61	·8500	·9130	·8706
·12	·9933	·9962	·9943	·62	·8457	·9105	·8669
·13	·9922	·9955	·9933	·63	·8414	·9080	·8632
·14	·9909	·9948	·9922	·64	·8371	·9054	·8595
·15	·9896	·9940	·9910	·65	·8328	·9028	·8557
·16	·9882	·9932	·9898	·66	·8284	·9003	·8519
·17	·9867	·9924	·9886	·67	·8240	·8977	·8481
·18	·9851	·9915	·9872	·68	·8196	·8950	·8442
·19	·9834	·9905	·9857	·69	·8151	·8924	·8403
·20	·9816	·9895	·9842	·70	·8107	·8897	·8364
·21	·9798	·9884	·9826	·71	·8062	·8871	·8325
·22	·9779	·9873	·9810	·72	·8017	·8844	·8286
·23	·9758	·9862	·9793	·73	·7972	·8817	·8247
·24	·9738	·9850	·9775	·74	·7927	·8790	·8207
·25	·9716	·9837	·9756	·75	·7881	·8762	·8167
·26	·9693	·9824	·9736	·76	·7835	·8735	·8127
·27	·9670	·9811	·9717	·77	·7790	·8708	·8087
·28	·9646	·9797	·9696	·78	·7744	·8680	·8047
·29	·9621	·9783	·9675	·79	·7698	·8653	·8007
·30	·9595	·9768	·9653	·80	·7652	·8625	·7967
·31	·9569	·9753	·9630	·81	·7606	·8597	·7927
·32	·9542	·9737	·9607	·82	·7560	·8569	·7887
·33	·9514	·9721	·9583	·83	·7513	·8541	·7847
·34	·9486	·9705	·9558	·84	·7467	·8513	·7807
·35	·9457	·9688	·9533	·85	·7421	·8485	·7766
·36	·9427	·9671	·9507	·86	·7374	·8457	·7725
·37	·9396	·9653	·9481	·87	·7328	·8429	·7684
·38	·9365	·9635	·9454	·88	·7282	·8400	·7643
·39	·9333	·9617	·9427	·89	·7235	·8372	·7601
·40	·9301	·9598	·9399	·90	·7189	·8344	·7560
·41	·9268	·9579	·9371	·91	·7143	·8315	·7519
·42	·9234	·9559	·9342	·92	·7096	·8287	·7478
·43	·9200	·9539	·9312	·93	·7050	·8259	·7437
·44	·9165	·9519	·9282	·94	·7004	·8230	·7396
·45	·9129	·9499	·9252	·95	·6958	·8202	·7355
·46	·9094	·9478	·9221	·96	·6912	·8173	·7314
·47	·9057	·9456	·9189	·97	·6866	·8145	·7273
·48	·9020	·9435	·9157	·98	·6820	·8117	·7232
·49	·8983	·9413	·9125	·99	·6774	·8088	·7192

TABLE II (*continued*)

α Radians	F(α)	Φ(α)	Ψ'(α)	α Radians	F(α)	Φ(α)	Ψ'(α)
1·00	·6728	·8060	·7152	1·30	·5429	·7229	·5985
1·01	·6683	·8031	·7112	1·31	·5389	·7202	·5948
1·02	·6637	·8003	·7072	1·32	·5349	·7175	·5912
1·03	·6592	·7975	·7031	1·33	·5309	·7149	·5875
1·04	·6547	·7946	·6991	1·34	·5269	·7123	·5839
1·05	·6501	·7918	·6950	1·35	·5230	·7097	·5803
1·06	·6456	·7890	·6910	1·36	·5191	·7071	·5767
1·07	·6411	·7861	·6870	1·37	·5152	·7045	·5732
1·08	·6367	·7833	·6830	1·38	·5114	·7019	·5697
1·09	·6322	·7805	·6790	1·39	·5075	·6993	·5662
1·10	·6278	·7777	·6750	1·40	·5037	·6967	·5627
1·11	·6233	·7749	·6711	1·41	·4999	·6942	·5593
1·12	·6189	·7721	·6672	1·42	·4962	·6916	·5559
1·13	·6145	·7693	·6633	1·43	·4924	·6891	·5525
1·14	·6102	·7665	·6594	1·44	·4887	·6866	·5491
1·15	·6058	·7637	·6555	1·45	·4851	·6840	·5457
1·16	·6015	·7609	·6516	1·46	·4814	·6815	·5423
1·17	·5972	·7582	·6477	1·47	·4778	·6790	·5389
1·18	·5929	·7554	·6438	1·48	·4742	·6766	·5355
1·19	·5886	·7527	·6399	1·49	·4706	·6741	·5321
1·20	·5843	·7499	·6360	1·50	·4670	·6716	·5288
1·21	·5801	·7472	·6322	1·51	·4635	·6692	·5255
1·22	·5759	·7444	·6284	1·52	·4600	·6668	·5222
1·23	·5717	·7417	·6246	1·53	·4565	·6643	·5189
1·24	·5675	·7390	·6208	1·54	·4530	·6619	·5157
1·25	·5633	·7363	·6170	1·55	·4496	·6595	·5125
1·26	·5592	·7336	·6133	1·56	·4462	·6571	·5093
1·27	·5551	·7309	·6096	1·57	·4428	·6547	·5061
1·28	·5510	·7282	·6059	1·58	·4395	·6524	·5030
1·29	·5469	·7255	·6022	1·59	·4361	·6500	·4999
				1·60	·4328	·6476	·4968

TABLE III

Tanh α.

α Radians	Tanh α	α Radians	Tanh α	α Radians	Tanh α	α Radians	Tanh α
0·00	·00000	0·50	·46212	1·00	·76159	1·50	·90515
·01	·01000	·51	·46995	·01	·76576	·51	·90694
·02	·02000	·52	·47770	·02	·76987	·52	·90870
·03	·02999	·53	·48538	·03	·77391	·53	·91043
·04	·03998	·54	·49299	·04	·77789	·54	·91212
·05	·04996	·55	·50052	·05	·78181	·55	·91379
·06	·05993	·56	·50798	·06	·78566	·56	·91542
·07	·06989	·57	·51536	·07	·78946	·57	·91703
·08	·07983	·58	·52267	·08	·79320	·58	·91860
·09	·08976	·59	·52990	·09	·79688	·59	·92015
0·10	·09967	0·60	·53705	1·10	·80050	1·60	·92167
·11	·10956	·61	·54413	·11	·80406	·61	·92316
·12	·11943	·62	·55113	·12	·80757	·62	·92462
·13	·12928	·63	·55805	·13	·81102	·63	·92606
·14	·13909	·64	·56490	·14	·81441	·64	·92747
·15	·14888	·65	·57167	·15	·81775	·65	·92886
·16	·15865	·66	·57836	·16	·82104	·66	·93022
·17	·16838	·67	·58498	·17	·82427	·67	·93155
·18	·17808	·68	·59152	·18	·82745	·68	·93286
·19	·18775	·69	·59798	·19	·83058	·69	·93415
0·20	·19738	0·70	·60437	1·20	·83365	1·70	·93541
·21	·20697	·71	·61068	·21	·83668	·71	·93665
·22	·21652	·72	·61691	·22	·83965	·72	·93786
·23	·22603	·73	·62307	·23	·84258	·73	·93906
·24	·23550	·74	·62915	·24	·84546	·74	·94023
·25	·24492	·75	·63515	·25	·84828	·75	·94138
·26	·25430	·76	·64108	·26	·85106	·76	·94250
·27	·26362	·77	·64693	·27	·85380	·77	·94361
·28	·27291	·78	·65271	·28	·85648	·78	·94470
·29	·28213	·79	·65841	·29	·85913	·79	·94576
0·30	·29131	0·80	·66404	1·30	·86172	1·80	·94681
·31	·30044	·81	·66959	·31	·86427	·81	·94783
·32	·30951	·82	·67507	·32	·86678	·82	·94884
·33	·31852	·83	·68048	·33	·86925	·83	·94983
·34	·32748	·84	·68581	·34	·87167	·84	·95080
·35	·33638	·85	·69107	·35	·87405	·85	·95175
·36	·34521	·86	·69626	·36	·87639	·86	·95268
·37	·35399	·87	·70137	·37	·87869	·87	·95359
·38	·36271	·88	·70642	·38	·88095	·88	·95449
·39	·37136	·89	·71139	·39	·88317	·89	·95537
0·40	·37995	0·90	·71630	1·40	·88535	1·90	·95624
·41	·38847	·91	·72113	·41	·88749	·91	·95709
·42	·39693	·92	·72590	·42	·88960	·92	·95792
·43	·40532	·93	·73059	·43	·89167	·93	·95873
·44	·41364	·94	·73522	·44	·89370	·94	·95953
·45	·42190	·95	·73978	·45	·89569	·95	·96032
·46	·43008	·96	·74428	·46	·89765	·96	·96109
·47	·43820	·97	·74870	·47	·89958	·97	·96185
·48	·44624	·98	·75307	·48	·90147	·98	·96259
·49	·45422	·99	·75736	·49	·90332	·99	·96331
						2·00	·96403

INDEX